HEATH
MIDDLE LEVEL
LITERATURE

GOLD LEVEL

AUTHORS

Donna Alvermann
Linda Miller Cleary
Kenneth Donelson
Donald Gallo
Alice Haskins
J. Howard Johnston
John Lounsbury
Alleen Pace Nilsen
Robert Pavlik
Jewell Parker Rhodes
Alberto Alvaro Ríos
Sandra Schurr
Lyndon Searfoss
Julia Thomason
Max Thompson
Carl Zon

D.C. Heath and Company
Lexington, Massachusetts / Toronto, Ontario

STAFF CREDITS

EDITORIAL Barbara A. Brennan, Helen Byers, Christopher Johnson, Kathleen Kennedy Kelley, Owen Shows, Rita M. Sullivan
Proofreading: JoAnne B. Sgroi

CONTRIBUTING WRITERS Nance Davidson, Florence Harris

SERIES DESIGN Robin Herr

BOOK DESIGN Caroline Bowden, Daniel Derdula, Susan Geer, Diana Maloney, Angela Sciaraffa, Bonnie Chayes Yousefian
Art Editing: Carolyn Langley

PHOTOGRAPHY *Series Photography Coordinator:* Carmen Johnson
Photo Research Supervisor: Martha Friedman
Photo Researchers: Wendy Enright, Po-yee McKenna, PhotoSearch, Inc., Gillian Speeth, Denise Theodores
Assignment Photography Coordinators: Susan Doheny, Gayna Hoffman, Shawna Johnston

COMPUTER PREPRESS Ricki Pappo, Kathy Meisl
Richard Curran, Michele Locatelli

PERMISSIONS Dorothy B. McLeod

PRODUCTION Patrick Connolly

Cover: *Electric Prisms* Sonia Delaunay, 1914, National Museum of Modern Art, Paris, France
Cover Design: Len Massiglia

Published simultaneously in Canada

Printed in the United States of America

International Standard Book Number: 0-669-32074-9
5 6 7 8 9 10-RRD-99 98

Middle Level Authors

Donna Alvermann, University of Georgia
Alice Haskins, Howard County Public Schools, Maryland
J. Howard Johnston, University of South Florida
John Lounsbury, Georgia College
Sandra Schurr, University of South Florida
Julia Thomason, Appalachian State University
Max Thompson, Appalachian State University
Carl Zon, California Assessment Collaborative

Literature and Language Arts Authors

Linda Miller Cleary, University of Minnesota
Kenneth Donelson, Arizona State University
Donald Gallo, Central Connecticut State University
Alleen Pace Nilsen, Arizona State University
Robert Pavlik, Cardinal Stritch College, Milwaukee
Jewell Parker Rhodes, Arizona State University
Alberto Alvaro Ríos, Arizona State University
Lyndon Searfoss, Arizona State University

Teacher Consultants

Suzanne Aubin, Patapsco Middle School, Ellicott City, Maryland
Judy Baxter, Newport News Public Schools, Newport News, Virginia
Saundra Bryn, Director of Research and Development, El Mirage, Arizona
Lorraine Gerhart, Elmbrook Middle School, Elm Grove, Wisconsin
Kathy Tuchman Glass, Burlingame Intermediate School, Burlingame, California
Lisa Mandelbaum, Crocker Middle School, Hillsborough, California
Lucretia Pannozzo, John Jay Middle School, Katonah, New York
Carol Schultz, Jerling Junior High, Orland Park, Illinois
Jeanne Siebenman, Grand Canyon University, Phoenix, Arizona
Gail Thompson, Garey High School, Pomona, California
Rufus Thompson, Grace Yokley School, Ontario, California
Tom Tufts, Conniston Middle School, West Palm Beach, Florida
Edna Turner, Harpers Choice Middle School, Columbia, Maryland
C. Anne Webb, Buerkle Junior High School, St. Louis, Missouri
Geri Yaccino, Thompson Junior High School, St. Charles, Illinois

CONTENTS

SPECIAL NOTE: *Because each unit of this book is also available as a separate volume, each page has two page numbers. In this book, use the page numbers in the boxes to locate what you want.*

THEME: Identity and Self-Esteem

BECOMING MYSELF

PROJECTS

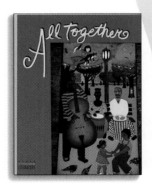

THEME: Community

ALL TOGETHER

THE LITERATURE

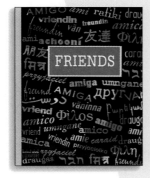

THEME: Friendship

FRIENDS

THEME: Conflict Resolution

OUT OF TUNE

THEME: Mystery and the Imagination

JUST IMAGINE

THE LITERATURE

PROJECTS

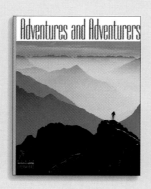

THEME: Challenges and Achievements

ADVENTURES AND ADVENTURERS

THEME: Survival

SURVIVAL!

THE LITERATURE

THEME: Myths, Legends, and Folktales

TALES FROM HERE AND THERE

PROJECTS

BECOMING MYSELF

HEATH
MIDDLE LEVEL
LITERATURE

HEATH
MIDDLE LEVEL
LITERATURE

Becoming Myself

▼ THEME ▼
IDENTITY AND SELF-ESTEEM

AUTHORS

Donna Alvermann
Linda Miller Cleary
Kenneth Donelson
Donald Gallo
Alice Haskins
J. Howard Johnston
John Lounsbury
Alleen Pace Nilsen
Robert Pavlik
Jewell Parker Rhodes
Alberto Alvaro Ríos
Sandra Schurr
Lyndon Searfoss
Julia Thomason
Max Thompson
Carl Zon

 D.C. Heath and Company
Lexington, Massachusetts / Toronto, Ontario
HEATH

17

STAFF CREDITS

EDITORIAL — Barbara A. Brennan, Helen Byers, Christopher Johnson, Kathleen Kennedy Kelley, Owen Shows, Rita M. Sullivan
Proofreading: JoAnne B. Sgroi

CONTRIBUTING WRITERS — Nance Davidson, Florence Harris

SERIES DESIGN — Robin Herr

BOOK DESIGN — Caroline Bowden, Daniel Derdula, Susan Geer, Diana Maloney, Angela Sciaraffa, Bonnie Chayes Yousefian
Art Editing: Carolyn Langley

PHOTOGRAPHY — *Series Photography Coordinator*: Carmen Johnson
Photo Research Supervisor: Martha Friedman
Photo Researchers: Wendy Enright, Linda Finigan, Po-yee McKenna, PhotoSearch, Inc., Gillian Speeth, Denise Theodores
Assignment Photography Coordinators: Susan Doheny, Gayna Hoffman, Shawna Johnston

COMPUTER PREPRESS — Ricki Pappo, Kathy Meisl, Richard Curran, Michele Locatelli

PERMISSIONS — Dorothy B. McLeod

PRODUCTION — Patrick Connolly

Cover Photograph: © Myron J. Dorf, The Stock Market. **Cover Design:** Robin Herr

Copyright © 1995 by D.C. Heath and Company, a division of Houghton Mifflin Company

Acknowledgments for copyrighted material are on page 125 and constitute an extension of this page.

Published simultaneously in Canada

Printed in the United States of America

International Standard Book Number: 0-669-32105-2 (soft cover)
4 5 6 7 8 9 10-RRD-99 98 97

International Standard Book Number: 0-669-38174-8 (hard cover)
4 5 6 7 8 9 10-RRD-99 98 97

Middle Level Authors

Donna Alvermann, University of Georgia
Alice Haskins, Howard County Public Schools, Maryland
J. Howard Johnston, University of South Florida
John Lounsbury, Georgia College
Sandra Schurr, University of South Florida
Julia Thomason, Appalachian State University
Max Thompson, Appalachian State University
Carl Zon, California Assessment Collaborative

Literature and Language Arts Authors

Linda Miller Cleary, University of Minnesota
Kenneth Donelson, Arizona State University
Donald Gallo, Central Connecticut State University
Alleen Pace Nilsen, Arizona State University
Robert Pavlik, Cardinal Stritch College, Milwaukee
Jewell Parker Rhodes, Arizona State University
Alberto Alvaro Ríos, Arizona State University
Lyndon Searfoss, Arizona State University

Teacher Consultants

Suzanne Aubin, Patapsco Middle School, Ellicott City, Maryland
Judy Baxter, Newport News Public Schools, Newport News, Virginia
Saundra Bryn, Director of Research and Development, El Mirage, Arizona
Lorraine Gerhart, Elmbrook Middle School, Elm Grove, Wisconsin
Kathy Tuchman Glass, Burlingame Intermediate School, Burlingame, California
Lisa Mandelbaum, Crocker Middle School, Hillsborough, California
Lucretia Pannozzo, John Jay Middle School, Katonah, New York
Carol Schultz, Jerling Junior High, Orland Park, Illinois
Jeanne Siebenman, Grand Canyon University, Phoenix, Arizona
Gail Thompson, Garey High School, Pomona, California
Rufus Thompson, Grace Yokley School, Ontario, California
Tom Tufts, Conniston Middle School, West Palm Beach, Florida
Edna Turner, Harpers Choice Middle School, Columbia, Maryland
C. Anne Webb, Buerkle Junior High School, St. Louis, Missouri
Geri Yaccino, Thompson Junior High School, St. Charles, Illinois

CONTENTS

Cornfield with Cypresses Vincent van Gogh. National Gallery, London

ASKING BIG QUESTIONS ABOUT THE LITERATURE

PROJECTS

1 WRITING WORKSHOP

DESCRIBING A HEROIC ACT   106-111

Write an eyewitness report describing an event in which an ordinary person became a hero.

2 COOPERATIVE LEARNING

A TIME CAPSULE   112-113

Create a time capsule of information about yourself and your world.

3 HELPING YOUR COMMUNITY

BECOME AN INSPIRATION   114-115

Express your unique creativity in artwork that will inspire others to see and appreciate their own special qualities.

Give Yourself a Hand

Who are you? Silly question, right? You're Sally Ling or Andrew Doyle or María Elena Ortíz or . . . whatever your name may be. You're X years old and a Yth grader at Z School.

But those details don't tell much—if anything—about you; they're just statistics. You, whoever you are, have a certain chin and talents and background and feelings. You're a complicated mixture, and you can't be labeled so easily.

So who are you really? Start figuring that out by giving yourself a hand—two hands, in fact—for all the things that are special about you.

1 A handsome list.

Look around you. What are the special characteristics of the people you see? Certain things are obvious, of course. Some wear glasses, are tall or short, have red hair or black hair. Some are terrific at basketball or math or art. But people have special qualities that aren't always obvious, too. Some are helpful to others or can keep a secret. Others are great puzzle-solvers. Some learn new languages easily or can dance. Others are natural leaders, or good sports, or good at fixing things.

With the whole class, brainstorm a long list of positive qualities people can have. Write the list in your journal.

2 Hand it to yourself.

Working alone, go over the list of qualities. Which ones could also describe you? Don't worry about seeming conceited. Be good to yourself, and be honest. For example, have you ever helped people with their homework? Then you can be helpful. Are you good at putting colors together in your clothes? Then you're creative as well as colorful. Put a check mark beside every quality that applies to you. Then, in your journal, copy the word for each quality into a second list. Entitle this list "My Special Qualities."

Now stretch the second list. Yes, there are more good things about you! Think of these qualities and add them too.

3 Hands down.

Spread one of your hands, palm down, on a piece of paper. (Leave room for the other hand.) Carefully trace it, going around each finger. Now put the other hand palm down and trace it. Go over your own list of special qualities and choose ten qualities that describe you most. Write one in each finger of the hands you traced.

Finally write your name on one palm. On the other, draw an item you think represents you—such as a basketball, a musical note, or a smile.

4 Hands up!

When you're satisfied, hand your hands to a partner. What does your partner think? Is he or she surprised by something you included—or left out?

Finally link your paper hands with those of your classmates in a classroom display that shows everyone's strengths, abilities, and special qualities.

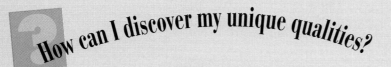

Asking Big Questions About the Theme

How can I discover my unique qualities?

List your unique qualities in one column of a chart like the one here. Next to each quality, write the name of an object the quality could also describe.

Choose the pair of words you like best and use them to finish the following sentence.

I am _____ than a _____. Are you *sharper* than a *pencil?* Or *brighter* than a *light bulb?*

Use the sentence in a shape poem in which the words form a picture of something in the poem.

Quality	Items
sharp	pencil
bright	light bulb

How can I improve my unique qualities?

Divide a sheet of paper into seven columns. Then label each column with the name of one of the following abilities.

Physical — Moving, acting out, playing
Social — Interacting with others
Personal — Understanding thoughts and feelings
Logical — Reasoning, problem solving
Musical — Making music, using rhythm
Verbal — Using language
Visual — Noticing shapes, creating art

Under each heading describe examples of how you have used that ability. Write a New Year's resolution telling which abilities you'd like to improve.

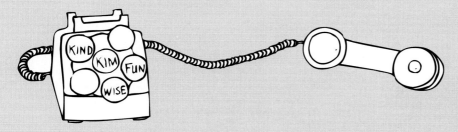

How can I share my unique qualities?

With a partner, think of ways to fill the blanks in the sentence "When I need help with _____, I call someone who's _____." Write them in your journal. Which qualities in the second blank also describe you? Circle them.

Draw an old-fashioned telephone like the one here. Write your name on the dial. Around it write five qualities—such as *creative* or *wise*—that tell why someone might call *you* for help.

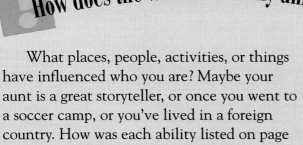

How does the world affect my unique qualities?

What places, people, activities, or things have influenced who you are? Maybe your aunt is a great storyteller, or once you went to a soccer camp, or you've lived in a foreign country. How was each ability listed on page 10 strengthened by that experience?

Design a postcard by drawing the place, activity, thing, or person who influenced you. On the back, explain to someone how your experience sparked one or more of your special qualities.

NOW

Think!

What are other questions you might ask about the qualities that make you unique? Make a list for yourself in your journal. In your reading, activities, and projects for *Becoming Myself*, think about these questions as well as the four Big Questions. Notice the ways that you uniquely answer them!

THE SUN AND THE MOON

ELAINE LARON

The Sun is filled with shining light
It blazes far and wide
The Moon reflects the sunlight back
But has no light inside.

I think I'd rather be the Sun
That shines so bold and bright
Than be the Moon, that only glows
With someone else's light.

Who Am I?

STELLA MANCILLAS

I walk through crowded streets

Dirt and broken glass beneath my feet.

I gaze up at the crying red sky

And ask, "Who am I?"

Natural Answer Helen Frankenthaler, 1976, acrylic on canvas, 8' x 11', Art Gallery of Ontario, Toronto

Young Ladies Don't Slay Dragons

JOYCE HOVELSRUD

A dragon with exceedingly evil intentions was plaguing[1] the Palace of Hexagon. Night and day he lurked about the courtyard walls, belching fire and smoke and roaring in a most terrible fashion. Things looked bad for the royal household.

"Mercy," said the queen.

"Dear me," said the king. "One of these days he'll get a royal blaze going, and when he does—poof! That'll be it."

"Well, what are you going to do about it?" asked the queen sharply. "I mean, you can't just sit there counting out your money and ignoring the problem."

"I have asked every brave man in the kingdom to slay the dragon," said the king. "They all said they had more important things to do."

"Nonsense," said the queen with a breathy sigh. "What could be more important than saving the palace from a monstrous dragon? Perhaps you should offer a reward."

"I *have* offered a reward," said the king. "No one seems interested."

"Well then, offer something of value to go with it," said the queen. And with that, she slammed the honey jar on the table and stomped out of the room.

"I'll slay the dragon," said the Princess Penelope, jumping from behind an antique suit of armor. There, she had just happened to be listening to the conversation while oiling a rusty joint.

The king blinked his eyes twice—once with shock because he was taken by surprise, and once with pride because he was taken by his daughter's dazzling beauty. "You can't

---

1. **plaguing** [plāg′ ing]: tormenting, troubling.

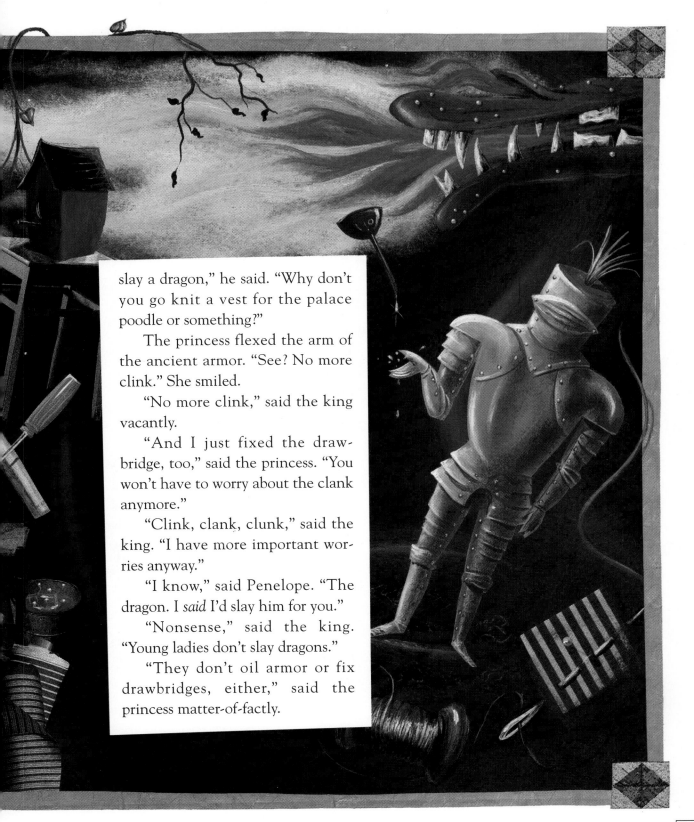

slay a dragon," he said. "Why don't you go knit a vest for the palace poodle or something?"

The princess flexed the arm of the ancient armor. "See? No more clink." She smiled.

"No more clink," said the king vacantly.

"And I just fixed the draw-bridge, too," said the princess. "You won't have to worry about the clank anymore."

"Clink, clank, clunk," said the king. "I have more important wor-ries anyway."

"I know," said Penelope. "The dragon. I *said* I'd slay him for you."

"Nonsense," said the king. "Young ladies don't slay dragons."

"They don't oil armor or fix drawbridges, either," said the princess matter-of-factly.

The king scratched his head and thought about that for a while. Princess Penelope was always giving him something to think about. For one thing, he thought her rare beauty was unsurpassed[2] by that of any princess on earth. For another, it seemed she never behaved as beautiful princesses should.

"Slaying dragons is men's work," he said finally, "and that's that."

The princess didn't really think that was that. But she knew her father did. So she said no more about it—to him, anyway.

It seemed to her that a young lady could do anything she wanted, if she set her mind to it. And in her tender years she had set her mind to many things the king and queen had said only men could do.

She once whittled[3] a whistle from a green willow stick when she was supposed to be sewing a fine seam.

She once built a birdhouse for the palace puffin[4] when she was supposed to be practicing her lute[5] lesson.

And once she even killed a mouse. She had come into the bedchamber to find her mother standing on a chair and screaming— as queens do in the presence of mice. "Don't worry, Mother, I'll get him," Penelope said.

"Young ladies don't kill mice," the queen said. "For heaven's sake, stand on a chair and scream along with me."

But Penelope didn't stand on a chair and scream. She caught the mouse and disposed of it tidily.

Well, she would dispose of the dragon, too. And she would get some ideas on how to go about it.

She went to speak to the royal cook. "How would you slay a dragon?" she asked.

"I would cut off his head with a carving knife," said the cook. "But of course you couldn't do that."

"Why not?" asked the princess.

"Young ladies don't slay dragons," the cook said.

"My father said that, too," said Penelope, and she went to speak to the royal tailor. "How would you slay a dragon?" she asked.

"I would stab him through the heart with a long needle," the tailor said.

2. **unsurpassed** [un′ sər pasd′]: not equaled.
3. **whittled** [hwit′ ld]: carved.
4. **puffin** [puf′ ən]: a sea bird with a thick body, a large head, and a bill of several colors.
5. **lute** [lüt]: a musical instrument, similar to a guitar, used in the 1500s and 1600s.

"Would you lend me a long needle?" asked the princess.

"Young ladies don't slay dragons," the tailor said. "Besides, I don't have a needle long enough or strong enough."

So Princess Penelope went to the royal court jester.[6] "How would you slay a dragon?" she asked.

"I would tell him such a funny story he would die laughing," said the jester.

"Do you have such a funny story?" asked Penelope.

"There aren't any stories *that* funny," said the jester. "Besides, young ladies don't slay dragons."

"You may be in for a surprise," said the princess, and she went to speak to the royal wizard. "How would you slay a dragon?" she asked.

The royal wizard thought a long time. Then he said, "Why do you want to know?"

"Because I want to slay the dragon," Penelope said matter-of-factly.

"Well, if you really want the truth," the wizard said, "the fact is, young ladies don't slay dragons."

"How do you know they don't?" Penelope asked.

"Everybody knows that," the wizard said. "Don't ask me how I know—it's just a fact."

"Well, then," the princess said, "if a brave young man wanted to save the palace from a smoke-blowing, flame-throwing, fierce and wicked dragon, what advice would you give him?"

The royal wizard wrinkled his forehead, squinted his eyes, and made arches with his fingers while he thought. Then he said, "I would advise him to fight fire with fire."

"I see," said Penelope.

"My feet are cold," said the wizard. "Do me a favor and slide that hot bucket over here. I want to warm my toes on it."

Penelope did as he bade. "How does the bucket stay hot?" she asked.

"It's filled with a magic liquid that burns without fire," said the wizard. "I conjured[7] it up myself."

"A good bit of magic," said Penelope admiringly. "Can you get the liquid to flame up?"

"If I want flames, I just drop a hot coal into the bucket," said the wizard. And then he fell asleep. He always fell asleep after talking three minutes, and now his three minutes were up. Besides, it was nap time for everybody in the palace.

6. **jester** [jes′ tər]: a man who told amusing stories to kings and their guests.
7. **conjured** [kon′ jərd]: caused to appear by using magic.

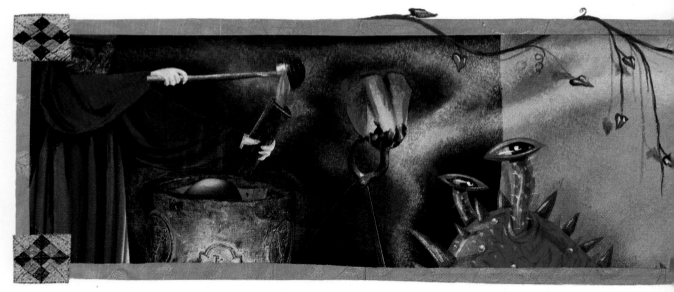

But how anybody could sleep through the dragon's terrible roaring was a mystery to Penelope. And how anybody could sleep while evil threatened the palace was another mystery to her.

The wizard had given the princess an idea, though, and she tiptoed out of the room.

She found a pipe in her collection of iron and sealed it at one end. She tiptoed back to the wizard's room and filled the pipe with liquid from the magic bucket. With a pair of tongs, she took a hot coal from the fire and tiptoed away. She paused in the great hall long enough to don a suit of armor—minus the helmet that hurt her ears and hung low over her eyes. Finally she found a shield she could lift.

Then, clanking, she made her way through the courtyard to the gates. Though she was not strong enough to open them, she managed to push herself sideways through the iron bars. And she wasn't the least bit afraid.

Now, the dragon was the biggest, the most ferocious dragon that ever lived. Princess Penelope didn't know that, but she rather suspected it, for why else wouldn't the brave men in the kingdom come to slay him?

And the dragon, who was also the wisest dragon that ever lived, had a hunch someone was after him. So he crept slowly around the walls to see who it was—roaring terrible roars and belching the sky full of fire and smoke as he went.

"I wish he wouldn't smoke so much," Penelope muttered as she crept after him. Rounding the corner, she could just make out the monstrous tip of the dragon's tail disappearing around the corner ahead.

"This will never do," she said after the third corner. Turning, she crept the other way—and she met the dragon face to face!

Now, it isn't easy to describe the ferocious battle that ensued, but it went something like this.

"Stop or I'll shoot," said Penelope calmly.

"What's a nice girl like you doing out slaying dragons?" sneered the dragon as he crept toward her, blinking several times because of her dazzling beauty.

"I said, stop or I'll shoot."

"You don't *shoot* dragons," the dragon said, coming closer. "Everybody I ever heard of slays them with swords."

"I'm not like everybody you ever heard of," Penelope said.

"I wonder why that is," the dragon said. And though he didn't know it at the time, the dragon had spoken his last words.

Princess Penelope raised her lead pipe, ignited the liquid with her hot coal, and dealt the deadly dragon a deadly blow.

Now, nobody would believe the terrible fire that followed, so it isn't necessary to describe it. But it was like the end of the world.

At last the smoke cleared away. And there, standing among the charred remains of the world's most ferocious dragon was—the world's most handsome prince. Penelope couldn't believe her eyes.

"I've been waiting for something like that to happen," said the prince, smiling a handsome smile and blinking a winsome[8] blink. "You'll marry me, of course."

8. **winsome** [win′ səm]: charming, pleasing.

But—Penelope was the world's most beautiful princess. Having her for a wife was more than the prince had dared dream, especially while bouncing about in the body of a dragon.

"I have a kingdom ten times the size of this pea patch," he added, "and it's all yours if you'll say yes."

Penelope gazed into his eyes a long time. Thoughtfully, she said, "I've been waiting for someone like you to ask me something like that. But there's something you should know about me first. I wouldn't be happy just being a queen and doing queen-things. I like to fix draw-bridges, build birdhouses, slay drag-ons—that sort of thing."

"It so happens I have bridges, birds, and dragons to spare," said the prince hopefully.

"Then my answer is yes," said Penelope.

And with that they saddled up a white horse and rode off into the sunset.

Now, even though this is the end of the story, you realize, of course, they are still living happily ever after.

MAYA ANGELOU

FROM

I KNOW WHY THE CAGED BIRD SINGS

L ater, my room had all the cheeriness of a dungeon and the appeal of a tomb. It was going to be impossible to stay there, but leaving held no attraction for me, either. Running away from home would be anticlimactic after Mexico, and a dull story after my month in the car lot. But the need for change bulldozed a road down the center of my mind.

I had it. The answer came to me with the suddenness of a collision. I would go to work. Mother wouldn't be difficult to convince; after all, in school I was a year ahead of my grade and Mother was a firm believer in self-sufficiency.[1] In fact, she'd be pleased to think that I had that much gumption,[2] that much of her in my character. (She liked to speak of herself as the original "do-it-yourself girl.")

1. **self-sufficiency** [self′ sə fish′ ən sē]: ability to take care of one's own needs.
2. **gumption** [gump′ shən]: fearlessness, energy.

Once I had settled on getting a job, all that remained was to decide which kind of job I was most fitted for. My intellectual pride had kept me from selecting typing, shorthand or filing as subjects in school, so office work was ruled out. War plants and shipyards demanded birth certificates, and mine would reveal me to be fifteen, and ineligible for work. So the well-paying defense jobs were also out. Women had replaced men on the streetcars as conductors and motormen, and the thought of sailing up and down the hills of San Francisco in a dark-blue uniform, with a money changer at my belt, caught my fancy.

Mother was as easy as I had anticipated. The world was moving so fast, so much money was being made, so many people were dying in Guam[3] and Germany, that hordes of strangers became good friends overnight. Life was cheap and death entirely free. How could she have the time to think about my academic career?

To her question of what I planned to do, I replied that I would get a job on the streetcars. She rejected the proposal with: "They don't accept colored people on the streetcars."

I would like to claim an immediate fury which was followed by the noble determination to break the restricting tradition. But the truth is, my first reaction was one of disappointment. I'd pictured myself, dressed in a neat blue serge suit, my money changer swinging jauntily[4] at my waist, and a cheery smile for the passengers which would make their own work day brighter.

From disappointment, I gradually ascended the emotional ladder to haughty[5] indignation, and finally to that state of stubbornness where the mind is locked like the jaws of an enraged bulldog.

I would go to work on the streetcars and wear a blue serge suit. Mother gave me her support with one of her usual terse[6] asides, "That's what you want to do? Then nothing beats a trial but a failure.

3. **Guam** [gwäm]: island and important U.S. military base in the western Pacific Ocean, east of the Philippines, which was heavily attacked during World War II.
4. **jauntily** [jôn′ tə lē]: in a carefree way.
5. **haughty** [hô′ tē]: too proud, scornful of others.
6. **terse** [tėrs]: brief and to the point.

Give it everything you've got. I've told you many times, 'Can't do is like Don't Care.' Neither of them have a home."

Translated, that meant there was nothing a person can't do, and there should be nothing a human being didn't care about. It was the most positive encouragement I could have hoped for.

In the offices of the Market Street Railway Company, the receptionist seemed as surprised to see me there as I was surprised to find the interior dingy and the décor drab. Somehow I had expected waxed surfaces and carpeted floors. If I had met no resistance, I might have decided against working for such a poor-mouth-looking concern. As it was, I explained that I had come to see about a job. She asked, was I sent by an agency, and when I replied that I was not, she told me they were only accepting applicants from agencies.

The classified pages of the morning papers had listed advertisements for motorettes and conductorettes and I reminded her of that. She gave me a face full of astonishment that my suspicious nature would not accept.

"I am applying for the job listed in this morning's *Chronicle* and I'd like to be presented to your personnel manager." While I spoke in supercilious[7] accents, and looked at the room as if I had an oil well in my own backyard, my armpits were being pricked by millions of hot pointed needles. She saw her escape and dived into it.

"He's out. He's out for the day. You might call tomorrow and if he's in, I'm sure you can see him." Then she swiveled her chair around on its rusty screws and with that I was supposed to be dismissed.

"May I ask his name?"

She half turned, acting surprised to find me still there.

"His name? Whose name?"

"Your personnel manager."

We were firmly joined in the hypocrisy[8] to play out the scene.

"The personnel manager? Oh, he's Mr. Cooper, but I'm not sure

---

7. **supercilious** [sü′ pər sil′ ē əs]: proud and filled with contempt for others.
8. **hypocrisy** [hi pok′ rə sē]: state of pretending to be good and polite.

you'll find him here tomorrow. He's . . . Oh, but you can try."

"Thank you."

"You're welcome."

And I was out of the musty room and into the even mustier lobby. In the street I saw the receptionist and myself going faithfully through paces that were stale with familiarity, although I had never encountered that kind of situation before and, probably, neither had she. We were like actors who, knowing the play by heart, were still able to cry afresh over the old tragedies and laugh spontaneously at the comic situations.

The miserable little encounter had nothing to do with me, the me of me, any more than it had to do with that silly clerk. The incident was a recurring dream, concocted[9] years before by stupid whites and it eternally came back to haunt us all. The secretary and I were like Hamlet and Laertes[10] in the final scene, where, because of harm done by one ancestor to another, we were bound to duel to the death. Also because the play must end somewhere.

I went further than forgiving the clerk, I accepted her as a fellow victim of the same puppeteer.

On the streetcar, I put my fare into the box and the conductorette looked at me with the usual hard eyes of white contempt. "Move into the car, please move on in the car." She patted her money changer.

Her Southern nasal accent sliced my meditation and I looked deep into my thoughts. All lies, all comfortable lies. The receptionist was not innocent and neither was I. The whole charade[11] we had played out in that crummy waiting room had directly to do with me, Black, and her, white.

I wouldn't move into the streetcar but stood on the ledge over the conductor, glaring. My mind shouted so energetically that the announcement made my veins stand out, and my mouth tighten into a prune.

9. **concocted** [kon kokt′ əd]: made up.
10. **Hamlet and Laertes** [ham′ lit lā ėr′ tēz]: in Shakespeare's *Hamlet*, the prince of Denmark, Hamlet, kills his friend Laertes in a duel at the end of the play.
11. **charade** [shə rād]: meaningless or false action or series of actions.

I WOULD HAVE THE JOB. I WOULD BE A CONDUC-
TORETTE AND SLING A FULL MONEY CHANGER FROM
MY BELT. I WOULD.

The next three weeks were a honeycomb of determination with apertures[12] for the days to go in and out. The Negro organizations to whom I appealed for support bounced me back and forth like a shuttlecock on a badminton court. Why did I insist on that particular job? Openings were going begging that paid nearly twice the money. The minor officials with whom I was able to win an audience thought me mad. Possibly I was.

12. **apertures** [ap′ ər chŭrz]: openings.

Downtown San Francisco became alien and cold, and the streets I had loved in a personal familiarity were unknown lanes that twisted with malicious[13] intent. Old buildings, whose gray rococo façades housed my memories of the Forty-Niners, and Diamond Lil, Robert Service, Sutter and Jack London, were then imposing structures viciously joined to keep me out. My trips to the streetcar office were of the frequency of a person on salary. The struggle expanded. I was no longer in conflict only with the Market Street Railway but with the marble lobby of the building which housed its offices, and elevators and their operators.

During this period of strain Mother and I began our first steps on the long path toward mutual adult admiration. She never asked for reports and I didn't offer any details. But every morning she made breakfast, gave me carfare and lunch money, as if I were going to work. She comprehended the perversity of life, that in the struggle lies the joy. That I was no glory seeker was obvious to her, and that I had to exhaust every possibility before giving in was also clear.

On my way out of the house one morning she said, "Life is going to give you just what you put in it. Put your whole heart in everything you do, and pray, then you can wait." Another time she reminded me that "God helps those who help themselves." She had a store of aphorisms[14] which she dished out as the occasion demanded. Strangely, as bored as I was with clichés, her inflection gave them something new, and set me thinking for a little while at least. Later when asked how I got my job, I was never able to say exactly. I only knew that one day, which was tiresomely like all the others before it, I sat in the Railway office, ostensibly waiting to be interviewed. The receptionist called me to her desk and shuffled a bundle of papers to me. They were job application forms. She said they had to be filled in triplicate. I had little time to wonder if I had won or not, for the standard questions reminded me of the necessity for dexterous[15] lying. How old was I? List my previous jobs, starting from the last held

13. **malicious** [mə lish′ əs]: cruel and spiteful.
14. **aphorisms** [af′ ə riz′ əmz]: short sentences that express a truth or piece of wisdom.
15. **dexterous** [dek′ stər əs]: skillful.

and go backward to the first. How much money did I earn, and why did I leave the position? Give two references (not relatives).

Sitting at a side table my mind and I wove a cat's ladder of near truths and total lies. I kept my face blank (an old art) and wrote quickly the fable of Marguerite Johnson, aged nineteen, former companion and driver for Mrs. Annie Henderson (a White Lady) in Stamps, Arkansas.

I was given blood tests, aptitude tests, physical coordination tests, and Rorschachs, then on a blissful[16] day I was hired as the first Negro on the San Francisco streetcars.

Mother gave me the money to have my blue serge suit tailored, and I learned to fill out work cards, operate the money changer and punch transfers. The time crowded together and at an End of Days I was swinging on the back of the rackety trolley, smiling sweetly and persuading my charges to "step forward in the car, please."

For one whole semester the streetcars and I shimmied up and scooted down the sheer hills of San Francisco. I lost some of my need for the Black ghetto's shielding-sponge quality, as I clanged and cleared my way down Market Street, with its honky-tonk homes for homeless sailors, past the quiet retreat of Golden Gate Park and along closed undwelled-in-looking dwellings of the Sunset District.

My work shifts were split so haphazardly[17] that it was easy to believe that my superiors had chosen them maliciously. Upon mentioning my suspicions to Mother, she said, "Don't worry about it. You ask for what you want, and you pay for what you get. And I'm going to show you that it ain't no trouble when you pack double."

She stayed awake to drive me out to the car barn at four thirty in the mornings, or to pick me up when I was relieved just before dawn. Her awareness of life's perils convinced her that while I would be safe on the public conveyances, she "wasn't about to trust a taxi driver with her baby."

When the spring classes began, I resumed my commitment with formal education. I was so much wiser and older, so much more

16. **blissful** [blis′ fəl]: extremely happy, joyful.
17. **haphazardly** [hap′ haz′ ərd lē]: without being planned ahead.

independent, with a bank account and clothes that I had bought for myself, that I was sure that I had learned and earned the magic formula which would make me a part of the gay life my contemporaries led.

Not a bit of it. Within weeks, I realized that my schoolmates and I were on paths moving diametrically away from each other. They were concerned and excited over the approaching football games, but I had in my immediate past raced a car down a dark and foreign Mexican mountain. They concentrated great interest on who was worthy of being student body president, and when the metal bands would be removed from their teeth, while I remembered sleeping for a month in a wrecked automobile and conducting a streetcar in the uneven hours of the morning.

Without willing it, I had gone from being ignorant of being ignorant to being aware of being aware. And the worst part of my awareness was that I didn't know what I was aware of. I knew I knew very little, but I was certain that the things I had yet to learn wouldn't be taught to me at George Washington High School.

I began to cut classes, to walk in Golden Gate Park or wander along the shiny counter of the Emporium Department Store. When Mother discovered that I was playing truant, she told me that if I didn't want to go to school one day, if there were no tests being held, and if my school work was up to standard, all I had to do was tell her and I could stay home. She said that she didn't want some white woman calling her up to tell her something about her child that she didn't know. And she didn't want to be put in the position of lying to a white woman because I wasn't woman enough to speak up. That put an end to my truancy, but nothing appeared to lighten the long gloomy day that going to school became.

To be left alone on the tightrope of youthful unknowing is to experience the excruciating beauty of full freedom and the threat of eternal indecision. Few, if any, survive their teens. Most surrender to the vague but murderous pressure of adult conformity. It becomes easier to die and avoid conflicts than to maintain a constant battle with the superior forces of maturity.

Until recently each generation found it more expedient to plead guilty to the charge of being young and ignorant, easier to take the punishment meted out by the older generation (which had itself confessed to the same crime short years before). The command to grow up at once was more bearable than the faceless horror of wavering purpose, which was youth.

The bright hours when the young rebelled against the descending sun had to give way to twenty-four-hour periods called "days" that were named as well as numbered.

The Black female is assaulted in her tender years by all those common forces of nature at the same time that she is caught in the tripartite crossfire of masculine prejudice, white illogical hate and Black lack of power.

The fact that the adult American Negro female emerges a formidable character is often met with amazement, distaste and even belligerence. It is seldom accepted as an inevitable outcome of the struggle won by survivors and deserves respect if not enthusiastic acceptance.

MAYA ANGELOU

Maya Angelou was born in 1928 in St. Louis, Missouri. When she was three years old, her parents divorced and sent Angelou and her brother to live with their grandmother in Stamps, Arkansas. Angelou grew up attending the segregated public school there; her high school years were spent in California. Over the years, she studied music, dance, and drama from private teachers.

Angelou had a hard time as a teenager but never gave up on herself. Today she says, "I believe all things are possible for a human being, and I don't think there's anything in the world I can't do." She has become one of the best-known American writers of books, plays, and poetry. She speaks six languages. She has worked in television and lectured in the United States and Ghana. All her life and work, Angelou believes, is about survival.

from *I Know Why the Caged Bird Sings*   35

74th Street

MYRA COHN LIVINGSTON

East Twelfth Street Ben Shahn, 1946, tempera, 22" x 30"

Hey, this little kid gets roller skates.
She puts them on.
She stands up and almost
flops over backwards.
She sticks out a foot like   5
she's going somewhere and
falls down and
smacks her hand. She
grabs hold of a step to get up and
sticks out the other foot and   10
slides about six inches and
falls and
skins her knee.

And then, you know what?

She brushes off the dirt and the   15
blood and puts some
spit on it and then
sticks out the other foot

again.

MYRA COHN LIVINGSTON

Myra Cohn Livingston was born in 1926 in Omaha, Nebraska. Livingston started out as a musician, playing the French horn professionally as a teenager. Then, at eighteen, she published her first poem and began channeling her creativity into writing.

Livingston is also a teacher. She instructs her writing students to "either tell me something I have never heard before or tell me in a new way something I have heard before." Two of her collections are *A Circle of Seasons* and *There Was a Place and Other Poems*.

Above, 1984 Olympic
high diving champion
Greg Louganis, U.S.A.,
and right, 1948
Olympic high diving
champion Sammy Lee,
U.S.A.

THE OLYMPIC GAMES

THEODORE KNIGHT

DETERMINED TO SUCCEED

Not all obstacles are physical. Adversity can take many forms, as the linked stories of Olympic divers Dr. Sammy Lee and Greg Louganis show. Lee was the winner of the gold medal in platform diving and the bronze medal in springboard diving in 1948 and the gold medal in platform diving again in 1952. When Lee captured his second gold medal in 1952 at the age of thirty-two, he went into the record books as the oldest athlete ever to win an Olympic diving medal, but that is not even close to the true measure of his achievement.

Lee was born in California to Korean parents who had fled the Japanese invasion of Korea.[1] Lee's family was too poor to attend the 1932 Games in Los Angeles, but when his father explained what the Olympics were all about, the boy announced that one day he would

1. **Japanese invasion of Korea:** Japan controlled Korea from 1910 until the end of World War II.

be an Olympic champion. "In what sport?" laughed his father. "Gee, I don't know, Pop," the boy replied, "but someday I'll find one." Not long afterward, Lee discovered that he could do things off a diving board that the other kids could not do. Soon he had heavier kids double-bouncing him off the diving board so he could get higher into the air and do more stunts. Diving was fast becoming Lee's passion.

DEALING WITH DISCRIMINATION

In 1936, two things happened that cemented young Lee's determination. The gold medal winner in the marathon[2] was a runner named Kitei Son.[3] Although he was listed as Japanese and running for the Japanese team, Korean-Americans knew that Kitei Son was really Sohn Kee Chung,[4] a Korean forced by the invading Japanese to compete for them. On the victory stand, Chung tore off his Japanese emblem and announced to the world, "I'm Korean, not Japanese." He was immediately seized and whisked away by the Japanese, but not before he had become a hero to Koreans everywhere and especially to young Sammy Lee. The other 1936 Olympian who made an indelible[5] impression on Lee was the black American runner Jesse Owens. Owens had overcome racial prejudice at home and abroad to run brilliantly in the 1936 Olympics. Smarting under the widespread prejudice against Asians in this country, Lee was inspired by Owens's feats and the respect they brought to him.

As a teenager, Lee had difficulty finding pools that would allow him to practice. The public pool in his hometown of Pasadena, California, for example, was open to him only on Mondays. Mondays were designated International Day, when non-whites were allowed to use the facilities. Each Monday evening, it was rumored, the pool was drained and then refilled with clean water. While still a teenager, Lee met and began to train with some of the best divers in the

2. **marathon** [marʹ ə thon]: a race run over a long distance, usually 26 miles, 385 yards.
3. **Kitei Son** [kēʹ tā sōn]
4. **Sohn Kee Chung** [sôn kēʹ chung]
5. **indelible** [in delʹ ə bəl]: permanent.

Sammy Lee (middle) accepts his Olympic gold medal in 1948 along with silver medalist P. Joachin Capilla of Mexico, (left), and bronze medalist Gunther Haase of Germany, (right).

country, among them several former Olympians. One former champion—Farid Simaika,[6] the Egyptian 1928 silver medalist who had moved to this country—gave Lee a piece of advice that he took to heart. He told the young diver that he might encounter prejudice in competition because he was of Korean descent. Simaika told Lee he would simply have to work twice as hard as other athletes. "You've got to be so much better that they have to give you the medal," Simaika said.

COMPETITION AND A CONTINUING COMMITMENT

Lee began to perfect more complex dives than had ever before been done in competition—forward three-and-a-half somersaults, reverse two-and-a-half somersaults and inward two-and-a-half somersaults. Despite his growing success as a diver and his impressive academic achievements, prejudice pursued Lee even to the Olympic Games themselves. In London in 1948, just as Lee began competition in the platform diving competition, he was told that an

6. **Farid Simaika** [fä rēd′ sim ī′ kä]

American swimming association official had been heard telling the diving judges, "I hope you don't favor that Korean." Only Lee's extraordinary confidence and self-control could have enabled him to make one perfect dive after another off that thirty-three-foot diving tower with those vicious words of his fellow countryman ringing in his ears.

Lee won a second gold medal in 1952 in Helsinki, Finland. Although this marked his last Olympic performance, it did not end his close ties to the Olympics. Lee later took time from his medical career to coach a young man named Greg Louganis. Louganis had suffered from a difficult childhood. He was born of Samoan and Swedish parents who gave him up for adoption at birth. He was called nigger by his schoolmates in California because of his dark skin and labeled retarded because he had a severe reading disability called dyslexia.[7] By age thirteen, Louganis was in trouble with the law and addicted to drugs and alcohol. But he also had developed an interest in diving. Lee spotted Louganis diving one day and saw promise in the young man's dives. With Lee's support, Louganis escaped from his difficulties into the world of competitive diving. He showed such promise that he qualified for the Montreal, Canada, Olympics at the age of sixteen. In Montreal in 1976, he finished sixth in the springboard competition and second in the platform diving. In 1984 at Los Angeles, he carried the day with gold medals in both springboard competition and platform diving, becoming the first diver to win the gold in both events since 1928.

The Seoul[8] Olympics in 1988 represented the third and last appearance in a long and remarkable career for Greg Louganis, and the Games provided a fitting conclusion. By 1988, at twenty-eight years old, Louganis was an old man in diving circles, but he was still the favorite in both diving events. Things began very badly, however, in the preliminaries[9] of the springboard competition. Louganis bounced

---

7. **dyslexia** [dis lek′ sē ə]: a brain problem that causes difficulty in reading.
8. **Seoul** [sōl]: the capital of South Korea.
9. **preliminaries** [pri lim′ ə ner′ ēz]: contests that come before the main event.

hard on the board and launched himself high into the air for a two-and-a-half pike.[10] As he twisted and rolled and then plunged back toward the water, his head slammed into the end of the diving board. Spectators and television viewers alike will never forget the loud, hollow sound of Louganis's head hitting the board, the splash as he tumbled into the water, or the suspenseful moments as everyone waited to see if he would surface. Incredibly, Louganis suffered only an ugly gash in

Greg Louganis accepts one of his Olympic gold medals in 1984.

his scalp that was closed with five stitches. He immediately returned to competition and still managed to qualify for the finals. He carried off both gold medals again and became the first man ever to repeat as Olympic champion in both events.

10. **pike** [pīk]: a dive in which the diver bends at the waist, keeps the knees straight, and usually touches the toes.

THEODORE KNIGHT

Theodore Knight was born and grew up in Rhode Island. At one time, Knight managed a large bookstore, but later became a freelance author and editor. Besides *The Olympic Games*, Knight has been writing a book about former President Jimmy Carter. Knight says he admires Carter partly because he didn't just retire but "went on to an important new career" after being president.

Through the Tunnel

DORIS LESSING

Going to the shore on the first morning of the vacation, the young English boy stopped at a turning of the path and looked down at a wild and rocky bay, and then over to the crowded beach he knew so well from other years. His mother walked on in front of him, carrying a bright striped bag in one hand. Her other arm, swinging loose, was very white in the sun. The boy watched that white, naked arm, and turned his eyes, which had a frown behind them, toward the bay and back again to his mother. When she felt he was not with her, she swung around. "Oh, there you are, Jerry!" she said. She looked impatient, then smiled. "Why, darling, would you rather not come with me? Would you rather—" She frowned, conscientiously worrying over what amusements he might secretly be longing for, which she had been too busy or too careless to imagine. He was very familiar with that anxious, apologetic smile. Contrition[1] sent him running after her. And yet, as he ran, he looked back over his shoulder at the wild bay; and all morning, as he played on the safe beach, he was thinking of it.

1. **contrition** [kən trish′ ən]: sorrow for having hurt someone, guilt.

Next morning, when it was time for the routine of swimming and sunbathing, his mother said, "Are you tired of the usual beach, Jerry? Would you like to go somewhere else?"

"Oh, no!" he said quickly, smiling at her out of that unfailing impulse of contrition—a sort of chivalry. Yet, walking down the path with her, he blurted out, "I'd like to go and have a look at those rocks down there."

She gave the idea her attention. It was a wild-looking place, and there was no one there; but she said, "Of course, Jerry. When you've had enough, come to the big beach. Or just go straight back to the villa, if you like." She walked away, that bare arm, now slightly reddened from yesterday's sun, swinging. And he almost ran after her again, feeling it unbearable that she should go by herself, but he did not.

She was thinking, Of course he's old enough to be safe without me. Have I been keeping him too close? He mustn't feel he ought to be with me. I must be careful.

He was an only child, eleven years old. She was a widow. She was determined to be neither possessive nor lacking in devotion. She went worrying off to her beach.

As for Jerry, once he saw that his mother had gained her beach, he began the steep descent to the bay. From where he was, high up among red-brown rocks, it was a scoop of moving bluish green fringed with white. As he went lower, he saw that it spread among small promontories[2] and inlets[3] of rough, sharp rock, and the crisping, lapping surface showed stains of purple and darker blue. Finally, as he ran sliding and scraping down the last few yards, he saw an edge of white surf and the shallow, luminous[4] movement of water over white sand, and, beyond that, a solid, heavy blue.

He ran straight into the water and began swimming. He was a

2. **promontories** [prom′ ən tôr′ ēz]: high points of land extending from the coast into the water.
3. **inlets** [in′ letz]: narrow bays or channels of water extending inland from a large body of water.
4. **luminous** [lü′ mə nəs]: shining, full of light.

good swimmer. He went out fast over the gleaming sand, over a middle region where rocks lay like discolored monsters under the surface, and then he was in the real sea—a warm sea where irregular cold currents from the deep water shocked his limbs.

When he was so far out that he could look back not only on the little bay but past the promontory that was between it and the big beach, he floated on the buoyant surface and looked for his mother. There she was, a speck of yellow under an umbrella that looked like a slice of orange peel. He swam back to shore, relieved at being sure she was there, but all at once very lonely.

On the edge of a small cape that marked the side of the bay away from the promontory was a loose scatter of rocks. Above them, some boys were stripping off their clothes. They came running, naked, down to the rocks. The English boy swam toward them, but kept his distance at a stone's throw. They were of that coast; all of them were burned smooth dark brown and speaking a language he did not understand. To be with them, of them, was a craving that filled his whole body. He swam a little closer; they turned and watched him with narrowed, alert dark eyes. Then one smiled and waved. It was enough. In a minute, he had swum in and was on the rocks beside them, smiling with a desperate, nervous supplication.[5] They shouted cheerful greetings at him; and then, as he preserved his nervous, uncomprehending smile, they understood that he was a foreigner strayed from his own beach, and they proceeded to forget him. But he was happy. He was with them.

They began diving again and again from a high point into a well of blue sea between rough, pointed rocks. After they had dived and come up, they swam around, hauled themselves up, and waited their turn to dive again. They were big boys—men, to Jerry. He dived, and they watched him; and when he swam around to take his place, they made way for him. He felt he was accepted and he dived again, carefully, proud of himself.

Soon the biggest of the boys poised himself, shot down into the

---

5. **supplication** [sup′ lə kā′ shən]: humble begging.

water, and did not come up. The others stood about, watching. Jerry, after waiting for the sleek brown head to appear, let out a yell of warning; they looked at him idly and turned their eyes back toward the water. After a long time, the boy came up on the other side of a big dark rock, letting the air out of his lungs in a sputtering gasp and a shout of triumph. Immediately the rest of them dived in. One moment, the morning seemed full of chattering boys; the next, the air and the surface of the water were empty. But through the heavy blue, dark shapes could be seen moving and groping.

Jerry dived, shot past the school of underwater swimmers, saw a black wall of rock looming at him, touched it, and bobbed up at once to the surface, where the wall was a low barrier he could see across. There was no one visible; under him, in the water, the dim shapes of the swimmers had disappeared. Then one, and then another of the boys came up on the far side of the barrier of rock, and he understood that they had swum through some gap or hole in it. He plunged down again. He could see nothing through the stinging salt water but the blank rock. When he came up the boys were all on the diving rock, preparing to attempt the feat again. And now, in a panic of failure, he yelled up, in English, "Look at me! Look!" and he began splashing and kicking in the water like a foolish dog.

They looked down gravely, frowning. He knew the frown. At moments of failure, when he clowned to claim his mother's attention, it was with just this grave, embarrassed inspection that she rewarded him. Through his hot shame, feeling the pleading grin on his face like a scar that he could never remove, he looked up at the group of big brown boys on the rock and shouted, *"Bonjour! Merci! Au revoir! Monsieur, monsieur!"*[6] while he hooked his fingers round his ears and waggled them.

Water surged into his mouth; he choked, sank, came up. The rock, lately weighted with boys, seemed to rear up out of the water as their weight was removed. They were flying down past him, now, into the water; the air was full of falling bodies. Then the rock was empty in the hot sunlight. He counted one, two, three. . . .

At fifty, he was terrified. They must all be drowning beneath him, in the watery caves of the rock! At a hundred, he stared around him at the empty hillside, wondering if he should yell for help. He counted faster, faster, to hurry them up, to bring them to the surface quickly, to drown them quickly—anything rather than the terror of counting on and on into the blue emptiness of the morning. And then, at a hundred and sixty, the water beyond the rock was full of boys blowing like brown whales. They swam back to the shore without a look at him.

He climbed back to the diving rock and sat down, feeling the hot roughness of it under his thighs. The boys were gathering up their bits of clothing and running off along the shore to another promontory. They were leaving to get away from him. He cried openly, fists in his eyes. There was no one to see him, and he cried himself out.

It seemed to him that a long time had passed, and he swam out to where he could see his mother. Yes, she was still there, a yellow spot under an orange umbrella. He swam back to the big rock, climbed up, and dived into the blue pool among the fanged and angry

6. *"Bonjour! Merci! Au revoir! Monsieur, monsieur!"* [bōn zhür′ mär sē′ ō rə vwär′ mə syœ′]: French for "Hello! Thank you! Good bye! Mister, mister!"

boulders. Down he went, until he touched the wall of rock again. But the salt was so painful in his eyes that he could not see.

He came to the surface, swam to shore and went back to the villa to wait for his mother. Soon she walked slowly up the path, swinging her striped bag, the flushed, naked arm dangling beside her. "I want some swimming goggles," he panted, defiant[7] and beseeching.

She gave him a patient, inquisitive look as she said casually, "Well, of course, darling."

But now, now, now! He must have them this minute, and no other time. He nagged and pestered until she went with him to a shop. As soon as she had bought the goggles, he grabbed them from her hand as if she were going to claim them for herself, and was off, running down the steep path to the bay.

Jerry swam out to the big barrier rock, adjusted the goggles, and dived. The impact of the water broke the rubber-enclosed vacuum, and the goggles came loose. He understood that he must swim down to the base of the rock from the surface of the water. He fixed the goggles tight and firm, filled his lungs, and floated, face down, on the water. Now, he could see. It was as if he had eyes of a different kind—fish eyes that showed everything clear and delicate and wavering in the bright water.

Under him, six or seven feet down, was a floor of perfectly clean, shining white sand, rippled firm and hard by the tides. Two grayish shapes steered there, like long, rounded pieces of wood or slate. They were fish. He saw them nose toward each other, poise motionless, make a dart forward, swerve off, and come around again. It was like a water dance. A few inches above them the water sparkled as if sequins were dropping through it. Fish again—myriads[8] of minute fish, the length of his fingernail, were drifting through the water, and in a moment he could feel the innumerable tiny touches of them against his limbs. It was like swimming in flaked silver. The great rock the big boys had swum through rose sheer out of the white

7. **defiant** [di fī′ ənt]: challenging authority, bold.
8. **myriads** [mir′ ē ədz]: a very great number.

sand—black, tufted lightly with greenish weed. He could see no gap in it. He swam down to its base.

Again and again he rose, took a big chestful of air, and went down. Again and again he groped over the surface of the rock, feeling it, almost hugging it in the desperate need to find the entrance. And then, once, while he was clinging to the black wall, his knees came up and he shot his feet out forward and they met no obstacle. He had found the hole.

He gained the surface, clambered about the stones that littered the barrier rock until he found a big one, and, with this in his arms, let himself down over the side of the rock. He dropped, with the weight, straight to the sandy floor. Clinging tight to the anchor of stone, he lay on his side and looked in under the dark shelf at the place where his feet had gone. He could see the hole. It was an irregular, dark gap; but he could not see deep into it. He let go of his anchor, clung with his hands to the edges of the hole, and tried to push himself in.

He got his head in, found his shoulders jammed, moved them in sidewise, and was inside as far as his waist. He could see nothing ahead. Something soft and clammy touched his mouth; he saw a dark frond[9] moving against the grayish rock, and panic filled him. He thought

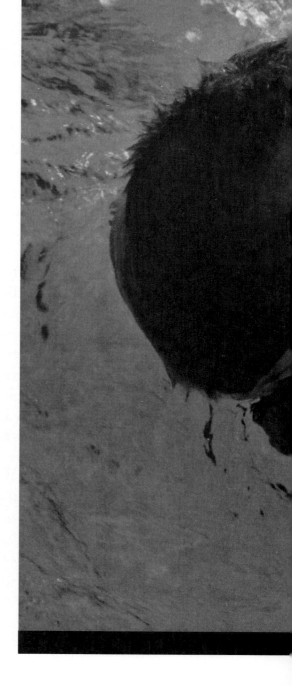

9. **frond:** a large leaf.

of octopuses, of clinging weed. He pushed himself out backward and caught a glimpse, as he retreated, of a harmless tentacle of seaweed drifting in the mouth of the tunnel. But it was enough. He reached the sunlight, swam to shore, and lay on the diving rock. He looked down into the blue well of water. He knew he must find his way through that cave, or hole, or tunnel, and out the other side.

First, he thought, he must learn to control his breathing. He let himself down into the water with another big stone in his arms, so that he could lie effortlessly on the bottom of the sea. He counted. One, two, three. He counted steadily. He could hear the movement of blood in his chest. Fifty-one, fifty-two. . . . His chest was hurting. He let go of the rock and went up into the air. He saw that the sun was low. He rushed to the villa and found his mother at her supper. She said only "Did you enjoy yourself?" and he said "Yes."

All night the boy dreamed of the water-filled cave in the rock, and as soon as breakfast was over he went to the bay.

That night, his nose bled badly. For hours he had been underwater, learning to hold his breath, and now he felt weak and dizzy. His mother said, "I shouldn't overdo things, darling, if I were you."

That day and the next, Jerry exercised his lungs as if everything, the whole of his life, all that he would become, depended upon it. Again his nose bled at night, and his mother insisted on his coming with her the next day. It was a torment to him to waste a day of his careful self-training, but he stayed with her on that other beach, which now seemed a place for small children, a place where his mother might lie safe in the sun. It was not his beach.

He did not ask for permission, on the following day, to go to his beach. He went, before his mother could consider the complicated rights and wrongs of the matter. A day's rest, he discovered, had improved his count by ten. The big boys had made the passage while he counted a hundred and sixty. He had been counting fast, in his fright. Probably now, if he tried, he could get through that long tunnel, but he was not going to try yet. A curious, most unchildlike persistence, a controlled impatience, made him wait. In the meantime, he lay underwater on the white sand, littered now by stones he had brought down from the upper air, and studied the entrance to the tunnel. He knew every jut and corner of it, as far as it was possible to see. It was as if he already felt its sharpness about his shoulders.

He sat by the clock in the villa, when his mother was not near, and checked his time. He was incredulous and then proud to find he could hold his breath without strain for two minutes. The words "two minutes," authorized by the clock, brought close the adventure that was so necessary to him.

In another four days, his mother said casually one morning, they must go home. On the day before they left, he would do it. He would do it if it killed him, he said defiantly to himself. But two days before they were to leave—a day of triumph when he increased his count by fifteen—his nose bled so badly that he turned dizzy and had to lie limply over the big rock like a bit of seaweed, watching the thick red blood flow on to the rock and trickle slowly down to the sea. He was frightened. Supposing he turned dizzy in the tunnel? Supposing he died there, trapped? Supposing—his head went around, in the hot sun, and he almost gave up. He thought he would return to the house and lie down, and next summer, perhaps, when he had another year's growth in him—*then* he would go through the hole.

But even after he had made the decision, or thought he had, he found himself sitting up on the rock and looking down into the water; and he knew that now, this moment, when his nose had only just stopped bleeding, when his head was still sore and throbbing—this was the moment when he would try. If he did not do it now, he never would. He was trembling with fear that he would not go; and he was trembling with horror at that long, long tunnel under the rock, under the sea. Even in the open sunlight, the barrier rock seemed very wide and very heavy; tons of rock pressed down on where he would go. If he died there, he would lie until one day—perhaps not before next year—those big boys would swim into it and find it blocked.

He put on his goggles, fitted them tight, tested the vacuum. His hands were shaking. Then he chose the biggest stone he could carry and slipped over the edge of the rock until half of him was in the cool, enclosing water and half in the hot sun. He looked up once at the empty sky, filled his lungs once, twice, and then sank fast to the bottom with the stone. He let it go and began to count. He took the edges of the hole in his hands and drew himself into it, wriggling his shoulders in sidewise as he remembered he must, kicking himself along with his feet.

Soon he was clear inside. He was in a small rock-bound hole filled with yellowish-gray water. The water was pushing him up against the roof. The roof was sharp and pained his back. He pulled himself along with his hands—fast, fast—and used his legs as levers. His head knocked against something; a sharp pain dizzied him. Fifty, fifty-one, fifty-two. . . . He was without light, and the water seemed to press upon him with the weight of rock. Seventy-one, seventy-two. . . . There was no strain on his lungs. He felt like an inflated balloon, his lungs were so light and easy, but his head was pulsing.

He was being continually pressed against the sharp roof, which felt slimy as well as sharp. Again he thought of octopuses, and wondered if the tunnel might be filled with weed that could tangle him. He gave himself a panicky, convulsive[10] kick forward, ducked his head, and swam. His feet and hands moved freely, as if in open water. The hole must have widened out. He thought he must be swimming fast, and he was frightened of banging his head if the tunnel narrowed.

A hundred, a hundred and one. . . . The water paled. Victory filled him. His lungs were beginning to hurt. A few more strokes and he would be out. He was counting wildly; he said a hundred and fifteen, and then, a long time later, a hundred and fifteen again. The water was a clear jewel-green all around him. Then he saw, above his head, a crack running up through the rock. Sunlight was falling through it, showing the clean, dark rock of the tunnel, a single mussel shell, and darkness ahead.

He was at the end of what he could do. He looked up at the crack as if it were filled with air and not water, as if he could put his mouth to it to draw in air. A hundred and fifteen, he heard himself say inside his head—but he had said that long ago. He must go on

10. **convulsive** [kən vul′ siv]: unintentionally violent and fast.

into the blackness ahead, or he would drown. His head was swelling, his lungs cracking. A hundred and fifteen, a hundred and fifteen pounded through his head, and he feebly clutched at rocks in the dark, pulling himself forward, leaving the brief space of sunlit water behind. He felt he was dying. He was no longer quite conscious. He struggled on in the darkness between lapses into unconsciousness. An immense, swelling pain filled his head, and then the darkness cracked with an explosion of green light. His hands, groping forward, met nothing; and his feet, kicking back, propelled him out into the open sea.

He drifted to the surface, his face turned up to the air. He was gasping like a fish. He felt he would sink now and drown; he could not swim the few feet back to the rock. Then he was clutching it and pulling himself up on to it. He lay face down, gasping. He could see nothing but a red-veined, clotted dark. His eyes must have burst, he thought; they were full of blood. He tore off his goggles and a gout of blood went into the sea. His nose was bleeding, and the blood had filled the goggles.

He scooped up handfuls of water from the cool, salty sea, to splash on his face, and did not know whether it was blood or salt water he tasted. After a time, his heart quieted, his eyes cleared, and he sat up. He could see the local boys diving and playing half a mile away. He did not want them. He wanted nothing but to get back home and lie down.

In a short while, Jerry swam to shore and climbed slowly up the path to the villa. He flung himself on his bed and slept, waking at the sound of feet on the path outside. His mother was coming back. He rushed to the bathroom, thinking she must not see his face with bloodstains, or tearstains, on it. He came out of the bathroom and met her as she walked into the villa, smiling, her eyes lighting up.

"Have a nice morning?" she asked, laying her hand on his warm brown shoulder a moment.

"Oh, yes, thank you," he said.

"You look a bit pale." And then, sharp and anxious, "How did you bang your head?"

"Oh, just banged it," he told her.

She looked at him closely. He was strained; his eyes were glazed-looking. She was worried. And then she said to herself, Oh, don't fuss! Nothing can happen. He can swim like a fish.

They sat down to lunch together.

"Mummy," he said, "I can stay under water for two minutes—three minutes, at least." It came bursting out of him.

"Can you, darling?" she said. "Well, I shouldn't overdo it. I don't think you ought to swim any more today."

She was ready for a battle of wills, but he gave in at once. It was no longer of the least importance to go to the bay.

DORIS LESSING

Doris Lessing was born in 1919 to a British family living in Iran. She grew up in the African country then called Southern Rhodesia, now Zimbabwe. She never visited England until she was thirty. Lessing became a writer in Africa, and she writes of life there.

Lessing left school early and began writing at eighteen. (She tore up her first six novels.) Her first published novel was a success. She went on to write more, including science fiction and nonfiction. Lessing has always been concerned with politics and social issues. But short stories are her favorite form.

As a recognized writer, Lessing tried an experiment. She wrote two novels under the pseudonym Jane Somers. They were published, but the critics ignored them and the publisher's lack of advertising kept them from selling well. It showed, Lessing said, why it can be so hard for unknown writers to become known, even when they write well!

Cornfield with Cypresses Vincent Van Gogh, 1889, oil on canvas, 28 ¹/₂" x 36", National Gallery, London

For Poets
AL YOUNG

Stay beautiful
but dont stay down underground too long
Dont turn into a mole
or a worm
or a root   5
or a stone

Come on out into the sunlight
Breathe in trees
Knock out mountains
Commune[1] with snakes   10
& be the very hero of birds

Dont forget to poke your head up
& blink
Think
Walk all around   15
Swim upstream

Dont forget to fly

---

1. **commune** [kə myün′]: communicate
   effortlessly as with a good friend.

AL YOUNG

Al Young was born in 1939 in Ocean Springs, Mississippi. His father
was an auto worker and professional musician. Following in his footsteps,
Young started out at eighteen as a jazz musician, playing guitar and flute
and singing professionally while attending the University of Michigan. He
also began writing poetry.

Young's first book, *Dancing: Poems,* was published in 1969; he
published his first novel the following year. Critics have praised him for
capturing the rhythms of African American music in his writing. They have
also praised his creation of convincing characters who struggle with the
problems of real life that face everyone.

You can find "For Poets" and other poems in Young's book, *The Song
Turning Back into Itself.*

RAYMOND'S RUN

TONI CADE BAMBARA

I don't have much work to do around the house like some girls. My mother does that. And I don't have to earn my pocket money by hustling; George runs errands for the big boys and sells Christmas cards. And anything else that's got to get done, my father does. All I have to do in life is mind my brother Raymond, which is enough.

Sometimes I slip and say my little brother Raymond. But as any fool can see he's much bigger and he's older too. But a lot of people call him my little brother cause he needs looking after cause he's not quite right. And a lot of smart mouths got lots to say about that too, especially when George was minding him. But now, if anybody has anything to say to Raymond, anything to say about his big head, they have to come by me. And I don't play the dozens or believe in standing around with somebody in my face doing a lot of talking. I much rather just knock you down and take my chances even if I am a little girl with skinny arms and a squeaky voice, which is how I got the name Squeaky. And if things get too rough, I run. And as anybody can tell you, I'm the fastest thing on two feet.

There is no track meet that I don't win the first place medal. I used to win the twenty-yard dash when I was a little kid in kindergarten. Nowadays, it's the fifty-yard dash. And tomorrow I'm subject to run the quarter-meter relay all by myself and come in first, second, and third. The big kids call me Mercury[1] cause I'm the swiftest thing in the neighborhood. Everybody knows that—except two people who know better, my father and me. He can beat me to Amsterdam Avenue with me having a two fire-hydrant headstart and him running with his hands in his pockets and whistling. But that's private information. Cause can you imagine some thirty-five-year-old man stuffing himself into PAL[2] shorts to race little kids? So as far as everyone's concerned, I'm the fastest and that goes for Gretchen, too, who has put out the tale that she is going to win the first-place medal this year. Ridiculous. In the second place, she's got short legs. In the third place, she's got freckles. In the first place, no one can beat me and that's all there is to it.

1. **Mercury** [mėr′ kyər ē]: in Roman myths, the fast-moving messenger of the gods.
2. **PAL:** Police Athletic League.

I'm standing on the corner admiring the weather and about to take a stroll down Broadway so I can practice my breathing exercises, and I've got Raymond walking on the inside close to the buildings, cause he's subject to fits of fantasy and starts thinking he's a circus performer and that the curb is a tightrope strung high in the air. And sometimes after a rain he likes to step down off his tightrope right into the gutter and slosh around getting his shoes and cuffs wet. Then I get hit when I get home. Or sometimes if you don't watch him he'll dash across traffic to the island in the middle of Broadway and give the pigeons a fit. Then I have to go behind him apologizing to all the old people sitting around trying to get some sun and getting all upset with the pigeons fluttering around them, scattering their newspapers and upsetting the waxpaper lunches in their laps. So I keep Raymond on the inside of me, and he plays like he's driving a stage coach which is O.K. by me so long as he doesn't run me over or interrupt my breathing exercises, which I have to do on account of I'm serious about my running, and I don't care who knows it.

Now some people like to act like things come easy to them, won't let on that they practice. Not me. I'll high-prance down 34th Street like a rodeo pony to keep my knees strong even if it does get my mother uptight so that she walks ahead like she's not with me, don't know me, is all by herself on a shopping trip, and I am somebody else's crazy child. Now you take Cynthia Procter for instance. She's just the opposite. If there's a test tomorrow, she'll say something like, "Oh, I guess I'll play handball this afternoon and watch television tonight," just to let you know she ain't thinking about the test. Or like last week when she won the spelling bee for the millionth time, "A good thing you got 'receive,' Squeaky, cause I would have got it wrong. I completely forgot about the spelling bee." And she'll clutch the lace on her blouse like it was a narrow escape. Oh, brother. But of course when I pass her house on my early morning trots around the block, she is practicing the scales on the piano over and over and over and over. Then in music class she always lets herself get bumped around so she falls accidently on purpose onto the piano stool and is so surprised to find herself sitting there that she decides just for fun to try out the ole keys. And what do you know—Chopin's[3] waltzes just spring out of her fingertips and she's the most surprised thing in the world. A regular prodigy.[4] I could kill people like that. I stay up all night studying the words for the spelling bee. And you can see me any time of day practicing running. I never walk if I can trot, and shame on Raymond if he can't keep up. But of course he does, cause if he hangs back someone's liable to walk up to him and get smart, or take his allowance from him, or ask him where he got that great big pumpkin head. People are so stupid sometimes.

So I'm strolling down Broadway breathing out and breathing in on counts of seven, which is my lucky number, and here comes Gretchen and her sidekicks: Mary Louise, who used to be a friend of mine when she first moved to Harlem from Baltimore and got beat up by everybody till I took up for her on account of her mother and my mother used to sing in the same choir when they were young girls, but people ain't grateful, so now she hangs out with the new girl Gretchen and talks about me like a dog; and Rosie, who is as fat as I am skinny and has a big mouth where Raymond is concerned and is too stupid to know that there is not a big deal of difference between herself and Raymond and that she can't afford to throw stones. So they are steady coming up Broadway and I see right away that it's going to be one of those Dodge City scenes cause the street ain't that big and they're close to the buildings just as we are. First I think I'll step into the candy store and look over the new comics and let them pass. But that's chicken and I've got a reputation to consider. So then I think I'll just walk straight on through them or even over them if necessary. But as they get to me, they slow down. I'm ready to fight, cause like I said I don't feature a whole lot of chit-chat, I much prefer to just knock you down right from the jump and save everybody a lotta precious time.

"You signing up for the May Day[5] races?" smiles Mary Louise,

---

3. **Chopin** [shō′ pan]: Polish composer and pianist of the nineteenth century who lived in France.
4. **prodigy** [prod′ ə jē]: young person who is extremely brilliant and talented.
5. **May Day:** May 1, in some countries the traditional day for celebrating spring with games and dancing around a pole decorated with colored ribbons.

only it's not a smile at all. A dumb question like that doesn't deserve an answer. Besides, there's just me and Gretchen standing there really, so no use wasting my breath talking to shadows.

"I don't think you're going to win this time," says Rosie, trying to signify with her hands on her hips all salty, completely forgetting that I have whupped her behind many times for less salt than that.

"I always win cause I'm the best," I say straight at Gretchen who is, as far as I'm concerned, the only one talking in this ventriloquist-dummy routine. Gretchen smiles, but it's not a smile, and I'm thinking that girls never really smile at each other because they don't know how and don't want to know how and there's probably no one to teach us how, cause grown-up girls don't know either. Then they all look at Raymond who has just brought his mule team to a stand-still. And they're about to see what trouble they can get into through him.

"What grade you in now, Raymond?"

"You got anything to say to my brother, you say it to me, Mary Louise Williams of Raggedy Town, Baltimore."

"What are you, his mother?" sasses Rosie.

"That's right, Fatso. And the next word out of anybody and I'll be *their* mother too." So they just stand there and Gretchen shifts from one leg to the other and so do they. Then Gretchen puts her hands on her hips and is about to say something with her freckle-face self but doesn't. Then she walks around me looking me up and down but keeps walking up Broadway, and her sidekicks follow her. So me and Raymond smile at each other and he says, "Gidyap" to his team and I continue with my breathing exercises, strolling down Broadway toward the ice man on 145th with not a care in the world cause I am Miss Quicksilver herself.

I take my time getting to the park on May Day because the track meet is the last thing on the program. The biggest thing on the program is the May Pole dancing, which I can do without, thank you, even if my mother thinks it's a shame I don't take part and act like a girl for a change. You'd think my mother'd be grateful not to have to make me a white organdy[6] dress with a big satin sash and buy me new white

---

6. **organdy** [ôr′ gən dē′]: fine, transparent material.

baby-doll shoes that can't be taken out of the box till the big day. You'd think she'd be glad her daughter ain't out there prancing around a May Pole getting the new clothes all dirty and sweaty and trying to act like a fairy or a flower or whatever you're supposed to be when you should be trying to be yourself, whatever that is, which is, as far as I am concerned, a poor Black girl who really can't afford to buy shoes and a new dress you only wear once a lifetime cause it won't fit next year.

I was once a strawberry in a Hansel and Gretel pageant when I was in nursery school and didn't have no better sense than to dance on tiptoe with my arms in a circle over my head doing umbrella steps and being a perfect fool just so my mother and father could come dressed up and clap. You'd think they'd know better than to encourage that kind of nonsense. I am not a strawberry. I do not dance on my toes. I run. That is what I am all about. So I always come late to the May Day program, just in time to get my number pinned on and lay in the grass till they announce the fifty-yard dash.

I put Raymond in the little swings, which is a tight squeeze this year and will be impossible next year. Then I look around for Mr. Pearson, who pins the numbers on. I'm really looking for Gretchen if you want to know the truth, but she's not around. The park is jam-packed. Parents in hats and corsages and breast-pocket handkerchiefs peeking up. Kids in white dresses and light-blue suits. The parkees unfolding chairs and chasing the rowdy kids from Lenox as if they had no right to be there. The big guys with their caps on backwards, leaning against the fence swirling the basketballs on the tips of their fingers, waiting for all these crazy people to clear out the park so they can play. Most of the kids in my class are carrying bass drums and glockenspiels[7] and flutes. You'd think they'd put in a few bongos or something for real like that.

Then here comes Mr. Pearson with his clipboard and his cards and pencils and whistles and safety pins and fifty million other things he's always dropping all over the place with his clumsy self. He sticks

---

7. **glockenspiels** [glok′ ən spēlz]: musical instruments played by striking two hammers on metal bells, bars, or tubes that are mounted in two rows in a frame.

out in a crowd because he's on stilts. We used to call him Jack and the Beanstalk to get him mad. But I'm the only one that can outrun him and get away, and I'm too grown for that silliness now.

"Well, Squeaky," he says, checking my name off the list and handing me number seven and two pins. And I'm thinking he's got no right to call me Squeaky, if I can't call him Beanstalk.

"Hazel Elizabeth Deborah Parker," I correct him and tell him to write it down on his board.

"Well, Hazel Elizabeth Deborah Parker, going to give someone else a break this year?" I squint at him real hard to see if he is seriously thinking I should lose the race on purpose just to give someone else a break. "Only six girls running this time," he continues, shaking his head sadly like it's my fault all of New York didn't turn out in sneakers. "That new girl should give you a run for your money." He looks around the park for Gretchen like a periscope in a submarine movie. "Wouldn't it be a nice gesture if you were . . . to ahhh . . . "

I give him such a look he couldn't finish putting that idea into words. Grownups got a lot of nerve sometimes. I pin number seven to myself and stomp away, I'm so burnt. And I go straight for the track and stretch out on the grass while the band winds up with "Oh, the Monkey Wrapped His Tail Around the Flag Pole," which my teacher calls by some other name. The man on the loudspeaker is calling everyone over to the track and I'm on my back looking at the sky, trying to pretend I'm in the country, but I can't, because even grass in the city feels hard as sidewalk, and there's just no pretending you are anywhere but in a "concrete jungle" as my grandfather says.

The twenty-yard dash takes all of two minutes cause most of the little kids don't know no better than to run off the track or run the wrong way or run smack into the fence and fall down and cry. One little kid, though, has got the good sense to run straight for the white ribbon up ahead so he wins. Then the second-graders line up for the thirty-yard dash and I don't even bother to turn my head to watch cause Raphael Perez always wins. He wins before he even begins by psyching the runners, telling them they're going to trip on their shoelaces and fall on their faces or lose their shorts or something,

which he doesn't really have to do since he is very fast, almost as fast as I am. After that is the forty-yard dash which I use to run when I was in first grade. Raymond is hollering from the swings cause he knows I'm about to do my thing cause the man on the loudspeaker has just announced the fifty-yard dash, although he might just as well be giving a recipe for angel food cake cause you can hardly make out what he's sayin for the static. I get up and slip off my sweat pants and then I see Gretchen standing at the starting line, kicking her legs out like a pro. Then as I get into place I see that ole Raymond is on line on the other side of the fence, bending down with his fingers on the ground just like he knew what he was doing. I was going to yell at him but then I didn't. It burns up your energy to holler.

Every time, just before I take off in a race, I always feel like I'm in a dream, the kind of dream you have when you're sick with fever and feel all hot and weightless. I dream I'm flying over a sandy beach in the early morning sun, kissing the leaves of the trees as I fly by. And there's always the smell of apples, just like in the country when I was little and used to think I was a choo-choo train, running through the fields of corn and chugging up the hill to the orchard. And all the time I'm dreaming this, I get lighter and lighter until I'm flying over the beach again, getting blown through the sky like a feather that weighs nothing at all. But once I spread my fingers in the dirt and crouch over the Get on Your Mark, the dream goes and I am solid again and am telling myself, Squeaky you must win, you must win, you are the fastest thing in the world, you can even beat your father up Amsterdam if you really try. And then I feel my weight coming back just behind my knees then down to my feet then into the earth and the pistol shot explodes in my blood and I am off and weightless again, flying past the other runners, my arms pumping up and down and the whole world is quiet except for the crunch as I zoom over the gravel in the track. I glance to my left and there is no one. To the right, a blurred Gretchen, who's got her chin jutting out as if it would win the race all by itself. And on the other side of the fence is Raymond with his arms down to his side and the palms tucked up behind him, running in his very own style, and it's the first time I ever saw that and I almost stop to watch my brother Raymond on his first run. But the white ribbon is bouncing toward me and I tear past it, racing into the distance till my feet with a mind of their own start digging up footfuls of dirt and brake me short. Then all the kids standing on the side pile on me, banging me on the back and slapping my head with their May Day programs, for I have won again and everybody on 151st Street can walk tall for another year.

"In first place . . ." the man on the loudspeaker is clear as a bell now. But then he pauses and the loudspeaker starts to whine. Then static. And I lean down to catch my breath and here comes Gretchen walking back, for she's overshot the finish line too, huffing and puffing with her hands on her hips taking it slow, breathing in steady time like a real pro and I sort of like her a little for the first time. "In first place . . ." and then three or four voices get all mixed up on the loudspeaker and I dig my sneaker into the grass and stare at Gretchen who's staring back, we both wondering just who did win. I can hear old Beanstalk arguing with the man on the loudspeaker and then a few others running their mouths about what the stopwatches say. Then I hear Raymond yanking at the fence to call me and I wave to shush him, but he keeps rattling the fence like a gorilla in a cage like in them gorilla movies, but then like a dancer or something he starts climbing up nice and easy but very fast. And it occurs to me, watching how smoothly he climbs hand over hand and remembering how he looked running with his arms down to his side and with the wind pulling his mouth back and his teeth showing and all, it occurred to me that Raymond would make a very fine runner. Doesn't he always keep up with me on my trots? And he surely knows how to breathe in counts of seven cause he's always doing it at the dinner table, which drives my brother George up the wall. And I'm smiling to beat the band cause if I've lost this race, or if me and Gretchen tied, or even if I've won, I can always retire as a runner and begin a whole new career as a coach with Raymond as my champion. After all, with a little more study I can beat Cynthia and her phony self at the spelling bee. And if I bugged my mother, I could get piano lessons and become a star. And I have a big rep as the baddest thing around.

And I've got a roomful of ribbons and medals and awards. But what has Raymond got to call his own?

So I stand there with my new plans, laughing out loud by this time as Raymond jumps down from the fence and runs over with his teeth showing and his arms down to the side, which no one before him has quite mastered as a running style. And by the time he comes over I'm jumping up and down so glad to see him—my brother Raymond, a great runner in the family tradition. But of course everyone thinks I'm jumping up and down because the men on the loudspeaker have finally gotten themselves together and compared notes and are announcing "In first place—Miss Hazel Elizabeth Deborah Parker." (Dig that.) "In second place—Miss Gretchen P. Lewis." And I look over at Gretchen wondering what the "P" stands for. And I smile. Cause she's good, no doubt about it. Maybe she'd like to help me coach Raymond; she obviously is serious about running, as any fool can see. And she nods to congratulate me and then she smiles. And I smile. We stand there with this big smile of respect between us. It's about as real a smile as girls can do for each other, considering we don't practice real smiling every day, you know, cause maybe we too busy being flowers or fairies or strawberries instead of something honest and worthy of respect . . . you know . . . like being people.

TONI CADE BAMBARA

Toni Cade Bambara was born in 1939 in New York City and grew up there, graduating from Queens College. Bambara became a civil rights activist, a professor of English and African American studies, an editor of anthologies of African American literature, and an author. At the same time, she has never stopped working in community programs.

"Raymond's Run" is one of the stories you'll find in Bambara's first book, *Gorilla, My Love*.

What a Boy

ALBERTO RÍOS

February, and the wind has begun
Milk cartons moving along the curb,
An occasional wrapper, Baby Ruth.

The young tree bends in a hoeing.
Cirrus[1] clouds, sparrows, jet trailings: 5
Each puts a line on the sky. February

Kites, too, their shapes: the way three
Boys have taken their baseball fields
Into the air, flying them on strings.

When I flew my kite I shouted, louder,   10
Anything, strong, boy wild and rocks:
February was here. I was helping.

1. **cirrus** [sir′ əs]: high, thin, feathery, white clouds.

Cañ Do

ALBERTO RÍOS

Alberto Ríos was born in 1952 in Nogales, Arizona. Since his father was born in Mexico and his mother in England, he is a first-generation American. Ríos majored in English literature and creative writing at the University of Arizona. He wrote poetry and later began also writing fiction and drama.

Ríos speaks Spanish and has written a great deal from the Mexican side of his heritage. England, he has said, "is supposed to always wait for me." But the death of his English grandmother, a woman he had never met, was a reminder that parts of life do not wait forever.

Ríos's poem "What a Boy Can Do" is from his book *Teodoro Luna's Two Kisses*.

THUMBPRINT

EVE MERRIAM

In the heel of my thumb
are whorls,[1] whirls, wheels
in a unique design:
mine alone.   5
What a treasure to own!
My own flesh, my own feelings.
No other, however grand or base,
can ever contain the same.
My signature,   10
thumbing the pages of my time.
My universe key,
my singularity.
Impress, implant,
I am myself,   15
of all my atom parts I am the sum.
And out of my blood and my brain
I make my own interior weather,
my own sun and rain.
Imprint my mark upon the world,   20
whatever I shall become.

1. **whorls** [hwôrlz]: circular fingerprint patterns on
   the fingertips by which people can be identified.

EVE MERRIAM

Eve Merriam [1916-1992] was born in Philadelphia, Pennsylvania. She began her long and busy career in New York as a radio writer for Columbia Broadcasting System during the early l940s. She published her first book of poems, *Family Circle,* in l946, and wrote for *Glamour* and other fashion magazines. Throughout her life Merriam wrote steadily, publishing many books of poetry as well as fiction and nonfiction.

Merriam's many interests included travel, sports, and living in the city. Most of all, she loved her work. "I am fortunate that my work is my main pleasure," she once said, "and, while I find all forms of writing absorbing, I like poetry as the most immediate and richest form of communication."

Merriam loved humor, too. One of her last books is called *Chortles: New and Selected Wordplay Poems.*

PICTURES ON A ROCK

One spring day a few years before the Rough Rock Demonstration School was opened, a five-year-old Navajo[1] boy named Fred Bia was watching the family sheep flock in the arid[2] countryside near the little town. It was his daily chore to follow the sheep as they drifted over the red, rocky earth in their endless search for grass and the leaves of semi-desert plants. He had covered this ground so many times that he no longer paid any attention to where he was, his thoughts wandering as he moved slowly with the animals.

When he saw the rock in front of him, he knew he was in a place that he had not been before, and he could not believe his eyes. The big red rock was covered with drawings of people and animals. Fred stood very still as he stared at them, and an excitement he had never felt before raced through his blood. Who had made these pictures? When? He had no idea. There were no drawings on the other rocks around him, only those he was staring at. He was almost hypnotized and though he had no way of knowing it, in that moment Fred Bia, Navajo artist, was born.

When he finally looked away from the rock, he saw that his sheep were nearly out of sight, and he ran to catch up with them. But he did not forget the drawings on the rock. He thought about them that night, and the next day he returned to the rock. The same feeling of excitement came back to him. He picked up a small chalky stone, went to a large rock nearby, and did his best to copy the drawings of people and animals he saw on the red rock.

1. **Navajo** [nav′ ə hō]: Native American nation of New Mexico, Arizona, and Utah.
2. **arid** [ar′ id]: dry, having little rainfall.

Later that day in another part of the rocky semidesert where he had followed his sheep, Fred drew the pictures from memory on other rocks. In the days and weeks that followed he drew other pictures, some from his imagination, some from the things in nature around him. By the time he entered first grade, Fred's pictures covered many of the big rocks around Rough Rock.

In school Fred discovered crayons, and fortunately he had teachers who quickly saw that the boy had a real drawing ability and an unusual fascination with making pictures. They encouraged him and saw that he had plenty of crayons and paper. When Fred went to high school in Chinle and Fort Wingate[3] the encouragement continued, and his powers as a pictorial artist grew.

After he graduated from high school, he was accepted as a student at the Institute of American Indian Art in Santa Fe.[4] Fred began in elementary classes, but his instructors at this special school for promising Indian artists moved him to advanced classes.

Fred spent two years at the art institute and then embarked on a career as a professional artist. Today he is one of a small number of Indian artists whose work sells steadily and brings substantial prices. Major fame remains in the future, but he has established himself as a solid professional painter whose work is in a number of western art galleries and museums and in such private collections as that of famous country-music singer Johnny Cash.

"I want to be thought of as a painter, not as a Navajo painter or an Indian painter," Fred says. "But I draw my subjects from the Navajo world, the people and the land, because that is what I know."

Fred returned to Rough Rock to live, and for the past three years he has given much of his time to illustrating a series of Navajo social studies books that the Rough Rock Demonstration School is producing for grades kindergarten through twelve. The books will be made available to all Navajo schools. His powerful black-and-white

3. **Chinle and Fort Wingate** [chin′ lē]: a town on the Navajo Reservation in northeastern Arizona; a town on the Navajo Reservation in northwestern New Mexico.
4. **Sante Fe** [san′ tə fā′]: capital of New Mexico, situated in the northern part of the state.

drawings of Black Mesa,[5] Shiprock,[6] and other Navajo landmarks, as well as faithful visual portraits of Navajo people and cultural objects, will give Navajo school-children a new and exciting look at themselves and their world as Navajos.

Fred sometimes talks about the day that changed his life, the day he saw the drawings on the rock in the desert. He never learned how the drawings got there or what they were. He does not think they were ancient pictographs, although there are many of them in Navajo country. They may have been the work of a shaman[7] or medicine man, but Fred does not think they were that either.

"They were just there, and I saw them," he says. "I am very glad I did."

5. **Black Mesa** [māʹ sə]: a mesa, a high plateau with a flat top and steep sides, in New Mexico.
6. **Shiprock:** a town on the Navajo Reservation in northwestern New Mexico.
7. **shaman** [shäʹ mən]

Navajo artist Fred Bía and his daughter

BRENT ASHABRANNER

Brent Ashabranner was born in 1921 in Shawnee, Oklahoma. He began writing as a young boy and published his first short story when he was twenty. Although Ashabranner has written more short stories, most of his writing has been nonfiction—some coauthored with his friend Russell Davis.

Ashabranner writes of the people he has come to know and their lives in the places where they live. He has drawn on his many years of travel and work in a score of countries around the world.

One of Ashabranner's books is a memoir, *The Times of My Life,* that tells of his experiences, from his Oklahoma childhood during the Great Depression through his volunteer work with the Peace Corps during the 1960s.

On SHARK'S TOOTH BEACH

E. L. KONIGSBURG

My dad is Hixon of Hixon's Landing, the fishing camp down on the intracoastal waterway just across Highway A1A. Our camp isn't a fancy one. Just two coolers, one for beer and one for bait, plus four boats and eight motors that we rent out.

Dad was raised on a farm in Nebraska, but he joined the Navy and signed on for the war in Vietnam[1] and came back knowing two things. One, he hated war, and two, he loved the sea. Actually, he came back with two loves. The other one was my mother. There wasn't *any* way *any*one could get him to settle *any*where that was far from the ocean when he got out of the service, so he bought this small stretch of land in north Florida, and we've been there for all of my life that I can remember.

Dad's got this small pension[2] for getting wounded over in Nam, so between what we sell, what we rent and what the government sends, we do all right. We're not what you're likely to call rich, but we are all right. Mom doubts that we'll ever make enough money to pay for a trip to her native country of Thailand, but she doesn't seem to mind. She says that it is more important to love where you're at than to love where you're from.

1. **Vietnam** [vē et′ näm′]: country in Southeast Asia where the United States was involved in a war from about 1957 to 1973.
2. **pension** [pen′ shən]: here, a fixed amount of money paid regularly by the government to a war veteran, especially one who has been wounded.

Mom makes and sells sandwiches for the fishermen. She does a right good job on them, I can tell you. There is this about Mom's sandwiches: you don't have to eat halfway through to the middle to find out what's between the bread, and once you get hold of a bite, you don't have to guess at whether it is egg salad or tuna that you're eating. The filling is high in size and in flavor.

The town next door to us is spreading south toward our landing, and both Mom and Dad say that our property will be worth a pretty penny in a few years. But both of them always ask, "What's a pretty penny worth when you can't buy anything prettier than what you already have?" I have to agree. Maybe because I don't know anything else, but I can't imagine what it would be like not to have a sandbox miles and miles long and a pool as big as an ocean for a playground across the street—even if the street is a highway. I can't ever remember going to sleep but that I heard some water shushing and slurping or humming and hollering for a lullaby.

Last spring, just as the days were getting long enough that a person could both start and finish something between the time he got home from school and the time he went to bed, I went out onto our dock and I saw this guy all duded up from a catalogue. Now that the town has grown toward us, we have more of these guys than we used to. When you've been in the business of fishing all your life, you come to know the difference between fishermen and guys who have a hobby. Here are some of the clues:

1. The hat. A real fisherman's hat is darkened along the edges where the sweat from his hand leaves marks. A non-fisherman's hat has perfect little dent marks in it.

2. The smile. Real fishermen don't smile while they're fishing unless someone tells them a joke. Real fishermen wear their faces in the same look people wear when they are in church—deliberate and far-off—the way they do when they don't want to catch the eye of the preacher. The only time that look changes is when they take a swig of beer and then it changes only a little and with a slow rhythm like watching instant replay on television. Non-fishermen twitch their necks around like pigeons, which are very

citified birds, and non-fishermen smile a lot.

3. The umbrella. Real fishermen don't have them.

This old guy sat on a wooden-legged, canvas-bottom folding campstool that didn't have any salt burns on it anywhere and put his rod into one of the holders that Dad had set up along the dock railing. Then he held out his hand and called out, "Hey, boy, do you know what I've got here?"

I walked on over to him and said, "Name's Ned."

"What's that?" he asked, cupping his hand over his ear so that the breeze wouldn't blow it past him.

"I said that my name is Ned," I repeated.

"All right, Ed," he said. "I have a question for you. Do you know what this is, boy?"

"Name's Ned," I repeated. I looked down at the palm of his hand and saw a medium-sized shark's tooth from a sand shark. "Not bad," I said.

"But do you know what it is, boy?" he asked.

I could tell that it wasn't the kind of question where a person is looking for an answer; it was the kind of question where a person just wants you to look interested long enough so that he can get on with telling you the answer. I decided that I wouldn't play it that way even if he was a customer. Three *boys* in a row made me mean, so I said, "Medium-sized sand."

"What's that?" he shouted, cupping his hand over his ear again.

"Medium-sized sand," I repeated louder.

"That's a shark's tooth," he said, clamping his hand shut.

Shoot! I knew that it was a shark's tooth. I was telling him what *kind* it was and what size it was.

"That is a fossilized[3] shark's tooth, boy," he said. "Found it just across the street."

"Name's Ned," I told him, and I walked away.

Sharks' teeth wash up all the time at the beach just across the road from Hixon's Landing. There's a giant fossil bed out in the

---

3. **fossilized** [fos′ ə līzd]: changed by time into a rock-like material.

On Shark's Tooth Beach   85   101

ocean somewheres, and a vent from it leads right onto our beach. When the undertow[4] gets to digging up out of that fossil bed and the tide is coming in, all kinds of interesting things wash in. Besides the sharks' teeth, there are also pieces of bones that wash up. I collect the backbones, the vertebraes, they're called; they have a hole in them where the spinal column went through. I have a whole string of them fixed according to size.

I collect sharks' teeth, too. I have been doing it for years. Mom started me doing it. It was Mom who made a study of them and found what kind of animal they might come from. Mom has these thorough ways about her. Dad says that Mom is smarter'n a briar and prettier'n a movie star.

Mom fixes the sharks' teeth that we collect into patterns and fastens them down onto a velvet mat and gets them framed into a shadowbox frame. She sells them down at the gift shop in town. And the gift shop isn't any tacky old gift shop full of smelly candles and ashtrays with the name of our town stamped on it. It's more like an art gallery. Matter of fact, it is called *The Artists' Gallery*, and Mom is something of an artist at how she makes those sharks' teeth designs. Some of the really pretty sharks' teeth Mom sells to a jeweler who sets them in gold for pendants. When she gets two pretty ones that match, he makes them into earrings.

4. **undertow** [un′ dər tō′]: the backward flow of water from waves breaking on the shore.

When I find her a really special or unusual one, Mom says to me, "Looks like we got a trophy, Ned." When we get us a trophy, one that needs investigating or one that is just downright super special, we don't sell it. Shoot! We don't even think about selling it. There's nothing that bit of money could buy that we'd want more than having that there trophy.

Most everyone who comes to Hixon's Landing knows about Mom and me being something of authorities on fossils, especially sharks' teeth, so I figured that this old dude would either go away and not come back or hang around long enough to find out. Either way, I figured that I didn't need to advertise for myself and my mom.

The next day after school there was the old fellow again. I wouldn't want to sound braggy or anything, but I could tell that he was standing there at the end of our dock waiting for me to come home from school.

"Hi," I said.

"Well, boy," he said, "did you have a good day at school?"

"Fair," I answered. I decided to let the *boy* ride. I figured that he couldn't hear or couldn't remember or both. "Catch anything?" I asked.

"No, not today," he said. "Matter of fact I was just about to close up shop." Then he began reeling in, looking back over his shoulder to see if I was still hanging around. He didn't even bother taking the hook off his line; he just dumped rod and reel down on the dock and stuck out his hand to me and said, "Well, son, you can call me President Bob."

"What are you president of?" I asked.

"President of a college, upstate Michigan. But I'm retired now."

"Then you're not a president," I said.

"Not at the moment, but the title stays. The way that people still call a retired governor, *Governor*. You can call me President Bob instead of President Kennicott. Bob is more informal, but I wouldn't want you to call me just Bob. It doesn't seem respectful for a boy to call a senior citizen just Bob."

"And you can call me Ned," I said. "That's my name."

"All right, son," he said.

"After the first day, I don't answer to *son* or to *boy*," I said.

"What did you say your name was, son?"

Shoot! He had to learn. So I didn't answer.

"What is your name again?"

"Ned."

"Well, Ned, would you like to take a walk on the beach and hunt for some of those sharks' teeth?"

"Sure," I said.

He must have counted on my saying yes, because the next thing I see is him dropping his pants and showing me a pair of skinny white legs with milky blue veins sticking out from under a pair of bathing trunks.

As we walked the length of the dock, he told me that he was used to the company of young men since he had been president of a college. "Of course, the students were somewhat older," he said. Then he laughed a little, like punctuation. I didn't say anything. "And, of course, I didn't often see the students on a one-to-one basis." I didn't say anything. "I was president," he added. He glanced over at me, and I still didn't say anything. "I was president," he added.

"There's supposed to be some good fishing in Michigan," I said.

"Oh, yes! Yes, there is. Good fishing. Fine fishing. Sportsmen's fishing."

We crossed A1A and got down onto the beach from a path people had worn between the dunes, and I showed him how to look for sharks' teeth in the coquina.[5] "There's nothing too much to learn," I said. "It's mostly training your eye."

He did what most beginners do, that is, he picked up a lot of wedge-shaped pieces of broken shell, mostly black, thinking they were fossil teeth. The tide was just starting on its way out, and that is the best time for finding sharks' teeth. He found about eight of them, and two of them were right nice sized. I found fourteen myself and three of mine were bigger than anything he collected. We compared, and I could tell that he was wishing he had mine, so I gave him one

5. **coquina** [kō kē′ nə]: soft, porous limestone formed of fragments of sea shells and corals.

of my big ones. It wasn't a trophy or anything like that because I would never do that to Mom, that is, give away a trophy or a jewelry one.

President Bob was waiting for me the next day and the day after that one. By the time Friday afternoon came, President Bob gave up on trying to pretend that he was fishing. He'd just be there on the dock, waiting for me to take him sharks' tooth hunting.

"There's no magic to it," I told him. "You can go without me."

"That's all right, Ned," he said, "I don't mind waiting."

On Saturday I had a notion to sleep late and was in the process of doing just that when Mom shook me out of my sleep and told me that I had a visitor. It was President Bob, and there he was standing on his vanilla legs right by my bedroom door. He had gotten tired of waiting for me on the dock. It being Saturday, he had come early so's we could have more time together.

Mom invited him in to have breakfast with me, and while we ate, she brought out our trophy boxes. Our trophies were all sitting on cotton in special boxes like the ones you see butterflies fixed in inside a science museum. Mom explained about our very special fossils.

"Oh, yes," President Bob said. Then, "Oh, yes," again. Then after he'd seen all our trophies and had drunk a second cup of coffee, he said, "We had quite a fine reference library in my college. I am referring to the college of which I was president. Not my alma mater, the college I attended as a young man. We had quite a fine library, and I must confess I used it often, so I am not entirely unfamiliar with these things."

That's when I said, "Oh, yes," except that it came out, "Oh, yeah!" and that's when Mom swiped my foot under the table.

President Bob plunked his empty cup down on the table and said, "Well, come on now, Ned, time and tide wait for no man. Ha! Ha!"

I think that I've heard someone say that at least four times a week. Everyone says it. Dad told me that it was a proverb,[6] an old, old saying. And I can tell you that it got old even before I reached my second birthday.

6. **proverb** [prov′ ėrb]: a short, wise saying used for a long time by many people.

When we got down to the beach, President Bob brought out a plastic bag and flung it open like a bag boy at the supermarket. But there wasn't much to fill it with that day because the currents had shifted and weren't churning up the fossil bed.

"I suppose you'll be going to church tomorrow," he said.

"Yes," I answered.

"I think I'll do some fishing in the morning. I'll probably have had enough of that by noon. I'll meet you at the dock about twelve-thirty. We can get started on our shark's tooth hunt then."

"Sorry," I said. "I help Mom with the sandwiches and then we clean things up and then we go to late services. Sunday is our busiest day."

"Of course it is," he said.

Mom and I got back about one-thirty and changed out of our good clothes before Dad came in as he always does on Sundays to grab some lunch before the men start coming back and he has to get busy with washing down motors and buying. (What he buys is fish from the men who have had a specially good run. Dad cleans them and sells them to markets back in town or to people who drive on out toward the beach of a Sunday. Sometimes, he gets so busy buying and cleaning that Mom and I pitch right in and give him a hand.)

Dad had not quite finished his sandwiches and had just lifted his beer when he got called out to the dock. There was this big haul of bass that some men were wanting to sell.

Mom and I were anxious to finish our lunch and clean up so's we could go on out and see if Dad would be needing some help when President Bob presented himself at the screen door to our kitchen.

"Knock, knock," he said, pressing his old face up against the screen. The minute we both looked up he opened the door without even an *if you please* and marched into our kitchen on his frosted icicle legs. "I think you're going to be interested in what I found today," he said. "Very interested."

Mom smiled her customer smile and said, "We are having very busy day, please to excuse if I continue with work."

"That's perfectly all right," President Bob said. "You're excused."
Then he sat down at the table that Mom was wiping off. He held up
the placemat and said, "Over here, Mama-san. You missed a spot."

Mom smiled her customer smile again and wiped the spot that he
had pointed to, and President Bob put the placemat back down and
emptied the contents of his plastic bag right on top of it. He leaned
over the pile and using his forefinger began to comb through it. "Ah!
here," he said. He picked up a small black thing between his thumb
and forefinger and said to Mom, "Come here, Mama-san." *Mama-san*
is some kind of Japanese for *mama*. A lot of people call my mom that,
but she says it's okay because it is a term of respect, and a lot of
people think that all Orientals are Japanese. Sometimes these same
people call me Boy-san, which is to *boy* what Mama-san is to *mama*.
They call me that because I have dark slanted eyes just like Mom's,
except that hers are prettier.

"Look at this," President Bob said. "Look at it closely. I suspect
that it is the upper palate[7] of an extinct species of deep water fish."

Mom took it from his hand and looked at it and said, "Dolphin
tooth." She put it back down and walked to the sink where she

7. **palate** [pal′ it]: roof of the mouth.

continued right on with washing up the dishes. She automatically handed me a towel to dry.

President Bob studied the dolphin's tooth and said to Mom, "Are you sure?"

She smiled and nodded.

"Quite sure?"

She nodded.

He asked once more, and she nodded again. Then he began poking through his collection again and came up with another piece. He beckoned to Mom to look at it closer, and she dried her hands and did that.

"Shell," she said.

"Oh, I beg to differ with you," he said.

"Shell," Mom said, looking down at it, not bothering to pick it up.

"Are you sure?"

She nodded.

"Quite sure?"

She nodded again, and I came over and picked it up off the table and held it up and broke it in two. I thought that President Bob was going to arrest me. "A piece of fossil that thick wouldn't break that easy. It's a sure test," I said.

"There are fragile fossils, I'm sure," President Bob said.

"I suppose so," I said. "But that shell ain't fossilized. Piece of fossil that thick wouldn't ever break that easy." I could see that you had to repeat yourself with President Bob. "That shell ain't fossilized."

"*Ain't* is considered very bad manners up North," President Bob said.

Shoot! *Bad manners* are considered bad manners down South, I thought. But I didn't say anything. President Bob kept sorting through his bag of stuff, studying on it so hard that his eyes winched up and made his bottom jaw drop open.

Mom finished washing the dishes, and I finished drying, and we asked if we could be excused, and President Bob told us (in our own kitchen, mind) that it was perfectly all right, but would we please

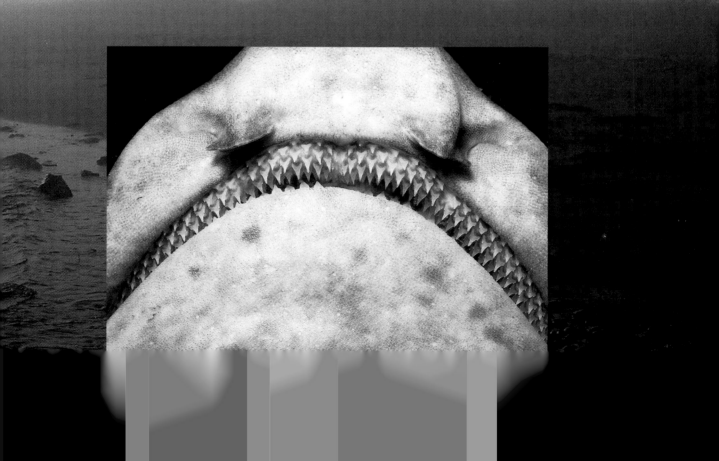

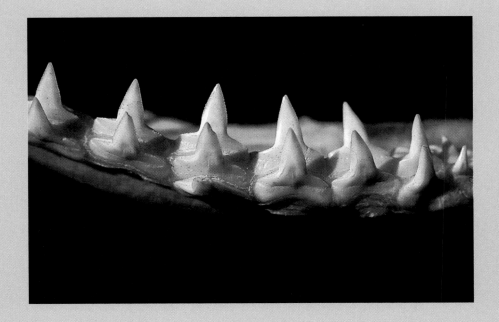

fetch him a glass of ice water before we left. We fetched it. He said, "Thank you. You may go now." I suppose that up North it's good manners to give people orders in their own house if you do it with *please* and *thank you* and no *ain'ts*.

It rained on Monday and it rained again on Tuesday, so I didn't see President Bob again until Wednesday after school. He was waiting for me at the end of the dock with his plastic sandwich bag already partly full. "Well," he said, "I guess I got a bit of a head start on you today."

I looked close at his bag and saw that he had a couple of nice ones—not trophies—but nice.

"I have homework," I said. "I can't walk the beaches with you today."

"What subject?"

"Math."

"Maybe I can help you. Did I tell you that I was president of a college."

"Really?" I said in my fakiest voice. "I think I better do my homework by myself."

"I'll wait for you," he said. "I promise I won't hunt for anything until you come back out."

"It'll probably take me the rest of daylight to do it," I said.

"Math must be hard for you," he said. "Always was my strongest subject."

"It's not hard for me," I lied. "I just have a lot of it."

"Let me show you what I found today," he said.

"I don't think I have the time."

"Just take a minute."

Before I could give him another polite no, he had spread the contents of his bag over the railing of the dock. I looked things over real good. I knew he was watching me, so I wouldn't let my eyes pause too long on any one thing in particular. "Very nice," I said. "I've got to go now."

As I turned to walk back to our house, he called, "See you tomorrow."

The next day I didn't even walk to the dock. Instead I walked around to the side door of our house and threw my books on the wicker sofa on the screened porch and went up to my room and changed into my cut-offs. I had a plan; I was going to go back out the side door and walk a bit to the north before crossing the highway and climbing over the dunes onto the beach. I knew a place where a sandbar often formed, and Mom and I sometimes went there. When I was little, she'd put me in the sloop[8] behind the sandbar, like at a wading pool at a regular Holiday Inn. As I got older, we'd go there on lazy days and take a picnic lunch and sift through the coquina of the sandbar. We've found about four trophies there. Not about, exactly four. Of the four, the first one was the most fun because it was the one we found by accident.

I felt if I could get out of the house and head north, I could escape President Bob and dig up some trophies that would make him flip.

But I didn't escape. When I came downstairs after changing my clothes, there he was sitting on the wicker sofa, his blueberry ripple

8. **sloop** [slüp]: a sailboat, usually having one sail.

legs crossed in front of him. He was leafing through my math book.

I told him hello.

He smiled at me. "Yes, yes, yes," he said, "I know exactly how it is to have to sit in school all day and have to hold your water. I am quite used to the habits of young men. I was president of a liberal arts college in Michigan." He noticed that I was wearing my cut-offs, my usual beachcombing outfit, so he slapped his thighs and set them to shimmying like two pots of vanilla yogurt. "I see you're ready. Let's get going. The tide's halfway out already, and as they say, 'Time and tide wait for no man.' Tide was better a few hours ago. I found a couple of real beauties. Locked them in the glove compartment of my car."

I walked with him to the beach, and we began our hunt. He wasn't bending over for falsies very much any more. Each time he bent over, he yelled, "Got one!" and then he'd hold it up in the air and wouldn't put it in his bag until I nodded or said something or both. President Bob ended up with about twenty teeth, one vertebra bone, and of the twenty, one was a real trophy, an inch long, heavy root and the whole edge serrated[9] with nothing worn away. A real trophy.

I found eight. Three of them were medium, four of them were itty-bitty and one had the tip crushed off.

I got up early the next day and checked the tide; it was just starting out. Good, I thought. I crossed the road and ran out onto the beach, rolling up my pajama bottoms as I walked along. The tide was just right; it was leaving long saw-tooth edges of coquina, and I managed to collect eight decent-sized teeth and one right-good-sized one before I ran back home and hosed off my feet and got dressed for school. I stuffed my collection into pockets of my cut-offs. I had to skip breakfast, a fact that didn't particularly annoy me until about eleven o'clock. That afternoon, for every two times President Bob stooped down and yelled, "Got one!" I did it three times.

On Friday I didn't want to skip breakfast again, and my mother for sure didn't want me to, so President Bob was way ahead.

9. **serrated** [ser′ ā tid]: notched like the edge of a saw.

On Saturday I got up before dawn and dressed and sat on our dock until I saw the first thin line of dawn. Dawn coming over the intracoastal is like watching someone draw up a Venetian blind. On a clear day the sky lifts slowly and evenly, and it makes a guy feel more than okay to see it happen. But on that Saturday, I sat on the dock just long enough to make sure that daylight was to the east of me before I crossed the highway and began heading north. Shoot! I think that if the Lord had done some skywriting that morning, I wouldn't have taken the time to read it, even if it was in English.

Finally, I climbed to the top of a tall dune and walked up one and down another. I was heading for a place between the dunes about a mile to the north. I knew that during spring, when the moon was new, there was a tidewater[10] between two of the dunes. Sharks' teeth got trapped in it, and sometimes Mom and I would go there if there was a special size she was looking for to finish an arrangement. You had to dig down into the coquina, and it wasn't much fun finding sharks' teeth this way instead of sauntering along the beach and happening to find them. But sometimes it was necessary.

I dug.

I dug and I dug and I dug.

I put all my findings into a clam shell that I found, and I dug, and I dug, and I dug. I felt the sun hot on my back, and I still dug. I had my back to the ocean and my face to the ground and for all I knew there was no sky and no sea and no sand and no colors. There was nothing, nothing and nothing except black, and that black was the black of fossil teeth.

I had filled the clam shell before I stopped digging. I sorted the teeth and put the best ones—there were fourteen of them—in my right side pocket—the one with a button—and I put all the smaller ones in my back pocket and started back toward home, walking along the strand. I figured that I had a good head start on the day and on President Bob. I would pepper my regular findings with the ones I had just dug up. I'd mix the little ones in with the fourteen big ones.

10. **tidewater** [tīd′ wô′ tər]: low-lying land along a seacoast through which the tide flows.

But, I decided, smiling to myself, I'd have a run of about eight big ones in a row just to see what he would do.

My back felt that it was near to burning up, and I looked toward the ocean, and it looked powerful good. The morning ocean in the spring can be as blue as the phony color they paint it on a geography book map. Sometimes there are dark patches in it, and the gulls sweep down on top of the dark spots. I decided that I needed to take a dip in that ocean. I half expected a cloud of steam to rise up off my back. I forgot about time and tide and sharks' teeth and ducked under the waves and licked the salt off my lips as I came back up.

I was feeling pretty good, ready to face President Bob and the world, and then I checked my pockets and found that about half the supply from my back pocket had tumbled out, and I had lost two big ones. I was pretty upset about that, so I slowed down on my walk back home. I crouched down and picked up shell pieces, something I thought that I had outgrown, but that is about how anxious I was not to let anything get by me. I found a couple of medium-sized ones and put them in my back pocket and began a more normal walk when my trained eye saw a small tooth right at the tide line.

I reached down to pick it up, figuring that, if nothing else, it would add bulk to my collection the way they add cereal to hot dog meat. I didn't have any idea how many baby teeth I had lost out of my back pocket.

When I reached down to pick up that little tooth, it didn't come up immediately, and I began to think that maybe it was the tip of a really big one. I stooped down and carefully scraped away the wet sand and saw that there were several teeth together. The tide was rushing back up to where I was, so I laid my hand flat down on the ground and shoveled up a whole fistful of wet, cool sand.

I walked back to the dune and gently scraped away the sand with the forefinger of my other hand, and then I saw what I had.

There were several teeth, and they were attached to a piece of bone, a piece of jaw bone. There was a space between the third tooth and the fourth, and the smallest tooth, the one on the end that I had first seen, was attached to the jaw bone by only a thin edge.

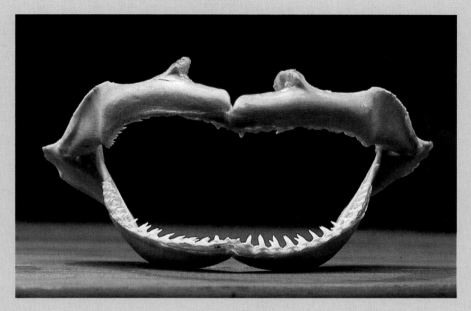

I had never seen such a trophy. I felt that the spirit of the Lord had come mightily upon me, like Samson.[11] Except that I had the jawbone of a shark and not the jawbone of an ass. And I wanted to smite[12] only one president, not a thousand Philistines.

I didn't run the rest of the way home. I was too careful for that. I walked, holding that trophy in my hand, making certain that it didn't dry out before I could see if the weak tooth was fossilized onto the bone.

I called to Mom when I came into the house and when she appeared at the door to the screened porch, I uncurled my fingers one by one until the whole bone and all four of the teeth were showing. I watched Mom's face, and it was like watching the dawn I had missed.

"Ah, Ned," she said, "it is the Nobel Prize[13] of trophies." We walked into the kitchen. She wet a good wad of paper towels and

11. **Samson** [sam′ sən]: a very strong man whose story is in the Bible; he used the jawbone of an ass to kill one thousand men in the army of the enemy Philistines.
12. **smite** [smīt]: strike with a weapon to cause serious injury or death.
13. **Nobel Prize** [nō bel′]: a yearly prize given to people who have done outstanding work in science, the arts, or for the good of humanity.

lifted the jawbone carefully from my hand and put it down on that pad of paper. And then we sat down at the kitchen table and I told her about how I found it, and I told it all to her in detail. Dad came in and Mom asked me to tell him, and I did and she listened just as hard the second time.

We ate our breakfast, and afterwards, we wet the paper towels again and moved the trophy onto a plastic placemat on the kitchen table. Mom looked at it through the magnifying glass and then handed me the glass so that I could look at it, too.

While we were studying it hard like that, President Bob came to the screen door and said, "Knock, knock."

Mom nodded at me, her way of letting me know that I was supposed to invite him on in.

"Well, well," he said. "Are we ready for today's treasure hunt?"

"I guess so," I said, as easy as you please, moving a little to the left so that he could catch a glimpse of what Mom and I were looking at.

He gave it a glance and then another one right quick.

Mom and I looked at each other as he came closer and closer to the table. He studied that trophy from his full height and from behind a chair. Next thing, he moved in front of the chair. And next after that he sat down in the chair. And then, not taking his eyes off that trophy, he held his hand out for the magnifying glass and Mom took it from me and gave it to him.

The whole time he did this, I watched his face. His eyes squinched up and his jaw dropped open and his nostrils flared. It was like watching a mini-movie called *Jealousy and Greed*.

I could feel myself smiling. "Found it this morning," I said.

Then I didn't say anything anymore. And I stopped smiling.

I thought about his face, and that made me think about mine. If his face was a movie called *Jealousy and Greed*, I didn't like the words I could put to mine.

I gently pushed the placemat closer to President Bob. "Look at it," I said. "Look at it good." I waited until his eyes were level with mine. "It's for you," I said. "It's a present from me."

"Why, thank you, boy," he said.

"Name's Ned," I answered, as I walked around to the other side of the table and emptied my pockets. "Do you think we can make something pretty out of these?" I asked Mom.

She gave me a Nobel Prize of a smile for an answer. President Bob didn't even notice, he was so busy examining the jawbone with which he had been smitten.

E. L. KONIGSBURG

Elaine Lobl Konigsburg was born in 1930 in New York City and grew up in a small mill town in Pennsylvania. She became a chemist before she became a writer—because, she says, "I was good at it." There was no guidance counselor at her high school, and she was the first person in her family to go to college; she knew no one who made a living from writing. At that time, you went to college to become a professional—such as a teacher or an engineer—who could make a living. But eventually, through teaching, Konigsburg found her way to writing.

Most of Konigsburg's amusing and serious books are for young people. "On Shark's Tooth Beach" is one of the five short stories in her book *Throwing Shadows*. Each story, set in a different place, will draw you into the experience of a different young character.

Asking Big Questions About the Literature

How can I discover my unique qualities?

LITERATURE STUDY
Point of View

Point of view is the way a story is told. When a story is told using pronouns such as *I, me, we,* or *us,* the author is using the *first-person* point of view. When the events of a story are told using pronouns such as *he, she, him, her,* or *them,* the author is using the *third-person* point of view.

Choose a literature selection from this unit and identify its point of view. Then rewrite part of it using a different point of view. (*See "Point of View" on page 118.*)

Write a
THANK-YOU NOTE

Write a thank-you note to a character or an author of one of the literature selections in this unit who has inspired you with a unique quality. Explain how the character or author revealed this quality to you and what you plan to do as a result.

COMPARE & CONTRAST

With a partner, discuss the qualities of several characters in the literature in this unit. Then make a chart like the one shown to compare and contrast the qualities of different characters. Use the chart to help you write a short essay comparing and contrasting the characters.

Selection Title	Character	Qualities
"Raymond's Run"	Squeaky	determined self-disciplined confident committed

How can I improve my unique qualities?

Write an
ADVERTISEMENT

With a group, make a list of real people in the news and characters in this unit who have improved themselves by strengthening qualities they already had. Then imagine one of them is running for political office. Write an advertisement for the candidate's campaign, pointing out how he or she has personally improved. Try out your ad on another group. How would its members vote?

Conflict

A **conflict** is a problem or struggle faced by a character. The conflict can be *internal*—within the character. Or it can be *external*—between the character and another person, nature, or society.

Make a comic strip or story board showing how one character from a literature selection in this unit dealt with a problem and ended up a better person because of it. (*See "Conflict" on page 119.*)

Improvement Scale

With a partner, discuss characters you've read about in the literature selections in this unit who have tried to improve themselves. How did they try? How well did they succeed? Make a Quality Improvement Scale like the one shown. Rate different characters with the same quality. Or rate different qualities of one character. The example is for Ned in "On Shark's Tooth Beach."

Ned's Quality Improvement Scale				
	none	a little	some	a lot
friendly			X	
generous				X
tolerant				X
observant			X	

Asking Big Questions About the Literature

How can I share my unique qualities?

ADVICE COLUMN

Share something you've learned with a person who might benefit from your experience. With a partner, choose a character from this unit who could use your advice. What problems does the character face? What similar problems have you solved? Write an advice column. One partner can write the character's letter, explaining the problem and asking for advice. The other can write the columnist's reply.

Reach Out

In "Pictures on a Rock," an artist shares his talent with the world. Other characters in this unit make a contribution to the world. With some classmates, discuss which characters these are and what they do.

What quality or ability do you have that might help one of the characters in the literature selections you've read? Write a letter to that character, offering what you'd like to share.

Conflict

In literature, how characters deal with the main problem or **conflict** reveals their inner qualities.

With a group, discuss how characters from this unit use their inner qualities to deal with conflict. List their qualities in character wheels like the one here. Then take turns playing the different characters, answering your classmates' questions about how you solve problems. Let your classmates identify which character you are. (*See "Conflict" on page 119.*)

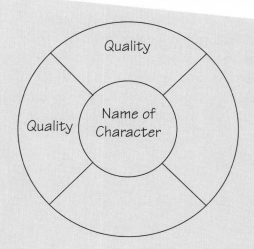

How does the world affect my unique qualities?

An Equation

Choose a character from one of the selections in this unit and set up an equation like the one shown for Penelope in "Young Ladies Don't Slay Dragons." In the first half circle, list things that affect the character. In the second half circle, list the character's inner qualities. Then, in the full circle, write the sum of both halves: the results in the character's life, such as goals achieved or lessons learned.

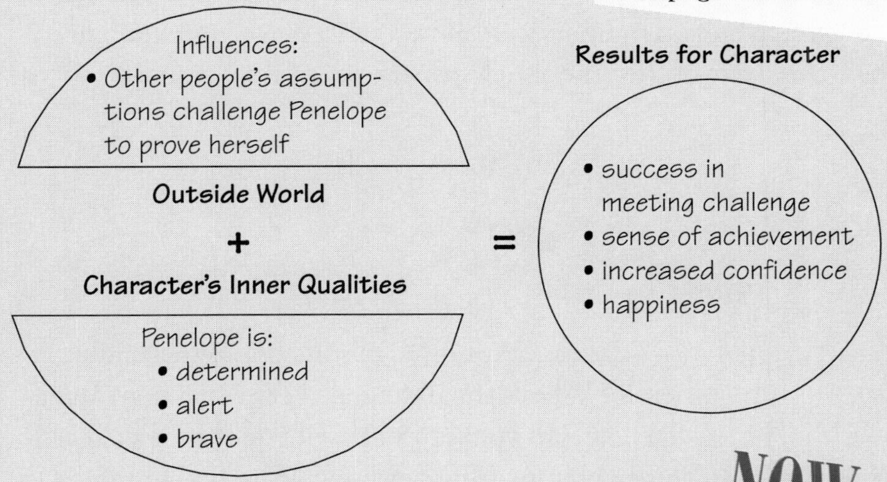

Influences:
- Other people's assumptions challenge Penelope to prove herself

Outside World

+

Character's Inner Qualities

Penelope is:
- determined
- alert
- brave

=

Results for Character

- success in meeting challenge
- sense of achievement
- increased confidence
- happiness

LITERATURE STUDY

Point of View

In fiction, a narrator who identifies himself or herself as *I* is using the *first-person* **point of view**. A narrator who uses pronouns like *he*, *she*, and *they* is using the third-person point of view.

Write one first-person and one third-person description of the same event from a story in this unit. (*See "Point of View" on page 118.*)

Tell Your Own Story

With a group, discuss how the world affects the unique qualities of characters in this unit. Then write a short essay about a time in your own life when your unique qualities were affected by your world.

NOW
Choose a Project!

Three projects about becoming yourself are described on the following pages.

Writing Workshop

DESCRIBING A HEROIC ACT

Heroes: who are they? We all know them when we find them in the movies or in the stories we read and tell. They're the ones everyone looks up to. But *who* are the people we call heroes? Are they somehow different from the rest of us? How did they get to be heroes? And *where* are they? Do they all live in Texas, or the White House, or Hollywood? Is it possible that ordinary people—such as you and people you know— can also be heroes by using their unique qualities to help others?

This project will give you a chance to decide what heroism is. Your **purpose** will be to write an eyewitness description of a real event that you observed when an ordinary person become a hero. Your **audience** will be the readers of the school newspaper or a local magazine.

Prewriting
THINKING ABOUT HEROISM

What is heroism? Can someone be naturally heroic? What's the difference between a hero and a daredevil? In your journal, write questions such as these about real-life heroism. Write one-sentence answers.

Next make a list of actual heroic acts you've seen or participated in. If you can't think of any, think again: maybe you didn't consider the act heroic at the time. Maybe you did something ordinary that "saved the day" for someone. This list may help you think of an event.

Heroism
- Saving an animal
- Defending a friend
- Helping someone in need

Prewriting
VISUALIZING

Your challenge is to describe every detail of the heroic act. Choose details that will help a reader imagine what happened. Imagine you're a film-maker whose pictures are made of words. Your details should bring to life all the sights, sounds, smells, and other parts of the event. Close your eyes and picture the whole event as vividly as possible. Then jot down a list of as many details as you remember.

Deciding
WHY, WHO, AND HOW

You can't decide *how* to describe the details of the heroic event until you know your **purpose**—*why* you're writing—and your **audience**—*who* your readers will be. Are you writing to describe some event? Are you writing for friends your own age, or for strangers of all ages and backgrounds, or for a group with special interests? Knowing your audience and purpose will help you decide whether to be formal or informal, humorous or serious.

Writing Workshop

Drafting
....
YOUR EYEWITNESS DESCRIPTION

Your eyewitness description should have three main parts: an introduction, a body, and a conclusion.

- In the **introduction,** try describing the setting: where and when the event takes place. Michelle Parisi, a student writer, introduces her description on page 110 by presenting a very ordinary setting—a school. She also tells the reader the names of the main characters and the person who will perform the heroic act—Maria.

- In the **body** of your eyewitness description, describe the parts of the event in the order in which they happened. Use some transitions, such as *first, next, later,* and *afterward,* to help readers keep track. Then go back to your list of details and be sure you've included them. To bring your description to life, try including some figurative language like similes and metaphors. Michelle, for example, compares Maria's classmates to a pack of wolves: "Instead of teenagers, they now looked more like a wolf pack in search of prey to rip to shreds." Finally remember to include dialogue—what people said during the incident—if it's appropriate.

- In the **conclusion,** tell your readers the results of the heroic action and leave them with some food for thought. It might be a lesson learned from the experience or an update on the heroic person's life since the event. Keep it short.

- Finally give your eyewitness description a **title.** You might want to make a list of ten or more possibilities before choosing a title that fits the purpose and tone of your report. It should spark the reader's interest without giving away too much information.

Revising
YOUR EYEWITNESS DESCRIPTION

Invite a partner or a group to read and respond to your eyewitness description. You may want to ask questions like these:

- Does the opening draw you into the event? Is it too long?
- Do the descriptive details help you picture what happened?
- Are there any clichés—overused expressions—that spoil the freshness of my description?
- Is the conclusion clear?

Based on your friends' suggestions, make some changes to improve your work. Read the student model on pages 110-111 for an example of a successful eyewitness description.

Editing
YOUR EYEWITNESS DESCRIPTION

Finally edit your description for errors in grammar, usage, punctuation, and spelling. Invite a friend or your writing group to help you check for mistakes. Correct any errors and make a clean copy. You don't want carelessness to be part of your reputation as a reporter.

Publishing
YOUR EYEWITNESS DESCRIPTION

Before you send your manuscript to the local newspaper or school magazine or share it with your family, make another copy for your records (in case an editor has questions, or the original copy gets lost). To share your report orally, read it to your class, your friends or family, the hero, or any person or group who might be inspired by it.

If you have photographs of the heroic event, include them with your report for visual interest. They'll also remind your audience that your hero or heroine is real, like them.

A Heroic Effort

by Michelle Parisi

St. Charles, Illinois

I never thought Maria was heroic in any way until Kevin arrived at school. At first I didn't pay any attention to Kevin either—he was always so silent and solitary, sitting at the back of the room. For some reason, no one wanted him in their group, and nobody tried to make friends with him.

Even though Maria and I hung out with a group of our own, something about the new boy's independence touched us. Maria in particular sensed his loneliness every time she looked at him. We didn't like the way kids called him "the loser" and attacked him because of his independence.

Maria was repulsed by this lack of respect for others, but what she found even more horrible was the lack of respect these people had for themselves. Kevin seemed to be the only one who had any real backbone and sense of self-worth, and this inspired us to become his friends.

One day, Maria and I scoured the lunch room for Kevin and discovered him in a secluded corner. I went with her as she squeezed through the packed room and plunked herself across from him. She placed her lunch on the table, hesitated slightly, and said "Hello."

Conversation was a bit slow at first, as we all three picked at our food uneasily. But soon enough, we warmed up to each other like old friends.

The next day Maria spotted Kevin in the cafeteria and waved, but as she walked toward him, she was stopped dead in her tracks. There seemed to be a human roadblock, formed for her inconvenience. She hardly recognized the people she had once called her friends. Instead of teenagers, they now looked more like a wolf pack in search of prey to rip to shreds. They resembled that same pack in another way—they were too cowardly to confront a creature alone.

To the mob's surprise, Maria solidly stood her ground. I stood a little behind her, to observe the situation.

"So you're hangin' out with the loser, huh?" Snickers traveled through the group like an electric current. The wolves licked their lips, anticipating and closing in for the kill. They awaited response from their victim.

"He's not a loser," Maria said, straining with the effort to keep her voice level. "He's my friend."

The pack was confused. Was she actually standing up to them—by herself? Then from the pack the voice spoke again, but this time more softly. "Why would you hang out with that loser if you could hang out with us?"

Maria's words came out in an angry explosion. "I don't even know who you guys are. You cover up your real identity because you're afraid people will laugh at the things that make each one of you different. That makes you the losers! Now if you'll excuse me." Maria shoved through the stunned crowd and joined her new friend.

I learned a lot about heroism that day. I saw how courage can come in many shapes and forms. And most of all, I learned that the secret to being a hero is simply helping someone in need.

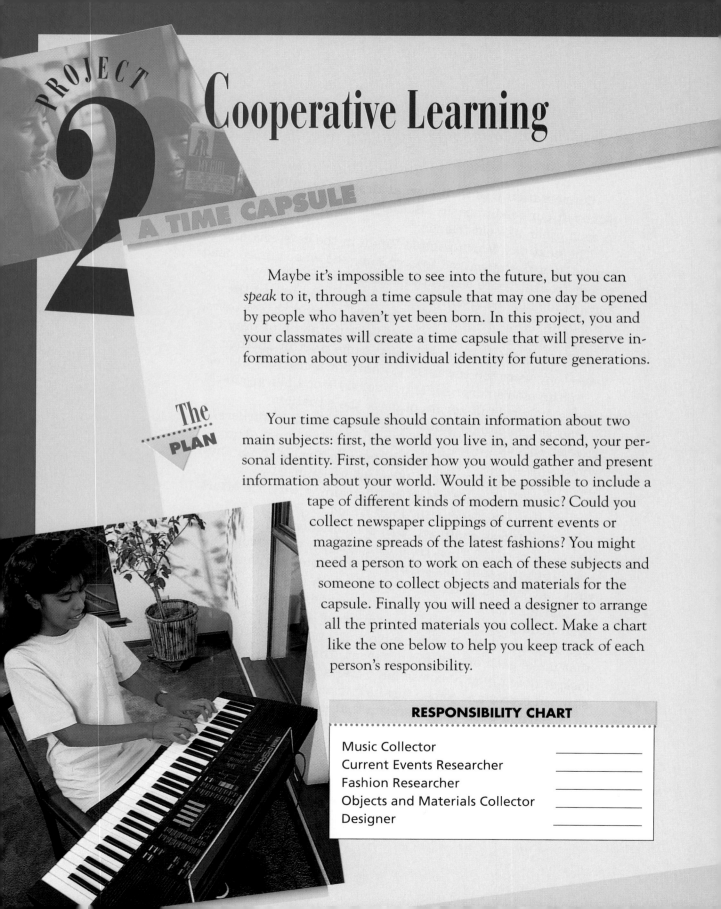

Cooperative Learning

A TIME CAPSULE

Maybe it's impossible to see into the future, but you can *speak* to it, through a time capsule that may one day be opened by people who haven't yet been born. In this project, you and your classmates will create a time capsule that will preserve information about your individual identity for future generations.

The PLAN

Your time capsule should contain information about two main subjects: first, the world you live in, and second, your personal identity. First, consider how you would gather and present information about your world. Would it be possible to include a tape of different kinds of modern music? Could you collect newspaper clippings of current events or magazine spreads of the latest fashions? You might need a person to work on each of these subjects and someone to collect objects and materials for the capsule. Finally you will need a designer to arrange all the printed materials you collect. Make a chart like the one below to help you keep track of each person's responsibility.

RESPONSIBILITY CHART

Music Collector	_____
Current Events Researcher	_____
Fashion Researcher	_____
Objects and Materials Collector	_____
Designer	_____

The PERSONAL INFORMATION

Now work on the personal information you'd like to include. Write a short introduction, giving your date of birth and a brief physical description. Then describe the kind of person you are. Think about your strengths and abilities. Do you have **physical** skills that you communicate through physical activities such as sports, dance, or charades? Do you have **musical** talents that help you in activities such as rap, choral reading, composing, and singing? Perhaps you have a strong **visual** sense, with a knack for copying, designing, sculpting, or repairing things, or **interpersonal** skills that give you the ability to cooperate, negotiate, empathize, or interact with others. Whatever your strengths, make sure you define them in your description of yourself. When you have finished your description, add it to the time capsule.

The PRODUCT

Now that you've gathered all the information that you'd like to preserve, discuss what to use as a time capsule and where to put it. Could you use a tin box or a plastic container? Should you bury it or send it to your local archives or museum? Think of a place that will safely preserve your identity for future generations.

PROJECT 3

Helping Your Community

BECOME AN INSPIRATION

A work of art not only expresses the individuality of its creator, but inspires others to create as well. In this project, you'll use your creativity to produce a work of art that expresses who you've become. Then, with a small group or your entire class, you'll decide how to present your work in a way that encourages others to express themselves, too.

Creating SOMETHING UNIQUE

Base the choice for your work of art on your talents. Are you a good musician? Then write a song! Do you like to paint? Create a self-portrait! Make a collage or a jigsaw puzzle, or construct a mobile of your childhood memories. Express yourself through dance or sculpture if you prefer. Create something that represents some aspect of your individuality—a work of art that will inspire others.

To help you think of things to express about yourself, try jotting down answers to questions like the ones below. Then brainstorm a list of the things that each question brings to mind—such as colors, tunes, places, events, pictures, or faces. Try to incorporate some of these into your creation.

- How do I see myself?
- What sort of things do I like?
- How did I get to be who I am?
- Does my identity remain the same, or do I change at different times and in different places?

Presenting YOUR WORK

Once you've completed your work of art, hold a small group or class meeting to decide where to present your work. Consider a homeless shelter, a hospice, a home for physically handicapped young people, a retirement community, or the pediatric unit of a hospital. Then contact the organization to see if it would like to provide a space for your presentation.

Use your presentation as an opportunity to encourage others to create something. Present a talk, a video tape, or a written explanation of your creative process. Show others how to ask the questions that you've asked yourself. Help them locate their own talents and hidden strengths. Include an introduction explaining the value of understanding the qualities that make each person unique.

Putting It All Together

What Have You Learned About the Theme?

Now that you've finished *Becoming Myself*, think about how your attitudes toward this theme and your own identity have changed. Look back at the writing you've done for this unit—in your journal, in response to your reading, in the Writing Workshop. Show what you have learned about this theme by writing an encyclopedia entry about yourself.

AN ENTRY OF YOUR OWN

Prewriting and Drafting   First, find an encyclopedia entry of someone famous, just to get an idea of how to write one about yourself. Notice that the entry gives information about the person's life and achievements. When you have finished studying the encyclopedia entry, make a web about what makes you who you are. Include your special qualities, the people and events that have especially influenced you, and the literature and activities in this unit that have most strongly affected you.

Begin your entry by giving information about your early life, such as where you were born, lived, and went to school.

Remember to refer to yourself in the third person, using the pronoun *he* or *she*. Then write about your interests and your special qualities and achievements. If you like, describe something that you will do in the future because of your special qualities; imagine what achievement might be listed in a future encyclopedia. Think of several possibilities and then pick one.

Revising and Editing   Exchange entries with a partner or writing group. Ask for comments on and advice about the content of your writing. Try making a few different drafts until you have one that pleases you. Finally, have your partner or writing group check for errors in grammar, spelling, and punctuation.

Publishing   Write your encyclopedia entry neatly and give it a title. Post it on a class bulletin board so that your classmates can read it or add it to your classmates' entries, arranging the entries alphabetically.

Evaluating Your Work

Think Back About the Big Questions

In a small group, discuss the Big Questions on pages 10-11. In your journal, comment on how your responses have changed following your work in this unit.

Think Back About Your Work

Now think about the unit you've just finished and evaluate your work, including your reading, your writing, your activities, and your projects. Be realistic and honest about your progress, but don't be too hard on yourself.

Write a note to your teacher explaining what you've accomplished during this unit. Use the following questions to help you write your note.

- How have your ideas about becoming yourself changed? What literature selections or activities in this unit helped to bring about this change?

- Which literature selections that you read in this unit did you enjoy most and least? Why?

- What did you learn as you worked on your project? What would you do differently if you worked on a similar project again?

- What suggestions would you make to your teacher about presenting this unit next time?

- How do you rate your work in this unit? Use the following scale and explain why you chose this number.

1 = Outstanding	3 = Fair
2 = Good	4 = Not as good as it could have been

POINT OF VIEW

What Is Point of View?

Point of view is the way a story is told. Sometimes a *narrator*, or speaker, tells the story from a personal point of view, referring to himself or herself using pronouns like *I*, *we*, *our* and *us*. This is called *first-person point of view*. For example, in the literature selection "Who Am I?" the speaker describes the world from a very personal point of view: "I walk through crowded streets. . . ." In *third-person point of view*, on the other hand, the narrator stands back from the action and describes what happens to others. A third-person narrator may be *omniscient* (all-knowing) or *limited* (taking the point of view of a particular character).

Rewriting a Story   Look through the literature selections you've read for a character whose point of view was never revealed, such as the dragon in "Young Ladies Don't Slay Dragons" or one of the boys in "Through the Tunnel." Then retell the story from the first-person point of view using that character's voice. Describe what you think about the other characters and how you feel about the events of the story.

Write About Your Life   Think of an important event in your life that you can remember clearly, such as your first day in a new school. Now step back from the event and write a short story about it from the third-person omniscient point of view. Remember that in this kind of narrative you must use the pronoun *he* or *she* when referring to yourself.

What Is Conflict?

Conflict is the struggle that a character must face in a work of literature. The conflict can be *external*—as in one character against another, one character against nature, or one character against society—or it can be *internal*—taking place inside the character's mind. Conflict is important to the story's plot and helps reveal a character's identity. In the literature selection from *I Know Why the Caged Bird Sings*, the narrator struggles to become the first African American to work on the San Francisco streetcars. Her victory reveals not only her strength of character but also the importance of conflict in both literature and life.

Write a Diary   Look through the literature selections you've read for a character facing a special conflict. This conflict could be internal or external. Then imagine you are that character and write a series of diary entries that parallel the action of the story. Describe how you feel about the story's events and tell what you hope to gain from the conflict.

Turning Reality into Fiction   The world is full of the raw material of stories. Look through a newspaper or magazine for examples of real-life conflict. The conflict could be between one person and another; it might also be between one person and society or nature. Choose an article about a person who is experiencing some kind of conflict. Then write a story about the conflict. Include dialogue and description.

Glossary of Literary Terms

A

alliteration   Repetition of the first sound—usually a consonant sound—in several words of a sentence or a line of poetry.

allusion   An author's indirect reference to someone or something that is presumed to be familiar to the reader.

anecdote   A short narrative about an interesting or a humorous event, usually in the life of a person.

antagonist   The person or force opposing the protagonist, or main character in a literary work. [See also *protagonist*.]

autobiography   A person's written account of his or her own life.

B

ballad   A poem, often a song, that tells a story in simple verse.

biography   An account of a person's life, written by another person.

blank verse   Unrhymed poetry.

C

character   A person or an animal that participates in the action of a work of literature. A *dynamic character* is one whose thoughts, feelings, and actions are changeable and lifelike; a *static character* always remains the same. [See also *protagonist, antagonist*.]

characterization   The creation of characters through the characters' use of language and through descriptions of their appearance, thoughts, emotions, and actions. [See also *character*.]

chronology   An arrangement of events in the order in which they happen.

cliché   An overused expression that is trite rather than meaningful.

climax   The highest point of tension in the plot of a work of literature. [See also *plot*.]

comedy   An amusing play that has a happy ending.

conclusion   The final part or ending of a piece of literature.

concrete poem   A poem arranged on the page so that its punctuation, letters, and lines make the shape of the subject of the poem.

conflict   A problem that confronts the characters in a piece of literature. The conflict may be *internal* (a character's struggle within himself or herself) or *external* (a character's struggle against nature, another person, or society). [See also *plot*.]

context   The general sense of words that helps readers to understand the meaning of unfamiliar words and phrases in a piece of writing.

D

description   An author's use of words to give the reader or listener a mental picture, an impression, or an understanding of a person, place, thing, event, or idea.

dialect   A form of speech spoken by people in a particular group or geographical region that differs in vocabulary, grammar, and pronunciation from the standard language.

dialogue   The spoken words and conversation of characters in a work of literature.

drama   A play that is performed before an audience according to stage directions and using dialogue. Classical drama has two genres: *tragedy* and *comedy*. Modern drama includes *melodrama, satire, theater of the absurd*, and *pantomime*. [See also *comedy, play*, and *tragedy*.]

dramatic poetry   A play written in the form of poetry.

E

epic   A long narrative poem—written in a formal style and meant to be read aloud—that relates the adventures and

experiences of one or more great heroes or heroines.

essay   Personal nonfiction writing about a particular subject that is important to the writer.

excerpt   A passage from a larger work that has been taken out of its context to be used for a special purpose.

exposition   Writing that explains, analyzes, or defines.

extended metaphor   An elaborately drawn out metaphor. [See also *metaphor*.]

F

fable   A short, simple story whose purpose is to teach a lesson, usually with animal characters who talk and act like people.

fantasy   Imaginative fiction about unrealistic characters, places, and events.

fiction   Literature, including the short story and the novel, that tells about imaginary people and events.

figurative language Language used to express ideas through figures of speech: descriptions that aren't meant to be taken literally. Types of figurative language include *simile, metaphor, extended metaphor, hyperbole,* and *personification*.

figure of speech   A type of figurative language, not meant to be taken literally, that expresses something in such a way that it brings the thing to life in the reader's or listener's imagination. [See also *figurative language*.]

flashback   A break in a story's action that relates a past happening in order to give the reader background information about a present action in the story.

folktale   A story that has been passed along from storyteller to storyteller for generations. Kinds of folktales include *tall tales, fairy tales, fables, legends,* and *myths*.

foreshadowing   The use of clues to create suspense by giving the reader or audience hints of events to come.

free verse   Poetry that has no formal rhyme scheme or metrical pattern.

G

genre   A major category of art. The three major literary genres are poetry, prose, and drama.

H

haiku   A three-line Japanese verse form. In most haiku, the first and third lines have five syllables, while the second line has seven. The traditional haiku describes a complicated feeling or thought in simple language through a single image.

hero/heroine   The main character in a work of literature. In heroic literature, the hero or heroine is a particularly brave, noble, or clever person whose achievements are unusual and important. [See also *character*.]

heroic age   The historical period in western civilization—from about 800 B.C. through A.D. 200—during which most works of heroic literature, such as myths and epics, were created in ancient Greece and Rome.

hubris   Arrogance or excessive pride leading to mistakes; the character flaw in a hero of classical tragedy.

hyperbole   An obvious exaggeration used for emphasis. [See also *figurative language*.]

I

idiom   An expression whose meaning cannot be understood from the ordinary meaning of the words. For example, *It's raining cats and dogs*.

imagery   The words and phrases in writing that appeal to the senses of sight, hearing, taste, touch, and smell.

irony   An effect created by a sharp contrast between what is expected and what is real. An *ironic twist* in a plot is an event that is the complete opposite of what the characters have been hoping or expecting will happen. An *ironic statement* declares the opposite of the speaker's literal meaning.

J

jargon   Words and phrases used by a group of people who share the same profession or special interests in order to refer to technical things or processes with which they are familiar. In general, jargon is any terminology that sounds unclear, overused, or pretentious.

L

legend   A famous folktale about heroic actions, passed along by word of mouth from generation to generation. The legend may have begun as a factual account of real people and events but has become mostly or completely fictitious.

limerick   A form of light verse, or humorous poetry, written in one five-line stanza with a regular scheme of rhyme and meter.

literature   The branch of art that is expressed in written language and includes all written genres.

lyric poem   A short poem that expresses personal feelings and thoughts in a musical way. Originally, lyrics were the words of songs that were sung to music played on the lyre, a stringed instrument invented by the ancient Greeks.

M

metamorphosis   The transformation of one thing, or being, into another completely different thing or being, such as a caterpillar's change into a butterfly.

metaphor   Figurative language in which one thing is said to be another thing. [See also *figurative language*.]

meter   The pattern of rhythm in lines of poetry. The most common meter, in poetry written in English, is iambic pentameter, that is, a verse having five metrical feet, each foot of verse having two syllables, an unaccented one followed by an accented one.

mood   The feeling or atmosphere that a reader senses while reading or listening to a work of literature.

motivation   A character's reasons for doing, thinking, feeling, or saying something. Sometimes an author will make a character's motivation obvious from the beginning. In realistic fiction and drama, however, a character's motivation may be so complicated that the reader discovers it gradually, by studying the character's thoughts, feelings, and behavior.

myth   A story, passed along by word of mouth for generations, about the actions of gods and goddesses or superhuman heroes and heroines. Most myths were first told to explain the origins of natural things or to justify the social rules and customs of a particular society.

N

narration   The process of telling a story. For both fiction and nonfiction, there are two main kinds of narration, based on whether the story is told from a first-person or third-person point of view. [See also *point of view*.]

narrative poem   A poem that tells a story containing the basic literary ingredients of fiction: character, setting, and plot.

narrator   The person, or voice, that tells a story. [See also *point of view, voice*.]

nonfiction   Prose that is factually true and is about real people, events, and places.

nonstandard English
Versions of English, such as slang and dialects, that use pronunciation, vocabulary, idiomatic expressions, grammar, and punctuation that differ from the accepted "correct" constructions of English.

novel   A long work of narrative prose fiction. A novel contains narration, a setting or settings, characters, dialogue, and a more complicated plot than a short story.

O

onomatopoeia   The technique of using words that imitate the sounds they describe, such as *hiss, buzz,* and *splash.*

oral tradition   Stories, poems, and songs that have been kept alive by being told, recited, and sung by people over many generations. Since the works were not originally written, they often have many different versions.

P

parable   A brief story—similar to a fable, but about people—that describes an ordinary situation and concludes with a short moral or lesson to be learned.

personification   Figurative language in which an animal, an object, or an idea is given human characteristics. [See also *figurative language.*]

persuasion   A type of speech or writing whose purpose is to convince people that something is true or important.

play   A work of dramatic literature written for performance by actors before an audience. In classical or traditional drama, a play is divided into five acts, each containing a number of scenes. Each act represents a distinct phase in the development of the plot. Modern plays often have only one act and one scene.

playwright   The author of a play.

plot   The sequence of actions and events in fiction or drama. A traditional plot has at least three parts: the *rising action,* leading up to a turning point that affects the main character; the *climax,* the turning point or moment of greatest intensity or interest; and the *falling action,* leading away from the conflict, or resolving it.

poetry   Language selected and arranged in order to say something in a compressed or nonliteral way. Modern poetry may or may not use many of the traditional poetic techniques that include *meter, rhyme, alliteration, figurative language, symbolism,* and *specific verse forms.*

point of view   The perspective from which a writer tells a story. *First-person* narrators tell the story from their own point of view, using pronouns such as *I* or *me. Third-person* narrators, using pronouns such as *he, she,* or *them,* may be *omniscient* (knowing everything about all characters), or *limited* (taking the point of view of one character). [See also *narration.*]

propaganda   Information or ideas that may or may not be true, but are spread as though they are true, in order to persuade people to do or believe something.

prose   The ordinary form of written and spoken language used to create fiction, nonfiction, and most drama.

protagonist   The main character of a literary work. [See also *character* and *characterization.*]

R

refrain   A line or group of lines that is repeated, usually at the end of each verse, in a poem or a song.

repetition   The use of the same formal element more than once in a literary work, for emphasis or in order to achieve another desired effect.

resolution   The falling action in fiction or drama,

including all of the developments that follow the climax and show that the story's conflict is over. [See also *plot*.]

rhyme scheme   A repeated pattern of similar sounds, usually found at the ends of lines of poetry or poetic drama.

rhythm   In poetry, the measured recurrence of accented and unaccented syllables in a particular pattern. [See also *meter*.]

S

scene   The time, place, and circumstances of a play or a story. In a play, a scene is a section of an act. [See also *play*.]

science fiction   Fantasy literature set in an imaginary future, with details and situations that are designed to seem scientifically possible.

setting   The time and place of a work of literature.

short story   Narrative prose fiction that is shorter and has a less complicated plot than a novel. A short story contains narration, at least one setting, at least one character, and usually some dialogue.

simile   Figurative language that compares two unlike things, introduced by the words "like" or "as." [See also *figurative language*.]

soliloquy   In a play, a short speech spoken by a single character when he or she is alone on the stage. A soliloquy usually expresses the character's innermost thoughts and feelings, when he or she thinks no other characters can hear.

sonnet   A poem written in one stanza, using fourteen lines of iambic pentameter. [See also *meter*.]

speaker   In poetry, the individual whose voice seems to be speaking the lines. [See also *narration*, *voice*.]

stage directions   The directions, written by the playwright, to tell the director, actors, and theater technicians how a play should be dramatized. Stage directions may specify such things as how the setting should appear in each scene, how the actors should deliver their lines, when the stage curtain should rise and fall, how stage lights should be used, where on the stage the actors should be during the action, and when sound effects should be used.

stanza   A group of lines in poetry set apart by blank lines before and after the group; a poetic verse.

style   The distinctive way in which an author composes a work of literature in written or spoken language.

suspense   An effect created by authors of various types of fiction and drama, especially adventure and mystery, to heighten interest in the story.

symbol   An image, person, place, or thing that is used to express the idea of something else.

T

tall tale   A kind of folk tale, or legend, that exaggerates the characteristics of its hero or heroine.

theme   The main idea or underlying subject of a work of literature.

tone   The attitude that a work of literature expresses to the reader through its style.

tragedy   In classical drama, a tragedy depicts a noble hero or heroine who makes a mistake of judgment that has disastrous consequences.

V

verse   A stanza in a poem. Also, a synonym for poetry as a genre. [See also *stanza*.]

voice   The narrator or the person who relates the action of a piece of literature. [See also *speaker*.]

ACKNOWLEDGMENTS

Grateful acknowledgment is made for permission to reprint the following copyrighted material.

"The Sun and the Moon" by Elaine Laron from *Free to Be...You and Me* by Marlo Thomas and Associates. Copyright © 1974 by Free to Be Foundation, Inc. Used by permission of Bantam Books, a division of Bantam Doubleday Dell Publishing Group, Inc.

"Who Am I?" by Stella Mancillas is reprinted from *I Heard a Scream in the Street : Poems by Young People in the City* selected by Nancy Larrick, copyright © 1970 by Nancy Larrick

"Young Ladies Don't Slay Dragons" by Joyce Hovelsrud is reprinted from *The Princess Book*, copyright © 1974 by Rand McNally & company. By permission of the author.

From *I Know Why the Caged Bird Sings* by Maya Angelou. Copyright © 1969 by Maya Angelou. Reprinted by permission of Random House, Inc.

"74th Street" from *The Malibu and Other Poems* by Myra Cohn Livingston. Copyright © 1972 by Myra Cohn Livingston (Atheneum). Reprinted by permission of Marian Reiner for the author.

from *The Olympic Games* by Theodore Knight. Reprinted by permission of Lucent Books, Inc., P.O. Box 289011, San Diego, CA 92198-9011.

"Through the Tunnel" from *The Habit of Loving* by Doris Lessing, copyright © 1957 by Doris Lessing. Originally appeared in *The New Yorker*. Reprinted by permission of HarperCollins Publishers.

"For Poets" by Al Young is reprinted from *The Song Turning Back Into Itself* by Al Young, copyright © 1965 by Al Young. By permission of the author.

"Raymond's Run" from *Gorilla, My Love* by Toni Cade Bambara. Copyright © 1971 by Toni Cade Bambara. Reprinted by permission of Random House.

"What a Boy Can Do" by Alberto Ríos is reprinted from *Teodoro Luna's Two Kisses*, Poems by Alberto Ríos, by permission of W.W. Norton & Company, Inc. Copyright © 1990 by Alberto Ríos.

"Thumbprint" from *It Doesn't Always Have to Rhyme* by Eve Merriam. Copyright © 1964 by Eve Merriam. © renewed 1992 by Eve Merriam. Reprinted by permission of Marian Reiner.

"Pictures on a Rock" from *To Live in Two Worlds: American Indian Youth Today* by Brent Ashabranner. Copyright © 1984 by Brent Ashabranner. Reprinted by permission of the author.

"On Shark's Tooth Beach" from *Throwing Shadows* by E. L. Konigsburg. Copyright ©1979 by E. L. Konigsburg. Reprinted with the permission of Atheneum Publishers, an imprint of Macmillan Publishing Company.

ILLUSTRATION

11 Heidi Lutts; 16-23 K. Boake W.

PHOTOGRAPHY

4 *l* Tony Freeman/PhotoEdit; *r* Jim Whitmer/Stock Boston; **5** Reproduced by the courtesy of the Trustees, The National Gallery, London; **6** Julie Bidwell/©D.C. Heath; **10** *t* Skjold/The Image Works; *b* John Owens/©D.C. Heath; **11** *t* Sarah Putnam/©D.C. Heath; *c* John Owens/©D.C. Heath; *b* Jim Whitmer/Stock Boston; **12** *inset* NASA; **12-13** *background* ©Jay Pasachoff; **13** *inset* Richard Hamilton Smith; **14-15** Art Gallery of Ontario, Toronto. Gift of Mr. and Mrs. Morris Emer, 1985. ©Helen Frankenthaler, 1993. Photo by Carlo Catenazzi; **24-25, 29** UPI/Bettmann; **29** *inset* Mary Ellen Mark Library; **32, 34-35** UPI/Bettmann; **35** *inset* AP/Wide World Photos; **36-37** Collection Mr. & Mrs. Albert Hackett, NY. ©Estate of Ben Shahn/VAGA, NY, 1995. **37** Courtesy of Holiday House; **38** Focus on Sports; *inset,* **41** UPI/Bettmann; **43** Dan Helms/Duomo; *inset* Anne Knight; **44-59** Clem Spalding; **59** *inset* Miriam Berkley; **60** Reproduced by courtesy of the Trustees, The National Gallery, London; **62-63, 64-65, 66-67** David Madison; **69** David Madison/Duomo; **70-71** David Madison; **72, 73** Focus on Sports; **73** *inset* Carole Dufrechou. Courtesy of Random House Group, Inc.; **74-75** *background* Dan Derdula; **75** *inset* Photo by Hal Martin Fogel. Courtesy of W.W. Norton and Company; **77** *inset* Courtesy of Macmillan Children's Book Group; **78-81** Lauren Shaw; **81** *t, inset* Paul Conklin; *b, inset* AP/Wide World Photos; **82-83** Richard Hamilton Smith; *insets* Sinclair Stammers/Photo Researchers; **86, 91** Kevin Aitken/Peter Arnold; **92-93** Daniel Derdula; **93** *inset* Jeffrey Rotman/Peter Arnold; **94** Norbert Wu/Peter Arnold; **99** James Karales/Peter Arnold; **101** Richard Hamilton Smith; **101** *inset* Stu Perry. Courtesy of Macmillan Children's Book Group.
Back cover *t* Julie Bidwell/©D.C. Heath; *c* Sarah Putnam/©D.C. Heath; *b* Julie Bidwell/©D.C. Heath.

Full Pronunciation Key for Footnoted Words

(Each pronunciation and definition is adapted from *Scott, Foresman Advanced Dictionary* by E.L. Thorndike and Clarence L. Barnhart.)

The pronunciation of each footnoted word is shown just after the word, in this way: **abbreviate** [ə brē′ vē āt]. The letters and signs used are pronounced as in the words below. The mark ′ is placed after a syllable with primary or heavy accent, as in the example above. The mark ′ after a syllable shows a secondary or lighter accent, as in **abbreviation** [ə brē′ vē ā′ shən].

Some words, taken from foreign languages, are spoken with sounds that do not otherwise occur in English. Symbols for these sounds are given in the key as "foreign sounds."

a	hat, cap	j	jam, enjoy	u	cup, butter
ā	age, face	k	kind, seek	ủ	full, put
ä	father, far	l	land, coal	ü	rule, move
		m	me, am	v	very, save
b	bad, rob	n	no, in	w	will, woman
ch	child, much	ng	long, bring	y	young, yet
d	did, red			z	zero, breeze
		o	hot, rock	zh	measure, seizure
e	let, best	ō	open, go		
ē	equal, be	ô	order, all	ə represents:
ėr	term, learn	oi	oil, voice	a in about
		ou	house, out	e in taken
f	fat, if			i in pencil
g	go, bag	p	paper, cup	o in lemon
h	he, how	r	run, try	u in circus
		s	say, yes	
i	it, pin	sh	she, rush	
ī	ice, five	t	tell, it	
		th	thin, both	
		ᵺH	then, smooth	

foreign sounds

Y as in French *du*. Pronounce (ē) with the lips rounded as for (ü).

à as in French *ami*. Pronounce (ä) with the lips spread and held tense.

œ as in French *peu*. Pronounce (ā) with the lips rounded as for (ō).

N as in French *bon*. The N is not pronounced, but shows that the vowel before it is nasal.

H as in German *ach*. Pronounce (k) without closing the breath passage.

All Together

HEATH
MIDDLE LEVEL
LITERATURE

HEATH
MIDDLE LEVEL
LITERATURE

All Together

THEME
COMMUNITY

AUTHORS

Donna Alvermann
Linda Miller Cleary
Kenneth Donelson
Donald Gallo
Alice Haskins
J. Howard Johnston
John Lounsbury
Alleen Pace Nilsen
Robert Pavlik
Jewell Parker Rhodes
Alberto Alvaro Ríos
Sandra Schurr
Lyndon Searfoss
Julia Thomason
Max Thompson
Carl Zon

D.C. Heath and Company
Lexington, Massachusetts / Toronto, Ontario

STAFF CREDITS

EDITORIAL Barbara A. Brennan, Helen Byers, Christopher Johnson,
Kathleen Kennedy Kelley, Owen Shows, Rita M. Sullivan
Proofreading: JoAnne B. Sgroi

CONTRIBUTING WRITERS Nance Davidson, Florence Harris

SERIES DESIGN Robin Herr

BOOK DESIGN Caroline Bowden, Daniel Derdula, Susan Geer, Diana Maloney,
Angela Sciaraffa, Bonnie Chayes Yousefian
Art Editing: Carolyn Langley

PHOTOGRAPHY *Series Photography Coordinator*: Carmen Johnson
Photo Research Supervisor: Martha Friedman
Photo Researchers: Wendy Enright, Linda Finigan, Po-yee McKenna,
PhotoSearch, Inc., Gillian Speeth, Denise Theodores
Assignment Photography Coordinators: Susan Doheny,
Gayna Hoffman, Shawna Johnston

COMPUTER PREPRESS Ricki Pappo, Kathy Meisl
Richard Curran, Michele Locatelli

PERMISSIONS Dorothy B. McLeod

PRODUCTION Patrick Connolly

Cover: © Superstock. **Cover Design:** Steve Snider

Published simultaneously in Canada

Printed in the United States of America

International Standard Book Number: 0-669-32098-6 (soft cover)
  3 4 5 6 7 8 9 10-RRD-99 98 97

International Standard Book Number: 0-669-38168-3 (hard cover)
  3 4 5 6 7 8 9 10-RRD-99 98 97

Middle Level Authors

Donna Alvermann, University of Georgia
Alice Haskins, Howard County Public Schools, Maryland
J. Howard Johnston, University of South Florida
John Lounsbury, Georgia College
Sandra Schurr, University of South Florida
Julia Thomason, Appalachian State University
Max Thompson, Appalachian State University
Carl Zon, California Assessment Collaborative

Literature and Language Arts Authors

Linda Miller Cleary, University of Minnesota
Kenneth Donelson, Arizona State University
Donald Gallo, Central Connecticut State University
Alleen Pace Nilsen, Arizona State University
Robert Pavlik, Cardinal Stritch College, Milwaukee
Jewell Parker Rhodes, Arizona State University
Alberto Alvaro Ríos, Arizona State University
Lyndon Searfoss, Arizona State University

Teacher Consultants

Suzanne Aubin, Patapsco Middle School, Ellicott City, Maryland
Judy Baxter, Newport News Public Schools, Newport News, Virginia
Saundra Bryn, Director of Research and Development, El Mirage, Arizona
Lorraine Gerhart, Elmbrook Middle School, Elm Grove, Wisconsin
Kathy Tuchman Glass, Burlingame Intermediate School, Burlingame, California
Lisa Mandelbaum, Crocker Middle School, Hillsborough, California
Lucretia Pannozzo, John Jay Middle School, Katonah, New York
Carol Schultz, Jerling Junior High, Orland Park, Illinois
Jeanne Siebenman, Grand Canyon University, Phoenix, Arizona
Gail Thompson, Garey High School, Pomona, California
Rufus Thompson, Grace Yokley School, Ontario, California
Tom Tufts, Conniston Middle School, West Palm Beach, Florida
Edna Turner, Harpers Choice Middle School, Columbia, Maryland
C. Anne Webb, Buerkle Junior High School, St. Louis, Missouri
Geri Yaccino, Thompson Junior High School, St. Charles, Illinois

149

CONTENTS

THE LITERATURE

ASKING BIG QUESTIONS ABOUT THE LITERATURE

What makes a community? 102

What communities do people belong to? 103

What responsibilities do people have to their community? 104

How do communities change? 105

PROJECTS

1 WRITING WORKSHOP

A PROPOSAL FOR CHANGE 106-111

Does something need work in your community? Here's your chance to change the world!

2 COOPERATIVE LEARNING

A COMMUNITY OF THE FUTURE 112-113

What will communities of the future be like? Use your imagination to create a futuristic community on a planet of your choice!

3 HELPING YOUR COMMUNITY

DEVELOPING A PLAN OF ACTION 114-115

What does your community need? Create a plan of action to help your school, neighborhood, or town.

A Picture of Us

The word *me* separates you from other people, but the word *us* links you to them. Using *us* means you see yourself not just as one person alone but as part of a *community*—a group of persons who have something in common or who share some daily experience, such as going to the same school or living in the same neighborhood.

What do you know about communities, and about the people and places that turn *me* into *us*? With a group of classmates, express what you know in a mural—a picture of *us*.

1 Think about your mural.

What does *community* mean to you? What groups of people do you feel part of? Think of how you could represent the idea of community in a mural. Could a community be represented by certain kinds of clothing, food, or a flag? Jot down your thoughts in your journal.

Make your mural.

Work with a group of five or six classmates to make a mural of a community you know, such as your school or neighborhood. Use poster paper or tape together sheets of notebook paper. Decide on a work plan before you start. Divide the mural into sections that you can work on individually, or come up with an overall design and work on it together.

Let's talk.

Discuss your mural. Use questions like these to guide your discussion:
- Why did we include the things we did?
- What do they mean to us?
- How are they linked to community?
- What do they tell us about communities?

Define community.

Think about the murals you've seen and then write your own definition of *community*. Let members of your group take turns reading their definitions. How do these definitions compare to yours? As your recorder takes notes, work toward a group definition. Keep revising until you come up with a definition that satisfies everyone. Finally write your definition on a piece of paper and attach it to the mural.

Asking Big Questions About the Theme

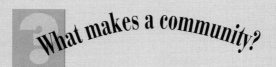

What makes a community?

Think about the communities that you belong to, such as your school or your neighborhood. Then, in your journal, complete these sentences with as many ideas as you can.

When I say *us*, I mean _____.

The things I associate with *us* are _____.

Now think of all the different kinds of communities in the world, from school communities like yours to the village communities in the rain forests of Costa Rica. Discuss what all these communities have in common. Decide what makes a community.

What communities do people belong to?

Your world is full of communities. Just look at your town, which is made up of many smaller communities. What are they? Work with one or more classmates. Draw a big circle and label it *TOWN*. Then take turns identifying the smaller communities within your town. To represent each of these communities, draw and label a small circle inside the big circle.

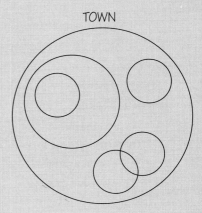

TOWN

What responsibilities do people have to their community?

What are your responsibilities to your school, neighborhood, and town? For example, have you ever volunteered to baby-sit while your neighbor voted? In your journal, draw the outline of your hand three times. Then label each outline with the name of one of these communities. In each finger, write a duty you have to that community. Compare your "hands" with those of your classmates.

How do communities change?

With a partner or small group, discuss changes in your school, neighborhood, and town over the years. Are your classes organized differently? Have stores opened or closed? Have bus routes changed? In your journal, make a chart to show the changes in one of your communities. Use the model below to help you.

Changes in My Neighborhood	
When I was 8	**Now**
Only grocery store, shoe store, pharmacy on Vine St.	Mini-mall

NOW *Think!*

How do you feel about your communities? As you read *All Together*, think about how your communities compare with the communities in the stories and poems. Do the characters in the selections say what you might say about your community? Do they feel how you feel about belonging to a group?

SEVENTH GRADE

GARY SOTO

On the first day of school, Victor stood in line half an hour before he came to a wobbly card table. He was handed a packet of papers and a computer card on which he listed his one elective, French. He already spoke Spanish and English, but he thought some day he might travel to France, where it was cool; not like Fresno,[1] where summer days reached 110 degrees in the shade. There were rivers in France, and huge churches, and fair-skinned people everywhere, the way there were brown people all around Victor.

Besides, Teresa, a girl he had liked since they were in catechism[2] classes at Saint Theresa's, was taking French, too. With any luck they would be in the same class. Teresa is going to be my girl this year, he promised himself as he left the gym full of students in their new fall clothes. She was cute. And good at math, too, Victor thought as he walked down the hall to his homeroom. He ran into his friend, Michael Torres, by the water fountain that never turned off.

1. **Fresno** [frez′ nō]: city in central California.
2. **catechism** [kat′ ə kiz əm]: a book of questions and answers about religion.

They shook hands, *raza*-style,[3] and jerked their heads at one another in a *saludo de vato*.[4] "How come you're making a face?" asked Victor.

"I ain't making a face, *ese*.[5] This *is* my face." Michael said his face had changed during the summer. He had read a *GQ* magazine that his older brother borrowed from the Book Mobile and noticed that the male models all had the same look on their faces. They would stand, one arm around a beautiful woman, and *scowl*. They would sit at a pool, their rippled stomachs dark with shadow, and *scowl*. They would sit at dinner tables, cool drinks in their hands, and *scowl*.

"I think it works," Michael said. He scowled and let his upper lip quiver. His teeth showed along with the ferocity of his soul. "Belinda Reyes walked by a while ago and looked at me," he said.

Victor didn't say anything, though he thought his friend looked pretty strange. They talked about recent movies, baseball, their parents, and the horrors of picking grapes in order to buy their fall clothes. Picking grapes was like living in Siberia, except hot and more boring.

"What classes are you taking?" Michael said, scowling.

"French. How 'bout you?"

"Spanish. I ain't so good at it, even if I'm Mexican."

"I'm not either, but I'm better at it than math, that's for sure."

A tinny, three-beat bell propelled students to their homerooms. The two friends socked each other in the arm and went their ways, Victor thinking, man, that's weird. Michael thinks making a face makes him handsome.

On his way to his homeroom, Victor tried a scowl. He felt foolish, until out of the corner of his eye he saw a girl looking at

---

3. *raza*-style [rä′ sä]: Spanish slang, here meaning in a special style known by friends.
4. *saludo de vato* [sä lü′ dō dä vä′ tō]: Spanish slang, meaning a greeting between "cool" guys.
5. *ese* [ā′ sā]: Spanish slang, here meaning "dude" or "you."

him. Umm, he thought, maybe it does work. He scowled with greater conviction.

In homeroom, roll was taken, emergency cards were passed out, and they were given a bulletin to take home to their parents. The principal, Mr. Belton, spoke over a crackling loudspeaker, welcoming the students to a new year, new experiences, and new friendships. The students squirmed in their chairs and ignored him. They were anxious to go to first period. Victor sat calmly, thinking of Teresa, who sat two rows away, reading a paperback novel. This would be his lucky year. She was in his homeroom, and would probably be in his English and math classes. And, of course, French.

The bell rang for first period, and the students herded noisily through the door. Only Teresa lingered, talking with the homeroom teacher.

"So you think I should talk to Mrs. Gaines?" she asked the teacher. "She would know about ballet?"

"She would be a good bet," the teacher said. Then added, "Or the gym teacher, Mrs. Garza."

Victor lingered, keeping his head down and staring at his desk. He wanted to leave when she did so he could bump into her and say something clever.

He watched her on the sly. As she turned to leave, he stood up and hurried to the door, where he managed to catch her eye. She smiled and said, "Hi, Victor."

He smiled back and said, "Yeah, that's me." His brown face blushed. Why hadn't he said, "Hi, Teresa," or "How was your summer?" or something nice?

As Teresa walked down the hall, Victor walked the other way, looking back, admiring how gracefully she walked, one foot in front of the other. So much for being in the same class, he thought. As he trudged to English, he practiced scowling.

In English they reviewed the parts of speech. Mr. Lucas, a portly man, waddled down the aisle, asking, "What is a noun?"

"A person, place, or thing," said the class in unison.

"Yes, now somebody give me an example of a person—you, Victor Rodriguez."

"Teresa," Victor said automatically. Some of the girls giggled. They knew he had a crush on Teresa. He felt himself blushing again.

"Correct," Mr. Lucas said. "Now provide me with a place."

Mr. Lucas called on a freckled kid who answered, "Teresa's house with a kitchen full of big brothers."

After English, Victor had math, his weakest subject. He sat in the back by the window, hoping that he would not be called on. Victor understood most of the problems, but some of the stuff looked like the teacher made it up as she went along. It was confusing, like the inside of a watch.

After math he had a fifteen-minute break, then social studies, and, finally, lunch. He bought a tuna casserole with buttered rolls, some fruit cocktail, and milk. He sat with Michael, who practiced scowling between bites.

Girls walked by and looked at him.

"See what I mean, Vic?" Michael scowled. "They love it."

"Yeah, I guess so."

They ate slowly, Victor scanning the horizon for a glimpse of Teresa. He didn't see her. She must have brought lunch, he thought, and is eating outside. Victor scraped his plate and left Michael, who was busy scowling at a girl two tables away.

The small, triangle-shaped campus bustled with students talking about their new classes. Everyone was in a sunny mood. Victor hurried to the bag lunch area, where he sat down and opened his math book. He moved his lips as if he were reading, but his mind was somewhere else. He raised his eyes slowly and looked around. No Teresa.

He lowered his eyes, pretending to study, then looked slowly to the left. No Teresa. He turned a page in the book and stared at some math problems that scared him because he knew he would have to do them eventually. He looked to the right. Still no sign of her. He stretched out lazily in an attempt to disguise his snooping.

Then he saw her. She was sitting with a girlfriend under a plum tree. Victor moved to a table near her and daydreamed about taking her to a movie. When the bell sounded, Teresa looked up, and their eyes met. She smiled sweetly and gathered her books. Her next class was French, same as Victor's.

They were among the last students to arrive in class, so all the good desks in the back had already been taken. Victor was forced to sit near the front, a few desks away from Teresa, while Mr. Bueller wrote French words on the chalkboard. The bell rang, and Mr. Bueller wiped his hands, turned to the class, and said, "*Bonjour.*" [6]

"*Bonjour,*" braved a few students.

"*Bonjour,*" Victor whispered. He wondered if Teresa heard him.

Mr. Bueller said that if the students studied hard, at the end of the year they could go to France and be understood by the populace.

One kid raised his hand and asked, "What's 'populace'?"

"The people, the people of France."

Mr. Bueller asked if anyone knew French. Victor raised his hand, wanting to impress Teresa. The teacher beamed and said, "*Très bien. Parlez-vous français?*" [7]

Victor didn't know what to say. The teacher wet his lips and asked something else in French. The room grew silent. Victor felt all eyes staring at him. He tried to bluff his way out by making noises that sounded French.

"La me vava me con le grandma," [8] he said uncertainly.

Mr. Bueller, wrinkling his face in curiosity, asked him to speak up.

Great rosebushes of red bloomed on Victor's cheeks. A river of nervous sweat ran down his palms. He felt awful. Teresa sat a few desks away, no doubt thinking he was a fool. Without looking at Mr. Bueller, Victor mumbled, "Frenchie oh wewe gee in September." [9]

Mr. Bueller asked Victor to repeat what he had said.

---

6. **bonjour** [bôN zhür']: French for "hello."
7. **Très bien. Parlez-vous français?** [tre byen pär lā' vü frän se']: French for "Very good. Do you speak French?"
8. **La me vava me con le grandma** [lä mä vä' vä mä côn lä grän' mä]: Victor is pretending to speak French.
9. **Frenchie oh wewe gee in September:** Victor is talking nonsense.

"Frenchie oh wewe gee in September," Victor repeated.

Mr. Bueller understood that the boy didn't know French and turned away. He walked to the blackboard and pointed to the words on the board with his steel-edged ruler.

"*Le bateau,*"[10] he sang.

"*Le bateau,*" the students repeated.

"*Le bateau est sur l'eau,*"[11] he sang.

"*Le bateau est sur l'eau.*"

Victor was too weak from failure to join the class. He stared at the board and wished he had taken Spanish, not French. Better yet, he wished he could start his life over. He had never been so embarrassed. He bit his thumb until he tore off a sliver of skin.

The bell sounded for fifth period, and Victor shot out of the room, avoiding the stares of the other kids, but had to return for his math book. He looked sheepishly at the teacher, who was erasing the board, then widened his eyes in terror at Teresa who stood in front of him. "I didn't know you knew French," she said. "That was good."

Mr. Bueller looked at Victor, and Victor looked back. Oh please, don't say anything, Victor pleaded with his eyes. I'll wash your car, mow your lawn, walk your dog—anything! I'll be your best student, and I'll clean your erasers after school.

10. **le bateau** [lə bä tō′]: French for "boat."
11. **le bateau est sur l'eau** [lə bä tō′ ā syr lō]: French for "The boat is on the water."

Mr. Bueller shuffled through the papers on his desk. He smiled and hummed as he sat down to work. He remembered his college years when he dated a girlfriend in borrowed cars. She thought he was rich because each time he picked her up he had a different car. It was fun until he had spent all his money on her and had to write home to his parents because he was broke.

Victor couldn't stand to look at Teresa. He was sweaty with shame. "Yeah, well, I picked up a few things from movies and books, and stuff like that." They left the class together. Teresa asked him if he would help her with her French.

"Sure, anytime," Victor said.

"I won't be bothering you, will I?"

"Oh no, I like being bothered."

"*Bonjour*," Teresa said, leaving him outside her next class. She smiled and pushed wisps of hair from her face.

"Yeah, right, *bonjour*," Victor said. He turned and headed to his class. The rosebushes of shame on his face became bouquets of love. Teresa is a great girl, he thought. And Mr. Bueller is a good guy.

He raced to metal shop. After metal shop there was biology, and after biology a long sprint to the public library, where he checked out three French textbooks.

He was going to like seventh grade.

GARY SOTO

Gary Soto was born in 1952 in Fresno, California, and grew up in a poor Mexican American family. Like the boys in "Seventh Grade," Soto earned money as a farm worker. Later he began to write poetry about his childhood memories and published his first book of poems in 1977. Soto has gone on to write fiction—much of it for young adults—while teaching Chicano Studies and English at the University of California in Berkeley.

Most of Soto's short stories are based on his experiences while growing up. "Seventh Grade" is one of the stories in *Baseball in April*. You can find more of Soto's stories in his book *Local News*.

The Arizona Republic   Sunday, December 27, 1992

'They think I'm an expert'

Girl's diary spurs letters by peers, notice of Hollywood

By Catherine Crocker
Associated Press

Latoya Hunter

NEW YORK—Latoya Hunter is just 14 years old, but recently, the mail brought a packet of letters from teen-agers in Brooklyn, many of them girls seeking advice about boys and their parents.

"As I was reading it, I couldn't believe it," said Latoya, whose face still has the softness of childhood.

"I mean, I'm going through those problems now, and they think I am an expert."

They think she is an expert because they know her deepest thoughts, expressed in a diary she kept during her first year in junior high school.

The Diary of Latoya Hunter, published earlier this year, is about the stuff of young girls' lives— school, friendships, boys, television, the urge for independence and conflicts with her mother.

But the slim volume, which runs 131 pages, goes deeper. It is also about being a black, immigrant girl growing up in the Bronx.

Latoya wrote in her diary about the gray, treeless streets of her neighborhood, the deadly violence around her, teen-age pregnancy, the poverty of caring and learning at her school and her homesickness for Jamaica.[1]

1. **Jamaica** [jə māʹ kə]: island country in the West Indies, south of Cuba.

It's the ordinariness of her preadolescent world against this troubled background that draws the reader into her diary. Latoya rhapsodizes[2] about her passion for junk food and TV, and then, in painfully clear prose, writes about the gunshots that killed a store clerk who sold her candy.

"Today gunshots echo in my head," Latoya wrote on Jan. 9, 1991.

"They are the same gunshots that killed an innocent human being right across from my house last night. They are the same gunshots that have scarred me, I think, forever."

'It was mostly luck'

Latoya's world has expanded beyond its old Bronx borders because of a devoted teacher, a chance newspaper article and her gift for writing.

"I think it was mostly luck," Latoya said.

But then she added, "I think, like, I am a good spokesperson for people around my age, for kids who feel that they don't count in anything, that they're being held back from being who they really want to be by outside things, like parents and friends and the kind of environment you live in."

A 1990 newspaper article about the graduation of Latoya's sixth-grade class said her English teacher wrote, "The world is waiting for Latoya!" on her report card. An editor at a publishing company saw the story and was inspired.

He contacted the teacher to ask whether Latoya would be interested in keeping a diary her first year in junior high. Latoya was offered a $3,000 advance and will receive $25,000 for the paperback rights.

Her first entries began "Dear Diary," then she decided to personalize her journal because "you've become like a best friend to me." She named it Janice Page, after her best friend in Jamaica.

"I like guys," Latoya wrote. "There, I said it. It's easy to say to you, but my mother would give me a real hard time if she heard me say that. She believes a normal 12-year-old should only obey her parents, go to school, learn her lessons, and come home

2. **rhapsodizes** [rap′ sə dīz əz]: talks or writes in an overly enthusiastic way.

everyday and listen to her parents some more."

She recounts her first relationship with a boy (they didn't go out, they just opened their hearts over the telephone), her brother's wedding (she was a bridesmaid in blue), the birth of her unmarried sister's boy, and a much-anticipated trip to Jamaica that left her deeply disappointed.

Her conclusion: "With understanding, I think I will achieve anything I want."

'Colors I see are . . . dull'

On a cold and windy afternoon, Latoya, dressed in jeans and gold hoop earrings, was back in her old Bronx neighborhood, giving a reporter a tour. She harbors no nostalgia[3] for it.

"It really makes you feel down to walk around and see the things around you," she wrote. "The only colors I see are brown and gray—dull colors. Maybe there are others, but the dull ones are the ones I see. Maybe if the streets were cleaner, and I would see colors like red and yellow, my surroundings would be more appealing."

Until she was 8, Latoya was raised by relatives in Jamaica while her parents were in the New York area struggling to make a new life for themselves. Latoya's old house, where she lived with her family on the second floor, has a chain-link fence in front and flowers in the planters that, she said, make it look better than it did when she lived there.

"It was the ugliest house on the whole block," she said. "And I never liked to bring anybody over."

Relatives live in the ground-floor apartment. Eager to see a newborn cousin, Latoya drops by for a visit. A stale smell fills the dark, sparsely[4] furnished rooms. The walls are stained and cracked.

Today, her mother, Linneth, works evenings as a nurse's aide; her father, Linton, works overnight as a security guard. And Latoya now lives in a well-kept apartment in a blue house on a tree-lined street in Mount Vernon, N.Y., a city just north of the Bronx.

---

3. **nostalgia** [no stal′ jə]: a painful loneliness that results from thinking about one's home, country, city, and so forth.
4. **sparsely** [spärs′ lē]: thinly; very little spread out.

Overwhelming response

The book's sales started out slowly, but the media response has been overwhelming. Latoya has been interviewed by reporters, appeared on television talk shows and news programs—including one that airs in Japan—and met the Jamaican prime minister.

Two movie companies are bidding for the rights to the book, said Richard Marek, her editor at Crown Publishing Inc.

But Latoya says wistfully[5] that her parents have never talked to her directly about the diary's contents, although she believes both have read it.

"If I do an interview or something," she said, "they say 'I'm proud of you' and stuff, but they never really said that to me about the book, like, you know, 'You did a good job and I'm proud of you.'"

She's a sophomore in high school, having skipped a grade. Ithaca College and Columbia University already have approached her, she said.

She wants to study psychology[6]

and be a writer. She also says that after she has had a job for a year, she wants to have a baby.

Sitting at her dining-room table, she fidgets with a pendant necklace belonging to her mother. She is shy, soft-spoken, but articulate.

"It's like everybody's dream to be in America," Latoya said. "And now that I am here, I just don't want to waste the opportunities I have."

But as doors open to worlds she never dreamed existed, there is a loss of innocence to which she is still adjusting. In her diary, she wrote, "I've never come across discrimination against me for being black."

Now she has.

A few weeks ago, when she went to the Manhattan office of a national women's magazine to be interviewed about her book, the woman at the front desk asked "if I was there to deliver anything."

"She could have said, like, 'Could I help you?' or something," Latoya said. "I guess they didn't expect someone like me to be there."

---

5. **wistfully** [wist′ fəl ē]: longingly, yearningly.
6. **psychology** [sī kol′ ə jē]: study of the mind.

From *The Diary of Latoya Hunter*

LATOYA HUNTER

Mural painted by children from the nearby community, 1989, Col. Young Park, New York City

September 17, 1990

Dear Diary,

I have good news. On Thursday and Friday there'll be no school. It's the Jewish New Year. It doesn't count for me because I'm not Jewish. I really respect these people though. Last year in school I learned about Adolph Hitler[1] and all the terrible things he did to them. He was a psycho if you ask me. I can't understand why people

1 **Adolph Hitler** [ā′ dolf hit′ lər]: Nazi dictator of Germany from 1933 to 1945.

discriminate against others for simple things like skin color and religion. I strongly believe this world should be non-racist. I've never come across discrimination against me for being black. I know racism is going on in all parts of the world but the fight is still going on too. That is something to be thankful for. Things like Mandela[2] recently being freed has kept my hope alive.

September 18, 1990

Dear Diary,

Today felt like a sneak preview of winter and a sad end to summer. It was fun while it lasted. I spent most of August in Toronto.[3] It's such a beautiful city. It's clean and peaceful. In other words, not my style. I like action. It's not so much the place that appeals to me, it's my relatives living there. That includes my grandparents on my mom's side, my aunt Chunnie, and four of my cousins. The oldest is 20 and the youngest is now 16. That's the only girl, Ann. We grew up like sisters! Like me their mom lived apart from them (in Canada), then took them up. Then she took up my grandparents. My cousins are who I grew up with excluding my Aunt Chunnie and her youngest son, and they were the only people I knew how to love until I was eight. That's when I left Jamaica, my homeland, the place where my life was crafted. Sadly, until that time, my life was crafted without my parents. They were here in N.Y., struggling to make enough money to get my sister, two brothers and me to share with them the American dream. I didn't know my father until he met us at the airport. He left when I was a baby. I've really gotten to know him over the past four years though. When I first saw him at the airport, I thought "Well this is the famous Daddy!" Everyone, even my cousins call him Daddy. Our families were that close. I can't forget he was in a hurry to get home to watch a big baseball game on t.v. After

2. **Mandela** [man del′ ə]: Nelson, black South African lawyer and leader of the African National Congress, who fought for civil rights and was imprisoned by the South African government from 1964 to 1990.
3. **Toronto** [tə ron′ tō]: city in southeast Canada, capital of the province of Ontario.

that was over, he pretty much put all his attention into us. I can remember once when I was sick, and I'll never forget this, he made me soup and made me stay in bed. I was like, "Wow! This is like t.v." I guess in Jamaica I never pictured a father making soup for his kid. I pictured the mother doing those things, never the man. He isn't easily upset or worked up. He hardly yells at me. That works with me because if I do something wrong and someone yells at me, I don't feel guilty about what I've done, just angry at the person yelling. He just goes with the flow. He was really easy to get used to.

My mother is really complex though. I still don't understand her. I had a faint memory of her while I was in Jamaica. She had left when I was 3 or 4. Anyways, they succeeded in getting my brothers, sister and myself up here. When we first got here she worked as a live-in housekeeper in Poughkeepsie[4] for some very rich people. She only came home on Friday and left again on Sunday. We hardly ever saw her but she called all the time. What got her to quit was when I first started going to P.S. 94. I was in computer class for the first time and when I saw that everyone knew what to do, I got depressed. I never saw one before in my life. I cried and cried and the teacher sent me home because I said I had a stomach ache.

Anyway, my mom heard about it and decided she didn't want to be away when things like that happened. I finally had her full-time. We enjoyed ourselves at first, being together all the time. But the excitement wore off and when I was around ten, we began the phase we're in now.

As I said, I'm living in the Bronx,[5] a place where walking alone at night is a major risk. The streets are so dirty and there's graffiti everywhere. It really makes you feel down to walk around and see the things around you. The only colors I see are brown and grey—dull colors. Maybe there are others but the dull ones are the ones I see. Maybe if the streets were cleaner, and I would see colors like red and yellow, my surroundings would be more appealing but for now, all I see is dullness and cloudiness. There aren't any pleasant smells

4. **Poughkeepsie** [pə kip′ sē]: city in southeastern New York, on the Hudson River.
5. **Bronx** [brongks]: section of New York City.

from *The Diary of Latoya Hunter*   27

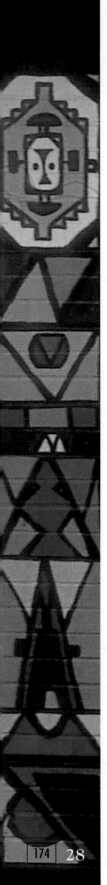

coming from anywhere as I walk the neighborhood—just the smell of nothingness. There are a few stores very close to where I live. They are one of the few things that are familiar to me in this neighborhood. Everyone knows me in these stores because if nothing else, I'm a junk food fanatic! There's one at the corner, one around the corner and one in between. Besides them, everything is grey.

Am I lucky or what? I would say not but it wouldn't be true entirely. There are so many opportunities we've gotten that we wouldn't dream of getting in Jamaica. I guess that's why they call this the land of opportunity. My mom works in a hospital not far from our house. She's a nurses assistant, my father does security work. It isn't a big income family but I'll make it. I think we all will.

September 19, 1990

Dear Diary,

Just knowing I don't have to go to school tomorrow made my entire day today. I stayed outside with my friends after school. I haven't done that for such a long time. I almost forgot how much fun I had with them.

I'll tell you about Deborah first, she's a distant cousin. She's the one who showed me around at first and introduced me to people. She's like the leader of our crew. She can act pushy sometimes but I like her. We would call her a Don Girl in Jamaican. That means she's someone you just respect.

Then there's Denise and Monique, they're sisters, but they don't really get along. Denise changes her personality a lot and frankly I can't keep up with her. Monique however, stays the same. She's funny and just a fun-loving person. There's also Lisa and Isabelle. Lisa's cool, Isabelle's someone I can't explain. I'm not really crazy about her.

They, especially Deborah, have taught me a lot. Over the years they've shown me how to come out of my shell and have fun. They were the ones who introduced me to things like parties, music, boys . . . some crazy things we've done! One time we planned to go visit a cemetery at night. Is that crazy or what? Only we would do something like that!

September 20, 1990

Dear Diary,

I spent the day helping out my friend Anika. She's moving out of her apartment. I'll still get to see her though, she's still going to go to my school.

We met an old lady on the street. We walked with her to the bus stop. I think in that short time we spent walking, she actually told us her life story. She told us she's going back to high school and she seemed to be proud of herself. She told us about God and that He had been her best friend ever since she was our age. It was really interesting to listen to someone who has lived and experienced so much. At first, I was just trying not to be rude so I listened, but soon I found myself wanting to hear what she had to say. I realize now that everyone has a life to them. I see so many faces everyday, it was nice to go beyond the face for once.

September 21, 1990

Dear Diary,

Today three of my relatives from Canada came for a visit; my grandfather and two boy cousins Glendon and Dexton. They'll be here until Sunday. I hope God keeps them safe for the few days they'll be here. The other day a guy from Utah was stabbed to death while protecting his family on the train. That is a sad example of the crime in New York especially since he was just visiting for the weekend. The crime is really getting ridiculous here.

If I had a choice now, I would choose to leave this place. I just can't feel safe here. I have good reasons too. My father was almost shot when he used to drive a cab at nights. My brother also came close to being a victim of crime. He was held up at gunpoint at the movie theater where he works in Manhattan. Fortunately he wasn't hurt. I'm really scared to be here.

My friend Lisa wasn't as lucky with brothers as I was. Her brother was shot 12 times just the other day. I heard he was on the way to the

store and someone waited for him and did the job. It was probably drug-related. He looked like someone involved in those things, sorry to say. She's still mourning his death. Anyways Diary, that's the way things are in New York city, my home.

September 23, 1990

Dear Diary,

The weekend was great as always. On Saturday I went to see my aunt Rita. She lives 15 minutes away in the Bronx. Everyone went: my parents, sister, and my relatives visiting from Canada. It was a nice evening. Afterwards I went to my friend's sister's baby shower. I couldn't stay long though because I wasn't supposed to be there in the first place. My mother disapproves of me being at that house. I don't know what she thinks goes on up there but I know she's wrong. She wrong about everything. She thinks there are things going on that she doesn't know about, but there aren't. I think in her mind she sees Deborah and everyone else with a bunch of guys partying and making out—what else could she think? I think she knows I wouldn't do anything like drugs. If only she'd understand, then I wouldn't feel guilty every time I want to be with my friends.

Today, Sunday, I went to church. My relatives left and went back home. It was nice having them here, even for a short time. I get to take communion[6] now. Personally I don't like the bread but it's supposed to be the body of Christ so I eat it. I always make sure however that I have candy to get the taste out of my mouth. Well Diary, the vacation is over. I have to face school tomorrow. I don't mind though, I'm going to try to feel comfortable there—I'll really like my classes and make more friends. I think things would really look up then. So far I like Home and Careers. I'm not so crazy about the teacher but I like the idea of planning and thinking about later on in life.

6. **communion** [kə myü′ nyən]: the act of receiving bread as a part of some Christian religious services.

September 25, 1990

Dear Diary,

Why does school have to come with music teachers?! You would not believe what mine is going to make the class do. I'm talking major embarrassing! The whole class has to sing "We Are the World" in front of the whole school! Can you believe it? I mean, the song is so old. It's not fair! I bet the kids will boo us off the stage, they're good at that if anything. We're supposed to do this thing on Wednesday. Talk about short notice! We rehearsed and I must say, sound terrible. The boys are off key and it's just a mess. I hope we get it together before Wednesday, we can't afford to give the older kids more reason not to like us.

September 30, 1990

Dear Diary,

I think I need a name for you. You've become like a best friend to me, you're someone I can talk to without being argued with. I think I know just the name for you. I'll call you Janice after my best friend from Jamaica. We were like sisters before I left. Over the years we've grown apart though, the letters have stopped but that friendship is still going on within me!

So today I christen[7] you diary, Janice Page.

7. **christen** [kris′ n]: to give a name to someone or something, as in baptism.

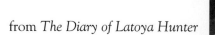

from *The Boston Globe*   April 22, 1993

Empowered

Clinton to honor Brockton

By Michael Grunwald

GLOBE STAFF

BROCKTON[1]—There was a war raging on the streets of this troubled city, a violent clash of well-armed teen-agers who neither feared death nor shrunk from causing it. And there was a new group declaring war on that war: Our Positive Posse,[2] eight teen-agers determined to educate their peers about the dangers of gangs and drugs.

So there was a meeting, held in the Crescent Court housing project,[3] on Nov. 2, 1991. The Posse's peer leaders spoke about peace, about taking back Brockton, about setting a positive example. Forty teen-agers pledged their support for the Posse.

This afternoon, President Clinton will recognize the Posse's work by awarding it the President's Volunteer Action Award in a Rose Garden ceremony.

The Posse is one of 20 groups selected for the honor out of more than 4,300 nominees, stirring up an outpouring of pride in a city that

---

1. **Brockton** [brokʹ tən]: city in southeastern Massachusetts.
2. **posse** [posʹ ē]: group working together.
3. **housing project** [projʹ ekt]: group of apartment houses run as a unit, especially as a part of public housing.

to heal

antiviolence group

has grown accustomed to numbing headlines about its chronic[4] woes: not enough water, too much political infighting, not enough money, too much crime.

Things weren't always so bright. At that 1991 meeting was a rising young singer named Christopher Bender. The next day, Bender was gunned down in a car parked outside his mother's Crescent Court home. And for a fleeting time, the Posse's leaders wondered if there was any use even trying to save their crumbling community.

4. **chronic** [kron′ ik]: lasting a long time.

"Yeah, when Chris got killed, we were really down," said Ollie Spears Jr., 18. "I figured the program would probably fall through the cracks. But we had a powerful, positive message to deliver."

"You hear all these horrible things about Brockton," said Police Chief Paul Studenski. "Well, these kids are making a real difference."

Members of the Posse swung into action soon after Bender was killed, organizing a Holiday Peace Bazaar to help heal their traumatized neighborhood. The group has led peace marches, peace forums and dozens of peace workshops for Brockton youngsters. It has branched out from the Crescent Court and Hillside Village development—where requests for police assistance have decreased more than 90 percent since the group began its grass-roots work—to the entire city.

The concept behind the Posse is as revolutionary as it is simple: Instead of telling kids what to do, let kids tell kids what to do. It is a concept at the heart of Teen Empowerment Inc., a private company hired by the Brockton Housing Authority to get the Posse off the ground.

"People always talk about empowerment, but they're usually just talking," said Tina Freimuth, 31, project coordinator for the Posse. "You've really got to believe in the power of youth. Kids won't always listen to adults, but they listen to each other."

Teen Empowerment administers similar teen-run programs in Lowell, Lawrence, New Bedford and Boston, as well as a citywide initiative[5] in Louisville, Ky. Director Stanley Pollack says programs run by teen-agers for teen-agers could offer Clinton an inexpensive, effective and easily replicated[6] strategy for reinvigorating[7] the nation's urban centers.

"This isn't a cure-all, but it will save a lot of lives," said Pollack, who said the Brockton program cost only $70,000 last year. "You could start this all across the country, no problem whatsoever, and

---

5. **initiative** [i nish ē ə tiv]: the first step in starting a task.
6. **replicated** [rep′ lə kat əd]: exactly reproduced, copied.
7. **reinvigorating** [rē in vig′ ə rāt ing]: filling again with life and energy.

you'd save millions of dollars in the long run."

It's hard to put a dollar value on crimes that never happen, on potential criminals whose lives are turned around, and potential victims who win unseen reprieves. Spears says that if he hadn't gotten involved in the Posse, he probably would be in jail today. Marcia Fernandes, 17, can only wonder if the Posse could have saved her brother Wayne, who was shot in the back and killed at a Brockton party in 1984.

"Adults haven't been able to solve young people's problems," Fernandes said. "We've got to solve them ourselves."

Yesterday, the Posse was dined (but not wined—peer leaders' contracts prohibit them from touching alcohol) by a horde of smiling politicians. Today, they will be honored by the president. Tomorrow, the group will be back on the streets of Brockton, and its battle will continue. Gangs, drugs and violence still tear at the fabric of this struggling city, still pose a constant threat to Brockton's youth.

"People are beginning to see that we can make a change, but everything isn't roses yet," Spears said. "We've still got a war to fight."

Break a Leg

JOEL SCHWARTZ

I wouldn't have gone to the "Getting to Know You" dance at school if it hadn't been for my father. He wouldn't have talked to me about it if it hadn't been for my mother. She wouldn't have talked to him about it if it hadn't been for my best friend Myron's mother. My best friend's mother wouldn't have talked to my mother about it if it hadn't been for my best friend. Myron wouldn't have talked to his mother about it if I hadn't talked to him about it, so I guess I'm to blame for everything.

It's not that I don't like dances and it's certainly not that I don't like girls. It's just that, well, all the twelve-year-old girls in the world are much taller than all the twelve-year-old boys. I wouldn't mind having to look at them straight in the eye, but having to look up all the time is embarrassing and it hurts my neck too. When you dance with a girl, they are supposed to be able to put their head on your shoulder, not their chin on your head.

So when Myron asked me at lunch, "Are you going to the 'Getting to Know You' dance?" I said, "Are you kidding? Nobody's going to that dance."

Myron took a giant bite of his sandwich and said, "Emrymoday ish gowig."

"Every Monday, what did you say?" I asked.

Myron wiped a large glob of mustard off his chin with his sleeve. "I said, everybody I know is going." Myron looked at the glob of mustard that now decorated his sleeve and without hesitation ground it into his pants. "Everybody, that is, except you."

I stared down at the spot on Myron's pants and then up at a new glob on his chin. At this rate, by the end of lunch, he would be wearing palomino-colored[1] pants and a white shirt with gold cuffs. "Name one person who's going."

"Me!"

"Besides you."

"Todd Murray."

"Mr. Murray, our math teacher?" Myron nodded. "He has to go. He's the chaperon. Besides, teachers don't count."

"Come on, go." I shook my head no. "For me?" I shook my head no again. "Why not?" This time the mustard had migrated up both cheeks.

"Why do you use so much mustard on your sandwich?" I asked, purposely changing the subject.

"Because I hate the taste of the meat," replied Myron.

"If you hate the taste of the meat so much, why don't you put a different kind of meat on your sandwich?"

"If I put on the meat that I liked, I wouldn't put on any mustard, and I like mustard on my sandwich." I stood up to go. "Not so fast. Why won't you go to the dance? Are you too chicken to go?"

"I don't want to talk about it anymore," I replied. "Finish eating your mustard sandwich and have a good time at the dance. You can tell me about it on Monday."

I thought I had heard the last of it, but after dinner that night my father asked me to go into the den because he wanted to talk to me about something. This usually means I've done something wrong and my mother has delegated my father to handle it.

"I've cleaned up my room," I said. "I did all my homework. I'll read a book for half an hour before I go to sleep, and I took out the trash."

My father smiled. "Why aren't you going to the 'Getting to Know You' dance?"

"How do you know that?" I asked.

"Your mother was talking to Myron's mother and—"

1. **palomino-colored** [pal´ ə me´ nō]: the cream color of a palomino horse.

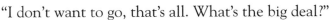

"I don't want to go, that's all. What's the big deal?"

My father lit his pipe and leaned back in his chair. This usually meant he was going to tell a story about himself when he was my age. "When I was your age and just starting seventh grade like you, my school had a 'Getting to Know You' dance too, and I didn't want to go either. My dad sat me down, just like this, and said to me, 'I'll bet you're a little afraid to go to the dance.' 'Afraid?' I replied. 'I'm not afraid of any school dance.' 'Not of the dance,' he continued, 'but of the girls. Girls can be scary at your age. They act like they feel more comfortable in social situations than boys, but they're just as scared as you are. Go to the dance, act like you know what you're doing, and I'll bet you'll have a good time.' I didn't want to admit it then, but what your grandfather said to me that day made sense and I decided to go to the dance. The night of the dance my father drove me to the school and as I got out of the car he said 'Break a leg.' That's an expression actors use when they want to wish another actor good luck on the night of a performance. I think he did that purposely because he knew I'd have to be a good actor that night to hide my nervousness. I was nervous that night, but I covered it well and I ended up having a great time. Think about it."

I sat by myself in the den for a long time after Dad left and thought about what he just said. Usually what Dad says is either dumb or old-fashioned. This time he surprised me with something right on. Was he getting smarter?

After I called Myron and told him I had decided to go to the dance I spent half of the next twenty-four hours in and out of the bathroom. It was certainly a local record and probably a national and international one too. I could see myself in the Guinness Book of World Records for Most Trips in One Day to the Bathroom Without Actually Doing Anything.

I hardly ate dinner. After showering I smoothed on a manly hair gel, splashed on a mentholly after-shave, and sprayed on a musky deodorant. I smelled muskmantholly magnificent. I almost got out of the house with my old sneakers, but my mom made me go back and put on my new slippery loafers.

My father drove Myron and me to the dance. "Break a leg," he yelled as I got out of the car.

"What's that all about?" asked Myron.

"Who knows," I replied. "Probably some weird expression he picked up when he was my age."

When we got to the gym steps, I scuffed the bottom of my new shoes to take away some of the slipperiness. The gym was decorated with blue and white streamers and red, white, and yellow balloons. At one end was a large sign picturing a boy and girl dancing. It said WELCOME, SEVENTH GRADERS. Tables with punch, cookies, pretzels, and potato chips lined both side walls. The bleachers were filled with boys and the dance floor was filled with girls.

Myron and I walked to the top of the bleachers and sat down. I would have been very happy sitting there all evening, but the teacher chaperons had a different agenda. Without any warning they went into the stands and shooed all the boys out onto the floor. *Time to start acting*, I told myself.

Mr. Murray grabbed the microphone and said, "Girls make a circle." When they finished he said, "Boys make a circle around the girls' circle."

"Just what I wanted to do," I said to Myron. "Hold your hand and go around and around in a circle."

"When the music starts," instructed Mr. Murray, "I want the girls to circle clockwise and the boys to circle counterclockwise." The music started, and around both circles went. "When the music stops I want you to take the person in front of you for a partner."

Things were beginning to get serious. My heart was beating double time to the music and my muskmantholly mist was turning to must.[2] I secretly prayed for the song never to end. My prayer went unanswered and I found myself face to face with a girl—a tall girl—a very tall, muscular girl.

Act calm, I told myself. So what if her grandfather was Paul Bunyan. I smiled, she smiled back. I didn't know what to do next, so I smiled again.

2. **must** [must]: mold.

"Introduce yourself to your partner," said Mr. Murray.

"I'm Elliot."

"I'm Paula."

Paula Bunyan, I thought. Should I ask if she has a pet ox at home? *Be calm, Elliot. Be Calm.*

"To get things warmed up," said Mr. Murray, "I thought we might start off with a Mexican hat dance. Cross your hands and take hold of your partner." My palms were soaking wet and I wiped them on my pants before I grabbed Paula's hands. "Left foot, right foot, left-right-left. Do that combination two times. Go." Even though I could tell everyone around me thought this was dumb, we all did it. I could tell my shoes were still a little slippery. "Now, with your hands still crossed, swing your partner around. Go." *Next thing he'll want us to do is a whole dance of this,* I thought. "Now I want you to put both steps together and do them in time to the music."

The music started and Paula jerked me toward her. The one good thing about this kind of dance was that we were still far enough away from each other that I didn't have to talk to her. With a little luck I'd be back in the stands watching in a few minutes.

"Left, right, left-right-left," barked Mr. Murray. "Left, right, left-right-left. . . . Now swing." Paula started off slowly, but as the music got louder she swung harder. The faster she swung, the dizzier I got. At the apex[3] of the spin either she let go or my sweaty hands slipped away from hers. Either way I found myself spinning and twirling across the floor, straight for the punch bowl. The kids around us stopped to watch this whirling dervish. It seemed as if everyone was staring and pointing.

My left leg hit the table first, full force, causing it to tip forward. The strength of the blow caused my feet to slide out from under me and before I knew it I was on the ground and the table

3. **apex** [ā′ peks]: the highest point.

was on top of my legs. My pants were soaked with punch and my shirt was covered with smushed, smashed slivers of pretzels and potato chips.

There was almost complete silence until one of the kids started to laugh. Then everyone laughed. I felt stupid, dumb, and wet. I saw Mr. Murray running toward me to help, but Myron arrived first. I brushed myself off. He helped me stand up. I started to take a step, but my left leg refused to bear any weight and I collapsed in a heap.

The doctor at the hospital showed me the break in the X ray and told me my leg would be in a full leg cast for at least six weeks.

Since Myron came to the hospital with me, he was the first to sign my cast. He laughed the whole time he was writing. When he finished he said, "Read it."

What he wrote started at my thigh and went down the entire length of the cast. It said, "Remember what your dad said to you when you got out of the car? I know you're supposed to listen to your parents, but this is ridiculous." I looked up at Myron, who was still smiling. "Your cast will be off just in time for the Thanksgiving Dance. Going?"

JOEL SCHWARTZ

Joel Schwartz was born in 1940 in Philadelphia, Pennsylvania. His father was a doctor, and when Schwartz grew up he went to medical school too. After doing graduate work in psychiatry, Schwartz served as a medic in the Air Force. He came back to work and write in Pennsylvania.

Schwartz's first book, *Upchuck Summer,* was followed by a sequel called *Best Friends Don't Come in Three's,* and later by *Shrink.* Like all good writers, Schwartz believes in writing about what he knows. "My books," he says, "are about boys from a boy's point of view."

FOUNDERS OF THE CHILDREN'S RAIN FOREST

PHILLIP HOOSE

Children from the Fagervik School, Sweden

Forty first- and second-grade students from a small school in Sweden became upset when their teacher told them that rain forests[1] were being destroyed rapidly throughout the world. They wondered what they—so young, so few, and so far away from the tropics—could do that could really matter. Their answer has helped preserve rain forests around the world.

It all began in the first week of school when Eha Kern,[2] from the Fagervik[3] School, in the Swedish countryside, showed her forty first- and second-grade students pictures of hot, steamy jungles near the Equator. It was there, she said, that half the types of plants and animals in the whole world could be found. She read to them about monkeys

1. **rain forests:** very dense forests in regions, usually tropical, where rain is heavy all year.
2. **Eha Kern** [e′ hä kärn]
3. **Fagervik** [fä′ gär vēk]

and leopards and sloths,[4] about snakes that can paralyze your nerves with one bite, about strange plants that might hold a cure for cancer, about the great trees that give us oxygen to breathe and help keep the earth from becoming too hot.

And then she told them that the world's rain forests were being destroyed at the rate of one hundred acres a *minute*. In the past thirty years, she said, nearly half the world's rain forests have been cut down, often by poor people who burn the wood for fire. Sometimes forests are cleared to make pastures for cattle that are slaughtered and sold to hamburger chains in the U.S. and Europe. Sometimes the trees are sold and shipped away to make

4. **sloths** [slôths]: slow-moving mammals of South and Central America that live in trees and hang upside down from tree branches.

furniture and paper. More often they are just stacked up and burned. At this rate, there might not be any rain forests left in thirty years!

The children were horrified. The creatures of the rain forest could be gone before the students were even old enough to have a chance to see them. It didn't matter that they lived thousands of miles away in cold, snowy Sweden. It seemed to them that their future was being chopped and cleared away.

During the autumn, as the sunlight weakened and the days became short, the Fagervik children continued to think about the rain forest. Whenever they went on walks past the great fir trees on the school grounds, they imagined jaguars crouched in the limbs just above them, their long tails twitching impatiently.

They begged Mrs. Kern to help them think of something— anything—they could do to rescue the creatures of the tropics. And then one afternoon during a music lesson, a student named Roland Tiensuu asked suddenly, "Can't we just *buy* some rain forest?"

The lesson stopped. It was a simple, clear idea that all the others understood at once. The class began to cheer, and then they turned to their teacher. "Please, Mrs. Kern," they said. "Please, won't you find us a forest to buy?"

"PLEASE BUY MINE."

Mrs. Kern had no idea how to find a rain forest for sale. But then, the very weekend after Roland's idea, she was introduced to an American biologist[5] named Sharon Kinsman. As they chatted, Ms. Kinsman explained that she had been working in a rain forest called Monte Verde,[6] or Green Mountain.

When Mrs. Kern told Ms. Kinsman of the nearly impossible mission her students had given her, she expected the biologist to laugh. Instead her expression turned serious. "Oh," she said quickly, "please buy mine."

5. **biologist** [bī olʹ ə jist]: an expert in biology, which is the scientific study of plant and animal life.
6. **Monte Verde** [mônʹ tā värʹ dā]

Ms. Kinsman said that some people in Monte Verde were trying desperately to buy land so that more trees wouldn't be cut. Much land had already been protected, but much more was needed. Land was cheap there, she said—only about twenty-five dollars per acre.

Ms. Kinsman agreed to visit the Fagervik School. She would bring a map and slides of the Monte Verde forest and tell the children where they could send money to buy rain forest land. When Mrs. Kern told the children what had happened, they didn't even seem surprised. As they put it, "We knew you would find one."

"There Are No Bad Ideas."

In the days before Sharon Kinsman's visit, the Fagervik students began to think about how to raise money. They asked Mrs. Kern to write down all their ideas. As she picked up a piece of chalk, several children spoke at once.

"Pony rides!"

"Let's collect old things and sell them!"

"What about a rain forest evening here at school?"

"Dog washing!"

Dog washing? They began to laugh. "That would never work," someone said. "Who would give money for that?" Mrs. Kern put her chalk down. "Look," she said. "Let's make this our rule: there are no bad ideas. The only bad thing is if you have an idea and don't say it. Then we can't use it." She returned to the blackboard. Were there more ideas?

"A rabbit jumping contest!"

"Rabbit jumping?" said Mrs. Kern. "Be serious. You can't *make* a rabbit jump."

"Oh, yes, we all have rabbits. We can train them. We can. We *can!*"

Mrs. Kern tried to imagine someone actually paying money to watch children try to make rabbits jump. She couldn't. This idea was crazy.

"Mrs. Kern . . . there's no such thing as a bad idea . . . remember?" She did. "Rabbit jumping," she wrote, dutifully putting her doubts aside.

GIANT SPIDERS AND DEADLY SNAKES

On November 6, 1987, Sharon Kinsman arrived at the Fagervik School. She was just as enthusiastic as the students. They put on skits for her about rain forests and showed her the many books they had written about tropical creatures. Then at last, it was her turn to show them slides of the Monte Verde forest.

First she unfolded a map of the forest and pointed to the area their money could preserve from cutting. She told them that 400 bird species live in the forest, more than in all of Sweden, as well as 490 kinds of butterflies and 500 types of trees. Monte Verde is also the only home in

the world, she said, for the golden toad, a creature that seems to glow in the dark.

Then she showed her slides. As the room became dark, the students were swept into a hot, steamy jungle half the world away. The slides took them sloshing along a narrow, muddy trail, crisscrossed with roots and vines. A dark canopy of giant trees, thick with bright flowering plants, closed in above them.

They saw giant spiders and deadly snakes. Ms. Kinsman's tape recorder made the forest ring with the shriek of howler monkeys calling to each other and with the chattering of parrots above the trees. They saw the golden toad, the scarlet macaw, and the red-backed poison-arrow frog.

And they saw the forest disappearing, too. They saw hard-muscled men, their backs glistening with sweat, pushing chain saws deep into the giant trees. They could almost smell the smoke of burning tree limbs and feel the thunder of thick, brown trunks crashing down. Behind great piles of ragged wood, the tropical sky was hazy with smoke. Time seemed very short.

When the lights came on, the students were back in Sweden, but they were not the same. Now they had seen their forest—and the danger it faced. There was no time to lose. Mrs. Kern had inspired them with a problem, and Roland had given them an idea they could work with. Sharon Kinsman had shown them their target. Now it was up to them.

"We Knew What We Wanted."

Two weeks later, more than a hundred people crowded into an old schoolhouse near the Fagervik School for a rain forest evening. Students stood by the door and collected ten crowns (about $1.50) from each person. Special programs cost another crown. Even though it was winter, rain splattered steadily onto the roof, just as it must have been raining in the Monte Verde forest. To the students, rain was a good sign.

First they performed a play containing a dramatic scene in which trees of the rain forest were cut and creatures killed. That way guests would understand the problem they were trying to help solve. As the applause died down, the children passed an old hat around, urging audience members to drop money in it.

Then they sold rain forest books and rain forest poems. "We were not afraid to ask for money," remembers Maria Karlsson, who was nine. "We knew what we wanted was important." One boy stood at a table keeping track of how much they were making. Whenever a classmate would hand over a fresh delivery of cash, he would count it quickly and shout above the noise, "Now we've got two hundred crowns!!" "Now it's three hundred!!"

The evening's total came to 1,600 crowns, or about $240. The next day, they figured out that they had raised enough money to save about twelve football fields worth of rain forest. It was wonderful . . . but was it enough space for a sloth? A leopard? They all knew the answer. They needed more.

They filled up another blackboard with ideas and tried them out. Everything seemed to work. Mrs. Kern brought in a list of prominent people who might make donations. Two girls wrote a letter to the richest woman on the list. A few days later, a check arrived. Someone else wrote to the king of Sweden and asked if he would watch them perform plays about the rain forest. He said yes.

One day they went to a recording studio and made a tape of their rain forest songs. From the very beginning, Mrs. Kern and a music teacher had been helping them write songs. They started with old melodies they liked, changing them a little as they went along. As soon as anybody came up with a good line, they sang it into a tape recorder so they wouldn't forget it by the end of the song. They rehearsed the songs many times on their school bus before recording them, then designed a cover and used some of their money to buy plastic boxes for the tapes. Within months, they had sold five hundred tapes at ten dollars each.

The more they used their imaginations, the more money they raised. They decided to have a fair. "We had a magician and charged admission," remembers Lia Degeby, who was eight. "We charged to see who could make the ugliest face. We had a pony riding contest. We had a market. We had a lady with a beard. We had the strongest lady in the world. Maria forecast the future in a cabin. We tried everything." The biggest money maker of all was the rabbit jumping contest, even though each rabbit sat still when its time came to jump! Even carrots couldn't budge them. One simply flopped over and went to sleep, crushing its necklace of flowers.

Soon they needed a place to put all the money they had earned. Mrs. Kern's husband, Bernd, helped them form an organization called Barnens Regnskog,[7] which means Children's Rain Forest. They opened a bank account with a post office box where people could continue to mail donations.

By midwinter, they had raised $1,400. The children addressed an envelope to the Monte Verde Cloud Forest Protection League, folded a check inside, and sent it on its way to Costa Rica.[8] Weeks later, they received a crumpled package covered with brightly colored stamps. It contained a map of the area that had been bought with their money. A grateful writer thanked them for saving nearly ninety acres of Costa Rican rain forest.

In the early spring, the Fagervik students performed at the Swedish Children's Fair, which led to several national television appearances. Soon schools from all over Sweden were joining Barnens Regnskog and sending money to Monte Verde. At one high school

7. **Barnens Regnskog** [bär′ nenz rän′ skog]
8. **Costa Rica** [kos′ tə rē′ kə]: country in Central America, northwest of Panama.

near Stockholm, two thousand students did chores all day in the city and raised nearly $15,000. And inspired by the students, the Swedish government gave a grant of $80,000 to Monte Verde.

"I THINK OF MY FUTURE."

After another year's work, the children of Fagervik had raised $25,000 more. The families who could afford it sent their children to Costa Rica to see Monte Verde. Just before Christmas, ten Fagervik children stepped off the plane, blinking in the bright Costa Rican sunlight. It was hot! They stripped off their coats and sweaters, piled into a bus, and headed for the mountains.

A few hours later, the bus turned onto a narrow, rocky road that threaded its way through steep mountains. The children looked out upon spectacular waterfalls that fell hundreds of feet. Occasionally they glimpsed monkeys swinging through the trees.

Ahead, the mountaintops disappeared inside a dark purple cloud. For a few moments they could see five rainbows at once. Soon it began to rain.

The next morning, they joined ten Costa Rican children and went on a hike through the Monte Verde rain forest. Sometimes the thick mud made them step right out of their boots. But it didn't matter. "There were plants everywhere," says Lia. "I saw monkeys and flowers."

On Christmas day, the children of the Fagervik School proudly presented the staff of the Monte Verde Cloud Forest with their check for $25,000. They said it was a holiday present for all the children of the world.

The Monte Verde Conservation League used their gift, and funds that had been donated by other children previously, to establish what is now known as El Bosque Eterno de los Niños,[9] or the Eternal International Children's Rain Forest. It is a living monument to the caring and power of young people everywhere. So far, kids from twenty-one nations have raised more than two million dollars to preserve nearly 33,000 acres of rain forest, plenty of room for jaguars and ocelots[10] and tapirs.[11] The first group of Fagervik students have now graduated to another school, but the first- and second-graders who have replaced them are still raising great sums of money. The school total is now well over $50,000.

The Fagervik students continue to amaze their teacher. "I never thought they could do so much," Mrs. Kern says. "Sometimes I say to them, 'Why do you work so hard?' They say, 'I think of my future.' They make me feel optimistic. When I am with them, I think maybe anything can be done."

9. **El Bosque Eterno de los Niños** [el bos′ kā ā tār′ nō dā lōs nē′ nyōs]
10. **ocelots** [os′ ə lotz]: spotted cats smaller than leopards.
11. **tapirs** [tā′ pərz]: large piglike animals of tropical America with hooves and a flexible snout.

My name is Roy Vargas Garcia. I am twelve years old. I live in a small community called La Cruz de Abangares,[12] in Costa Rica. There are seven in my family. My father is a dairyman, my mother a housewife.

I love to listen to the songs of birds and insects of the forest. Often I see sloths, gray foxes, armadillos, opossums, birds, monkeys, and butterflies. The climate here is cool, and trees are tall and green, with many mosses.

I am very pleased that other children from around the world want to protect our forest. I want children to know that we who live here are protecting it, too.

In the past, our farmers cut the forest. Not because they did not care about it, but because they needed to make their farms and their vegetable gardens and to get firewood and lumber and so to raise their children.

But now many farmers are planting trees in windbreaks on the farms. In my community we are buying a small piece of land we call a community reserve to protect where our water comes from. We are doing this with help and training from the Monte Verde Conservation League.

I want to thank all the children who are helping save forests. Thank you.

Roy Vargas Garcia

12. **La Cruz de Abangares** [lä krüs dā ä bän gä′ räs]

PHILLIP HOOSE

Phillip Hoose was born in 1947 in South Bend, Indiana. Like many young people, Hoose grew up seeing things in the world that he thought were wrong and felt powerless to fix them. It was only when he had children of his own that he realized how badly "kids are underestimated by adults." He was amazed when his kindergarten-aged daughter helped figure out a way to raise money to help homeless people. Her experience gave him the idea for *It's Our World, Too!*

Beni Seballos

PHILLIP HOOSE

*V*olunteering to take care of others can be just as important to a community as standing up to an injustice. It can be just as challenging, too. Beni Seballos of Racida, California, overcame her self-doubt and volunteered to take care of older people with diseases that affect their ability to think, remember, and move. The things she learned gave her confidence and helped her solve one of the biggest problems in her own life.

One day when she was fifteen, Beni Seballos stepped onto a plane with ten of her aunts, uncles, cousins, nieces, and nephews and said good-bye to everything she loved. Soon her home, her friends, and her school in the Philippines were far behind her.

When they arrived in Los Angeles, they drove to a small house. There they would stay with her aunt and grandparents until they could find enough money to buy a home of their own.

The fourteen of them tried their best to be cheerful. For Beni, the hardest part was trying to get along with her grandmother. She was a stern, quiet woman, used to the respect that elders commanded in the Philippines. Beni was noisy and opinionated. Her grandmother always seemed to disapprove of her. Each day Beni would ask her grandmother if she could help with dinner, and the answer was always no. That "no" filled the kitchen, leaving no space for Beni. She always left the room in anger, wondering how long she could take living there.

Racida High School was no better. She didn't know anybody at first. She made the basketball team but rarely got in the games. "Academic Decathlon was even worse," Beni recalls. "A team of kids from Racida High tried to answer questions faster than a team from another school. It wasn't about learning. All they wanted to do was kick butt. I hated it."

The one thing she really liked was a volunteer organization called Youth Community Services, or YCS. After hearing about it at school, Beni went on a weekend field trip to plant trees in a farm area. There was no feeling of competition here. Everyone was working together. She volunteered for YCS at a blood bank, at a recycling center, and with a program that helped keep young kids off drugs. At last, she was having fun in the United States.

Her parents didn't understand. To them, volunteering just kept her away from home. She wasn't even getting school credit for it. When Beni put on her jacket to go to a YCS event, her grandmother would glare, and her mother would say, softly but pointedly, "Oh, you're going off again, aren't you, Beni?"

During the summer break, a YCS counselor urged Beni to volunteer at a senior citizens center. The staff needed volunteers to help take care of old people who had Alzheimer's and Parkinson's diseases. Think of all you could learn, the counselor kept saying.

Beni wasn't so sure. She found herself wondering what a sixteen-year-old could really have in common with someone who was seventy-five or eighty. She hated to admit it to herself, but old people sounded boring. Even worse, what if they all treated her the way her grandmother did?

But maybe the counselor was right. After all, she thought, you learn most by doing what you understand least. Beni signed up for four days a week, five hours a day, and then walked to the library to find out about Alzheimer's and Parkinson's diseases.

A medical encyclopedia said that both diseases affect the brain's ability to function. Alzheimer's patients gradually lose their memories, and Parkinson's patients gradually lose control of their muscles. After reading less than a page, Beni closed the book, unable to go on. "I was terrified," she remembers. "I could see myself having to force-feed these drooling people. I'd have to pick them up off the ground all the time. I thought they'd be vegetables.

"I practically ran out of the library. I was ready to quit before I had ever met a single patient. By the time I got home, I was wondering, 'What did I get myself into?'"

"WHAT DO YOU THINK ABOUT THIS?"

The first day, Beni introduced herself to the center's supervisor, Kathleen, and the six other volunteers, all in their forties and fifties. They were friendly, but she wondered if they really believed a teenager could handle the work.

Kathleen explained that the volunteers were supposed to feed the patients, take them for walks, and help give them their medicine. She went over each patient's medicine and diet. She kept looking at Beni and saying, "Don't worry, you'll do fine."

Then Kathleen opened the door, and they all walked out into the hallway, where about fifteen patients and their relatives were waiting. Some patients were in wheelchairs. Others were in walkers. A few leaned on canes.

Beni hung back and watched as the other volunteers rushed forward to greet the patients. Was she supposed to help them into their wheelchairs? How did you do it, anyway? What if she dropped someone? "I could see some of the patients' relatives looking at me. I felt them thinking, She's just a kid. She doesn't look like she knows what she's doing."

She followed the crowd into a big room, where the volunteers were supposed to serve the patients coffee and doughnuts. Beni's mind went blank. She couldn't remember who was supposed to have only half a doughnut and who wasn't supposed to get a doughnut at all. Kathleen was nowhere in sight. Beni fought back tears. This was terrible. It was the Alzheimer's patients who were supposed to have memory problems, not her.

After coffee, Kathleen was reading a newspaper article to a group of patients when one of them interrupted. He pointed to Beni. "You're a young person," he said. "What do you think about this?" Beni was startled. An older person actually wanted her opinion? This was certainly different from home. Well, actually she *did* have an opinion on the topic of the article, and so she gave it. They listened carefully and discussed it. This part isn't so bad, Beni thought.

She went home that night exhausted and determined to do better tomorrow. As always, her grandmother was in the kitchen. They went through the usual routine again, with Beni offering to help and her grandmother refusing her. Beni walked out fuming. She had to get out of there.

The next morning, Beni went to the center early and memorized the patients' names. When the patients arrived, she sat down beside a frail woman named Lil with a sparse crown of thin white hair. Beni peeled an orange for her and filled up her cup of coffee halfway with a single lump of sugar, just as Lil's chart said. As she was working, Beni told Lil about what it had been like to move from the Philippines.

Lil began to talk, too. She said she had spent much of her life raising five wonderful children.

"Where are they now?" Beni asked.

"Who?"

"Your children."

"What?"

"Your children. You were saying you have five children."

Lil wrung the hem of her dress in her hands, looking frantically around the room. "What do you mean? I-I-I can't remember." She seemed to be growing more desperate by the second. Beni quickly changed the subject to her own college plans, and gradually Lil relaxed. It was Beni's first real contact with Alzheimer's disease. It taught her that she had to listen and be flexible, alert to each patient's needs. Patients wouldn't always be able to stick to the same subject for very long.

Later that week, Beni was leading a patient named Oscar outside for a game of shuffleboard when she heard the sharp scrape of metal behind her. His walker had become caught between two chairs. Trembling, he tried to shake loose. Beni knelt to pry the walker free, but it was no use. Oscar was growing enraged and started to shout. His face was turning red. Here it is, Beni thought, the emergency I can't handle. She sprinted into the kitchen to get help. Three volunteers and Kathy rushed out, and in a moment, they had him free. "You handled it well," Kathy said to Beni later. "Just get help."

As the summer went by, Beni faced many different kinds of challenges. A few patients tried to wander off. Some became angry because they couldn't remember when to take their medicine. One refused to go back inside after a walk.

After a few weeks at the center, Beni found herself thinking differently about the patients. She could no longer think of them as "old people" or "senior citizens," or "Alzheimer's patients" or even "patients." They had become individuals, like her, who just happened to be at a different stage of their lives. Like her, they all had their own interests and families, hopes and fears, opinions and problems.

She discovered that if she listened carefully, she could find something in common with almost everyone. Alex wrote poetry, just like Beni. Sometimes at the shuffleboard court, they recited their poems to each other. Beni and Oscar spoke Spanish together. Blackie told her World War II stories. Mary taught her a few words of Czech. Lil loved to talk about children.

By the end of the summer, it seemed to Beni that being young had been an advantage, not a handicap, at the center. "I was special to some of the Alzheimer's patients," she says. "I think maybe having me around helped them remember how they were when they were young themselves."

BEANS AND FRIENDSHIP

In September, Beni said a tearful good-bye to the patients and staff and took a week off before school started. She had some unfinished business.

All summer long, things had gotten worse and worse with her grandmother until finally she had moved out of her aunt's house in order to find some peace in her life. But she didn't feel at peace. She loved her grandmother, and she wanted to put things right between them.

For a while it had seemed strange that she could have fun with Lil or Oscar or Alex but not her own grandmother. Then it came to her: When things got tough with a patient at the center, she kept trying patiently until she found a way to get through. But when things got tough with her grandmother, she gave up.

So one afternoon, she walked over to her aunt's house, determined to treat her grandmother as she had learned to treat the people at the center.

As usual, Beni's grandmother was in the kitchen. "Hi," Beni said. "Is there anything I can do?" "No," said her grandmother. This time Beni didn't leave. She noticed a bowl of string beans on the counter and carried them to the kitchen table. She sat down, picked up a bean, and snapped off the end.

She began to tell her grandmother about her summer. Though her grandmother didn't say anything, Beni could sense that she was listening. After a while, her grandmother wiped her hands on a towel, pulled up a chair, and sat down at the other end of the table. She picked up a bean and snapped the top off. A half hour later, there was a big pile of beans between them—and the beginning of a friendship.

Beni says that friendship was maybe the greatest gift of the summer. It couldn't have happened until she herself changed, and volunteering at the center was the key that opened doors within her. "The summer started working for me when I began to share myself with the patients, not just log time," she says. "Then it was fun. I know I did a good job at the center, but I probably got more out of it than the patients. I learned that caring is like a muscle. The more you exercise it, the more you *can* share."

I FEEL MYSELF
    GROW OLD
MY EYES GO BLIND
    MY HANDS SHAKE
PLEASE LORD, LET
    SOMEONE ALSO
    HELP ME OUT
WHEN TOMORROW'S DAWNS
    GROW DARK ON
    ME.
          —Beni Seballos

PHILLIP HOOSE

Phillip Hoose was born in 1947 in South Bend, Indiana. Like many young people, Hoose grew up seeing things in the world that he thought were wrong and felt powerless to fix them. It was only when he had children of his own that he realized how badly "kids are underestimated by adults." He was amazed when his kindergarten-aged daughter helped figure out a way to raise money to help homeless people. Her experience gave him the idea for *It's Our World, Too!*

For the book, Hoose conducted nearly a hundred interviews with young people who had taken action to help others. "I wish I'd had a book like this when I was a kid," Hoose says, "or known people like the kids I interviewed. I would have felt less alone."

ISAAC ASIMOV

THE FUN THEY HAD

Margie even wrote about it that night in her diary. On the page headed May 17, 2157, she wrote, "Today Tommy found a real book!"

It was a very old book. Margie's grandfather once said that when he was a little boy *his* grandfather told him that there was a time when all stories were printed on paper.

They turned the pages, which were yellow and crinkly, and it was awfully funny to read words that stood still instead of moving the way they were supposed to— on a screen, you know. And then, when they turned back to the page before, it had the same words on it that it had had when they read it the first time.

"Gee," said Tommy, "what a waste. When you're through with the book, you just throw it away, I guess. Our television screen must have had a million books on it and it's good for plenty more. I wouldn't throw *it* away."

"Same with mine," said Margie. She was eleven and hadn't seen as many telebooks as Tommy had. He was thirteen.

She said, "Where did you find it?"

"In my house." He pointed without looking, because he was busy reading. "In the attic."

"What's it about?"

"School."

Margie was scornful. "School? What's there to write about school? I hate school."

Margie always hated school, but now she hated it more than ever. The mechanical teacher had been giving her test after test in geography and she had been doing worse and worse until her mother had shaken her head sorrowfully and sent for the County Inspector.

He was a round little man with a red face and a whole box of tools with dials and wires. He smiled at Margie and gave her an apple, then took the teacher apart. Margie had hoped he wouldn't know how to put it together again, but he knew how all right, and, after an hour or so, there it was again, large and black and ugly, with a big screen on which all the lessons were shown and the questions were asked. That wasn't so bad. The part Margie hated most was the slot where she had to put homework and test papers. She always had to write them out in a punch code they made her learn when she was six years old, and the mechanical teacher calculated the mark in no time.

The Inspector had smiled after he was finished and patted Margie's head. He said to her mother, "It's not the little girl's fault, Mrs. Jones. I think the geography sector was geared a little too quick. Those things happen sometimes. I've slowed it up to an average ten-year level. Actually, the over-all pattern of her progress is quite satisfactory." And he patted Margie's head again.

Margie was disappointed. She had been hoping they would take the teacher away altogether. They had once taken Tommy's teacher away for nearly a month because the history sector had blanked out completely.

So she said to Tommy, "Why would anyone write about school?"

Tommy looked at her with very superior eyes. "Because it's not our kind of school, stupid. This is the old kind of school that they had hundreds and hundreds of years ago." He added loftily, pronouncing the word carefully, "*Centuries* ago."

Margie was hurt. "Well, I don't know what kind of school they had all that time ago." She read the book over his shoulder for a while, then said, "Anyway, they had a teacher."

"Sure they had a teacher, but it wasn't a *regular* teacher. It was a man."

"A man? How could a man be a teacher?"

"Well, he just told the boys and girls things and gave them homework and asked them questions."

"A man isn't smart enough."

"Sure he is. My father knows as much as my teacher."

"He can't. A man can't know as much as a teacher."

"He knows almost as much, I betcha."

Margie wasn't prepared to dispute that. She said, "I wouldn't want a strange man in my house to teach me."

Tommy screamed with laughter. "You don't know much, Margie. The teachers didn't live in the house. They had a special building and all the kids went there."

"And all the kids learned the same thing?"

"Sure, if they were the same age."

"But my mother says a teacher has to be adjusted to fit the mind of each boy and girl it teaches and that each kid has to be taught differently."

"Just the same they didn't do it that way then. If you don't like it, you don't have to read the book."

"I didn't say I didn't like it," Margie said quickly. She wanted to read about those funny schools.

They weren't even half-finished when Margie's mother called, "Margie! School!"

Margie looked up. "Not yet, Mamma."

"Now!" said Mrs. Jones. "And it's probably time for Tommy, too."

Margie said to Tommy, "Can I read the book some more with you after school?"

"Maybe," he said nonchalantly.[1] He walked away whistling, the dusty old book tucked beneath his arm.

Margie went into the schoolroom. It was right next to her bedroom, and the mechanical teacher was on and waiting for her. It was always on at the same time every day except Saturday and Sunday, because her mother said little girls learned better if they learned at regular hours.

The screen was lit up, and it said: "Today's arithmetic lesson is on the addition of proper fractions. Please insert yesterday's homework in the proper slot."

Margie did so with a sigh. She was thinking about the old schools they had when her grandfather's grandfather was a little boy. All the kids from the whole neighborhood came, laughing and shouting in the schoolyard, sitting together in the schoolroom, going home together at the end of the day. They learned the same things, so they could help one another on the homework and talk about it.

And the teachers were people. . . .

The mechanical teacher was flashing on the screen: "When we add the fractions 1/2 and 1/4—"

Margie was thinking about how the kids must have loved it in the old days. She was thinking about the fun they had.

1. **nonchalantly** [non´ shə länt´ lē]: indifferently, casually.

ISAAC ASIMOV

Isaac Asimov [1920-1992] was born in Petrovichi, U.S.S.R., and came to the United States when he was three years old. He grew up in Brooklyn, New York, where his family had a candy store. He discovered science fiction through magazines for sale on the store's newsstand.

At seventeen, he wrote his first science fiction story, "The Cosmic Corkscrew." Later he became one of the best-known science fiction writers in the world. His last books include *The Asimov Chronicles* and *Robot Visions*.

Something

from *Children of the Dust Bowl*

JERRY STANLEY

On a bright September morning in 1940 the Kern County[1] superintendent of education waved good-bye to his wife and left for work. On this day, instead of his usual coat and tie, Leo Hart was wearing old overalls and work boots. Leo told Edna he would be home late, but she already knew that. They had talked about this special day for weeks and had worked for it for months.

Leo drove the flatbed truck[2] to the field next to Weedpatch Camp. On the odd-looking stretch of land marked by piles of bricks, boards, and boxes of whatnot, Leo met with the teachers he had hired and introduced them to the fifty children from Weedpatch Camp whose parents had agreed to let Leo have them for the day. Then he told them all to get to work. They did. Brick by brick, board by board, the children of the Dust Bowl, eight teachers, and Leo Hart built Weedpatch School.

On the first day a team of children dug a hundred-yard trench from the water tower in the camp to the condemned buildings in the

1. **Kern County** [kern]: California county in the San Joaquin Valley where Weedpatch Camp and other farm-labor camps were located.
2. **flatbed truck:** truck with flat back section for carrying items.

to Watch

field. They laid a three-quarter-inch pipe in the trench, and on the second day the school had running water. Teachers instructed the children on hygiene, while Leo and some of the boys dug two huge holes in the ground and built two outhouses. After that, Leo said, "All the children used them."

"It was something to watch," Leo remembered. "It was the first time where they were working for something of their own. It was the first time where they could be proud of who they were and what they were doing." Pete Bancroft, the newly hired principal of the school, worked side by side with the teachers and the Okie kids, building the school and instilling in the Dust Bowl children a spirit of confidence and self-worth. "There was no partiality," Leo said, "no embarrassment or ridicule." Instead, "There was friendship, understanding, guidance, and love."

As the weeks stretched into months, the school rose from the field. Within two months the two condemned buildings had been renovated and made into four general-purpose classrooms. Following that, the twenty-five thousand bricks donated by the National Youth Authority were turned into three more classrooms and a cafeteria. This took an additional three months. A home economics building was needed. No problem. An old railroad car was located and moved to the school, where the boys added plumbing and wiring, and remodeled its interior. A shop building where mechanics and other trades could be learned was also needed. No problem. Leo persuaded the district to donate an abandoned auditorium, which was disassembled, hauled to the school, and remanufactured into a shop room. The Okie children learned a dozen useful trades—including plumbing, electrical wiring, carpentry, plastering, and masonry.[3] Scrap lumber was sawed into bookshelves. Discarded sinks were fixed in place for a chemistry lab. Orange crates and wooden boxes were fashioned into chairs, desks, and tables.

There was more. By October the field was alive with the sound of a dozen hoes and clattering farm machinery striking hard earth. The Okie children plowed part of the school field and planted vegetables and other crops. "Edna said we should start with potatoes and so we did," Leo recalled. "Potatoes and alfalfa. Tomatoes, carrots, celery, corn, and watermelon. The children especially liked the watermelon." Toiling in the sun for hours, tilling, planting, weeding, and harvesting was welcome labor to children who could still remember the taste of apple seeds, carrot stems, and coffee grounds.

The Okie kids also raised their own livestock. They built pens for sheep, pigs, chickens, and cows and dug a basement to store slaughtered livestock. Sometime in December 1940 a local butcher heard about "the Okie school" and

3. **masonry** [mā′ sn rē]: the trade of building with stone or brick.

wandered out to the site. The man spent ten hours at the school that day slaughtering pigs and cows and instructing the children until they learned the basic skills of a butcher.

During the early months of the school, Edna Hart helped the women at Weedpatch Camp cook meals for the children. But by the time Edna went to work in the school's new cafeteria in the spring of 1941, the school had become completely self-sufficient in potatoes, vegetables, milk, eggs, and beef.

The teachers, Leo said, "went out of their way to help these children and teach them things about themselves and the world that they couldn't learn anywhere else." Jim McPherson taught the Okie children history, geography, math, science—and shoe cobbling, so they could repair their parents' shoes. Rose Gilger taught them science, typing—and sewing, so their families didn't have to wear oversize clothes or rags. Chemistry teacher Barbara Sabovitch even taught the girls how to make face cream, rouge, and lipstick—in a chemistry lab!

Principal Pete Bancroft bought a C-46[4] airplane from military surplus for two hundred dollars and had it carted to the school. "I taught them aircraft mechanics," Pete said, "and if they maintained a grade of 90 percent or better in arithmetic, I let them drive the plane down the makeshift runway and back." Both Pete and Leo enrolled their own children in the school and Pete brought a doctor and nurse out to care for sick children. Pete dispensed cod-liver oil and orange juice until the first crops came in and the school cafeteria was built. Rose Gilger and Beverly Ahrens worked in that cafeteria as well as in the classroom and, like the other teachers, took the Okie children into Bakersfield on Sundays to go to church and to accept donations of food and clothing from local merchants and the Salvation Army. Other teachers—Edith Houghan, for instance—spent weekends at the school with children who were sick, because, Edith said, "They were better off in the nurse's room than at home in their one-room huts."

Fred Smith heard about the school and applied for a job as a music teacher. Leo only had enough money to hire Fred for one day a week, but Fred usually worked on weekends for nothing. When Leo sent Fred his yearly check of six hundred dollars, Fred sent it back.

Determination and a lot of hard work combined to change the fate of the Okie children from Weedpatch Camp. As discards and donations were slowly turned into a school, the children came to believe that anything was possible—and none of them doubted this after Leo picked up a shovel one day and started to dig at the east end of the field between the school and the camp. When twelve-year-old Bob Farley asked Leo what he was digging, Leo said, "Swimming pool."

4. C-46: a military airplane of the 1940s.

If the migrant[5] children did not "goof off," Leo said, "if they kept up on their academics," he would let them dig in their spare time. "Dig in the hole," the children called it.

"We used the twelve-by-twelve forms that were the floors of the tents over in the camp and built a wall around the inside," Leo recalled. "We poured concrete walls and a deck all the way around."

Leo made a game out of building the swimming pool during recess and after school. He helped the children set the frames and lay reinforcement rods. Then two, sometimes three wheelbarrows would be filled with cement, and Leo and the children would race the wheelbarrows to the hole in four-person teams. "The hole" became the first public swimming pool in Kern County.

When the swimming pool was finished, Elyse Phillips recalled, she pinched her nose and fell face forward into the water, "crying because I was so happy."

5. **migrant** [miʹgrənt]: person who moves from place to place, especially for farm work.

Our School

While the children of Weedpatch Camp were building a school for themselves, they were also attending classes, doing homework, and taking tests on a regular basis. Besides practical training in aircraft mechanics, sewing, cobbling, and canning fruits and vegetables, they learned the basic subjects taught in elementary school and junior high: English, arithmetic, geography, history. As many as two hundred students aged between six and sixteen attended the school during its first year of operation, from September 1940 to May 1941.

Their day was divided into two three-hour periods. Half the children went to classes in the morning, normally from nine A.M. until noon, while the other half worked on building the school and tending the crops. After lunch, the groups switched places.

But it is impossible to describe a "normal" day at Weedpatch School. For example, in October 1940, twelve-year-old Doyle Powers from Ardmore, Oklahoma, was studying arithmetic with others in an unfinished classroom, which was framed with two-by-fours[6] but had no roof. Suddenly, "The sky fell in on us. It started to rain, and classes were canceled for two days until the storm passed." In November a severe dust storm forced suspension of classes in one unfinished building when two of its walls collapsed. Della Stewart, from Duncan, Oklahoma, who was eleven, remembered missing school for nearly two weeks when her family found temporary employment in the fields of Tulare County, north of Kern. Instead of attending school every day, some children had to baby-sit siblings in the camp while adult members of the family worked.

Because attendance at the school was sometimes sporadic[7] and because many students were learning from scratch, Leo recalled "There were no quantum leaps in knowledge. There were only little victories, when a student understood addition or learned to write a complete sentence. But the main thing was they were learning." And they were. As weeks stretched into months and months into years, addition led to subtraction, English led to literature, and American history led to world history.

For some students at Weedpatch School, education had an immediate practical effect. For example, Joyce Foster lived with her parents and two younger brothers in two tents in Weedpatch Camp for more than three years. Joyce was ten in 1941 when she started attending the school. She was twelve when her father, thirty-six-year-old Roy Foster from Clinton, Oklahoma, contracted a lung disease while working grapes and died. Joyce cried for weeks because she

6. **two-by-fours**: pieces of lumber four inches wide and two inches thick used in building.
7. **sporadic** [spə rad′ ik]: occasional, happening at uneven intervals.

missed her father. She was appointed the task of writing a letter to relatives in Clinton conveying the sad news. She was the only member of her family who could write.

Joyce also wrote an essay about her father and read it aloud to the Okie families gathered in the auditorium at Weedpatch Camp. The Okie school children sometimes read stories and poems before the dances on Saturday nights, but it was a special moment when Joyce stood on the makeshift bandstand. She remembered riding with her father on a tractor in Clinton and picking beans with him in Arizona. And as she recalled each memory she thanked her father for giving his family food, shelter, and love. Her essay was called "An Okie Man" and it was composed in an English class at Weedpatch School.

At the same time, the children who studied at Weedpatch School had life experiences they would never forget. Patsy Lamb told the story of the first Thanksgiving at the school. Leo, Edna, and the teachers prepared a turkey dinner for the children. "Mrs. Hunter told us all to go to this one big room. We were so happy," Patsy recalled. But "when we sat down and tried to eat the turkey, most of us couldn't. We never had turkey before. We didn't like the taste. We pushed the food around on our plates. Later we got some beans from the camp and we ate beans for our Thanksgiving dinner."

Other students have vivid memories of the outings at the school. On Saturdays, for students who had shown improvement and for those who scored 90 percent or better in arithmetic for the week, Leo and the teachers took the children on one-day vacations, which Leo called "outings." Nathan Reed, twelve years old out of Guymon in the Panhandle,[8] which had few lakes or streams, caught his first fish on an outing in the Kern River Canyon. Leo's flatbed truck carried a dozen Okie children that day. The catfish were spawning in the shallows below the banks of the wild Kern River, and all of the children caught fish by hand-casting ten-foot lengths of string with hooks and

8. **Panhandle** [pan′ han dl]: a narrow stretch of land connected to a larger section of land, such as the Texas Panhandle.

worms attached. On that day, Nathan recalled, "We stayed out too long and it started to rain. It rained so hard that the truck sunk down to its frame in the mud when we got on it. We all piled off and dug it out with our bare hands while it poured cats and dogs." The children were soaked and covered with mud, and so was Leo. It was a memorable end to "a great day," and Nathan was hooked on fishing for life.

Students remember a thousand other "great days" at Weedpatch School. There was the day Edna gave Beth Stewart her first pair of earrings, and the day Beth made her first dress in sewing class for her mother. There was the day Doyle Powers got 92 percent on his arithmetic test and got to taxi the C-46 down the runway and back. There was the day when the school's first crop of potatoes came in and sold for two hundred fifty dollars. Most of the money went toward building the cafeteria, but fifty dollars was used for a trip to the Kern County Fair in Bakersfield, where over one hundred kids, Leo estimated, rode the Ferris wheel and the merry-go-round—and ate ice cream! A year later, Eddie Davis's hand-raised hog, "Eddie," placed third at the fair, but that's not what made that day special. The highlight of the day came when another boy, taller than Eddie, called Eddie a dumb Okie and Eddie stood up for himself. Eddie punched the boy in the nose and knocked him into the hog slop.

Eddie was also present during what came to be known as the Fight. It was a Saturday, and most of the parents of Weedpatch Camp were working in the fields. Perhaps as many as fifty children were playing baseball at the school or swimming in the pool when three cars driven by teenage boys began to circle the playground. The teenage boys got out of the cars and squared off in front of Eddie and a line of other sixteen-year-old boys from the camp. When the intruders hurled rocks into the swimming pool, the Okie boys charged forward and the Fight was on. Some men from the camp rushed over to the playground to restore order, but by then the invaders were in retreat with bloody noses and scuffed faces. That was what the Okie children meant when they said, "It was *our school.*"

"When we started to build the school, it gave the parents hope," Leo said. "They could see what the school meant to the children.

They could see it every day in their faces, in their laughter. And the longer we ran the school, the longer the families stayed. The greater portion of them stayed there and would stay the year round and work so their kids could stay in this school. They understood what we were trying to do. It was the first time the children ever had anything of their own, where all the attention was on them, where they were given the best and they knew everyone was for them." Teacher Mariel Hunter recalled a girl in the eighth grade whose family was about to move away. The girl wanted to stay in school so badly and go on to high school that she planned to marry so she could stay in town. Mariel took the problem to Leo, and Leo found the girl a home where she could live in return for doing household chores.

"Everyone pitched in to make it grow," Mariel said. "We all worked together like one big family, and grow we did together. . . . The kids appreciated everything you did for them because they had so little to light up their lives."

"The teachers made us feel important and like someone really cared," Trice Masters said. "The school gave us pride and dignity and honor when we didn't have those things. It was *our school*. It did a great deal to cause us to believe we were special."

Bob Rutledge was fourteen when his family moved into the camp. He spoke for his classmates while studying old photos of Weedpatch School. "Look at these people," he said. "They're not dumb." He spoke of poverty as being "in the mind" and said, "We never accepted poverty." He described the "Okie attitude" at the school as "This is what we are now, but it's not what we're going to be. Give us some time. Everybody should have had this experience," he added. "You have to live it to understand it."

Bob talked of a "pervading[9] affection" between the students, the teachers, and Leo and related an example of what he meant. "The girls, when they got old enough, couldn't wear nylons because their hands were too rough from picking cotton. And they had to pick cotton to buy their dresses for the prom. But we understood," he added. "It was part of all of us, what we were and where we were going."

Surely every day was special to the four hundred or so students who attended Weedpatch School. For it was there that they learned a most important lesson: they were as good as anybody else.

9. **pervading** [pər vād′ ing]: spreading everywhere.

JERRY STANLEY

Jerry Stanley was born in 1941 in Highland Park, Michigan. When he was seventeen, Stanley joined the Air Force and was stationed in California. After becoming a civilian again, he finished college and went to graduate school in Arizona—but liked California so much that he moved back. Stanley now teaches history at California State University in Bakersfield. He says he likes driving his motor scooter to work every day.

To research the story of Weedpatch School, Stanley interviewed the school superintendent and principal as well as all the former teachers and students he could locate. *Children of the Dust Bowl* is his first book.

Knoxville, Tennessee

NIKKI GIOVANNI

I always like summer
best
you can eat fresh corn
from daddy's garden
and okra[1]   5
and greens[2]
and cabbage
and lots of
barbecue
and buttermilk   10
and homemade ice-cream
at the church picnic
and listen to
gospel music[3]
outside   15
at the church
homecoming
and go to the mountains with
your grandmother
and go barefooted   20
and be warm
all the time
not only when you go to bed
and sleep

---

1. **okra** [ŏ′ krə]: a tall plant with sticky pods used in soups and as a vegetable.
2. **greens:** leaves and stems of plants, such as beets, used for food.
3. **gospel music** [gos′ pəl]: intense, joyful songs about the teachings of Christ and the apostles.

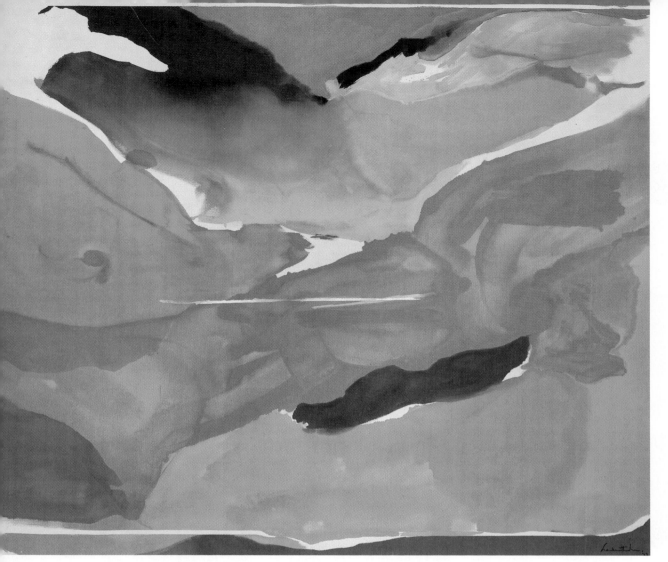

Nature Abhors a Vacuum Helen Frankenthaler, 1973, acrylic on canvas, 103" x 112", Private collection

N I K K I   G I O V A N N I

Nikki Giovanni was born in 1943 in Knoxville, Tennessee, and grew up there, in the shadow of the Smoky Mountains. In college, Giovanni majored in history and went on to Columbia University School of the Arts. During the civil rights days of the 1960s, she discovered her interest in writing poetry.

Giovanni tells young people, "The older you get, the better you will write. Not just because a writer's skills grow, but because of insight. One isn't born with insight, one obtains it."

Los Encuentros Javier Arévalo, 1991, Private collection

THOSE WHO DON'T

SANDRA CISNEROS

Those who don't know any better come into our neighborhood scared. They think we're dangerous. They think we will attack them with shiny knives. They are stupid people who are lost and got here by mistake.

But we aren't afraid. We know the guy with the crooked eye is Davey the Baby's brother, and the tall one next to him in the straw brim, that's Rosa's Eddie V. and the big one that looks like a dumb grown man, he's Fat Boy, though he's not fat anymore nor a boy.

All brown all around, we are safe. But watch us drive into a neighborhood of another color and our knees go shakity-shake and our car windows get rolled up tight and our eyes look straight. Yeah. That is how it goes and goes.

SANDRA CISNEROS

Sandra Cisneros was born in 1954 and raised in Chicago. She later went to live in San Antonio, Texas. Calling herself a migrant writer and professor, she has said that her memories of her old neighborhood—the neighborhood of *The House on Mango Street*—move with her, wherever she may live and work.

Cisneros writes both poetry and prose. So far, she has published two books of poems as well as two collections of short stories.

It's All in How

MICKEY ROBERTS

You Say It

*E*ver since I was a small girl in school, I've been aware of what the school textbooks say about Indians. I am an Indian and, naturally, am interested in what the school teaches about natives of this land.

One day in the grammar school I attended, I read that a delicacy of American Indian people was dried fish, which, according to the textbook, tasted "like an old shoe, or was like chewing on dried leather." To this day I can remember my utter dismay at reading these words. We called this wind-dried fish "sleet-schus," and to us, it was our favorite delicacy and, indeed, did not taste like shoe leather. It took many hours of long and hard work to cure[1] the fish in just this particular fashion. Early fur traders and other non-Indians must have agreed, for they often used this food for subsistence as they traveled around isolated areas.

I brought the textbook home to show it to my father, leader of my tribe at that time. My father was the youngest son of one of the last chiefs of the Nooksack Indian Tribe of Whatcom County in the state of Washington. On this particular day, he told me in his wise and humble manner that the outside world did not always understand Indian people, and that I should not let it hinder me from learning the good parts of education.

1. **cure** [kyŭr]: preserve meat or fish by drying, salting, smoking, or pickling.

Woven cup Nooksack tribe, Burke Museum, Seattle, Washington

Since those early years I have learned we were much better off with our own delicacies, which did not rot our teeth and bring about the various dietary problems that plague Indian people in modern times. I was about eight years old when this incident happened and it did much to sharpen my desire to pinpoint terminology in books used to describe American Indian people, books which are, most often, not very complimentary.

At a later time in my life, I had brought a group of Indian people to the county fairgrounds to put up a booth to sell Indian-made arts and crafts. My group was excited about the prospect of making some money selling genuine Indian artifacts. We thanked the man who showed us our booth and told him it was nice of him to remember the people of the Indian community. The man expanded a little and remarked that he liked Indian people. "In fact," he went on to state, "we are bringing some professional Indians to do the show!"

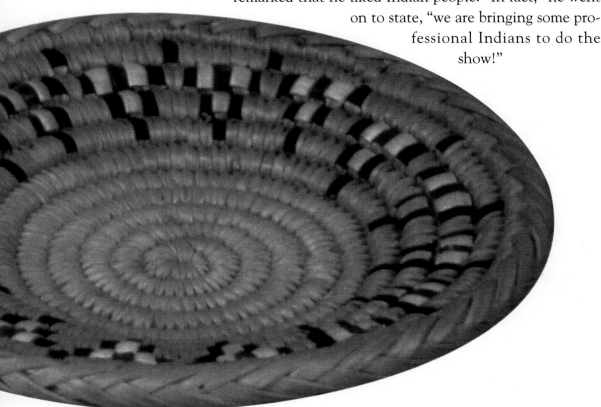

Dish Nooksack tribe, Burke Museum, Seattle, Washington

As we stood there in shock, listening to this uninformed outsider, I looked at my dear Indian companion, an eighty-year-old woman who could well remember the great chiefs of the tribe who once owned all the land of this county before the white man came bringing "civilization," which included diseases and pollution. My friend said not a word, but took the hurt as Indian people have done for many years, realizing outsiders are very often tactless and unthinking.

Of course, we all knew that the "professional Indians" were not Indians at all, but dressed in leather and dancing their own dances. And, anyway, how does one become a "professional Indian"?

I remembered my father's words of so long ago and said to my friend as my father had said to me, "They just don't understand Indian people."

Sugar bowl
Nooksack tribe,
Burke Museum,
Seattle, Washington

The Forest Cries

IGNATIA BROKER

"When the forest weeps, the Anishinabe[1] who listen will look back at the years. In each generation of Ojibway[2] there will be a person who will hear the si-si-gwa-d,[3] who will listen and remember and pass it on to the children."

I got off the city bus and walked the short one-and-a-half blocks home as I have been doing for years around five o'clock each evening. Because this evening was warm, I walked slower than usual, enjoying the look and feel of the early spring. The earth that had been white was now brown, left uncovered by the melting snow. This brown was turning to green and the air was fragrant with the opening of spring.

Daylight still lingered and as I walked I looked at my neighborhood and thought about it. When I first moved here in the mid-1950s this was a mixed neighborhood of Spanish-speaking people and Catholic whites, and there were many children. Now the Spanish-speaking people are all gone. They left when the parochial school closed its doors, although the church is still here. Now the neighborhood is only four blocks long and two blocks wide, whittled down by urban renewal and the freeways which reach their tentacles all around us.

I reached my doorstep and sat enjoying the good day and remembering the past. It was funny, really, when I think about it. That day thirty years ago when we moved here, me and my children, we were the aliens looking for a place to fit in, looking for a chance of a new life, moving in among these people, some of whose 'forefathers' had

1. **Anishinabe** [ä nish in ä′ bā]: Native Americans of northeast Montana and adjacent parts of Canada, members of the Sioux nation.
2. **Ojibway** [ō jib′ wā]: Native Americans from the region of Lake Superior in the United States and Canada.
3. **si-si-gwa-d** [sē sē qwäd]: the traditional oral story of the Ojibway.

Racing with the Moon Jaune Quick-to-See Smith,
1986, pastel on paper, 30″ x 22″, Private collection

displaced my ancestors for the same reason: looking for a new life. Their fathers were the aliens then, and now they, the children, are in possession of this land.

For a long time I was that Indian person with the two children. But it is good that children have a natural gift of accepting people, and so my children became a part of the neighborhood.

Thirty years in this neighborhood. My children went to school from here, they went to church from here, they were married from here and even though they are in faraway places they seem to have their roots here, for they had lived no other place while growing up.

I talked to my children, even when they were very small, about the ways of the Ojibway people. They were good children and they listened, but I had a feeling that they listened the same as when I read a story about the Bobbsey twins[4] or Marco Polo.[5] I was speaking of another people, removed from them by rock and roll, juvenile singers, and the bobbing movement of the new American dance.

My two, born and raised in Minneapolis, are of that generation of Ojibway who do not know what the reservation[6] means, or the Bureau of Indian Affairs,[7] or the tangled treaties and federal—so called—Indian laws which have spun their webs for a full century around the Native People, the First People of this land.

Now my children are urging me to recall all the stories and bits of information that I ever heard my grandparents or any of the older Ojibway tell. It is important, they say, because now their children are asking them. Others are saying the same thing. It is well that they are asking, for the Ojibway young must learn their cycle.

I have been abroad in this society, the dominating society, for two-thirds of my life, and yet I am a link in a chain to the past. Because of this, I shall do as they ask. I can close my eyes and I am back in the past.

4. **Bobbsey twins:** stories featuring the Bobbsey twins, by Laura Lee Hope.
5. **Marco Polo** [mär′ kō pō′ lō]: Italian merchant of the thirteenth and fourteenth centuries who wrote about his travels in Asia.
6. **reservation** [rez′ ər va′ shən]: place set aside by the government as a place for Native Americans to live.
7. **Bureau of Indian Affairs:** a Civil Service branch related to Native Americans.

I came to the Twin Cities[8] from the reservation in 1941, the year Pearl Harbor was attacked. I went to work in a defense plant and took night classes in order to catch up on the schooling I had missed. I was twenty-two years old and aching for a permanent, settling-down kind of life, but the war years were unstable years for everyone, and more so for the Indian people.

Although employment was good because of the labor demand of the huge defense plants, Indian people faced discrimination in restaurants, night clubs, retail and department stores, in service organizations, public offices, and worst of all, in housing. I can remember hearing, "This room has been rented already, but I got a basement that has a room. I'll show you." I looked at the room. It had the usual rectangular window, and pipes ran overhead. The walls and floors were brown cement, but the man with a gift-giving tone in his voice said, "I'll put linoleum on the floor for you and you'll have a toilet all to yourself. You could wash at the laundry tubs."

There was of course, nothing listed with the War Price and Rationing Board, but the man said it would cost seven dollars a week. I know that he would have made the illegal offer only to an Indian because he knew of the desperate housing conditions we, the first Americans, faced.

I remember living in a room with six others. It was a housekeeping room, nine by twelve feet in size, and meant for one person. It was listed with the price agency at five dollars a week, but the good landlady collected five dollars from each of us each week. However, she did put in a bunk bed and a rollaway which I suppose was all right because we were on different shifts and slept different times anyway. It was cramped and crowded but we had a mutual respect. We sometimes shared our one room with others who had no place, so that there might be nine or ten of us. We could not let friends be out on the street without bed or board. As long as our landlady did not mind, we helped and gave a place of rest to other Ojibway people.

Our paydays were on different days and so whoever had money

---

8. **Twin Cities:** Minneapolis and the nearby city of St. Paul, Minnesota.

lent carfare and bought meat and vegetables. Stew was our daily fare because we had only a hot plate and one large kettle.

I mention this practice because I know other Indian people did the same thing, and sometimes whole families evolved[9] from it. This was how we got a toehold in the urban areas—by helping each other. Perhaps this is the way nonmaterialistic people do. We were a sharing people and our tribal traits are still within us.

I think now that maybe it was a good thing, the migration of our people to the urban areas during the war years, because there, amongst the millions of people, we were brought to a brotherhood. We Indian people who worked in the war plants started a social group not only for the Ojibway but for the Dakota, the Arikara, the Menominee, the Gros Ventres, the Cree[10], the Oneida[11], and all those from other tribes and other states who had made the trek to something new. And because we, all, were isolated in this dominant[12] society, we became an island from which a revival of spirit began.

It was not easy for any of us during the war years and it became more difficult after the war had ceased. Many Native People returned to the reservations after our soldiers came home from the foreign lands, but others like me stayed and took the buffeting[13] and the difficulties shown us by an alien society.

The war plants closed and people were without jobs. The labor market tightened up and we, the Native People—even skilled workers—faced bias, prejudice, and active discrimination in employment. I know because when I was released from my defense job I answered many advertisements and always I was met with the words, "I'm sorry but we don't hire Indians because they only last the two weeks till payday. Then they quit."

9. **evolved** [i volvd′]: developed gradually; here it means that the families moved into the area gradually.
10. **Dakota** [də kō′ tə] **Arikara** [ə rē′ kə rə] **Menominee** [mə nom′ ə nē] **Gros Ventres** [grō vän′ trə] **Cree** [krē] Native Americans, from the northern United States and southern Canada.
11. **Oneida** [ō nī′ də]: Native Americans from central New York State.
12. **dominant** [dom′ ə nənt]: powerful, controlling; here the word refers to those in the area who are not Native American.
13. **buffeting** [buf′ it ing]: the hurts involved in being different.

It was around this time that I met and married a veteran who was passing through to the reservation. He got a job with the railroad. To be close to that job and because of the bias in housing, we moved to the capitol side of the river, to an area of St. Paul called the river flats. It was a poor area. Many of the houses had outdoor toilets; many were but tar-paper shacks. Surprising, but it was so in this very large city. It was here our two children were born and I, like a lot of other Indian women, went out and did day work—cleaning and scrubbing the homes of the middle-income people.

Many Indian families lived on the river flats, which became vibrant with their sharing. People gave to each other because times were bad. No Indian family dared approach the relief and welfare agencies of the Twin Cities. They knew that they would only be given a bus ticket and be told to go back to the reservation where the government would take care of them as usual. This was the policy of the public service agencies, and we put up with it by not asking for the help to which we had a legal right. We also suffered in other ways of their making. My husband was recalled to service and died in Korea. After this I moved from the river flats. I took the clerical training and got my first job at a health clinic.

Because my husband died fighting for a nation designed for freedom for all, I felt that I must help extend that freedom to our people. I joined a group of Indians who had banded together to form an Indian help agency. We built a welfare case to challenge the policy of sending our people back to the reservation, and we were successful. After that, the tide of Indians moving to Minnesota's urban areas increased, and today there are ten thousand of us. As the number grew, new-fangled types of Indian people came into being: those demanding what is in our treaties, those demanding service to our people, those working to provide these services—and all reaching back for identity.

When I see my people every day and know how they are doing, I do not feel so lost in the modern times. The children of our people who come to our agency have a questioning look, a dubious but seeking-to-learn look, and I truly believe that they are reaching back to learn those things of which they can be proud. Many of these children were born and raised in the urban areas and they do not make any distinctions as to their tribes. They do not say, "I am Ojibway," or "I am Dakota," or "I am Arapaho,"[14] but they say, "I am an Indian." Now they, too, are looking to their tribal identity.

These children are again honoring the Old People by asking them to speak, and I like other older people will search my memory and tell what I know. I, myself, shall tell you what I have heard my grandmother tell and I shall try to speak in the way she did and use the words that were hers.

My grandchildren,

I am glad that you, the young Ojibway of today, are seeking to learn the beliefs, the customs, and the practices of our people, for these things have too long been alive only within the memories of the Old Ones. I am glad that you are asking, for it has always been the custom for us to tell what must be passed on so that our ways will be known to the Ojibway children of the future.

Many times when I was a young girl I was fortunate to hear my grandmother tell of the lives and deeds of our grandfathers, grandmothers, and other people of our clan. I listened to these stories, but I really did not know their worth. "What good are these tales in today's world?" asked many people, never realizing that the Ojibway tales teach a philosophy for living. They tell of the purity of man and nature and keeping them in balance.

It is important that you learn the past and act accordingly, for that will assure us that we will always people the earth. I say this because our people who have gone before have said this. They have said that there will be five generations of Ojibway who will make a circle. The first people will start the circle and the others will move from the Ojibway ways. There will be those who will ask questions and those who remember, and the last generation will again act as the Ojibway have acted in years before. Then the circle will be closed.

14. **Arapaho** [ə rap′ ə hō]: Native Americans from Colorado who now live on reservations in Wyoming and Oklahoma.

I do not know which generation the children of today are, but the questions are beginning.

We, the Ojibway, are a forest people. A long time before a strange people came to this country, we lived east and north of this land now called Minnesota in the country of the eastern longhouses. Once we even lived on the big water of salt. We peopled both the north and south banks of what is now called the St. Lawrence River, and by 1770 we reached the north and south shores of what are now called the Great Lakes. We lived in harmony with our kinsmen of the Algonquin nation—the Ottawa, the Menominee, and the Potawatomi[15]—for they, too, were forest peoples. We were the westernmost and perhaps the largest tribe of this nation. The forests were huge and thick, and they were filled with our brethren, the animal people.

We did not own the land acre by acre as is done today, but we respected the right of all people to share in the gifts given by the Great Being to the Anishinabe, which means us, the original people.

The Mi-de-wi-wi-n[16] was a society within all Ojibway communities. Its basic philosophy was the prolonging of life and its practice was the use of herbs, the setting of bones, and the healing of wounds. The use of Mi-de-wi-wi-n rites was restricted to the society's members. They were consulted for their deeper knowledge of medicine.

The gathering and use of herbs was not, however, restricted to the Mi-de-wi-wi-n. Most adult Ojibway had a general knowledge of herbs and medicine, and there were also the Medicine People who had a greater knowledge. This they taught to the younger members of the family so that the practice continued from one generation to the next.

Our family traveled a tortuous path, trying to escape alien contact and retain a satisfying life. As the strange new people, the

15. **Algonquin nation** [al gong´ kən]: Native Americans from the valleys of the Ottawa River and northern parts of the St. Lawrence River. **Ottawa** [ot´ ə wə]: Native Americans, part of the Algonquin nation, from the areas around Lake Superior and Lake Huron. **Potawatomi** [pot´ ə wot´ ə mē]: Native Americans of the Algonquin nation from Michigan and Wisconsin.

16. **Mi-de-wi-wi-n** [mē də wē wn]

voyageurs,[17] came into our homeland, pushing and disrupting, many of the Ojibway met with them and became their friends. But our family group preferred to remain in the paths of our ancestors. They moved toward the setting sun and southward to the land of lakes and rivers. They would not deal with the strange people. We, the descendants who now live in the urban areas or on the reservation, have never put a foot in the many places where our ancestors lived, but our roots are in the land of forests where they made their homes.

The best way to learn why we were separated from the first generation is to tell you about the people who lived then. This I shall do by telling you of my great-great-grandmother, who is your grandmother five times removed. Her name was Ni-bo-wi-se-gwe,[18] which means Night Flying Woman. Her nickname was Oona.

The village in which Oona was born was very large and had many lodges. It was north and west of the Lake of Nettles, which is now called Nett Lake, where the A-sa-bi-ig-go-na-ya,[19] the People of the Nettle Fibers, lived. Although Ojibway people had been there many years, they were still thought of as newcomers by the People of the Nettle Fibers. But indeed they had been together a long, long time. They had shared the joy of birth and the sadness of the last journey. They had feasted together in time of plenty and had shared in time of little. They had been happy and there had always been peace among them.

In the early 1800s the strangers, those people who had robbed the white pine from the land of the Cherokee,[20] began looking at the tall trees in the forests of the Ojibway. Soon their clamor reached the communities of the Ojibway. "We need lumber for building homes and ships and the shops in our towns." The industry that ate the forests became king and then the Great White Father, who was de-

---

17. **voyageurs** [vwä yä zhėr′]: French-Canadian woodsmen, boaters, guides, and workers for early fur-trading companies; the word is French for "travelers."
18. **Ni-bo-wi-se-gwe** [nē bō wē sə gwā]
19. **A-sa-bi-ig-go-na-ya** [ä sä bē ig gō nä yä]
20. **Cherokee** [cher′ ə kē]: Native Americans of the Iroquois nation from the southern Appalachians, now living mostly in Oklahoma.

clared chief of all the people, sent treaty papers to the Ojibway. Six times groups of Ojibway were required to mark the treaties. Each time their lands passed into the hands of the alien peoples, and each group was required to move to a Native Area. These Native Areas are now called the Chippewa[21] reservations of Minnesota.

The strangers rapidly settled in the Ojibway territory. They soon surrounded the Native Areas and ripped away the forests. After them came more strangers who plowed the lands and made the laws and demanded the restriction of the Ojibway to the Native Areas. The council fires burned low because the agents of the strangers now said what must be so and what the Ojibway must do. Then came the peoples with the books, each saying his was the best. They told the Ojibway to mend their ways and follow the words of the book.

This is the time when Oona lived and these were the things that Oona faced. The adjustments that Oona and her family group made were much the same as those made by other family groups. This was the time when the generations of Ojibway began the travel on the circle away from the beginning, clinging in memory to what had been before. What was before must again be there when the circle closes.

21. **Chippewa** [chip′ ə wä]: (Ojibway) Native Americans from the region of Lake Superior in the United States and Canada.

I G N A T I A   B R O K E R

Ignatia Broker [1919-1987] was born on the White Earth Indian Reservation in Minnesota.

In 1966, Broker started working with Minneapolis Public Schools to develop an Indian Studies curriculum. She also was head researcher of the Upper Midwest American Indian Center and founder of the Minnesota Indian Historical Society.

Following the example of her mother, who had recorded many of her memories on tape, Broker recorded her own. Her book, *Night Flying Woman,* is based on the life of her great-great-grandmother.

Pittsburgh Memories Romare Beardon, 1984, collage on board, 28 5/8" x 23 1/2"

BLOCK PARTY

JEWELL PARKER RHODES

We lived in the dark green hills of Pittsburgh where the smoke from J. L. Steel dusted our clothes gray and blanketed the sky, causing sunsets to streak bright pink and orange. Streetcar wires crisscrossed overhead, making perches for the hungry crows who flew high when the lumbering cars came, spewing electric sparks. Sometimes we'd put pennies in the metal tracks and wait for them to be squashed flat as the streetcars rumbled over them, carrying passengers down the hills into the heart of the city that rested by the three rivers: Ohio, Monongahela, and Allegheny.

But what I remember most about growing up in Pittsburgh was living in a neighborhood where everyone acted like a relative—an aunt, an uncle, a brother, or a sister. Lots of women acted like my mother, bossing me, feeding me. Many would hold me on their laps and tell me stories about High John the Conqueror or John Henry. Some felt no shame about whipping out a comb and fixing my hair when they thought I looked too raggedy. And days when I was lucky, one of my neighborhood mothers would jump in the circle and join me in a waist-twisting, hip-rolling hula-hoop.[1] Sometimes it drove me crazy to have so many mothers, but it also made me feel safe. My real mother was gone—divorced from us—living in another city. But I lived with my dad, my grandparents, an aunt, a sister, and a cousin whom I called sister.

---

1. **hula-hoop** [hü′ lə hüp′]: a brand name for a ring-shaped, plastic toy that is spun around the hips, introduced in the 1950s.

Dad, Aunt, and Grandpa went off to work while Grandma took care of us. On Tuesdays, she did laundry in the basement and she let us stir the Argo starch and turn the roller drums to wring out all the wet in the clothes. Then we'd help hang the clothes on the line and, when the sheets were dry, she turned a blind eye while we played hide and seek among them. In the house we'd hike to the third floor and slide down the two banisters, smooth and fast, convinced it was better than any roller coaster ride at Kennywood Park.

We had a red tricycle with a bell. My sister, Tonie, had outgrown it. I was just the right size, while cousin Aleta was too small. But when Grandma made chitlins,[2] we would share the bike and make a game of driving through the stinking kitchen while Grandma cleaned out the pig's guts (yuck!) and boiled them. We'd ride our bike through dangerous territory, ringing our bell once we hit the kitchen linoleum, hollering and hooting like "wild ones"—or, as Grandma would say, like "Silly children with no sense!" If you held your nose you couldn't ring the bell and steer at the same time. So we'd count how many bells to figure out who won, who braved the skunky odor and didn't hold their nose the most.

The best part of growing up was the world we saw from our front stoop. Widow Chalmers mothered all the children, watching over us from her porch, waving her fan from the Methodist Church to cool herself in the summer heat. Mr. Berry, who had a splotch of pink roses on his cheek, liked checkers and would roam the street looking for a partner, carrying his own lawn chair. He even played with Aleta, who was five and had to be told every move. There was Jim, who played ball, spinning, ducking and diving, and throwing hoops into a basketball net and would only stop if someone was in any trouble. "Jim, my car stalled." "Jim, can you drive me to the grocery?" "Jim, my sink is clogged." Jim later joined the Army and came home and dunked three baskets in his clod-hopper[3] black shoes and khaki uniform. My sister Tonie, at eleven, swore she'd marry him.

---

2. **chitlins** [chit′ linz]: the intestines of pigs, cooked as food.
3. **clod-hopper** [klod′ hop′ ər]: strong, heavy shoe.

Detail from **Pittsburgh Memories** Romare Beardon

Stuck-up Rachel liked to cheat at Jacks and had to be black-mailed into playing Double Dutch.[4] "I'll give you some of Grandma's chicken from Sunday dinner," I'd offer. I promised a drumstick for each twenty minutes she turned the rope while I sang and dreamed of winning Double Dutch Champion at the "Y." Truth be told, Grandma would have given anyone who asked a piece of her chicken. Rachel knew it, I knew it. Everyone knew it. But Rachel was two years older than I and, like another big sister, she was nice enough to let me think I was putting one over on her.

Sitting on the steps, looking up and down the block, I saw and felt a world where I was safe, where I knew everybody and everybody knew me. Everybody was brown and black and when babies were born, we'd all wait for them to grow into their skin. Their shades would sometimes grow lighter, sometimes darker. Even the color of their eyes would change—blue became brown, hazel changed to deep green, and brown irises could mellow to a luminous black. Hair textures all varied: soft, bouncy, waves; strands curled in fuzzy, tight spirals; or even hair thick and straight because of a throwback to a Cherokee.[5] I knew we all were beautiful.

Summer block parties were the best. We'd close off traffic and sometimes the Fire Department would open the hydrants and we'd dance and sing while water gushed at us. A spray of wet beneath the moon and stars. Tonie, Aleta, and I pushed boxes together to make a stage and lipsynched to the record player, pretending we were The Supremes. "*Stop, in the name of love! Before you break my heart. Think it o-o-over! . . .* " and we'd giggle as the grown-ups clapped and the other children squealed, and everyone danced, even fat Charlie who could boogie so well you'd swear there was magic in his shoes.

The best block parties happened for no reason. Anyone—even a child—could wake up one day and call for "Block Party Day." And we'd share ribs, corn, chicken, tater pie, and collard greens, and Miss

4. **Double Dutch** [dub′ əl duch]: a game of jump rope in which two people swing two ropes at the same time, usually in opposite directions.
5. **Cherokee** [cher′ ə kē′]: Native Americans of the southern Appalachians, now living mostly in Oklahoma.

Sarah who never married always made punch with vanilla ice cream and it would melt into a swishy mess. Finally, when legs wouldn't move another dance step, then the record player was taken away, the street was swept. There were cries and whispers of good night. My real family and I, we'd go into the house. Grandma, Grandpa, Aunt, and Daddy would tuck us in bed and kiss me, Tonie, and Aleta good night. And I would wait until Tonie and Aleta were asleep in the small twin beds (I didn't want them to think I was off my head) and I'd go to the window. Then, peeking over the ledge, I'd whisper my own private "G'night" to the rest of my family, tucked in their beds inside the tall houses all along my street, there in the city where the three rivers meet.

JEWELL PARKER RHODES

Jewell Parker Rhodes teaches at Arizona State University in Tempe, Arizona. Despite what she calls her "fondness for gloomy days," she lives with her family in the sunny Arizona desert.

As a child, some of Parker Rhodes's happiest times were block parties. "I loved lipsynching to records," she says, "and I often imagined I'd grow up to become a singer or an actress." Instead, in college she chose to earn degrees in drama criticism, English, and creative writing.

As a writer, Parker Rhodes says, "I can be anything and everything in my imagination." She has written scholarly nonfiction as well as magazine articles, stories, and a novel. She is a co-author of the school book series that includes this literature book.

Asking Big Questions About the Literature

? What makes a community?

MAKE A COMMUNITY CHART

How would you define a community? Is it a group of people who share the same surroundings? Do members of a community see each other frequently or share certain responsibilities to their community? Does a community have its own customs like those of a clan or a tribe? Make a chart that shows what makes a community in each literature selection that you read. Use the chart below to help you get started.

Selection Title	Community Features
"Seventh Grade"	Small campus; school routines

LITERATURE STUDY

Setting

The **setting** of a work of fiction is the time and place in which the action occurs. For example, if you wrote a story about life in a community, you would probably want to include details of the neighborhood and the things your characters see every day. These details would be part of the setting.

Choose a fiction selection, such as "Seventh Grade." Write a paragraph describing how the setting helps you imagine when and where the action takes place. (*See "Setting" on page 118.*)

Write a LETTER

Many people get a sense of community from helping others. Imagine that you are Beni Seballos. Write a letter to a newspaper, suggesting ways of helping the sick or homeless in your community.

What communities do people belong to?

Theme

In a short story the main idea that the writer wishes to convey is called the **theme**. With a small group, take turns presenting the theme of a short fiction selection from this unit. In other words, what do you think the author is saying about communities? Let your classmates guess the title of the selection you have chosen. (*See "Theme" on page 119.*)

Create A QUESTIONNAIRE

Discuss the variety of communities described in the literature selections you've read. Then, with a partner, write a survey questionnaire about communities. Ask about the kinds of communities people belong to, how long they have been involved, and so on. Distribute copies of your questionnaire and collect the completed forms. Then write a report about the results. When you have finished your report, compare your results with the communities in the literature in the unit.

C.L.A.S.S.I.F.Y
COMMUNITIES

Classifying—grouping together things that have something in common—can help you understand communities. With a partner, list as many kinds of communities as you can—from the literature in this unit and from your own experience. Then decide if each community is a community of *place*, such as a neighborhood, or a community of *culture*, such as the Ojibway. Use a chart like the one here to classify these communities.

Title	Community	Place	Culture
"Block Party"	Neighborhood	X	
"The Forest Cries"	Ojibway		X

Asking Big Questions About the Literature

What responsibilities do people have to their community?

Giving Instructions

Some of the characters in the literature selections in this unit became involved in activities that revealed their sense of community responsibility. For example, in "Beni Seballos," the main character volunteers at a senior citizens center. Look through the literature selections and find an example of such an activity. Then show how it is done. Use a chart like the one below to break the activity down into steps. Present your instructions to the class.

Theme

Many of the selections in this unit present the **theme** of responsibility to a community, as in "Empowered to heal." Choose a fiction selection and write an essay discussing the theme of community responsibility in that selection. (See "Theme" on page 119.)

Step 1 — Step 2 — Step 3 — Step 4 — Step 5

MAKE A RESPONSIBILITIES CHART

What responsibilities do the characters in the literature selections have to their communities? For example, in "Empowered to heal," eight teenagers try stop the violence in their communities. Make a chart showing the community responsibilities that you find in each literature selection in this unit.

How do communities change?

*C*reate A DOCUMENTARY

As a group, choose a literature selection from this unit in which a community has experienced some kind of change. Collect information about the historical background of this change. Then present your documentary in the form of a video, an exhibit, or a lecture.

Write a
SPEECH

Listen to or read the "I Have a Dream" speech by Martin Luther King, Jr. How would you like to change your community or world? Prepare an "I Have a Dream" speech of your own. Use note cards to practice your speech with a partner. Then give your speech to your classmates. Post a written version of your speech on the bulletin board.

Setting

A story's **setting**—its time and place—influences the way its characters behave. With a partner, choose characters from several of the fiction selections in this unit. Discuss the good and bad effects of the setting on each character. Organize this information into a chart like the one below. (*See "Setting" on page 118.*)

Selection	"The Fun They Had"	
Positive Effects		
Negative Effects	Machines replace school community.	

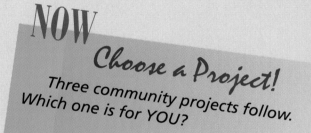

NOW

Choose a Project!

Three community projects follow. Which one is for YOU?

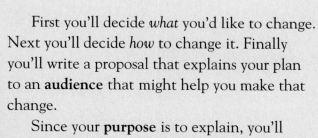

All communities change. Some may change so slowly that you can't tell they're changing. But sometimes communities change suddenly because people *make* them change—for the better, as in "Empowered to heal," or for the worse, as in "The Forest Cries." In this project, you'll have a chance to propose a change for the better in your own community and explain how this change can be brought about. Maybe you'd like to introduce a recycling program or new bike paths. Haven't you ever declared, "Would I like to do something about *that!*" Well, here's your chance.

First you'll decide *what* you'd like to change. Next you'll decide *how* to change it. Finally you'll write a proposal that explains your plan to an **audience** that might help you make that change.

Since your **purpose** is to explain, you'll need to present the proposal clearly and carefully. If your audience can understand and appreciate your plan, they'll be more likely to carry it out.

Prewriting
GETTING STARTED

If you could change one thing in your community, what would it be? Look around your school, neighborhood, or town. Talk to people; read editorials in local newspapers. What bothers you and others? How might these things be changed? Take notes as you explore. Then write a sentence that clearly states what change you're proposing for the community. This will be the main idea of your proposal.

Planning
YOUR PROPOSAL

After you decide what should be changed in your community, you'll need to plan your project before you start to write. Ask yourself these questions:

- What other information do I need and where can I get it?
- Who is an appropriate audience for my proposal?
- How will the change be brought about?

To help you answer the last question, complete a planning chart like the one below. Remember that you'll have to explain to your audience *how* the change will be brought about.

Tasks	People needed	Supplies	Timing	Expenses

Now think of the procedure that will be necessary to make the change. Break the procedure down into steps that can be easily explained to an audience. Create another chart showing the steps in your procedure for change.

Step 1	
Step 2	
Step 3	

Drafting
YOUR PROPOSAL

Now that you know what you want to change and how you want to change it, you're ready to draft your proposal.

- Begin with an introductory paragraph that presents the problem that you would like to solve. Jenny Szesterniak, a student writer, introduces her proposal on page 111 with a strong, forceful opening statement: "Our community needs bike paths." Next explain specific ways in which the change would benefit the community. Notice that the rest of Jenny's opening paragraph explains why the community needs these paths and how these paths would improve the quality of life.

- Explain the effects of your proposed change. In her second paragraph, Jenny begins with a topic sentence: "Bike paths would not only be more convenient, they would also be safer . . . . " She then explains how safety would benefit the community.

- Explain how people can bring change about. Give facts, examples, and details. It's easier to convince your audience if they understand how your plan can be carried out. In her third paragraph, Jenny shows what steps to follow to get the support of the whole community. Use your prewriting charts to help you write about the procedure for change.

- Finally write a conclusion. Restate your main idea in different words. Jenny ended her proposal with a final appeal to the community: "Hopefully everyone will realize that bike paths would make life a lot easier and safer."

Remember your purpose—to explain how the change can be brought about—and your audience when you write.

Revising YOUR PROPOSAL

Read your proposal to a writing partner or writing group and get their comments. Also try to read it to someone in the community who might have helped you in the early stages of your project. Do you have a clear topic sentence that expresses your main idea? Did you present the problem clearly? Did you explain the procedure for making the change in clear, logical steps? Do you have a strong concluding sentence?

Editing YOUR PROPOSAL

After you've revised your draft, work with a partner or group to edit your proposal. A final fine tuning will help you win over your audience. Read one another's proposals and check for errors in grammar, spelling, and punctuation. Correct your errors and make a publishable copy of your proposal.

Publishing YOUR PROPOSAL

Be sure your final copy is neat and attractive. Think about adding photos or illustrations.

Mail the proposal, or make an appointment to deliver it yourself. If classmates or friends are your audience, read it aloud or use a copy machine to make copies for everyone. For example, Jenny made a list of groups that might be interested in her proposal, such as the Brookfield Bicycle Club and the P.T.A. of her school. When she had completed her list, Jenny decided which group would be best able to carry out the plan.

Follow up with a note, phone call, or question to find out what people thought. Are they interested in making the change? If so, perhaps you too can be "Empowered to heal"!

A Proposal for Bike Paths
by Jennifer Szesterniak
Brookfield, Wisconsin

Our community needs bike paths. Transportation is very important to our community. Many people who can't drive or don't have a car have a difficult time getting around. Bike paths would make getting around much easier.

Bike paths would not only be more convenient, they would also be safer because cyclists would stop using busy roads. This would help decrease accidents. Adults would like bike paths because they would enjoy riding on them and also feel safer about their children being away from fast-moving cars. Paths would also help people stay physically fit.

We could get bike paths for the city by writing a proposal for the mayor to present to the

city council. Then we could plan a publicity campaign to let people know about this problem and gather support. Finally we could survey people to see if they would be willing to support this expense.

Bike paths may sound expensive to build but they are much better than having people's lives endangered by riding on busy roads. Bike paths would also add beauty to the city and keep it on the move in a healthy way. Hopefully everyone will realize that bike paths would make life a lot easier and safer.

PROJECT 2

Cooperative Learning

A COMMUNITY OF THE FUTURE

"What makes a community?" asks one of the Big Questions in this unit. For this project you'll be asking that question as you work with others to create a model of a community of the future.

The PLAN

With your class, brainstorm a list of futuristic communities, such as a flying school, a floating housing development, a moon colony, an underground mining village, or a fishing village at the bottom of the sea. Then join a group that has chosen to work on one of these communities.

How will you build a model of this community? Decide if you will make a blueprint or a papier-mâché model. Before you build your model, you need to plan. And to plan, you must decide what this community will need.

Brainstorm a list of community wants and needs and sort these into groups. Elect an expert to lead each group, someone who will research his or her subject thoroughly. You may need experts in architecture, science, politics, education, social work, medicine, and so on.

Finally, make a jobs map like the one shown.

FUTURE COMMUNITIES
- Flying school
- Floating City
- Moon town
- underground village

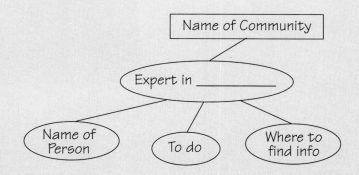

Now it's time to put your community together. Let each expert present a short research report to the team. Then ask yourselves these questions:

- What needs to be done?
- Who will do it?
- When will it be done?
- What supplies are needed?

Make a planning chart like the one below. Decide who'll perform each task. Then build the future!

Task	Person responsible	What is needed	Date to be done

Before you reveal your community to the world, consider your method of presentation. Provide the model with labels identifying the different parts and functions of your community.

You'll probably want to present your project to your class or school first. Perhaps you can work with the other project teams to create a Futuristic World's Fair. Contact a town official to see if you can display the exhibit in a public building. You might also want to make documentary-style audiotapes about your community.

Consider getting in touch with a community related to yours. Show them what their future might look like!

Helping Your Community

DEVELOPING A PLAN OF ACTION

Remember the Big Question "What responsibilities do people have to their community?" If you believe that people should help their community, then this project may be for you. Your community has needs, and you have talents. Here's a chance to bring them together by developing an action plan for a community project.

Identifying ···· NEEDS

With a partner or a group, brainstorm a list of community needs. How can you help your community? Could you start a Story Hour at the library or pick up litter in the playground?

Use a map like the one below to find ways of meeting your community's needs.

```
                      ┌─ Need 1 ── Do what? ── How? ── Where + When?
Possible Plans ───────┤
                      └─ Need 2 ── Do what? ── How? ── Where + When?
```

Before you choose a need for your project, ask yourselves the questions below. Then agree on what you would like to do.

- Is it realistic? Can it really be done?
- Can it be done by people our age?
- Can we complete it in time?
- Is the community likely to want it done?
- Can we get the materials we need?

Drawing Up YOUR PLAN OF ACTION

With your partner or group, decide just how you're going to carry out your project. List the kinds of information you'll need before you can make your plan. Visit and talk to the people involved. Contact officials. Be sure your project is something the community actually *wants*. Keep notes in your journal on everything you do and learn. Here are some of the questions you'll have to ask yourselves.

- Will our project require special permission or permits?
- What materials will be necessary? How will we get them?
- Is any money needed? How much? Where will it come from?
- How many volunteers will be necessary?
- How many people will we be dealing with?
- How will we get the word out? What publicity will we use?

When you have all the information, put your plan together. Use a project chart like the one below.

Steps (in order)	Dates	Materials	Workers
1.			
2.			
3.			

Carrying Out YOUR PLAN OF ACTION

Can you actually carry out your plan of action? Write an introduction, explaining what you would like to do and why. Then add your project chart, adding any explanation that might be helpful. Finally make a neat copy and try sending your plan to the appropriate persons for approval. You might also want to submit a copy to the local newspaper. Who knows what will happen next!

Putting It All Together
What Have You Learned About the Theme?

In this unit, you've thought about many different kinds of communities. How have the literature and activities in this unit affected your ideas about what makes a good community? Look back at the writing you've done for this unit—in your journal, in response to your reading, and in the Writing Workshop. Share your thoughts about community with your classmates by writing an essay, a short story, or a poem about a *Utopian*, or perfect, community. How would such a Utopian community differ from the communities that you know or have read about? Add your writing to a poster of your classmates' writing on the same subject.

A PERFECT COMMUNITY

Prewriting and Drafting   Brainstorm a list of problems facing the modern communities you know or have read about. How would you solve problems such as poverty, pollution, crime, and violence? Is there a way of creating a community in which everyone is happy? Where would such a community be located? Would it be in the city or the country?

Now draft an essay, a short story, or a poem about a perfect, Utopian community. Describe how the people of such a community live without the problems of the modern world and how such a community was created.

Revising and Editing   Work with a writing group or partner. Read your writing aloud to one another. Ask questions that you have about your draft, or ask your partner or group to suggest improvements to the content of your writing. Have your partner check for errors in grammar, punctuation, and spelling too.

Publishing   After you have made your final revisions, rewrite your essay neatly. Add your essay to your classmates' essays. Arrange your essays to fill a bulletin board or a poster with the title "My Utopia."

Evaluating Your Work

Think Back About the Big Questions

Think about the Big Questions on pages 10-11. Discuss your thoughts with a partner, especially your thoughts about questions that still seem hard to answer. Compare your ideas now with your ideas when you started this unit. Record your current thoughts in your journal.

Think Back About Your Work

Now think about the whole unit. What did you do? *How* did you do? To evaluate your work, including your reading, your writing, your activities, and your project, write a note to your teacher. Explain what you've done during this unit and what you've learned. Use the following questions to help you write your note.

- Which literature selections in this unit did you like the most? Why?

- What was your favorite activity in this unit? Why?

- What was your least favorite activity? Why?

- If you were to do your project again, what parts would you do the same way? What parts would you do differently?

- What did you learn as you worked on your project or projects?

- What have you learned in this unit about communities?

- How would you rate your work in this unit? Use the following scale and give at least three reasons for your rating.

  1 = Outstanding   3 = Fair
  2 = Good   4 = Not as good as it could have been

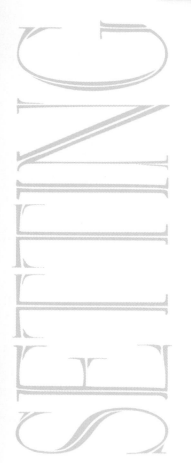

SETTING

What Is Setting?

Setting is the time and place in which the action of a work of fiction takes place. An author may describe the setting at the beginning of the story or present it through details that appear as the story unfolds. Sometimes the setting dominates the plot. In "Seventh Grade," for example, all the action takes place in a school setting, which is described in great detail. A story's setting may also have an important influence on the story's characters. It can often determine a character's attitudes and way of looking at the world.

Creating a New Setting Choose one of the fiction selections that you've read in this unit. With a partner, discuss how the setting influences both the main character and the plot of the story. Then try to imagine the selection with a very different setting. How would this affect the main character or the plot of the story? Rewrite the beginning of the story, using a different setting. Then discuss the change with a partner.

A Story Based on Your Life Write a story based on a real incident in your life or the life of your community, changing the name of your main character so that your story is a work of fiction. Begin the story by describing the setting. Think about the things you see or used to see every day. You might want to scan some of the selections to see how each author introduced the setting of a story. When you have finished your story, present it to the class. See if anyone is familiar with the setting you describe.

What Is Theme?

Theme in a piece of literature is the main idea or message that the author wishes to convey. The theme of a story can communicate the writer's attitude or way of looking at the world and can be expressed through setting, plot, or even the words of the characters. In the unit that you have just finished, each selection presented a particular idea or view of community. This idea is the theme. For example, in "The Fun They Had," the story is set in the year 2157, when students will no longer attend school but will be taught individually by machines. The main character, Margie, longs for the time when all the kids met daily in the school community. In this selection, the theme is the importance of community and the warning that one day this community might be lost forever.

Express a Theme Choose a fiction selection that you've read from the unit. Write what you think is the theme of that selection. Then make a list of details and passages that express the main theme. Think of how you could express the same theme in a story or poem of your own. Write your own piece of literature on the theme of community.

Writing a Skit With a partner, choose a theme or message, such as the importance of getting along with your neighbors or the responsibilities of friendship. Then write a short skit or dialogue that expresses that theme. When you have rehearsed your skit, present it to the class.

GLOSSARY OF LITERARY TERMS

A

alliteration Repetition of the first sound—usually a consonant sound—in several words of a sentence or a line of poetry.

allusion An author's indirect reference to someone or something that is presumed to be familiar to the reader.

anecdote A short narrative about an interesting or a humorous event, usually in the life of a person.

antagonist The person or force opposing the protagonist, or main character in a literary work. [See also *protagonist*.]

autobiography A person's written account of his or her own life.

B

ballad A poem, often a song, that tells a story in simple verse.

biography An account of a person's life, written by another person.

blank verse Unrhymed poetry.

C

character A person or an animal that participates in the action of a work of literature. A *dynamic character* is one whose thoughts, feelings, and actions are changeable and lifelike; a *static character* always remains the same. [See also *protagonist, antagonist*.]

characterization The creation of characters through the characters' use of language and through descriptions of their appearance, thoughts, emotions, and actions. [See also *character*.]

chronology An arrangement of events in the order in which they happen.

cliché An overused expression that is trite rather than meaningful.

climax The highest point of tension in the plot of a work of literature. [See also *plot*.]

comedy An amusing play that has a happy ending.

conclusion The final part or ending of a piece of literature.

concrete poem A poem arranged on the page so that its punctuation, letters, and lines make the shape of the subject of the poem.

conflict A problem that confronts the characters in a piece of literature. The conflict may be *internal* (a character's struggle within himself or herself) or *external* (a character's struggle against nature, another person, or society). [See also *plot*.]

context The general sense of words that helps readers to understand the meaning of unfamiliar words and phrases in a piece of writing.

D

description An author's use of words to give the reader or listener a mental picture, an impression, or an understanding of a person, place, thing, event, or idea.

dialect A form of speech spoken by people in a particular group or geographical region that differs in vocabulary, grammar, and pronunciation from the standard language.

dialogue The spoken words and conversation of characters in a work of literature.

drama A play that is performed before an audience according to stage directions and using dialogue. Classical drama has two genres: *tragedy* and *comedy*. Modern drama includes *melodrama, satire, theater of the absurd*, and *pantomime*. [See also *comedy, play*, and *tragedy*.]

dramatic poetry A play written in the form of poetry.

E

epic A long narrative poem—written in a formal style and meant to be read aloud—that relates the adventures and

experiences of one or more great heroes or heroines.

essay   Personal nonfiction writing about a particular subject that is important to the writer.

excerpt   A passage from a larger work that has been taken out of its context to be used for a special purpose.

exposition   Writing that explains, analyzes, or defines.

extended metaphor   An elaborately drawn out metaphor. [See also *metaphor*.]

F

fable   A short, simple story whose purpose is to teach a lesson, usually with animal characters who talk and act like people.

fantasy   Imaginative fiction about unrealistic characters, places, and events.

fiction   Literature, including the short story and the novel, that tells about imaginary people and events.

figurative language Language used to express ideas through figures of speech: descriptions that aren't meant to be taken literally. Types of figurative language include *simile*, *metaphor*, *extended metaphor*, *hyperbole*, and *personification*.

figure of speech   A type of figurative language, not meant to be taken literally, that expresses something in such a way that it brings the thing to life in the reader's or listener's imagination. [See also *figurative language*.]

flashback   A break in a story's action that relates a past happening in order to give the reader background information about a present action in the story.

folktale   A story that has been passed along from storyteller to storyteller for generations. Kinds of folktales include *tall tales*, *fairy tales*, *fables*, *legends*, and *myths*.

foreshadowing   The use of clues to create suspense by giving the reader or audience hints of events to come.

free verse   Poetry that has no formal rhyme scheme or metrical pattern.

G

genre   A major category of art. The three major literary genres are poetry, prose, and drama.

H

haiku   A three-line Japanese verse form. In most haiku, the first and third lines have five syllables, while the second line has seven. The traditional haiku describes a complicated feeling or thought in simple language through a single image.

hero/heroine   The main character in a work of literature. In heroic literature, the hero or heroine is a particularly brave, noble, or clever person whose achievements are unusual and important. [See also *character*.]

heroic age   The historical period in western civilization—from about 800 B.C. through A.D. 200—during which most works of heroic literature, such as myths and epics, were created in ancient Greece and Rome.

hubris   Arrogance or excessive pride leading to mistakes; the character flaw in a hero of classical tragedy.

hyperbole   An obvious exaggeration used for emphasis. [See also *figurative language*.]

I

idiom   An expression whose meaning cannot be understood from the ordinary meaning of the words. For example, *It's raining cats and dogs*.

imagery   The words and phrases in writing that appeal to the senses of sight, hearing, taste, touch, and smell.

irony An effect created by a sharp contrast between what is expected and what is real. An *ironic twist* in a plot is an event that is the complete opposite of what the characters have been hoping or expecting will happen. An *ironic statement* declares the opposite of the speaker's literal meaning.

J

jargon Words and phrases used by a group of people who share the same profession or special interests in order to refer to technical things or processes with which they are familiar. In general, jargon is any terminology that sounds unclear, overused, or pretentious.

L

legend A famous folktale about heroic actions, passed along by word of mouth from generation to generation. The legend may have begun as a factual account of real people and events but has become mostly or completely fictitious.

limerick A form of light verse, or humorous poetry, written in one five-line stanza with a regular scheme of rhyme and meter.

literature The branch of art that is expressed in written language and includes all written genres.

lyric poem A short poem that expresses personal feelings and thoughts in a musical way. Originally, lyrics were the words of songs that were sung to music played on the lyre, a stringed instrument invented by the ancient Greeks.

M

metamorphosis The transformation of one thing, or being, into another completely different thing or being, such as a caterpillar's change into a butterfly.

metaphor Figurative language in which one thing is said to be another thing. [See also *figurative language*.]

meter The pattern of rhythm in lines of poetry. The most common meter, in poetry written in English, is iambic pentameter, that is, a verse having five metrical feet, each foot of verse having two syllables, an unaccented one followed by an accented one.

mood The feeling or atmosphere that a reader senses while reading or listening to a work of literature.

motivation A character's reasons for doing, thinking, feeling, or saying something. Sometimes an author will make a character's motivation obvious from the beginning. In realistic fiction and drama, however, a character's motivation may be so complicated that the reader discovers it gradually, by studying the character's thoughts, feelings, and behavior.

myth A story, passed along by word of mouth for generations, about the actions of gods and goddesses or superhuman heroes and heroines. Most myths were first told to explain the origins of natural things or to justify the social rules and customs of a particular society.

N

narration The process of telling a story. For both fiction and nonfiction, there are two main kinds of narration, based on whether the story is told from a first-person or third-person point of view. [See also *point of view*.]

narrative poem A poem that tells a story containing the basic literary ingredients of fiction: character, setting, and plot.

narrator The person, or voice, that tells a story. [See also *point of view, voice*.]

nonfiction Prose that is factually true and is about real people, events, and places.

nonstandard English
Versions of English, such as slang and dialects, that use pronunciation, vocabulary, idiomatic expressions, grammar, and punctuation that differ from the accepted "correct" constructions of English.

novel   A long work of narrative prose fiction. A novel contains narration, a setting or settings, characters, dialogue, and a more complicated plot than a short story.

O

onomatopoeia   The technique of using words that imitate the sounds they describe, such as *hiss*, *buzz*, and *splash*.

oral tradition   Stories, poems, and songs that have been kept alive by being told, recited, and sung by people over many generations. Since the works were not originally written, they often have many different versions.

P

parable   A brief story—similar to a fable, but about people—that describes an ordinary situation and concludes with a short moral or lesson to be learned.

personification   Figurative language in which an animal, an object, or an idea is given human characteristics. [See also *figurative language*.]

persuasion   A type of speech or writing whose purpose is to convince people that something is true or important.

play   A work of dramatic literature written for performance by actors before an audience. In classical or traditional drama, a play is divided into five acts, each containing a number of scenes. Each act represents a distinct phase in the development of the plot. Modern plays often have only one act and one scene.

playwright   The author of a play.

plot   The sequence of actions and events in fiction or drama. A traditional plot has at least three parts: the *rising action*, leading up to a turning point that affects the main character; the *climax*, the turning point or moment of greatest intensity or interest; and the *falling action*, leading away from the conflict, or resolving it.

poetry   Language selected and arranged in order to say something in a compressed or nonliteral way. Modern poetry may or may not use many of the traditional poetic techniques that include *meter*, *rhyme*, *alliteration*, *figurative language*, *symbolism*, and *specific verse forms*.

point of view   The perspective from which a writer tells a story. *First-person* narrators tell the story from their own point of view, using pronouns such as *I* or *me*. *Third-person* narrators, using pronouns such as *he*, *she*, or *them*, may be *omniscient* (knowing everything about all characters), or *limited* (taking the point of view of one character). [See also *narration*.]

propaganda   Information or ideas that may or may not be true, but are spread as though they are true, in order to persuade people to do or believe something.

prose   The ordinary form of written and spoken language used to create fiction, nonfiction, and most drama.

protagonist   The main character of a literary work. [See also *character* and *characterization*.]

R

refrain   A line or group of lines that is repeated, usually at the end of each verse, in a poem or a song.

repetition   The use of the same formal element more than once in a literary work, for emphasis or in order to achieve another desired effect.

resolution   The falling action in fiction or drama,

including all of the developments that follow the climax and show that the story's conflict is over. [See also *plot*.]

rhyme scheme   A repeated pattern of similar sounds, usually found at the ends of lines of poetry or poetic drama.

rhythm   In poetry, the measured recurrence of accented and unaccented syllables in a particular pattern. [See also *meter*.]

S

scene   The time, place, and circumstances of a play or a story. In a play, a scene is a section of an act. [See also *play*.]

science fiction   Fantasy literature set in an imaginary future, with details and situations that are designed to seem scientifically possible.

setting   The time and place of a work of literature.

short story   Narrative prose fiction that is shorter and has a less complicated plot than a novel. A short story contains narration, at least one setting, at least one character, and usually some dialogue.

simile   Figurative language that compares two unlike things, introduced by the words "like" or "as." [See also *figurative language*.]

soliloquy   In a play, a short speech spoken by a single character when he or she is alone on the stage. A soliloquy usually expresses the character's innermost thoughts and feelings, when he or she thinks no other characters can hear.

sonnet   A poem written in one stanza, using fourteen lines of iambic pentameter. [See also *meter*.]

speaker   In poetry, the individual whose voice seems to be speaking the lines. [See also *narration*, *voice*.]

stage directions   The directions, written by the playwright, to tell the director, actors, and theater technicians how a play should be dramatized. Stage directions may specify such things as how the setting should appear in each scene, how the actors should deliver their lines, when the stage curtain should rise and fall, how stage lights should be used, where on the stage the actors should be during the action, and when sound effects should be used.

stanza   A group of lines in poetry set apart by blank lines before and after the group; a poetic verse.

style   The distinctive way in which an author composes a

work of literature in written or spoken language.

suspense   An effect created by authors of various types of fiction and drama, especially adventure and mystery, to heighten interest in the story.

symbol   An image, person, place, or thing that is used to express the idea of something else.

T

tall tale   A kind of folk tale, or legend, that exaggerates the characteristics of its hero or heroine.

theme   The main idea or underlying subject of a work of literature.

tone   The attitude that a work of literature expresses to the reader through its style.

tragedy   In classical drama, a tragedy depicts a noble hero or heroine who makes a mistake of judgment that has disastrous consequences.

V

verse   A stanza in a poem. Also, a synonym for poetry as a genre. [See also *stanza*.]

voice   The narrator or the person who relates the action of a piece of literature. [See also *speaker*.]

ACKNOWLEDGMENTS

Grateful acknowledgment is made for permission to reprint the following copyrighted material.

"Seventh Grade" from *Baseball in April and Other Stories* by Gary Soto, copyright ©1990 by Gary Soto, reprinted by permission of Harcourt Brace and Company.

"They think I'm an expert" by Catherine Crocker is reprinted by permission of the Associated Press.

From *The Diary of Latoya Hunter* by Latoya Hunter. Copyright ©1992 by Latoya Hunter. Reprinted by permission of Crown Publishers, Inc.

"Empowered to heal" by Michael Grunwald from *The Boston Globe*, April 22, 1993. Reprinted by courtesy *The Boston Globe*.

"Break a Leg" by Joel Schwartz. Copyright © 1992 by Joel Schwartz, from *Funny You Should Ask* by David Gale, Editor. Used by permission of Dell Books, a division of Bantam Doubleday Dell Publishing Group, Inc.

"Founders of the Children's Rain Forest" from *It's Our World Too!* by Phillip Hoose. Copyright © 1993 by Phillip Hoose. By permission of Little, Brown and Company.

"Beni Seballos" from *It's Our World Too!* by Phillip Hoose. Copyright © 1993 by Phillip Hoose. By permission of Little, Brown and Company.

"The Fun They Had" by Isaac Asimov from *Earth Room is Enough* by Isaac Asimov. Copyright © 1957 by Isaac Asimov. Used by permission of Doubleday, a division of Bantam Doubleday Dell Publishing Group, Inc.

"Something to Watch" and "Our School" from *Children of the Dust Bowl* by Jerry Stanley. Copyright © 1992 by Jerry Stanley. Reprinted by permission of Crown Publishers, Inc.

"Knoxville, Tennessee" by Nikki Giovanni from *Ego Tripping and Other Poems for Young Readers*. Copyright © 1973 by Nikki Giovanni. By permission of the author.

"Those Who Don't" from *The House On Mango Street* by Sandra Cisneros. Copyright © 1989 by Sandra Cisneros. Published in the United States by Vintage Books, a division of Random House, Inc., New York, and distributed in Canada by Random House of Canada Limited, Toronto. Originally published by Arte Publico Press in somewhat different form in 1984 and revised in 1989. Reprinted by permission of Susan Bergholz Literary Services, New York.

"It's All In How You Say It" by Mickey Roberts, from *Talking Leaves*, edited by Craig Lesley, copyright © 1991 by Craig Lesley. By permission of Dell Publishing, a division of Bantam Doubleday Dell Publishing Group, Inc.

"The Forest Cries" by Ignatia Broker, reprinted from *Night Flying Woman: An Ojibway Narrative* by Ignatia Broker, copyright © 1983 by the Minnesota Historical Society.

"Block Party" by Jewell Parker Rhodes, copyright © 1993 by Jewell Parker Rhodes, is reprinted by permission of the author.

ILLUSTRATION

36-41 Peter Horjus.

PHOTOGRAPHY

4 *l* John Owens/©D.C. Heath; *r* Sarah Putnam/©D.C. Heath; 5 Michael Fogden/DRK Photo; 6 Julie Bidwell/©D.C. Heath; 8 *t* Bob Daemmrich/Stock Boston; *b* Elizabeth Zuckerman/PhotoEdit; 9 *t* Bob Daemmrich/Stock Boston; *b* Kolvoord/The Image Works; 10 *l* Sarah Putnam/©D.C. Heath; *r* Sandy Roessler/The Stock Market; 11 *t* Skjold/The Image Works; *c* Jim Whitmer/Stock Boston; *b* Mary Kate Denny/PhotoEdit; 12, 18 Carol Palmer/©D.C. Heath; 19 Photo by Caroline Soto; 20 Porter Gifford/Gamma Liaison; 24-25, 26-31 *border* Curtis Willocks/Brooklyn Image Group; 31 Courtesy of Crown Publishers, Inc.; 33 Shayna Brennan/AP; 41 Courtesy of Bantam Doubleday Dell; 42-43 Gary Braasch; 43 Courtesy of Bernd W. Kern/The Children's Rain Forest of Sweden; 44 Michael Fogden/Animals Animals/Earth Scenes; 44-53 *border* Gary Braasch; 47 John Cancalosi/DRK Photo; 48, 51 Michael Fogden/DRK Photo; 52 Courtesy of The Children's Rain Forest of Sweden; 53 Photo by Richard Connelly; 54 *tl, tr, b* Joel Gordon; 54 *inset, 55-61 background* H.D. Thoreau/Westlight; 60 Jennifer Appleton; 61 Photo by Richard Connelly; 62-63, 64-65 *background* Jook Leung Photography; 65 *inset* AP/Wide World Photos; 66-67 U.S. Department of Agriculture Soil Conservation Service/The Oklahoma Historical Society; 68, 69, 71, 72, 76 Courtesy of Jerry Stanley; 68-77 *background* U.S. Department of Agriculture Soil Conservation Service/The Oklahoma Historical Society; 77 *inset* Photo by Joe Bariffi/Courtesy of Random House, Inc.; 79 *t* Private Collection, New York. Courtesy Andre Emmerich Gallery; *b* Photo by Jill Oxendine; 80 Private Collection, Iturralde Gallery, Los Angeles, CA; 81 AP/Wide World Photos; 82-85 Courtesy of the Burke Museum, Seattle, WA; 86 Steinbaum Krauss Gallery, New York, NY; 87-95 *top border* National Anthropological Archives, Smithsonian Institution, Washington, D.C. 596-E-48; 95 *b* Staff photo by Darlene Pfister/*Star Tribune*, Minneapolis and St. Paul, MN; 96, 99 Museum of Art, The Carnegie Institute, Pittsburgh, PA. Gift of Mr. and Mrs. Ronald R. Davenport and Mr. and Mrs. Milton A. Washington. 84.63; 104 Nancy Sheehan/©D.C. Heath; 106 *t* Elizabeth Hamlin/Stock Boston; *b* Alan McClennen, Jr.; 110 Mark C. Flannery; 111 Jonathan Stoke/Rails-to-Trails; 112 Jean-Claude LeJeune/Stock Boston; 113 Masahiro Sano/The Stock Market; 114 *t* J. Sulley/The Image Works; *b* Bob Daemmrich/Stock Boston.
Back cover *t* Sarah Putnam/©D.C. Heath; *c* Julie Bidwell/©D.C. Heath; *b* Jim Whitmer/Stock Boston.

Full Pronunciation Key for Footnoted Words

(Each pronunciation and definition is adapted from *Scott, Foresman Advanced Dictionary* by E.L. Thorndike and Clarence L. Barnhart.)

The pronunciation of each footnoted word is shown just after the word, in this way: **abbreviate** [ə brē′ vē āt]. The letters and signs used are pronounced as in the words below. The mark ′ is placed after a syllable with primary or heavy accent, as in the example above. The mark ′ after a syllable shows a secondary or lighter accent, as in **abbreviation** [ə brē′ vē ā′ shən].

Some words, taken from foreign languages, are spoken with sounds that do not otherwise occur in English. Symbols for these sounds are given in the key as "foreign sounds."

a	hat, cap	j	jam, enjoy	u	cup, butter	**foreign sounds**
ā	age, face	k	kind, seek	u̇	full, put	
ä	father, far	l	land, coal	ü	rule, move	Y as in French *du*.
		m	me, am	v	very, save	Pronounce (ē) with
b	bad, rob	n	no, in	w	will, woman	the lips rounded as
ch	child, much	ng	long, bring	y	young, yet	for (ü).
d	did, red			z	zero, breeze	
		o	hot, rock	zh	measure, seizure	à as in French *ami*.
e	let, best	ō	open, go			Pronounce (ä) with
ē	equal, be	ô	order, all	ə represents:		the lips spread and
ėr	term, learn	oi	oil, voice		a in about	held tense.
		ou	house, out		e in taken	
f	fat, if				i in pencil	œ as in French *peu*.
g	go, bag	p	paper, cup		o in lemon	Pronounce (ā) with the
h	he, how	r	run, try		u in circus	lips rounded as for (ō).
		s	say, yes			
i	it, pin	sh	she, rush			N as in French *bon*.
ī	ice, five	t	tell, it			The N is not pro-
		th	thin, both			nounced, but shows
		ŦH	then, smooth			that the vowel before
						it is nasal.

H as in German *ach*. Pronounce (k) without closing the breath passage.

AMIGO ami rafiki drauge
vriendin freundin
freundin vän amica
ami achooní 友達 Φιλη
朋友 caraic
FRIENDS amie
przyjaciel amiga umngane
freund AMIGA друган
väninna ընկերուհի
vriend Φιλος draugas
amico amigo ami
vriend umngane amico
vriendin amie caraid drauge
amica przyjaciolka Φιλη
HEATH
MIDDLE LEVEL
LITERATURE
przyjaciel
draugas freund

HEATH
MIDDLE LEVEL
LITERATURE

Friends

▼ THEME ▼
FRIENDSHIP

AUTHORS

Donna Alvermann
Linda Miller Cleary
Kenneth Donelson
Donald Gallo
Alice Haskins
J. Howard Johnston
John Lounsbury
Alleen Pace Nilsen
Robert Pavlik
Jewell Parker Rhodes
Alberto Alvaro Ríos
Sandra Schurr
Lyndon Searfoss
Julia Thomason
Max Thompson
Carl Zon

D.C. Heath and Company
Lexington, Massachusetts / Toronto, Ontario

STAFF CREDITS

EDITORIAL	Barbara A. Brennan, Helen Byers, Christopher Johnson, Kathleen Kennedy Kelley, Owen Shows, Rita M. Sullivan
	Proofreading: JoAnne B. Sgroi
CONTRIBUTING WRITERS	Nance Davidson, Florence Harris
SERIES DESIGN	Robin Herr
BOOK DESIGN	Caroline Bowden, Daniel Derdula, Susan Geer, Diana Maloney, Angela Sciaraffa, Bonnie Chayes Yousefian
	Art Editing: Carolyn Langley
PHOTOGRAPHY	*Series Photography Coordinator:* Carmen Johnson
	Photo Research Supervisor: Martha Friedman
	Photo Researchers: Wendy Enright, Linda Finigan, Po-yee McKenna, PhotoSearch, Inc., Gillian Speeth, Denise Theodores
	Assignment Photography Coordinators: Susan Doheny, Gayna Hoffman, Shawna Johnston
COMPUTER PREPRESS	Ricki Pappo, Kathy Meisl, Richard Curran, Michele Locatelli
PERMISSIONS	Dorothy B. McLeod
PRODUCTION	Patrick Connolly

Cover Design: Steve Snider

International Standard Book Number: 0-669-32099-4 (soft cover)
3 4 5 6 7 8 9 10-RRD-99 98 97

International Standard Book Number: 0-669-38169-1 (hard cover)
3 4 5 6 7 8 9 10-RRD-99 98 97

Middle Level Authors

Donna Alvermann, University of Georgia
Alice Haskins, Howard County Public Schools, Maryland
J. Howard Johnston, University of South Florida
John Lounsbury, Georgia College
Sandra Schurr, University of South Florida
Julia Thomason, Appalachian State University
Max Thompson, Appalachian State University
Carl Zon, California Assessment Collaborative

Literature and Language Arts Authors

Linda Miller Cleary, University of Minnesota
Kenneth Donelson, Arizona State University
Donald Gallo, Central Connecticut State University
Alleen Pace Nilsen, Arizona State University
Robert Pavlik, Cardinal Stritch College, Milwaukee
Jewell Parker Rhodes, Arizona State University
Alberto Alvaro Ríos, Arizona State University
Lyndon Searfoss, Arizona State University

Teacher Consultants

Suzanne Aubin, Patapsco Middle School, Ellicott City, Maryland
Judy Baxter, Newport News Public Schools, Newport News, Virginia
Saundra Bryn, Director of Research and Development, El Mirage, Arizona
Lorraine Gerhart, Elmbrook Middle School, Elm Grove, Wisconsin
Kathy Tuchman Glass, Burlingame Intermediate School, Burlingame, California
Lisa Mandelbaum, Crocker Middle School, Hillsborough, California
Lucretia Pannozzo, John Jay Middle School, Katonah, New York
Carol Schultz, Jerling Junior High, Orland Park, Illinois
Jeanne Siebenman, Grand Canyon University, Phoenix, Arizona
Gail Thompson, Garey High School, Pomona, California
Rufus Thompson, Grace Yokley School, Ontario, California
Tom Tufts, Conniston Middle School, West Palm Beach, Florida
Edna Turner, Harpers Choice Middle School, Columbia, Maryland
C. Anne Webb, Buerkle Junior High School, St. Louis, Missouri
Geri Yaccino, Thompson Junior High School, St. Charles, Illinois

CONTENTS

Midtown Sunset Romare Bearden, Private collection

ASKING BIG QUESTIONS ABOUT THE LITERATURE

INVENT-A-FRIE

Develop 1 your theory.

Scientists begin their experiments with a theory or unproven idea. First, they decide what the task is; then they think of ways to accomplish it. Think about what your perfect or ideal friend would be like. What character traits are important to you—appearance, age, special abilities? On a sheet of paper, develop your theory by brainstorming a list of character traits to complete this sentence: An ideal friend is someone who _____.

Collect 2 and evaluate your data.

Because they know that not all data is useful, scientists try to weed out details that weaken their theories. Once you've brainstormed a list of character traits, evaluate them and decide which ones you want to keep. To help you select the most important traits, discuss situations in which a special personality trait or physical characteristic would be a positive feature to have. For example, if you are shy, a friend who is outgoing may make social events less awkward for you.

hink of it! You're a scientist puttering in your laboratory—but your laboratory is a writing laboratory. It's your task to invent an ideal friend by using a mixture of words. What words will you choose, and how will you combine them? To test your ideas about friendship, complete the following steps individually, in a small group, or with your whole class.

Organize 3 your data.

Scientists have to present their data well to get others to understand and support them. To organize your data, create a chart or poster. Write your theory at the top. Under the theory, write the traits you've selected from your list. Be sure you can provide specific examples and reasons to support your choices.

Test your 4 conclusions.

If scientists didn't evaluate their results, they'd have no idea if their theories would work. Test your conclusions by comparing and contrasting the character traits of your ideal friend with the ones selected by other students. What are the similarities and differences? What new perspective did you get on the ideal friend?

Asking Big Questions About the Theme

What does it mean to be a friend?

In your journal, write a recipe for how to be a friend. List the ingredients and their measurements first, followed by instructions for combining them. Then compare your recipe with those of your classmates.

What does it mean to have a friend?

In your journal, create a web like the one started here. At the center of the web, write the name of someone, either real or imaginary, that you think would be a good friend. Then fill in the web with nouns, verbs, adjectives, and adverbs describing the friend's importance in your life. Share the web with a partner.

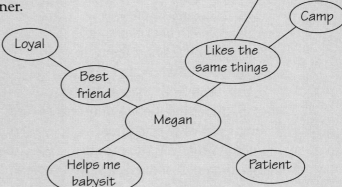

Horses — Camp — Likes the same things — Megan — Patient

Loyal — Best friend — Megan — Helps me babysit

What are different kinds of friendship?

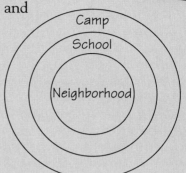

In your journal, draw several concentric circles like the ones shown and label them with the places you spend time, such as neighborhood, school, and camp. Then write the names of friends within the appropriate circles. Some friends' names may appear in more than one circle. Discuss with a partner the similarities and differences among these friendships.

Camp
School
Neighborhood

How can friendships change?

What events in your life have caused changes in your friendships? In your journal, create a time line like the one shown to trace the progress of your friendships. Divide the line into the different periods of your life and place important events in their appropriate position. Share your time line with several classmates and explain why these particular events are important to you.

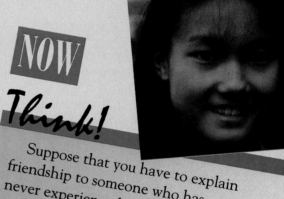

NOW Think!

Suppose that you have to explain friendship to someone who has never experienced it. With a partner, brainstorm ways to explain it and record your ideas in your journal. Then, as you read the literature in this unit, compare your ideas about friendship with the types of friendships experienced by the characters in the selections. Does your explanation of friendship change?

Billy and I go to camp.	Join Little League	Best friends with Kyle	Started junior high
8 yrs. old	10 yrs. old	11 yrs. old	12 yrs. old

THE BRACELET

Evacuee Family and Baggage   Minè Okubo, 1943, gouache on paper, 15^1/$_2$″ x 19^1/$_2$″

Yoshiko Uchida

"*Mama*, is it time to go?"

I hadn't planned to cry, but the tears came suddenly, and I wiped them away with the back of my hand. I didn't want my older sister to see me crying.

"It's almost time, Ruri," my mother said gently. Her face was filled with a kind of sadness I had never seen before.

I looked around at my empty room. The clothes that Mama always told me to hang up in the closet, the junk piled on my dresser, the old rag doll I could never bear to part with; they were all gone. There was nothing left in my room, and there was nothing left in the rest of the house. The rugs and furniture were gone, the pictures and drapes were down, and the closets and cupboards were empty. The house was like a gift box after the nice thing inside was gone; just a lot of nothingness.

It was almost time to leave our home, but we weren't moving to a nicer house or to a new town. It was April 21, 1942. The United States and Japan were at war, and every Japanese person on the West Coast was being evacuated[1] by the government to a concentration camp.[2] Mama, my sister Keiko[3] and I were being sent from our home, and out of Berkeley, and eventually, out of California.

The doorbell rang, and I ran to answer it before my sister could. I thought maybe by some miracle, a messenger from the government might be standing there, tall and proper and buttoned into a uniform, come to tell us it was all a terrible mistake; that we wouldn't have to leave after all. Or maybe the messenger would have a telegram from Papa, who was interned in a prisoner-of-war camp in Montana because he had worked for a Japanese business firm.

1. **evacuated** [i vak′ yü āt əd]: forced to leave.
2. **concentration camp** [kon′ sən trā′ shən]: in this case, a relocation camp; one of several inland detention camps established by the United States government during World War II for all Japanese Americans living on the West Coast.
3. **Keiko** [kā′ kō]

The FBI had come to pick up Papa and hundreds of other Japanese community leaders on the very day that Japanese planes had bombed Pearl Harbor.[4] The government thought they were dangerous enemy aliens.[5] If it weren't so sad, it would have been funny. Papa could no more be dangerous than the mayor of our city, and he was every bit as loyal to the United States. He had lived here since 1917.

When I opened the door, it wasn't a messenger from anywhere. It was my best friend, Laurie Madison, from next door. She was holding a package wrapped up like a birthday present, but she wasn't wearing her party dress, and her face drooped like a wilted tulip.

"Hi," she said. "I came to say goodbye."

She thrust the present at me and told me it was something to take to camp. "It's a bracelet," she said before I could open the package. "Put it on so you won't have to pack it." She knew I didn't have one inch of space left in my suitcase. We had been instructed to take only what we could carry into camp, and Mama had told us that we could each take only two suitcases.

"Then how are we ever going to pack the dishes and blankets and sheets they've told us to bring with us?" Keiko worried.

"I don't really know," Mama said, and she simply began packing those big impossible things into an enormous duffel bag—along with umbrellas, boots, a kettle, hot plate, and flashlight.

"Who's going to carry that huge sack?" I asked.

But Mama didn't worry about things like that. "Someone will help us," she said. "Don't worry." So I didn't.

Laurie wanted me to open her package and put on the bracelet before she left. It was a thin gold chain with a heart dangling on it. She helped me put it on, and I told her I'd never take it off, ever.

"Well, good-bye then," Laurie said awkwardly. "Come home soon."

"I will," I said, although I didn't know if I would ever get back to Berkeley again.

4. **Pearl Harbor:** United States naval base in Hawaii, which Japan attacked on December 7, 1941, bringing the United States into World War II.
5. **aliens** [āʹ lē ənz]: people who are not citizens of the country in which they live.

I watched Laurie go down the block, her long blond pigtails bouncing as she walked. I wondered who would be sitting in my desk at Lincoln Junior High now that I was gone. Laurie kept turning and waving, even walking backwards for a while, until she got to the corner. I didn't want to watch anymore, and I slammed the door shut.

The next time the doorbell rang, it was Mrs. Simpson, our other neighbor. She was going to drive us to the Congregational church, which was the Civil Control Station where all the Japanese of Berkeley were supposed to report.

It was time to go. "Come on, Ruri. Get your things," my sister called to me.

It was a warm day, but I put on a sweater and my coat so I wouldn't have to carry them, and I picked up my two suitcases. Each

Drawing by detention camp internee Minè Okubo

one had a tag with my name and our family number on it. Every Japanese family had to register and get a number. We were Family Number 13453.

Mama was taking one last look around our house. She was going from room to room, as though she were trying to take a mental picture of the house she had lived in for fifteen years, so she would never forget it.

I saw her take a long last look at the garden that Papa loved. The irises beside the fish pond were just beginning to bloom. If Papa had been home, he would have cut the first iris blossom and brought it inside to Mama. "This one is for you," he would have said. And Mama would have smiled and said, "Thank you, Papa San,"[6] and put it in her favorite cut-glass vase.

But the garden looked shabby and forsaken now that Papa was gone and Mama was too busy to take care of it. It looked the way I felt, sort of empty and lonely and abandoned.

Drawing by detention camp internee Minè Okubo

When Mrs. Simpson took us to the Civil Control Station, I felt even worse. I was scared, and for a minute I thought I was going to lose my breakfast right in front of everybody. There must have been over a thousand Japanese people gathered at the church. Some were old and some were young. Some were talking and laughing, and some were crying. I guess everybody else was scared too. No one knew exactly what was going to happen to us. We just knew we were being taken to the Tanforan Racetracks, which the army had turned into a camp for the Japanese. There were fourteen other camps like ours along the West Coast.

What scared me most were the soldiers standing at the doorway of the church hall. They were carrying guns with mounted bayonets. I wondered if they thought we would try to run away, and whether they'd shoot us or come after us with their bayonets if we did.

6. **San** [sän]: term of respect added to Japanese names.

A long line of buses waited to take us to camp. There were trucks, too, for our baggage. And Mama was right; some men were there to help us load our duffel bag. When it was time to board the buses, I sat with Keiko and Mama sat behind us. The bus went down Grove Street and passed the small Japanese food store where Mama used to order her bean-curd cakes and pickled radish. The windows were all boarded up, but there was a sign still hanging on the door that read, "We are loyal Americans."

The crazy thing about the whole evacuation was that we were all loyal Americans. Most of us were citizens because we had been born here. But our parents, who had come from Japan, couldn't become citizens because there was a law that prevented any Asian from becoming a citizen. Now everybody with a Japanese face was being shipped off to concentration camps.

"It's stupid," Keiko muttered as we saw the racetrack looming up beside the highway. "If there were any Japanese spies around, they'd have gone back to Japan long ago."

Drawing by detention camp internee Minè Okubo

"I'll say," I agreed. My sister was in high school and she ought to know, I thought.

When the bus turned into Tanforan, there were more armed guards at the gate, and I saw barbed wire strung around the entire grounds. I felt as though I were going into a prison, but I hadn't done anything wrong.

We streamed off the buses and poured into a huge room, where doctors looked down our throats and peeled back our eyelids to see if we had any diseases. Then we were given our housing assignments. The man in charge gave Mama a slip of paper. We were in Barrack[7] 16, Apartment 40.

"Mama!" I said. "We're going to live in an apartment!" The only apartment I had ever seen was the one my piano teacher lived in. It was in an enormous building in San Francisco with an elevator and thick carpeted hallways. I thought how wonderful it would be to have our own elevator. A house was all right, but an apartment seemed elegant and special.

We walked down the racetrack looking for Barrack 16. Mr. Noma, a friend of Papa's, helped us carry our bags. I was so busy looking around, I slipped and almost fell on the muddy track. Army barracks had been built everywhere, all around the racetrack and even in the center oval.

Mr. Noma pointed beyond the track toward the horse stables. "I think your barrack is out there."

He was right. We came to a long stable that had once housed the horses of Tanforan, and we climbed up the wide ramp. Each stall had a number painted on it, and when we got to 40, Mr. Noma pushed open the door.

"Well, here it is," he said. "Apartment 40."

The stall was narrow and empty and dark. There were two small windows on each side of the door. Three folded army cots were on the dust-covered floor and one light bulb dangled from the ceiling. That was all. This was our apartment, and it still smelled of horses.

Mama looked at my sister and then at me. "It won't be so bad when we fix it up," she began. "I'll ask Mr. Simpson to send me some material for curtains. I could make some cushions too, and . . . well . . . ." She stopped. She couldn't think of anything more to say.

Mr. Noma said he'd go get some mattresses for us. "I'd better hurry before they're all gone." He rushed off. I think he wanted to leave so that he wouldn't have to see Mama cry. But he needn't have

7. **barrack** [bar′ək]: a large building in which soldiers usually live.

run off, because Mama didn't cry. She just went out to borrow a broom and began sweeping out the dust and dirt. "Will you girls set up the cots?" she asked.

It was only after we'd put up the last cot that I noticed my bracelet was gone. "I've lost Laurie's bracelet!" I screamed. "My bracelet's gone!"

We looked all over the stall and even down the ramp. I wanted to run back down the track and go over every inch of ground we'd walked on, but it was getting dark and Mama wouldn't let me.

I thought of what I'd promised Laurie. I wasn't ever going to take the bracelet off, not even when I went to take a shower. And now I had lost it on my very first day in camp. I wanted to cry.

I kept looking for it all the time we were in Tanforan. I didn't stop looking until the day we were sent to another camp, called Topaz, in the middle of a desert in Utah. And then I gave up.

But Mama told me never mind. She said I didn't need a bracelet to remember Laurie, just as I didn't need anything to remember Papa or our home in Berkeley or all the people and things we loved and had left behind.

"Those are things we can carry in our hearts and take with us no matter where we are sent," she said.

And I guess she was right. I've never forgotten Laurie, even now.

YOSHIKO UCHIDA

Yoshiko Uchida [1921-1992] was born in Alameda, California. The Uchida family members' lives changed terribly during World War II, when the government interned all Japanese Americans in concentration camps. Suddenly the Uchidas became Family Number 13453 and were taken first to one and then to another prison camp. The camps were so crowded, Uchida said, that people had "no place to cry and no place to hide."

Uchida said the story of the Japanese American internments, "as painful as it may be to hear, needs to be told and retold and never forgotten." You can read more about her family's experience in her books *Journey to Topaz* and *Journey Home*.

A bald display of solidarity

ASSOCIATED PRESS

YORKVILLE, Ill.—Treatment for leukemia[1] soon may cost Mark Lowry his hair, but his bald head won't stand out in the classrooms at Cross Lutheran School.

When the school's 15 other seventh- and eighth-grade boys learned that Mark, 13, would undergo the chemotherapy,[2] they decided to have their own heads shaved in a show of support.

By Thursday, only two of the 16 weren't bald. One, Robert Erickson, was waiting for the weekend for his clipping. The other was Mark, who came home Wednesday from the hospital with a full head of hair.

"It probably won't be for long though," he said. "And my dad might cut my hair so I look like the rest of the guys."

Mark, an eighth-grader, learned only recently that he had leukemia, and started chemotherapy treatments last week.

How long do the boys plan to go hairless?

"Until Mark grows his hair back," was the unanimous[3] response.

1. **leukemia** [lü kē′ mē ə]: cancer in which there are too many white cells in the blood.
2. **chemotherapy** [kē′ mō ther′ ə pē]: treatment of a disease with chemicals that destroy the organisms of the disease.
3. **unanimous** [yü nan′ ə məs]: in complete agreement.

OUR GOOD DAY

SANDRA CISNEROS

If you give me five dollars I will be your friend forever. That's what the little one tells me.

Five dollars is cheap since I don't have any friends except Cathy who is only my friend till Tuesday.

Five dollars, five dollars.

She is trying to get somebody to chip in so they can buy a bicycle from this kid named Tito. They already have ten dollars and all they need is five more.

Electric Prisms Sonia Delaunay, 1914, National Museum of Modern Art, Paris, France

Only five dollars, she says.

Don't talk to them, says Cathy. Can't you see they smell like a broom.

But I like them. Their clothes are crooked and old. They are wearing shiny Sunday shoes without socks. It makes their bald ankles all red, but I like them. Especially the big one who laughs with all her teeth. I like her even though she lets the little one do all the talking.

Five dollars, the little one says, only five.

Cathy is tugging my arm and I know whatever I do next will make her mad forever.

Wait a minute, I say, and run inside to get the five dollars. I have three dollars saved and I take two of Nenny's. She's not home, but I'm sure she'll be glad when she finds out we won a bike. When I get back, Cathy is gone like I knew she would be, but I don't care. I have two new friends and a bike too.

My name is Lucy, the big one says. This here is Rachel my sister.

I'm her sister, says Rachel. Who are you?

And I wish my name was Cassandra or Alexis or Maritza—anything but Esperanza—but when I tell them my name they don't laugh.

We come from Texas, Lucy says and grins. Her was born here, but me I'm Texas.

You mean *she*, I say.

No, I'm from Texas, and doesn't get it.

This bike is three ways ours, says Rachel who is thinking ahead already. Mine today, Lucy's tomorrow and yours day after.

But everybody wants to ride it today because the bike is new, so we decide to take turns *after* tomorrow. Today it belongs to all of us.

I don't tell them about Nenny just yet. It's too complicated. Especially since Rachel almost put out Lucy's eye about who was going to get to ride it first. But finally we agree to ride it together. Why not?

Because Lucy has long legs she pedals. I sit on the back seat and Rachel is skinny enough to get up on the handlebars which makes the bike all wobbly as if the wheels are spaghetti, but after a bit you get used to it.

We ride fast and faster. Past my house, sad and red and crumbly in places, past Mr. Benny's grocery on the corner, and down the avenue which is dangerous. Laundromat, junk store, drug store, windows and cars and more cars, and around the block back to Mango.

People on the bus wave. A very fat lady crossing the street says, You sure got quite a load there.

Rachel shouts, You got quite a load there too. She is very sassy.

Down, down Mango Street we go. Rachel, Lucy, me. Our new bicycle. Laughing the crooked ride back.

SANDRA CISNEROS

Sandra Cisneros was born in Chicago in 1954 and grew up there, in a neighborhood like the one in "Our Good Day." Later she moved to San Antonio, Texas. When she isn't teaching, she writes what she calls the "kind of stories I didn't get growing up. Stories about poor families, brown families. People I knew and loved, but never saw in the pages of the books I borrowed from the Chicago Public Library."

Cisneros writes both prose and poetry. She says, "Fiction is a way to change the community, right wrongs, wail about grievances, fight back, push, shove, shake, terrorize. Poems are more like howls of the heart." "Our Good Day" is from her book of short stories, *The House on Mango Street*.

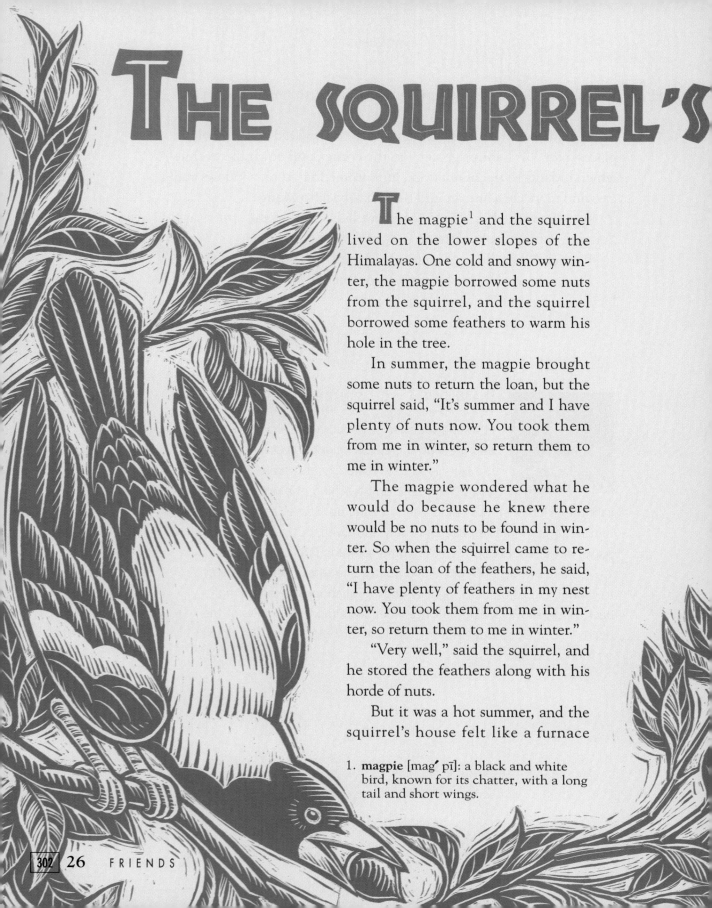

THE SQUIRREL'S

The magpie[1] and the squirrel lived on the lower slopes of the Himalayas. One cold and snowy winter, the magpie borrowed some nuts from the squirrel, and the squirrel borrowed some feathers to warm his hole in the tree.

In summer, the magpie brought some nuts to return the loan, but the squirrel said, "It's summer and I have plenty of nuts now. You took them from me in winter, so return them to me in winter."

The magpie wondered what he would do because he knew there would be no nuts to be found in winter. So when the squirrel came to return the loan of the feathers, he said, "I have plenty of feathers in my nest now. You took them from me in winter, so return them to me in winter."

"Very well," said the squirrel, and he stored the feathers along with his horde of nuts.

But it was a hot summer, and the squirrel's house felt like a furnace

1. **magpie** [mag′ pī]: a black and white bird, known for its chatter, with a long tail and short wings.

LOAN

Partap Sharma

with all those feathers in it. So he threw the feathers out, thinking he'd pick them up when winter came around and it was time to return the loan.

In winter, there was ice and snow everywhere. The feathers were buried underneath. Try as he might, the squirrel could not dig them out.

He said to the magpie, "I'm afraid I can't find feathers in winter."

"Nor can I find nuts at this time," said the magpie.

And the squirrel remembered his loan and his words to the magpie, and he was ashamed. He said, "I should expect you to return the nuts when you can, not when you cannot. A loan is meant to help a friend, not to give him trouble."

From then on they helped each other in winter and repaid their debts in summer. They continued to live happily and became even better friends thereafter.

Ring, Ring Roy Lichtenstein, 1961, oil on canvas, 24" x 16"

TELEPHONE TALK

X. J. KENNEDY

Back flat on the carpet,
Cushion under my head,
Sock feet on the wallpaper,
Munching raisin bread,

Making easy whispers   5
Balance on high wire,
Trading jokes and laughing,
The two of us conspire, [1]

Closer than when walking
Down the street together,   10
Closer than two sparrows
Hiding from wet weather.

How would my shrill whistle
Sound to you, I wonder?
Give a blow in *your* phone,   15
My phone makes it thunder.

Through the night, invisibly
Jumping over space,
Back and forth between us
All our secrets race.   20

1. **conspire** [kən spīrʹ]: plan secretly
   together.

X. J. KENNEDY
....

    X. J. Kennedy was born in 1929 in Dover, New
Jersey. After graduating from Seton Hall University and
serving in the Navy during the Korean War, he became
an English professor and writer of textbooks. Later he
began to write poetry and prose for both adults and young people.

    Kennedy enjoys writing poems that make use of traditional patterns
of rhyme and meter. He thinks composing this kind of poetry can be both
challenging and fun, "an enormous, meaningful game" that includes
interesting discoveries for the poet.

    Besides *The Kite That Braved Old Orchard Beach*, you can look up
collections of Kennedy's humorous verse for young people, including
The Phantom Ice Cream Man, *The Forgetful Wishing Well*, and *Brats*.

A Time To Talk

ROBERT FROST

When a friend calls to me from the road
And slows his horse to a meaning[1] walk,
I don't stand still and look around
On all the hills I haven't hoed,
And shout from where I am, "What is it?"   5
No, not as there is a time to talk.
I thrust my hoe in the mellow ground,
Blade-end up and five feet tall,
And plod:[2] I go up to the stone wall
For a friendly visit.   10

1. meaning: expressive, significant.
2. plod: walk heavily or slowly.

ROBERT FROST

Robert Frost [1874-1963] was born in San Francisco but later moved to Lawrence, Massachusetts. After high school he worked as a bobbin boy in a textiles mill, a cobbler, a newspaper editor, a teacher, and a farmer—but always dreamed of making poetry his career.

Frost moved to England in 1912, where he published two books of poems about rural New England. In 1915, he returned to America and became known as New England's poet and one of the great American poets. You can find Frost's poems in many collections, including *You Come Too: Favorite Poems for Young Readers*.

Wood engraving
Thomas W. Nason,
Boston Public Library
Print Department

The Osage Orange

WILLIAM STAFFORD

On that first day of high school in the prairie town where the tree was, I stood in the sun by the flagpole and watched, but pretended not to watch, the others. They stood in groups and talked and knew each other, all except one—a girl though—in a faded blue dress, carrying a sack lunch and standing near the corner looking everywhere but at the crowd.

I might talk to her, I thought. But of course it was out of the question.

That first day was easier when the classes started. Some of the teachers were kind; some were frightening. Some of the students didn't care, but I listened and waited; and at the end of the day I was relieved, less conspicuous from then on.

But that day was not really over. As I hurried to carry my new paper route, I was thinking about how in a strange town, if you are quiet, no one notices, and some may like you, later. I was thinking about this when I reached the north edge of town where the scattering houses dwindle. Beyond them to the north lay just openness, the plains, a big swoop of nothing. There, at the last house, just as I cut across a lot and threw to the last customer, I saw the girl in the blue dress coming along the street, heading on out of town, carrying books. And she saw me.

"Hello."

"Hello."

And because we stopped we were friends. I didn't know how I could stop, but I didn't hurry on. There was nothing to do but to act

as if I were walking on out too. I had three papers left in the bag, and I frantically began to fold them—box them, as we called it—for throwing. We had begun to walk and talk. The girl was timid; I became more bold. Not much, but a little.

"Have you gone to school here before?" I asked.

"Yes, I went here last year."

A long pause. A meadowlark sitting on a fencepost hunched his wings and flew. I kicked through the dust of the road.

I began to look ahead. Where could we possibly be walking to? I couldn't be walking just because I wanted to be with her.

Fortunately, there was one more house, a gray house by a sagging barn, set two hundred yards from the road.

"I thought I'd see if I could get a customer here," I said, waving toward the house.

"That's where I live."

"Oh."

We were at the dusty car tracks that turned off the road to the house. The girl stopped. There was a tree at that corner, a straight but little tree with slim branches and shiny dark leaves.

"I could take a paper tonight to see if my father wants to buy it."

A great relief, this. What could I have said to her parents? I held out a paper, dropped it, picked it up, brushing off the dust. "No, here's a new one"—a great action, putting the dusty paper in the bag over my shoulder and pulling out a fresh one. When she took the paper we stood there a minute. The wind was coming in over the grass. She looked out with a tranquil[1] expression.

She walked away past the tree, and I hurried quickly back toward town. Could anyone in the houses have been watching? I looked back once. The girl was standing on the small bridge halfway into her house. I hurried on.

The next day at school I didn't ask her whether her father wanted to take the paper. When the others were there I wouldn't say anything. I stood with the boys. In American history the students could choose their seats, and I saw that she was too quiet and plainly dressed for many to notice her. But I crowded in with the boys, pushing one aside, scrambling for a seat by the window.

That night I came to the edge of town. Two papers were left, and I walked on out. The meadowlark was there. By some reeds in a ditch by the road a dragonfly—snake feeders, we called them—glinted. The sun was going down, and the plains were stretched out and lifted, some way, to the horizon. Could I go on up to the house? I didn't think so, but I walked on. Then, by the tree where her road turned off, she was standing. She was holding her books. More confused than ever, I stopped.

"My father will take the paper," she said.

She told me always to leave the paper at the foot of the tree. She insisted on that, saying their house was too far; and it is true that I was far off my route, a long way, a half-mile out of my territory. But I didn't think of that.

And so we were acquainted. What I remember best in that town is those evening walks to the tree. Every night—or almost every night—the girl was there. Evangeline was her name. We didn't say much. On Friday night of the first week she gave me a dime, the cost

---

1. **tranquil** [trang′ kwəl]: calm, peaceful.

of the paper. It was a poor newspaper, by the way, cheap, sensational,[2] unreliable. I never went up to her house. We never talked together at school. But all the time we knew each other; we just happened to meet. Every evening.

There was a low place in the meadow by that corner. The fall rains made a pond there, and in the evenings sometimes ducks would be coming in—a long line with set wings down the wind, and then a turn, and a skimming glide to the water. The wind would be blowing and the grass bent down. The evenings got colder and colder. The wind was cold. As winter came on the time at the tree was dimmer, but not dark. In the winter there was snow. The pond was frozen over; all the plains were white. I had to walk down the ruts of the road and leave the paper in the crotch of the tree, sometimes, when it was cold. The wind made a sound through the black branches. But usually, even on cold evenings, Evangeline was there.

At school we played ball at noon—the boys did. And I got acquainted. I learned that Evangeline's brother was janitor at the school. A big dark boy he was—a man, middle-aged I thought at the time. He didn't ever let on that he knew me. I would see him sweeping the halls, bent down, slow. I would see him and Evangeline take their sack lunches over to the south side of the building. Once I slipped away from the ball game and went over there, but he looked at me so steadily, without moving, that I pretended to be looking for a book, and quickly went back, and got in the game and struck out.

You don't know about those winters, and especially that winter. Those were the dust years.[3] Wheat was away down in price. Everyone was poor—poor in a way that you can't understand. I made two dollars a week, or something like that, on my paper route. I could tell about working for ten cents an hour—and then not getting paid; about families that ate wheat, boiled, for their main food, and burned wheat for fuel. You don't know how it would be. All through that

2. **sensational** [sen sā′ shə nəl]: trying to arouse strong feelings.
3. **dust years:** the Great Depression in the 1930s, when the American Midwest and Southwest suffered droughts and destructive dust storms.

hard winter I carried a paper to the tree by the pond, in the evening, and gave it to Evangeline.

In the cold weather Evangeline wore a heavier dress, a dark, straight, heavy dress, under a thick black coat. Outdoors she wore a knitted cap that fastened under her chin. She was dressed this way when we met and she took the paper. The reeds were broken now. The meadowlark was gone.

And then came the spring. I have forgotten to tell just how Evangeline looked. She was of medium height, and slim. Her face was pale, her forehead high, her eyes blue. Her tranquil face I remember well. I remember her watching the wind come in over the grass. Her dress was long, her feet small. I can remember her by the tree, with her books, or walking on up the road toward her house and stopping on the bridge halfway up there, but she didn't wave, and I couldn't tell whether she was watching me or not. I always looked back as I went over the rise toward town.

And I can remember her in the room at school. She came into American history one spring day, the first really warm day. She had changed from the dark heavy dress to the dull blue one of the last fall; and she had on a new belt, a gray belt, with blue stitching along the edges. As she passed in front of Jane Wright, a girl who sat on the front row, I heard Jane say to the girl beside her, "Why look at Evangeline—that old dress of hers has a new belt!"

"Stop a minute, Evangeline," Jane said; "let me see your new dress."

Evangeline stopped and looked uncertainly at Jane and blushed. "It's just made over," she said, "it's just . . . "

"It's cute, Dear," Jane said; and as Evangeline went on Jane nudged her friend in the ribs and the friend smothered a giggle.

Well, that was a good year. Commencement[4] time came, and—along with the newspaper job—I had the task of preparing for finals and all. One thing, I wasn't a student who took part in the class play or anything like that. I was just one of the boys—twenty-fourth in line to get my diploma.

---

4. **commencement** [kə mens′ ment]: graduation.

And graduation was bringing an end to my paper-carrying. My father covered a big territory in our part of the state, selling farm equipment; and we were going to move at once to a town seventy miles south. Only because of my finishing the school year had we stayed till graduation.

I had taught another boy my route, always leaving him at the end and walking on out, by myself, to the tree. I didn't really have to go around with him that last day, the day of graduation, but I was going anyway.

At the graduation exercises, held that May afternoon, I wore my brown Sunday suit. My mother was in the audience. It was a heavy day. The girls had on new dresses. But I didn't see her.

I suppose that I did deserve old man Sutton's "Shhh!" as we lined up to march across the stage, but I for the first time in the year forgot my caution, and asked Jane where Evangeline was. She shrugged, and I could see for myself that she was not there.

We marched across the stage; our diplomas were ours; our parents filed out; to the strains of a march on the school organ we trailed to the hall. I unbuttoned my brown suit coat, stuffed the diploma in my pocket, and sidled out of the group and upstairs.

Evangeline's brother was emptying wastebaskets at the far end of the hall. I sauntered toward him and stopped. I didn't know what I wanted to say. Unexpectedly, he solved my problem. Stopping his work, holding a partly empty wastebasket over the canvas sack he wore over his shoulder, he stared at me, as if almost to say something.

"I noticed that your sister wasn't here," I said. The noise below was dwindling. The hall was quiet, an echoey place; my voice sounded terribly loud. He emptied the rest of the wastebasket and shifted easily. He was a man, in big overalls. He stared at me.

"Evangeline couldn't come," he said. He stopped, looked at me again, and said, "She stole."

"Stole?" I said. "Stole what?"

He shrugged and went toward the next wastebasket, but I followed him.

"She stole the money from her bank—the money she was to use

for her graduation dress," he said. He walked stolidly[5] on, and I stopped. He deliberately turned away as he picked up the next wastebasket. But he said something else, half to himself. "You knew her. You talked to her . . . I know." He walked away.

I hurried downstairs and outside. The new carrier would have the papers almost delivered by now; so I ran up the street toward the north. I took a paper from him at the end of the street and told him to go back. I didn't pay any more attention to him.

No one was at the tree, and I turned, for the first time, up the road to the house. I walked over the bridge and on up the narrow, rutty tracks. The house was gray and lopsided.[6] The ground of the yard was packed; nothing grew there. By the back door, the door to which the road led, there was a grayish-white place on the ground where the dishwater had been thrown. A gaunt shepherd dog trotted out growling.

And the door opened suddenly, as if someone had been watching me come up the track. A woman came out—a woman stern-faced, with a shawl over her head and a dark lumpy dress on—came out on the back porch and shouted, "Go 'way, go 'way! We don't want no papers!" She waved violently with one hand, holding the other on her shawl, at her throat. She coughed so hard that she leaned over and put her hand against one of the uprights of the porch. Her face was red. She glanced toward the barn and leaned toward me. "Go 'way!"

Behind me a meadowlark sang. Over all the plains swooped the sky. The land was drawn up somehow toward the horizon.

I stood there, half-defiant, half-ashamed. The dog continued to growl and to pace around me, stiff-legged, his tail down. The windows of the house were all blank, with blinds drawn. I couldn't say anything.

I stood a long time and then, lowering the newspaper I had held out, I stood longer, waiting, without thinking of what to do. The

5. **stolidly** [stol′ id lē]: showing no emotion.
6. **lopsided** [lop′ sī′ did]: leaning to one side.

meadowlark bubbled over again, but I turned and walked away, looking back once or twice. The old woman continued to stand, leaning forward, her head out. She glanced at the barn, but didn't call out any more.

My heels dug into the grayish place where the dishwater had been thrown; the dog skulked along behind.

At the bridge, halfway to the road, I stopped and looked back. The dog was lying down again; the porch was empty; and the door was closed. Turning the other way, I looked toward town. Near me stood our ragged little tree—an Osage orange tree it was. It was feebly coming into leaf, green all over the branches, among the sharp thorns. I hadn't wondered before how it grew there, all alone, in the plains country, neglected. Over our pond some ducks came slicing in.

Standing there on the bridge, still holding the folded-boxed-newspaper, that worthless paper, I could see everything. I looked out along the road to town. From the bridge you would see the road going away, to where it went over the rise.

Glancing around, I flipped that last newpaper under the bridge and then bent far over and looked where it had gone. There they were—a pile of boxed newspapers, thrown in a heap, some new, some worn and weathered, by rain, by snow.

WILLIAM STAFFORD

William Stafford [1914–1993] was born in Kansas and raised on a farm there. Stafford's college career was interrupted during World War II when he served as as a conscientious objector in civilian public service camps and relief organizations.

Stafford has taught at colleges in the Midwest and in Oregon. His fame as a writer comes from his poetry, although he is well known for stories such as "The Osage Orange Tree."

One poem of Stafford's that is especially well known is "Fifteen." You can find it in his book *The Rescued Year*. Other Stafford books include *West of Your City* and *Traveling Through the Dark*.

Where Are You Now, William Shakespeare?

My very first boyfriend was named William Shakespeare. This was his real name, and he lived over on Highland Hill, about a block from my house.

Billy Shakespeare didn't call at seven for dates, or suffer my father's inspection, or give me a silver identification bracelet. We didn't have a song, either.

I often went to his house to get him, or I met him down in the empty lot on Alden Avenue, or over at Hoopes Park, where we caught sunfish and brought them from the pond in bottles of murky water with polliwogs.

Marijane is ten [my father wrote in his journal]. *She plays with boys and looks like one.*

This was true.

My arms and knees were full of scabs from falls out of trees and off my bicycle. I was happiest wearing the pants my brother'd grown out of, the vest to one of my father's business suits over one of my brother's old shirts, Indian moccasins, and a cap. Everything I said came out of the side of my mouth, and I strolled around with my fists inside my trouser pockets.

you peare?

M. E. KERR

This did not faze Billy Shakespeare, whose eyes lit up when he saw me coming, and who readily agreed that when we married we'd name our first son Ellis, after my father, and not William after him.

"Because William Shakespeare is a funny name," I'd say.

"It isn't funny. It's just that there's a famous writer with the same name," he'd say.

"Do you agree to Ellis Shakespeare then?"

"Sure, if it's all right with your father."

"He'll be pleased," I'd tell Billy.

Around this time, I was always trying to think of ways to please my father. (The simplest way would have been to wear a dress and a big hair ribbon, stay out of trees, stop talking out of the side of my mouth, and act like a girl . . . but I couldn't have endured such misery even for him.)

Billy Shakespeare accepted the fact, early in our relationship, that my father was my hero. He protested only slightly when I insisted that the reason my father wasn't President of the United States was that my father didn't want to be.

That was what my father told me, when I'd ask him why he wasn't President. I'd look at him across the table at dinner, and think, He knows more than anybody knows, he's handsome, and he always gets things done—so he ought to be President. If he was, I'd think, there'd be no problems in the world.

Sometimes I'd ask him: "Daddy, why aren't you President of the United States?"

His answer was always the same.

"I wouldn't want that job for anything. We couldn't take a walk without Secret Service[1] men following us. Do you think we could go up to the lake for a swim by ourselves? No. There'd be Secret Service men tagging along. It'd ruin our lives. It'd end our privacy. Would you want that?"

Billy Shakespeare would say, "He's not President because nobody elected him President."

"He won't let anyone elect him," I'd answer. "He doesn't want Secret Service men around all the time."

"I'm not sure he could *get* elected," Billy would venture.

"He could get elected," I'd tell Billy. "He doesn't want to! We like our privacy!"

"Okay." Billy'd give in a little. "But he never tried getting elected, so he really doesn't know if he could."

I'd wave that idea away with my dirty hands. "Don't worry. He'd be elected in a minute if he wanted to be. You don't know *him*."

Billy Shakespeare's other rivals for my attention were movie stars. I'd write Clark Gable and Henry Fonda and Errol Flynn, and they'd send back glossy photos of themselves and sometimes letters, too.

These photographs and letters were thumbtacked to the fiberboard walls of a playhouse my father'd had built for me in our backyard.

When I did play with a girl, the game was always the same: getting dinner ready for our husbands. I had an old set of dishes back in the playhouse, and my girl friend and I played setting the table for dinner. During this game, Billy Shakespeare was forgotten. When my husband came through the playhouse door, he would be one of the movie stars pinned to the wall.

I played this game with Dorothy Spencer, who lived behind our house.

She was a tall redhead who looked like a girl,

1. **Secret Service:** the branch of the United States Department of the Treasury that provides protection for the President and his immediate family.

and who always had it in her head to fix meat loaf with mashed potatoes for a movie star named Spencer Tracy.

I changed around a lot—the menu as well as the movie star—but Dorothy stuck to meat loaf with mashed for Spencer.

I'd be saying, "Well, Clark is a little late tonight and the turkey is going to be overdone," or "Gee, Henry isn't here yet and the ham is going to be dried up." But Dorothy would persist with "Spencer's going to love this meat loaf when he gets here. I'll wait until I hear his footsteps to mash the potatoes."

Billy Shakespeare was jealous of this game and tried his best to ruin it with reality.

He'd say, "What are two famous movie stars doing living in the same house?"

He'd say, "How come famous movie stars only have a one-room house with no kitchen?"

But Dorothy Spencer and I went on happily playing house, until the movie *Brother Rat* came to town.

That was when we both fell in love with the movie star Ronald Reagan.[2]

Suddenly we were both setting the table for the same movie star—different menus, but the same husband.

"You've always stuck to meat loaf and mashed for Spencer!" I said angrily. "Now you want my Ronald!"

"He's not *your* Ronald," she said.

"It's my playhouse, though," I reminded her.

"But I won't play if I can't have Ronald," she said.

"We both can't have Ronald!" I insisted.

We took the argument to her mother, who told us to pretend Ronald Reagan was twins. Then we could both have him.

"He isn't twins, though," Dorothy said.

"And if he is," I put in, "I want the real Ronald, and not his twin."

Our game came to a halt, but our rivalry did not. Both of us had written to Ronald Reagan and were waiting for his reply.

2. **Ronald Reagan:** former movie star who became the fortieth president of the United States.

"No matter what he writes her," I told Billy Shakespeare, "my letter from him will be better."

"You might not even get a letter," Billy said. "She might not get one either."

"She might not get one," I said, "but I will."

"You don't know that," Billy said.

"Do you want to know why I know I'll get one?" I asked him.

I made him cross his heart and hope to die if he told anyone what I'd done.

Billy was a skinny little kid with big eyes that always got bigger when I was about to confess to him something I'd done.

"Crossmyheartandhopetodie," he said very fast. "What'd you do?"

"You know that Ronald Reagan isn't like any of the others," I said.

"Because Dorothy Spencer likes him, too."

"That's got nothing to do with it!" I said. "He's just different. I never felt this way about another movie star."

"Why?"

"*Why?* I don't know why! That's the way love is."

"Love?" Billy said.

"Yes. What did you think made me write him that I was a crippled child, and had to go to see him in a wheelchair?"

"Oh migosh!" Billy exclaimed. "Oh migosh!"

"I had to get his attention somehow."

"Oh migosh!"

"Just shut up about it!" I warned him. "If word gets out I'll know it's you."

Dorothy Spencer was the first to hear from Ronald Reagan. She didn't get a letter, but she got a signed photograph.

"Since I heard from him first," she said, "he's my husband."

"Not in my playhouse!" I said.

"He wrote me back first," she said.

"Just wait," I said.

"I don't have to wait," she said. "I'm setting the table for him in my own house."

"It's not even your house, it's your father's," I said. "At least when he's married to me, we'll have our own house."

"He's married to me now," she said.

"We'll see about that," I said.

I was beginning to get a panicky feeling as time passed and no mail came from Ronald Reagan. You'd think he'd write back to a crippled child first. . . . Meanwhile Dorothy was fixing him meat loaf and mashed at her place.

I had pictures of him cut out of movie magazines scotch-taped to my bedroom walls. I went to sleep thinking about him, wondering why he didn't care enough to answer me.

The letter and photograph from Ronald Reagan arrived on a Saturday.

I saw the Hollywood postmark and let out a whoop, thereby attracting my father's attention.

"What's all the excitement?"

I was getting the photograph out of the envelope. "I got a picture from Ronald Reagan!"

"Who's he?"

"Some movie star," my mother said.

By that time I had the photograph out. My heart began to beat nervously as I read the inscription at the bottom. "To a brave little girl, in admiration, Ronald Reagan."

"What does it say?" my father said.

"Nothing, it's just signed," I said, but he already saw what it said as he stood behind me looking down at it.

"Why are you a brave little girl?" he asked.

"How do I know?" I said.

"There's a letter on the floor," said my mother.

"That's my letter," I said, grabbing it.

"Why are you considered a brave little girl?" asked my father again. "Why does *he* admire *you?*"

I held the letter to my chest. "Those are just things they say," I said.

"They say you're *brave?*" my father said.

"Brave or honest or any dumb thing," I said weakly.

"Read the letter, Marijane," said my father.

I read the letter to myself.

Dear Marijane,
Thank you for your letter.
Remember that a handicap can be a challenge.
Always stay as cheerful as you are now.
Yours truly,
Ronald Reagan

"What does it say?" my mother asked.

"Just the usual," I said. "They never say much."

"Let me see it, brave little girl," my father said.

"It's to me."

"Marijane . . ." and he had his hand out.

After my father read the letter, and got the truth out of me concerning my correspondence with Ronald Reagan, he told me what I was to do.

What I was to do was to sit down immediately and write Ronald Reagan, telling him I had lied. I was to add that I thanked God for my good health. I was to return both the letter and the photograph.

No Saturday in my entire life had ever been so dark.

My father stood over me while I wrote the letter in tears, convinced that Ronald Reagan would hate me all his life for my deception. I watched through blurred eyes while my father took my letter, Ronald Reagan's letter, and the signed photograph, put them into a manila envelope, addressed it, sealed it, and put it in his briefcase to take to the post office.

For weeks and weeks after that, I dreaded the arrival of our postman. I was convinced a letter'd come beginning,

Dear Marijane,
How very disappointed I am in you. . . .

"I don't think he'll write back," Billy Shakespeare told me. "I don't think he'll want anything more to do with you."

That ended getting dinner for movie stars in my playhouse.

I told Dorothy Spencer that I'd outgrown all that.

Three years after I wrote Ronald Reagan that letter, I slumped way down in my seat in humiliation as I watched him lose a leg in the movie *King's Row*. . . . I was sure he thought of the little liar from upstate New York who'd pretended she was crippled.

Many, many years later, the man I always thought should be President of the United States was dead, and Ronald Reagan was President of the United States.

I didn't vote for him.

I heard Dorothy Spencer got married, and I envision her making meat loaf and mashed for her husband.

The only remaining question is, Where are you now, William Shakespeare?

M. E. KERR

M. E. Kerr was born in 1927 in Auburn, New York. Her real name is Meaker—M. E. Kerr pronounced another way! Like many writers, Kerr has used different "pen names" when writing such different kinds of books as suspense novels and nonfiction. Kerr has said it was after writing her first young adult novel that "things that happened to me long ago came back clear as a bell and ringing." Those memories gave her the ideas she was looking for.

M. E. Kerr has written many books, including *The Son of Someone Famous* and *I'll Love You When You're More Like Me*. The nonfiction story you've just read is a chapter in her autobiography, *Me, Me, Me, Me, Me: Not a Novel*.

"Mom" Sammy Henry Bozeman Jones, 1938, lithograph, 9" x 6 3/4", The Howard University Gallery of Art, Washington, D.C.

Thank You, M'am

LANGSTON HUGHES

She was a large woman with a large purse that had everything in it but hammer and nails. It had a long strap and she carried it slung across her shoulder. It was about eleven o'clock at night, and she was walking alone, when a boy ran up behind her and tried to snatch her purse. The strap broke with the single tug the boy gave it from behind. But the boy's weight and the weight of the purse combined caused him to lose his balance, so instead of taking off full blast as he had hoped, the boy fell on his back on the sidewalk, and his legs flew up. The large woman simply turned around and kicked him right square in his blue-jeaned sitter. Then she reached down, picked the boy up by his shirt front, and shook him until his teeth rattled.

After that the woman said, "Pick up my pocketbook, boy, and give it here."

She still held him. But she bent down enough to permit him to stoop and pick up her purse. Then she said, "Now ain't you ashamed of yourself?"

Firmly gripped by his shirt front, the boy said, "Yes'm."

The woman said, "What did you want to do it for?"

The boy said, "I didn't aim to."

She said, "You a lie!"

By that time two or three people passed, stopped, turned to look, and some stood watching.

"If I turn you loose, will you run?" asked the woman.

"Yes'm," said the boy.

"Then I won't turn you loose," said the woman. She did not release him.

"I'm very sorry, lady, I'm sorry," whispered the boy.

"Um-hum! And your face is dirty. I got a great mind to wash your face for you. Ain't you got nobody home to tell you to wash your face?"

"No'm," said the boy.

"Then it will get washed this evening," said the large woman starting up the street, dragging the frightened boy behind her.

He looked as if he were fourteen or fifteen, frail and willow-wild, in tennis shoes and blue jeans.

The woman said, "You ought to be my son. I would teach you right from wrong. Least I can do right now is to wash your face. Are you hungry?"

"No'm," said the being-dragged boy. "I just want you to turn me loose."

"Was I bothering *you* when I turned that corner?" asked the woman.

"No'm."

"But you put yourself in contact with *me*," said the woman. "If you think that that contact is not going to last awhile, you got another thought coming. When I get through with you, sir, you are going to remember Mrs. Luella Bates Washington Jones."

Sweat popped out on the boy's face and he began to struggle. Mrs. Jones stopped, jerked him around in front of her, put a half nelson[1] about his neck, and continued to drag him up the street. When she got to her door, she dragged the boy inside, down a hall, and into a large kitchenette-furnished room at the rear of the house. She switched on the light and left the door open. The boy could hear other roomers laughing and talking in the large house. Some of their doors were open, too, so he knew he and the woman were not alone. The woman still had him by the neck in the middle of her room.

She said, "What is your name?"

"Roger," answered the boy.

"Then, Roger, you go to that sink and wash your face," said the

1. **half nelson:** in wrestling, a hold applied by hooking one arm under the opponent's armpit and putting a hand on the back of the opponent's neck.

Midtown Sunset Romare Bearden, 1981, collage on board, 14" x 22",
Private collection

woman, whereupon she turned him loose—at last. Roger looked at
the door—looked at the woman—looked at the door—*and went to
the sink.*

"Let the water run until it gets warm," she said. "Here's a
clean towel."

"You gonna take me to jail?" asked the boy, bending over the
sink.

"Not with that face, I would not take you nowhere," said the
woman. "Here I am trying to get home to cook me a bite to eat and
you snatch my pocketbook! Maybe you ain't been to your supper
either, late as it be. Have you?"

"There's nobody home at my house," said the boy.

"Then we'll eat," said the woman. "I believe you're hungry—
or been hungry—to try to snatch my pocketbook!"

"I wanted a pair of blue suede[2] shoes," said the boy.

"Well, you didn't have to snatch *my* pocketbook to get some suede shoes," said Mrs. Luella Bates Washington Jones. "You could of asked me."

"M'am?"

The water dripping from his face, the boy looked at her. There was a long pause. A very long pause. After he had dried his face and not knowing what else to do dried it again, the boy turned around, wondering what next. The door was open. He could make a dash for it down the hall. He could run, run, run, run, *run!*

The woman was sitting on the day-bed. After awhile she said, "I were young once and I wanted things I could not get."

There was another long pause. The boy's mouth opened. Then he frowned, but not knowing he frowned.

The woman said, "Um-hum! You thought I was going to say *but,* didn't you? You thought I was going to say, *but I didn't snatch people's pocketbooks.* Well, I wasn't going to say that." Pause. Silence. "I have done things, too, which I would not tell you, son—neither tell God, if he didn't already know. So you set down while I fix us something to eat. You might run that comb through your hair so you will look presentable."

In another corner of the room behind a screen was a gas plate and an icebox. Mrs. Jones got up and went behind the screen. The woman did not watch the boy to see if he was going to run now, nor did she watch her purse which she left behind her on the day-bed. But the boy took care to sit on the far side of the room where he thought she could easily see him out of the corner of her eye, if she wanted to. He did not trust the woman *not* to trust him. And he did not want to be mistrusted now.

"Do you need somebody to go to the store," asked the boy, "maybe to get some milk or something?"

"Don't believe I do," said the woman, "unless you just want sweet milk yourself. I was going to make cocoa out of this canned milk I got here."

2. **suede** [swād]: a soft leather that feels velvety on one or both sides.

"That will be fine," said the boy.

She heated some lima beans and ham she had in the icebox, made the cocoa, and set the table. The woman did not ask the boy anything about where he lived, or his folks, or anything else that would embarrass him. Instead, as they ate, she told him about her job in a hotel beauty-shop that stayed open late, what the work was like, and how all kinds of women came in and out, blondes, red-heads, and Spanish. Then she cut him a half of her ten-cent cake.

"Eat some more, son," she said.

When they were finished eating she got up and said, "Now, here, take this ten dollars and buy yourself some blue suede shoes. And next time, do not make the mistake of latching onto *my* pocketbook *nor nobody else's*— because shoes come by devilish like that will burn your feet. I got to get my rest now. But I wish you would behave yourself, son, from here on in."

She led him down the hall to the front door and opened it. "Goodnight! Behave yourself, boy!" she said, looking out into the street.

The boy wanted to say something else other than, "Thank you, m'am," to Mrs. Luella Bates Washington Jones, but he couldn't do so as he turned at the barren stoop and looked back at the large woman in the door. He barely managed to say, "Thank you," before she shut the door. And he never saw her again.

LANGSTON HUGHES

Langston Hughes [1902-1967] was born in Joplin, Missouri. During his life, Hughes traveled so widely that he called his autobiography "I Wonder as I Wander." However, no matter how many continents he visited, the subject of his poems and stories continued to be the life he knew best—the daily experience of African Americans. Hughes wrote mainly of city life and everyday people whose strength of character could make a difference.

Fighter with Manager James Weeks, 1960, oil on canvas, 214" x 168", Private collection

AMIGO BROTHERS

PIRI THOMAS

*A*ntonio Cruz and Felix Varga were both seventeen years old. They were so together in friendship that they felt themselves to be brothers. They had known each other since childhood, growing up on the lower east side of Manhattan in the same tenement[1] building on Fifth Street between Avenue A and Avenue B.

Antonio was fair, lean, and lanky, while Felix was dark, short, and husky. Antonio's hair was always falling over his eyes, while Felix wore his black hair in a natural Afro[2] style.

Each youngster had a dream of someday becoming lightweight champion of the world. Every chance they had the boys worked out, sometimes at the Boys Club on 10th Street and Avenue A and sometimes at the pro's gym on 14th Street. Early morning sunrises would find them running along the East River Drive, wrapped in sweat shirts, short towels around their necks, and handkerchiefs Apache style around their foreheads.

While some youngsters were into street negatives, Antonio and Felix slept, ate, rapped, and dreamt positive. Between them, they had a collection of *Fight* magazines second to none, plus a scrapbook filled with torn tickets to every boxing match they had ever attended, and some clippings of their own. If asked a question about any given fighter, they would immediately zip out from their memory banks divisions, weights, records of fights, knockouts, technical knockouts, and draws or losses.

Each had fought many bouts representing their community and had won two gold-plated medals plus a silver and bronze medallion.

1. **tenement** [ten′ ə mənt]: an apartment house in a large city.
2. **Afro** [af′ rō]: a full, natural hair style.

The difference was in their style. Antonio's lean form and long reach made him the better boxer, while Felix's short and muscular frame made him the better slugger. Whenever they had met in the ring for sparring sessions, it had always been hot and heavy.

Now, after a series of elimination bouts, they had been informed that they were to meet each other in the division finals that were scheduled for the seventh of August, two weeks away—the winner to represent the Boys Club in the Golden Gloves Championship Tournament.

The two boys continued to run together along the East River Drive. But even when joking with each other, they both sensed a wall rising between them.

One morning less than a week before their bout, they met as usual for their daily workout. They fooled around with a few jabs at the air, slapped skin, and then took off, running lightly along the dirty East River's edge.

Antonio glanced at Felix who kept his eyes purposely straight ahead, pausing from time to time to do some fancy leg work while throwing one-twos followed by upper cuts to an imaginary jaw. Antonio then beat the air with a barrage of body blows and short devastating lefts with an overhand jaw-breaking right.

After a mile or so, Felix puffed and said, "Let's stop a while, bro. I think we both got something to say to each other."

Antonio nodded. It was not natural to be acting as though nothing unusual was happening when two ace-boon[3] buddies were going to be blasting . . . each other within a few short days.

They rested their elbows on the railing separating them from the river. Antonio wiped his face with his short towel. The sunrise was now creating day.

Felix leaned heavily on the river's railing and stared across to the shores of Brooklyn. Finally, he broke the silence.

"Gee . . . man. I don't know how to come out with it."

Antonio helped. "It's about our fight, right?"

---

3. **ace-boon** [ās bün]: skilled, best (friends).

"Yeah, right." Felix's eyes squinted at the rising orange sun.

"I've been thinking about it too, *panin*.[4] In fact, since we found out it was going to be me and you, I've been awake at night, pulling punches on you, trying not to hurt you."

"Same here. It ain't natural not to think about the fight. I mean, we both are *cheverote*[5] fighters and we both want to win. But only one of us can win. There ain't no draws in the eliminations."

Felix tapped Antonio gently on the shoulder. "I don't mean to sound like I'm bragging, bro. But I wanna win, fair and square."

Antonio nodded quietly. "Yeah. We both know that in the ring the better man wins. Friend or no friend, brother or no . . ."

Felix finished it for him. "Brother. Tony, let's promise something right here. Okay?"

"If it's fair, *hermano*,[6] I'm for it." Antonio admired the courage of a tug boat pulling a barge five times its welterweight size.

"It's fair, Tony. When we get into the ring, it's gotta be like we never met. We gotta be like two heavy strangers that want the same thing and only one can have it. You understand, don'tcha?"

"*Sí*,[7] I know," Tony smiled. "No pulling punches. We go all the way."

"Yeah, that's right. Listen, Tony. Don't you think it's a good idea if we don't see each other until the day of the fight? I'm going to stay with my Aunt Lucy in the Bronx. I can use Gleason's Gym for working out. My manager says he got some sparring partners with more or less your style."

Tony scratched his nose pensively. "Yeah, it would be better for our heads." He held out his hand, palm upward. "Deal?"

"Deal." Felix lightly slapped open skin.

"Ready for some more running?" Tony asked lamely.

"Naw, bro. Let's cut it here. You go on. I kinda like to get things together in my head."

4. *panin* [pä′ nēn]: Spanish slang for "friend."
5. *cheverote* [chā vä rō′ tā]: Spanish slang for "cool dude."
6. *hermano* [är mä′ nō]: Spanish for "brother."
7. *Sí* [sē]: Spanish for "Yes."

"You ain't worried, are you?" Tony asked.

"No way, man." Felix laughed out loud. "I got too much smarts for that. I just think it's cooler if we split right here. After the fight, we can get it together again like nothing ever happened."

The amigo brothers were not ashamed to hug each other tightly.

"Guess you're right. Watch yourself, Felix. I hear there's some pretty heavy dudes up in the Bronx. *Sauvecito*,[8] okay?"

"Okay. You watch yourself too, *sabe?*"[9]

Tony jogged away. Felix watched his friend disappear from view, throwing rights and lefts. Both fighters had a lot of psyching up to do before the big fight.

The days in training passed much too slowly. Although they kept out of each other's way, they were aware of each other's progress via the ghetto grapevine.

The evening before the big fight, Tony made his way to the roof of his tenement. In the quiet early dark, he peered over the ledge. Six stories below the lights of the city blinked and the sounds of cars mingled with the curses and the laughter of children in the street. He tried not to think of Felix, feeling he had succeeded in psyching his mind. But only in the ring would he really know. To spare Felix hurt, he would have to knock him out, early and quick.

Up in the South Bronx, Felix decided to take in a movie in an effort to keep Antonio's face away from his fists. The flick was *The Champion* with Kirk Douglas, the third time Felix was seeing it.

The champion was getting . . . beat, . . . his face being pounded into raw wet hamburger. His eyes were cut, jagged, bleeding, one eye swollen, the other almost shut. He was saved only by the sound of the bell.

Felix became the champ and Tony the challenger.

The movie audience was going out of its head, roaring in blood lust at the butchery going on. The champ hunched his shoulders grunting and sniffing red blood back into his broken nose. The challenger, confident that he had the championship in the bag,

8. *Sauvecito* [säü vā sē′ tō]: Spanish slang for "Take it easy."
9. *sabe* [sä′ bā]: Spanish slang for "You know?," or "Understand?"

threw a left. The champ countered with a dynamite right that exploded into the challenger's brains.

Felix's right arm felt the shock. Antonio's face, superimposed on the screen, was shattered and split apart by the awesome force of the killer blow. Felix saw himself in the ring, blasting Antonio against the ropes. The champ had to be forcibly restrained. The challenger was allowed to crumble slowly to the canvas, a broken bloody mess.

When Felix finally left the theater, he had figured out how to psyche himself for tomorrow's fight. It was Felix the Champion vs. Antonio the Challenger.

He walked up some dark streets, deserted except for small pockets of wary-looking kids wearing gang colors. Despite the fact that he was Puerto Rican like them, they eyed him as a stranger to their turf. Felix did a fast shuffle, bobbing and weaving, while letting loose a torrent of blows that would demolish whatever got in its way. It seemed to impress the brothers, who went about their own business.

Finding no takers, Felix decided to split to his aunt's. Walking the streets had not relaxed him, neither had the fight flick. All it had done was to stir him up. He let himself quietly into his Aunt Lucy's apartment and went straight to bed, falling into a fitful sleep with sounds of the gong for Round One.

Antonio was passing some heavy time on his rooftop. How would the fight tomorrow affect his relationship with Felix? After all, fighting was like any other profession. Friendship had nothing to do with it. A gnawing doubt crept in. He cut negative thinking real quick by doing some speedy fancy dance steps, bobbing and weaving like mercury. The night air was blurred with perpetual motions of left hooks and right crosses. Felix, his *amigo* brother, was not going to be Felix at all in the ring. Just an opponent with another face. Antonio went to sleep, hearing the opening bell for the first round. Like his friend in the South Bronx, he prayed for victory, via a quick clean knockout in the first round.

Large posters plastered all over the walls of local shops announced the fight between Antonio Cruz and Felix Vargas as the main bout.

The fight had created great interest in the neighborhood. Antonio and Felix were well liked and respected. Each had his own loyal following. Betting fever was high and ranged from a bottle of soda to cold hard cash on the line.

Antonio's fans bet with unbridled faith in his boxing skills. On the other side, Felix's admirers bet on his dynamite-packed fists.

Felix had returned to his apartment early in the morning of August 7th and stayed there, hoping to avoid seeing Antonio. He turned the radio on to *salsa* music[10] sounds and then tried to read while waiting for word from his manager.

The fight was scheduled to take place in Tompkins Square Park. It had been decided that the gymnasium of the Boys Club was not large enough to hold all the people who were sure to attend. In Tompkins Square Park, everyone who wanted could view the fight, whether from ringside or window fire escapes or tenement rooftops.

The morning of the fight Tompkins Square was a beehive of activity with numerous workers setting up the ring, the seats, and the guest speakers' stand. The scheduled bouts began shortly after noon and the park began filling up even earlier.

The local junior high school across from Tompkins Square Park served as the dressing room for all the fighters. Each was given a separate classroom with desk tops, covered with mats, serving as resting tables. Antonio thought he caught a glimpse of Felix waving to him from a room at the far end of the corridor. He waved back just in case it had been him.

The fighters changed from their street clothes into fighting gear. Antonio wore white trunks, black socks, and black shoes. Felix wore green trunks, white socks, and white boxing shoes. Each had dressing gowns to match their fighting trunks with their names neatly stitched on the back.

The loudspeakers blared into the open windows of the school. There were speeches by dignitaries, community leaders, and great boxers of yesteryear. Some were well prepared, some improvised on

10. **salsa music** [säl′ sä]: a popular kind of Hispanic music.

the spot. They all carried the same message of great pleasure and honor at being part of such a historic event. This great day was in the tradition of champions emerging from the streets of the lower east side.

Interwoven with the speeches were the sounds of the other boxing events. After the sixth bout, Felix was much relieved when his trainer Charlie said, "Time change. Quick knockout. This is it. We're on."

Waiting time was over. Felix was escorted from the classroom by a dozen fans in white T-shirts with the word FELIX across their fronts.

Antonio was escorted down a different stairwell and guided through a roped-off path.

As the two climbed into the ring, the crowd exploded with a roar. Antonio and Felix both bowed gracefully and then raised their arms in acknowledgment.

Antonio tried to be cool, but even as the roar was in its first birth, he turned slowly to meet Felix's eyes looking directly into his. Felix nodded his head and Antonio responded. And both as one, just as quickly, turned away to face his own corner.

Bong—bong—bong. The roar turned to stillness.

"Ladies and Gentlemen, *Señores y Señoras.*"[11]

The announcer spoke slowly, pleased at his bilingual efforts.

"Now the moment we have all been waiting for—the main event between two fine young Puerto Rican fighters, products of our lower east side."

"*Loisaida,*"[12] called out a member of the audience.

"In this corner, weighing 134 pounds, Felix Vargas. And in this corner, weighing 133 pounds, Antonio Cruz. The winner will represent the Boys Club in the tournament of champions, the Golden Gloves. There will be no draw. May the best man win."

11. **Señores y Señoras** [sā nyō′ räs ē sā nyō′ räs]: Spanish for "Gentlemen and Ladies."
12. **Loisaida** [lō ē sī′ dä]: the way people in the neighborhood say "lower east sider."

The cheering of the crowd shook the window panes of the old buildings surrounding Tompkins Square Park. At the center of the ring, the referee was giving instructions to the youngsters.

"Keep your punches up. No low blows. No punching on the back of the head. Keep your heads up. Understand. Let's have a clean fight. Now shake hands and come out fighting."

Both youngsters touched gloves and nodded. They turned and danced quickly to their corners. Their head towels and dressing gowns were lifted neatly from their shoulders by the trainers' nimble fingers. Antonio crossed himself. Felix did the same.

BONG! BONG! ROUND ONE. Felix and Antonio turned and faced each other squarely in a fighting pose. Felix wasted no time. He came in fast, head low, half hunched toward his right shoulder, and lashed out with a straight left. He missed a right cross as Antonio slipped the punch and countered with one-two-three lefts that snapped Felix's head back, sending a mild shock coursing through him. If Felix had any small doubt about their friendship affecting their fight, it was being neatly dispelled.

Antonio danced, a joy to behold. His left hand was like a piston,[13] pumping jabs one right after another with seeming ease. Felix bobbed and weaved and never stopped boring in. He knew that at long range he was at a disadvantage. Antonio had too much reach on him. Only by coming in close could Felix hope to achieve the dreamed-of knockout.

Antonio knew the dynamite that was stored in his *amigo* brother's fist. He ducked a short right and missed a left hook. Felix trapped him against the ropes just long enough to pour some punishing rights and lefts to Antonio's hard midsection. Antonio slipped away from Felix, crashing two lefts to his head, which set Felix's right ear to ringing.

Bong! Both *amigos* froze a punch well on its way, sending up a roar of approval for good sportsmanship.

Felix walked briskly back to his corner. His right ear had not stopped ringing. Antonio gracefully danced his way toward his stool

---

13. **piston** [pis′ tən]: a cylinder that is quickly moved back and forth by the force of steam.

none the worse, except for glowing glove burns, showing angry red against the whiteness of his midribs.

"Watch that right, Tony." His trainer talked into his ear. "Remember Felix always goes to the body. He'll want you to drop your hands for his overhand left or right. Got it?"

Antonio nodded, sprayed water out between his teeth. He felt better as his sore midsection was being firmly rubbed.

Felix's corner was also busy.

"You gotta get in there, fella." Felix's trainer poured water over his curly Afro locks. "Get in there or he's gonna chop you up from way back."

Bong! Bong! Round two. Felix was off his stool and rushed Antonio like a bull, sending a hard right to his head. Beads of water exploded from Antonio's long hair.

Antonio, hurt, sent back a blurring barrage of lefts and rights that only meant pain to Felix, who returned with a short left to the head followed by a looping right to the body. Antonio countered with his own flurry, forcing Felix to give ground. But not for long.

Felix bobbed and weaved, bobbed and weaved, occasionally punching his two gloves together.

Antonio waited for the rush that was sure to come. Felix closed in and feinted with his left shoulder and threw his right instead. Lights suddenly exploded inside Felix's head as Antonio slipped the blow and hit him with a pistonlike left, catching him flush on the point of his chin.

Bedlam broke loose as Felix's legs momentarily buckled. He fought off a series of rights and lefts and came back with a strong right that taught Antonio respect.

Antonio danced in carefully. He knew Felix had the habit of playing possum when hurt, to sucker an opponent within reach of the powerful bombs he carried in each fist.

A right to the head slowed Antonio's pretty dancing. He answered with his own left at Felix's right eye that began puffing up within three seconds.

Antonio, a bit too eager, moved in too close and Felix had him entangled into a rip-roaring, punching toe-to-toe slugfest that brought the whole Tompkins Square Park screaming to its feet.

Rights to the body. Lefts to the head. Neither fighter was giving an inch. Suddenly a short right caught Antonio squarely on the chin. His long legs turned to jelly and his arms flailed out desperately. Felix, grunting like a bull, threw wild punches from every direction. Antonio, groggy, bobbed and weaved, evading most of the blows. Suddenly his head cleared. His left flashed out hard and straight catching Felix on the bridge of his nose.

Felix lashed back with a haymaker, right off the ghetto streets. At the same instant, his eye caught another left hook from Antonio. Felix swung out trying to clear the pain. Only the frenzied screaming of those along ringside let him know that he had dropped Antonio. Fighting off the growing haze, Antonio struggled to his feet, got up, ducked, and threw a smashing right that dropped Felix flat on his back.

Felix got up as fast as he could in his own corner, groggy but still game. He didn't even hear the count. In a fog, he heard the roaring of the crowd, who seemed to have gone insane. His head cleared to hear the bell sound at the end of the round. He was . . . glad. His trainer sat him down on the stool.

In his corner, Antonio was doing what all fighters do when they are hurt. They sit and smile at everyone.

The referee signaled the ring doctor to check the fighters out. He did so and then gave his okay. The cold water sponges brought clarity to both *amigo* brothers. They were rubbed until their circulation ran free.

Bong! Round three—the final round. Up to now it had been tic-tac-toe, pretty much even. But everyone knew there could be no draw and that this round would decide the winner.

This time, to Felix's surprise, it was Antonio who came out fast, charging across the ring. Felix braced himself but couldn't ward off the barrage of punches. Antonio drove Felix hard against the ropes.

The crowd ate it up. Thus far the two had fought with *mucho corazón.*[14] Felix tapped his gloves and commenced his attack anew. Antonio, throwing boxer's caution to the winds, jumped in to meet him.

14. **mucho corazón** [mü′ chō kō rä sōn′]: Spanish for courage; literally, "a lot of heart."

Both pounded away. Neither gave an inch and neither fell to the canvas. Felix's left eye was tightly closed. Claret red blood poured from Antonio's nose. They fought toe-to-toe.

The sounds of their blows were loud in contrast to the silence of a crowd gone completely mute. The referee was stunned by their savagery.

Bong! Bong! Bong! The bell sounded over and over again. Felix and Antonio were past hearing. Their blows continued to pound on each other like hailstones.

Finally the referee and the two trainers pried Felix and Antonio apart. Cold water was poured over them to bring them back to their senses.

They looked around and then rushed toward each other. A cry of alarm surged through Tompkins Square Park. Was this a fight to the death instead of a boxing match?

The fear soon gave way to wave upon wave of cheering as the two *amigos* embraced.

No matter what the decision, they knew they would always be champions to each other.

BONG! BONG! BONG! "Ladies and Gentlemen. *Señores* and *Señoras*. The winner and representative to the Golden Gloves Tournament of Champions is . . ."

The announcer turned to point to the winner and found himself alone. Arm in arm the champions had already left the ring.

PIRI THOMAS

Piri Thomas was born in 1928 and grew up in New York City. Thomas's adult life did not begin well. At twenty-two, he was sent to prison for attempted armed robbery. In prison, he began to write. Four years later, after he was released, all his written work was accidentally destroyed. Back in the community, Thomas became involved in drug rehabilitation programs—and began writing again.

Much of Thomas's writing is autobiographical and makes use of the dialect of Spanish Harlem in New York. "Amigo Brothers" is from his book, *Stories from the Barrio*.

Hannah Armstrong

EDGAR LEE MASTERS

I wrote him a letter asking him for old times' sake
To discharge[1] my sick boy from the army;
But maybe he couldn't read it.
Then I went to town and had James Garber,
Who wrote beautifully, write him a letter;   5
But maybe that was lost in the mails.
So I traveled all the way to Washington.
I was more than an hour finding the White House.
And when I found it they turned me away,
Hiding their smiles. Then I thought: 10
"Oh, well, he ain't the same as when I boarded him
And he and my husband worked together
And all of us called him Abe, there in Menard."
As a last attempt I turned to a guard and said:
"Please say it's old Aunt Hannah Armstrong   15
From Illinois, come to see him about her sick boy
In the army."
Well, just in a moment they let me in!
And when he saw me he broke in a laugh,
And dropped his business as president,   20
And wrote in his own hand Doug's discharge,
Talking the while of the early days,
And telling stories.

---

1. **discharge** [dis chärj´]: release, let go.

The Great Good Man Marsden Hartley, 1942, oil on masonite, 40" x 30", Museum of Fine Arts, Boston

E D G A R   L E E   M A S T E R S

Edgar Lee Masters [1868-1950] was born in Garnett, Kansas, but grew up in the small Illinois towns of Petersburg and Lewistown. First he became a lawyer. Later, when he became a poet, he used a variety of pseudonyms to keep his literary life separate from his law practice.

Masters is best known for his *Spoon River Anthology*, which began as a novel about the kinds of people he knew in small-town Illinois. Following the example of the *Greek Anthology*, a collection of ancient Greek poems in which the dead comment on their own lives, Masters's characters in *Spoon River Anthology* are dead and each narrates his or her life story.

Graduates hear some Clinton advice

ASSOCIATED PRESS

WASHINGTON—President Clinton told new college graduates yesterday to "assume more personal responsibility" in the nation's future without losing sight of their personal priorities. "Always save time for your friends," he advised.

Speaking by telephone to a commencement audience at William Jewell College in Liberty, Mo., Clinton accepted an honorary doctorate.[1] His goddaughter, Sarah Staley of Little Rock, Ark., was among the graduates.

"I want to urge all who are here listening to me today to look out at the great adventures of your life and to seize them, but also to always save time for your friends," he said.

Clinton said one of the first things he did as president-elect was visit the home of Sarah's mother, Carolyn Staley, one of Clinton's oldest friends, who played host to a gathering of his pals.

"Amid life's challenges and disappointments, your friends are an anchor in a storm, and I urge you to keep them," the president said in the brief remarks.

1. **honorary doctorate** [on′ ə rer′ ē dok′ tər it]: a university doctor's degree given as an honor rather than earned through regular studies.

LOB'S GIRL

JOAN AIKEN

Some people choose their dogs, and some dogs choose their people. The Pengelly family had no say in the choosing of Lob; he came to them in the second way, and very decisively.

It began on the beach, the summer when Sandy was five, Don, her older brother, twelve, and the twins were three. Sandy was really Alexandra, because her grandmother had a beautiful picture of a queen in a diamond tiara[1] and high collar of pearls. It hung by Granny Pearce's kitchen sink and was as familiar as the doormat. When Sandy was born everyone agreed that she was the living spit of the picture, and so she was called Alexandra and Sandy for short.

On this summer day she was lying peacefully reading a comic and not keeping an eye on the twins, who didn't need it because they were occupied in seeing which of them could wrap the most seaweed around the other one's legs. Father—Bert Pengelly—and Don were up

1. tiara [tē er′ ə]: a band of gold, jewels, or flowers worn around the head as an ornament.

on the Hard painting the bottom boards of the boat in which
Father went fishing for pilchards.[2] And Mother—Jean Pengelly—
was getting ahead with making the Christmas puddings because
she never felt easy in her mind if they weren't made and safely put
away by the end of August. As usual, each member of the family
was happily getting on with his or her own affairs. Little did they
guess how soon this state of things would be changed by the large
new member who was going to erupt into their midst.

Sandy rolled onto her back to make sure that the twins were
not climbing on slippery rocks or getting cut off by the tide. At the
same moment a large body struck her forcibly in the midriff and
she was covered by flying sand. Instinctively she shut her eyes and
felt the sand being wiped off her face by something that seemed
like a warm, rough, damp flannel. She opened her eyes and looked.
It was a tongue. Its owner was a large and bouncy young Alsatian,

2. **pilchards** [pil' chərdz]: small fish related to herrings.

or German shepherd, with topaz[3] eyes, black-tipped prick ears, a thick, soft coat, and a bushy black-tipped tail.

"*Lob!*" shouted a man farther up the beach. "Lob, come here!"

But Lob, as if trying to atone[4] for the surprise he had given her, went on licking the sand off Sandy's face, wagging his tail so hard while he kept on knocking up more clouds of sand. His owner, a gray-haired man with a limp, walked over as quickly as he could and seized him by the collar.

"I hope he didn't give you a fright?" the man said to Sandy. "He meant it in play—he's only young."

"Oh, no, I think he's *beautiful*," said Sandy truly. She picked up a bit of driftwood and threw it. Lob, whisking easily out of his master's grip, was after it like a sand-colored bullet. He came back with the stick, beaming, and gave it to Sandy. At the same time he gave himself, though no one else was aware of this at the time. But with Sandy, too, it was love at first sight, and when, after a lot more stick-throwing, she and the twins joined Father and Don to go home for tea, they cast many a backward glance at Lob being led firmly away by his master.

"I wish we could play with him every day." Tess sighed.

"Why can't we?" said Tim.

Sandy explained. "Because Mr. Dodsworth, who owns him, is from Liverpool, and he is only staying at the Fisherman's Arms till Saturday."

"Is Liverpool a long way off?"

"Right at the other end of England from Cornwall, I'm afraid."

It was a Cornish fishing village where the Pengelly family lived, with rocks and cliffs and a strip of beach and a little round harbor, and palm trees growing in the gardens of the little whitewashed stone houses. The village was approached by a narrow, steep, twisting hill-road, and guarded by a notice that said LOW GEAR FOR 1 1/2 MILES, DANGEROUS TO CYCLISTS.

---

3. **topaz** [tō′ paz]: golden brown.
4. **atone** [ə tōn′]: make up for.

The Pengelly children went home to scones[5] with Cornish cream and jam, thinking they had seen the last of Lob. But they were much mistaken. The whole family was playing cards by the fire in the front room after supper when there was a loud thump and a crash of china in the kitchen.

"My Christmas puddings!" exclaimed Jean, and ran out.

"Did you put TNT[6] in them, then?" her husband said.

But it was Lob, who, finding the front door shut, had gone around to the back and bounced in through the open kitchen window, where the puddings were cooling on the sill. Luckily only the smallest was knocked down and broken.

Lob stood on his hind legs and plastered Sandy's face with licks. Then he did the same for the twins, who shrieked with joy.

"Where does this friend of yours come from?" inquired Mr. Pengelly.

"He's staying at the Fisherman's Arms—I mean his owner is."

"Then he must go back there. Find a bit of string, Sandy, to tie to his collar."

"I wonder how he found his way here," Mrs. Pengelly said, when the reluctant Lob had been led whining away and Sandy had explained about their afternoon's game on the beach. "Fisherman's Arms is right round the other side of the harbor."

Lob's owner scolded him and thanked Mr. Pengelly for bringing him back. Jean Pengelly warned the children that they had better not encourage Lob any more if they met him on the beach, or it would only lead to more trouble. So they dutifully took no notice of him the next day until he spoiled their good resolutions[7] by dashing up to them with joyful barks, wagging his tail so hard that he winded Tess and knocked Tim's legs from under him.

They had a happy day, playing on the sand.

The next day was Saturday. Sandy had found out that Mr. Dodsworth was to catch the half-past-nine train. She went out

5. **scones** [skōnz]: thick, round biscuits.
6. **TNT:** a yellow-colored solid used as an explosive.
7. **resolutions** [rez′ ə lü′ shənz]: decisions or intentions.

secretly, down to the station, nodded to Mr. Hoskins, the station-master, who wouldn't dream of charging any local[8] for a platform ticket, and climbed up on the footbridge that led over the tracks. She didn't want to be seen, but she did want to see. She saw Mr. Dodsworth get on the train, accompanied by an unhappy-looking Lob with drooping ears and tail. Then she saw the train slide away out sight around the next headland,[9] with a melancholy wail that sounded like Lob's last good-bye.

Sandy wished she hadn't had the idea of coming to the station. She walked home miserably, with her shoulders hunched and her hands in her pockets. For the rest of the day she was so cross and un-like herself that Tess and Tim were quite surprised, and her mother gave her a dose of senna.[10]

A week passed. Then, one evening, Mrs. Pengelly and the younger children were in the front room playing snakes and tadders. Mr. Pengelly and Don had gone fishing on the evening tide. If your father is a fisherman, he will never be home at the same time from one week to the next.

Suddenly, history repeating itself, there was a crash from the kitchen. Jean Pengelly leaped up, crying, "My blackberry jelly!" She and the children had spent the morning picking and the afternoon boiling fruit.

But Sandy was ahead of her mother. With flushed cheeks and eyes like stars she had darted into the kitchen, where she and Lob were hugging one another in a frenzy of joy. About a yard of his tongue was out, and he was licking every part of her that he could reach.

"Good heavens!" exclaimed Jean. "How in the world did *he* get here?"

"He must have walked," said Sandy. "Look at his feet."

They were worn, dusty, and tarry.[11] One had a cut on the pad.

---

8. **local** [lōʹ kəl]: local resident or person native to the area.
9. **headland:** a point of high land jutting into a body of water.
10. **senna** [senʹ ə]: dried leaves used as an herbal medicine.
11. **tarry** [tärʹ ē]: covered with tar.

"They ought to be bathed," said Jean Pengelly. "Sandy, run a bowl of warm water while I get the disinfectant."[12]

"What'll we do about him, Mother?" said Sandy anxiously.

Mrs. Pengelly looked at her daughter's pleading eyes and sighed.

"He must go back to his owner, of course," she said, making her voice firm. "Your dad can get the address from the Fisherman's tomorrow, and phone him or send a telegram. In the meantime he'd better have a long drink and a good meal."

Lob was very grateful for the drink and the meal, and made no objection to having his feet washed. Then he flopped down on the hearthrug and slept in front of the fire they had lit because it was a cold, wet evening, with his head on Sandy's feet. He was a very tired dog. He had walked all the way from Liverpool to Cornwall, which is more than four hundred miles.

The next day Mr. Pengelly phoned Lob's owner, and the following morning Mr. Dodsworth arrived off the night train, decidedly put out, to take his pet home. That parting was worse than the first. Lob whined, Don walked out of the house, the twins burst out crying, and Sandy crept up to her bedroom afterward and lay with her face pressed into the quilt, feeling as if she were bruised all over.

Jean Pengelly took them all into Plymouth to see the circus on the next day and the twins cheered up a little, but even the hour's ride in the train each way and the Liberty horses and performing seals could not cure Sandy's sore heart.

She need not have bothered, though. In ten days' time Lob was back—limping this time, with a torn ear and a patch missing out of his furry coat, as if he had met and tangled with an enemy or two in the course of his four-hundred-mile walk.

Bert Pengelly rang up Liverpool again. Mr. Dodsworth, when he answered, sounded weary. He said, "That dog has already cost me two days that I can't spare away from my work—plus endless time in police stations and drafting newspaper advertisements. I'm too old

12. **disinfectant** [dis′ in fek′ tənt]: a substance that destroys germs and may prevent infection.

for these ups and downs. I think we'd better face the fact, Mr. Pengelly, that it's your family he wants to stay with—that is, if you want to have him."

Bert Pengelly gulped. He was not a rich man; and Lob was a pedigreed[13] dog. He said cautiously, "How much would you be asking for him?"

"Good heavens, man, I'm not suggesting I'd *sell* him to you. You must have him as a gift. Think of the train fares I'll be saving. You'll be doing me a good turn."

"Is he a big eater?" Bert asked doubtfully.

By this time the children, breathless in the background listening to one side of this conversation, had realized what was in the wind and were dancing up and down with their hands clasped beseechingly.[14]

"Oh, not for his size," Lob's owner assured Bert. "Two or three pounds of meat a day and some vegetables and gravy and biscuits—he does very well on that."

Alexandra's father looked over the telephone at his daughter's swimming eyes and trembling lips. He reached a decision. "Well, then, Mr. Dodsworth," he said briskly, "we'll accept your offer and thank you very much. The children will be overjoyed and you can be sure Lob has come to a good home. They'll look after him and see he gets enough exercise. But I can tell you," he ended firmly, "if he wants to settle in with us he'll have to learn to eat a lot of fish."

So that was how Lob came to live with the Pengelly family. Everybody loved him and he loved them all. But there was never any question who came first with him. He was Sandy's dog. He slept by her bed and followed her everywhere he was allowed.

Nine years went by, and each summer Mr. Dodsworth came back to stay at the Fisherman's Arms and call on his erstwhile[15] dog. Lob always met him with recognition and dignified pleasure, accompanied

13. **pedigreed** [ped′ ə grēd]: having record of breeding or ancestry.
14. **beseechingly** [bi sēch′ ing lē]: as though asking or begging.
15. **erstwhile** [ėrst′ hwīl]: former, past.

him for a walk or two—but showed no signs of wishing to return to Liverpool. His place, he intimated,[16] was definitely with the Pengellys.

In the course of nine years Lob changed less than Sandy. As she went into her teens he became a little slower, a little stiffer, there was a touch of gray on his nose, but he was still a handsome dog. He and Sandy still loved one another devotedly.

One evening in October all the summer visitors had left, and the little fishing town looked empty and secretive. It was a wet, windy dusk. When the children came home from school—even the twins were at high school now, and Don was a full-fledged fisherman— Jean Pengelly said, "Sandy, your Aunt Rebecca says she's lonesome because Uncle Will Hoskins has gone out trawling,[17] and she wants one of you to go and spend the evening with her. You go, dear; you can take your homework with you."

Sandy looked far from enthusiastic.

"Can I take Lob with me?"

"You know Aunt Becky doesn't really like dogs—Oh, very well." Mrs. Pengelly sighed. "I suppose she'll have to put up with him as well as you."

Reluctantly Sandy tidied herself, took her schoolbag, put on the damp raincoat she had just taken off, fastened Lob's lead to his collar, and set off to walk through the dusk to Aunt Becky's cottage, which was five minutes' climb up the steep hill.

The wind was howling through the shrouds[18] of boats drawn up on the Hard.

"Put some cheerful music on, do," said Jean Pengelly to the nearest twin. "Anything to drown that wretched sound while I make your dad's supper." So Don, who had just come in, put on some rock music, loud. Which was why the Pengellys did not hear the truck hurtle down the hill and crash against the post office wall a few minutes later.

16. **intimated** [in′ tə māt əd]: hinted.
17. **trawling** [trôl′ ing]: fishing with a net.
18. **shrouds** [shrouds]: coverings made of cloth or some protective material.

Dr. Travers was driving through Cornwall with his wife, taking a late holiday before patients began coming down with winter colds and flu. He saw the sign that said STEEP HILL. LOW GEAR FOR 1 1/2 MILES. Dutifully he changed into second gear.

"We must be nearly there," said his wife, looking out of her window. "I noticed a sign on the coast road that said the Fisherman's Arms was two miles. What a narrow, dangerous hill! But the cottages are very pretty—Oh, Frank, stop, *stop!* There's a child, I'm sure it's a child—by the wall over there!"

Dr. Travers jammed on his brakes and brought the car to a stop. A little stream ran down by the road in a shallow stone culvert,[19] and half in the water lay something that looked, in the dusk, like a pile of clothes—or was it the body of a child? Mrs. Travers was out of the car in a flash, but her husband was quicker.

"Don't touch her, Emily!" he said sharply. "She's been hit. Can't be more than a few minutes. Remember that truck that overtook us half a mile back, speeding like the devil? Here, quick, go into that cottage and phone for an ambulance. The girl's in a bad way. I'll stay here and do what I can to stop the bleeding. Don't waste a minute."

Doctors are expert at stopping dangerous bleeding, for they know the right places to press. This Dr. Travers was able to do, but he didn't dare do more; the girl was lying in a queerly crumpled heap, and he guessed she had a number of bones broken and that it would be highly dangerous to move her. He watched her with great concentration, wondering where the truck had got to and what other damage it had done.

Mrs. Travers was very quick. She had seen plenty of accident cases and knew the importance of speed. The first cottage she tried had a phone; in four minutes she was back, and in six an ambulance was wailing down the hill.

Its attendants lifted the child onto a stretcher as carefully as if she were made of fine thistledown.[20] The ambulance sped off to

19. **culvert** [kul′ vərt]: a small channel or drain.
20. **thistledown** [this′ əl doun′]: soft, feathery fluff from thistle seeds.

Plymouth—for the local cottage hospital did not take serious accident cases—and Dr. Travers went down to the police station to report what he had done.

He found that the police already knew about the speeding truck—which had suffered from loss of brakes and ended up with its radiator halfway through the post-office wall. The driver was concussed[21] and shocked, but the police thought he was the only person injured—until Dr. Travers told his tale.

At half-past nine that night Aunt Rebecca Hoskins was sitting by her fire thinking aggrieved thoughts about the inconsiderateness of nieces who were asked to supper and never turned up, when she was startled by a neighbor, who burst in, exclaiming, "Have you heard about Sandy Pengelly, then, Mrs. Hoskins? Terrible thing, poor little soul, and they don't know if she's likely to live. Police have got the truck driver that hit her—ah, it didn't ought to be allowed, speeding through the place like that at umpty miles an hour, they ought to jail him for life—not that that'd be any comfort to poor Bert and Jean."

Horrified, Aunt Rebecca put on a coat and went down to her brother's house. She found the family with white shocked faces; Bert and Jean were about to drive off to the hospital where Sandy had been taken, and the twins were crying bitterly. Lob was nowhere to be seen. But Aunt Rebecca was not interested in dogs; she did not inquire about him.

"Thank the lord you've come, Beck," said her brother. "Will you stay the night with Don and the twins? Don's out looking for Lob and heaven knows when we'll be back; we may get a bed with Jean's mother in Plymouth."

"Oh, if only I'd never invited the poor child," wailed Mrs. Hoskins. But Bert and Jean hardly heard her.

That night seemed to last forever. The twins cried themselves to sleep. Don came home very late and grim-faced. Bert and Jean sat in a waiting room of the Western Counties Hospital, but Sandy was

21. **concussed** [kən kusd′]: injured in the head by a blow.

unconscious, they were told, and she remained so. All that could be done for her was done. She was given transfusions to replace all the blood she had lost. The broken bones were set and put in slings and cradles.

"Is she a healthy girl? Has she a good constitution?"[22] the emergency doctor asked.

"Aye, doctor, she is that," Bert said hoarsely. The lump in Jean's throat prevented her from answering; she merely nodded.

"Then she ought to have a chance. But I won't conceal from you that her condition is very serious, unless she shows signs of coming out from this coma."

But as hour succeeded hour, Sandy showed no signs of recovering consciousness. Her parents sat in the waiting room with haggard faces; sometimes one of them would go to telephone the family at home, or to try to get a little sleep at the home of Granny Pearce, not far away.

At noon next day Dr. and Mrs. Travers went to the Pengelly cottage to inquire how Sandy was doing, but the report was gloomy: "Still in a very serious condition." The twins were miserably unhappy. They forgot that they had sometimes called their elder sister bossy and only remembered how often she had shared her pocket money with them, how she read to them and took them for picnics and helped with their homework. Now there was no Sandy, no Mother and Dad, Don went around with a gray, shuttered face, and worse still, there was no Lob.

The Western Counties Hospital is a large one, with dozens of different departments and five or six connected buildings, each with three or four entrances. By that afternoon it became noticeable that a dog seemed to have taken up position outside the hospital, with the fixed intention of getting in. Patiently he would try first one entrance and then another, all the way around, and then begin again. Sometimes he would get a little way inside, following a visitor, but animals were, of course, forbidden, and he was always kindly but

22. **constitution:** [kon′ stə tü′ shən]: physical nature or makeup.

firmly turned out again. Sometimes the guard at the main entrance gave him a pat or offered him a bit of sandwich—he looked so wet and beseeching and desperate. But he never ate the sandwich. No one seemed to own him or to know where he came from; Plymouth is a large city and he might have belonged to anybody.

At tea time Granny Pearce came through the pouring rain to bring a flask of hot tea with brandy in it to her daughter and son-in-law. Just as she reached the main entrance the guard was gently but forcibly shoving out a large, agitated, soaking-wet Alsatian dog.

"No, old fellow, you can *not* come in. Hospitals are for people, not for dogs."

"Why, bless me," exclaimed old Mrs. Pearce. "That's Lob! Here, Lob, Lobby boy!"

Lob ran to her, whining. Mrs. Pearce walked up to the desk.

"I'm sorry, madam, you can't bring that dog in here," the guard said.

Mrs. Pearce was a very determined old lady. She looked the porter in the eye.

"Now, see here, young man. That dog has walked twenty miles from St. Killan to get to my granddaughter. Heaven knows how he knew she was here, but it's plain he knows. And he ought to have his rights! He ought to get to see her! Do you know," she went on, bristling, "that dog has walked the length of England—*twice*—to be with that girl? And you think you can keep him out with your fiddling rules and regulations?"

"I'll have to ask the medical officer," the guard said weakly.

"You do that, young man." Granny Pearce sat down in a determined manner, shutting her umbrella, and Lob sat patiently dripping at her feet. Every now and then he shook his head, as if to dislodge something heavy that was tied around his neck.

Presently a tired, thin, intelligent-looking man in a white coat came downstairs, with an impressive, silver-haired man in a dark suit, and there was a low-voiced discussion. Granny Pearce eyed them, biding her time.

"Frankly . . . not much to lose," said the older man. The man in the white coat approached Granny Pearce.

"It's strictly against every rule, but as it's such a serious case we are making an exception," he said to her quietly. "But only *outside* her bedroom door—and only for a moment or two."

Without a word, Granny Pearce rose and stumped upstairs. Lob followed close to her skirts, as if he knew his hope lay with her.

They waited in the green-floored corridor outside Sandy's room. The door was half shut. Bert and Jean were inside. Everything was terribly quiet. A nurse came out. The white-coated man asked her something and she shook her head. She had left the door ajar and through it could now be seen a high, narrow bed with a lot of gadgets around it. Sandy lay there, very flat under the covers, very still. Her head was turned away. All Lob's attention was riveted[23] on the bed. He strained toward it, but Granny Pearce clasped his collar firmly.

"I've done a lot for you, my boy, now you behave yourself," she whispered grimly. Lob let out a faint whine, anxious and pleading.

At the sound of that whine Sandy stirred just a little. She sighed and moved her head the least fraction. Lob whined again. And then Sandy turned her head right over. Her eyes opened, looking at the door.

"Lob?" she murmured—no more than a breath of sound. "Lobby, boy?"

The doctor by Granny Pearce drew a quick, sharp breath. Sandy moved her left arm—the one that was not broken—from below the covers and let her hand dangle down feeling as she always did in the mornings, for Lob's furry head. The doctor nodded slowly.

"All right," he whispered. "Let him go to the bedside. But keep a hold of him."

Granny Pearce and Lob moved to the bedside. Now she could see Bert and Jean, white-faced and shocked, on the far side of the bed. But she didn't look at them. She looked at the smile on her granddaughter's face as the groping fingers found Lob's wet ears and gently pulled them. "Good boy," whispered Sandy, and fell asleep again.

Granny Pearce led Lob out into the passage again. There she let go of him and he ran off swiftly down the stairs. She would have

23. **riveted** [riv′ it əd]: fixed firmly.

followed him, but Bert and Jean had come out into the passage, and she spoke to Bert fiercely.

"*I don't know why you were so foolish as not to bring the dog before! Leaving him to find the way here himself—*"

"But, Mother!" said Jean Pengelly. "That can't have been Lob. What a chance to take! Suppose Sandy hadn't—" She stopped, with her handkerchief pressed to her mouth.

"Not Lob? I've known that dog nine years! I suppose I ought to know my own granddaughter's dog?"

"Listen, Mother," said Bert. "Lob was killed by the same truck that hit Sandy. Don found him—when he went to look for Sandy's schoolbag. He was—he was dead. Ribs all smashed. No question of that. Don told me on the phone—he and Will Hoskins rowed a half mile out to sea and sank the dog with a lump of concrete tied to his collar. Poor old boy. Still—he was getting on. Couldn't have lasted forever."

"*Sank him at sea? Then what—?*"

Slowly old Mrs. Pearce, and then the other two, turned to look at the trail of dripping-wet footprints that led down the hospital stairs.

In the Pengellys' garden they have a stone, under the palm tree. It says: "Lob. Sandy's dog. Buried at sea."

JOAN AIKEN

Joan Aiken was born in England in 1924. She started writing stories and poems on "huge two-shilling writing blocks" when she was only five. When Aiken was seventeen, the British Broadcasting Corporation chose one of her stories to broadcast on their children's hour.

At different times, Aiken worked for the BBC, the United Nations Information Service, and *Argosy* magazine. At the age of thirty, when she was a widow with two small children, Aiken began writing steadily to support her family. She has written a dozen thrillers for adults and more than twenty books for young people, including *The Wolves of Willoughby Close* and *The Whispering Mountain*.

The CHINESE CHECKER PLAYERS

Richard Brautigan

Marbles V Charles Bell, 1982, oil on canvas, 48" x 84¹/₂"

When I was six years old
I played Chinese checkers[1]
   with a woman
who was ninety-three years old.
She lived by herself   5
in an apartment down the hall
   from ours.
We played Chinese checkers
every Monday and Thursday nights.
While we played she usually talked   10
about her husband
who had been dead for seventy years,
and we drank tea and ate cookies
   and cheated.

1. **Chinese checkers:** a game similar to
   checkers in which marbles are used on
   a board with holes.

RICHARD BRAUTIGAN

Copyright © by Jill Krementz

Richard Brautigan [1935-1984] was born in
Spokane, Washington. For many years he made a living
solely from writing poetry and novels, until he became
an instructor at Montana State University. His first book
of poems was published when he was twenty-two.

In all his work, Brautigan wrote about life and nature and poked fun at
both. One interesting collection is made up of eight poems, each printed on
a separate seed packet envelope, and is called *Please Plant This Book*.

MR. MISENHEIMER'S GARDEN

CHARLES KURALT

We've been wandering the back roads since 1967, and we've been to a few places we'll never forget. One of them was on Route 10, Surry County, Virginia. We rolled in here on a day in the spring of 1972 thinking this was another of those little roadside rest stops. But there were flowers on the picnic tables. That was the first surprise.

And beyond the tables, we found a paradise, a beautiful garden of thirteen acres, bright with azaleas, thousands of them, and bordered by dogwoods in bloom, and laced by a mile of paths in the shade of tall pines. In all our travels, it was the loveliest garden I'd ever seen. It made me wonder how large a battalion[1] of state-employed gardeners it took to keep the place up. The answer was it took one old man, and he was nobody's employee. Walter Misenheimer, a retired nurseryman,[2] created all this in the woods next to his house, created it alone after he retired at the age of seventy. He was eighty-three when I met him and was spending every day tending his garden for the pleasure of strangers who happened to stop.

Walter Misenheimer: I like people, and this is my way of following out some of the teachings of my parents. When I was a youngster, one of the things they said was, "If you don't try to make the world just a little bit nicer when you leave here, what is the reason for man's existence in the first place?" I have tried to give it to the state. The Parks Department says it is too small for them. The Highway Department says it is too big for them.

---

1. **battalion** [bə talʹ yən]: a large group of people with a common purpose.
2. **nurseryman** [nėrʹ sər ē mən]: person who grows or sells young trees and plants.

Kuralt: What's going to happen to this place after you're gone?

Misenheimer: Well, I imagine that within a very few years, this will be undergrowth, or nature will take it over again.

Kuralt: You mean, it's not going to survive?

Misenheimer: I doubt it.

Kuralt: That's a terribly discouraging thing, isn't it?

Misenheimer: Well, that's the way I see it now.

We watched for a while as people enjoyed the beauty of Walter Misenheimer's garden. And we left, and a few years later somebody sent me a clipping from the Surry County paper. It said Walter Misenheimer had died. I wondered what would happen to his garden. I wondered whether the Virginia sun still lights the branches of the dogwood, which he planted there.

Well, it does. Some stories have happy endings. Walter Misenheimer's garden does survive, and so does his spirit, in Haeja Namkoong. It seems that she stopped by the garden just a few months after we did, eleven years ago.

Haeja Namkoong: We slowed down and saw a sign and picnic tables and a lot of flowers blooming. We came to the picnic table, found a water spigot, helped ourselves, and we were sort of curious as to what this place was all about. Finally, we saw the old man sort of wobbling around and coming 'cross the lawn, saying "Hello," and just waving to us to stop. I guess he was afraid we were going to leave.

To please the old man, and herself, Haeja Namkoong stayed the afternoon with him, walking in his garden. It made her remember, she says, something she wanted once.

Haeja: I grew up in a large city in Korea, and I have never really seen rice grow. I always dreamed about living in the country, about a small, little cabin in the wilderness, with lots of flowers. That's what I dreamed about, but I guess that was just childhood dreams.

When the sun went down that day, the young woman said good-bye to the old man and headed home to Boston, but the roadside Eden called her back. That is, Walter Misenheimer did. He phoned her, long distance, and asked her to come for a little while and help in the garden.

Haeja: He was sort of pleading with me, "Please come down. Just help me for a couple of weeks."

A couple of weeks only, and then a few more, and then it was Christmas. Haeja Namkoong was twenty-six. She had no family. Neither did Walter Misenheimer and his wife.

Haeja: From wildflowers to man-grown shrubberies, he taught me. I was interested in learning the whole thing. I was out here almost every day with him.

They became as father and daughter working in the garden, and in time Haeja Namkoong was married in the garden.

Haeja: He was very proud to give me away. I guess he never thought, since he didn't have any children of his own, he would give someone away.

Brown earth was coaxed by the gentle old man into green growth and flowering red and pink and white. The earth rewards every loving attention it is paid. People repay such love, too, in memory.

Haeja: I was very, very close to my mother. But other than my mother, I can't remember anyone that loved me so much and cared for me so much as Mr. Misenheimer.

The garden is still here. Walter Misenheimer died in 1979 and left it to Haeja Namkoong. She pays a caretaker, Ed Trible, to help keep it beautiful for anybody who passes by. Haeja and her husband and their children live in Richmond now, but they return on weekends to work in the garden.

Haeja: So, knowing how much the garden meant to him, I want to keep it up and carry on.

Walter Misenheimer told me that he expected when he was gone the garden would soon be overgrown. He might have known better. His garden shows that something grows from seeds and cultivation. And if what you plant is love and kindness, something grows from that, too.

Haeja: Look at this purple one.
Child: I like the red.
Haeja: Aren't they pretty?

CHARLES KURALT

Charles Kuralt was born in 1934 in Wilmington, North Carolina. After attending college there, he became a reporter for the *Charlotte News* in Charlotte, North Carolina. When he moved to New York City to work as a writer and correspondent for CBS News, he began to travel.

For the television feature *On the Road,* Kuralt began a long career of traveling America's back roads in search of off-beat stories. With a camera and sound crew, Kuralt has averaged 50,000 miles a year, looking for—and finding—interesting, ordinary people. These stories of people who have quiet, productive lives in a noisy, troubled world help prove, Kuralt says, that "people go on living their lives in spite of big black headlines."

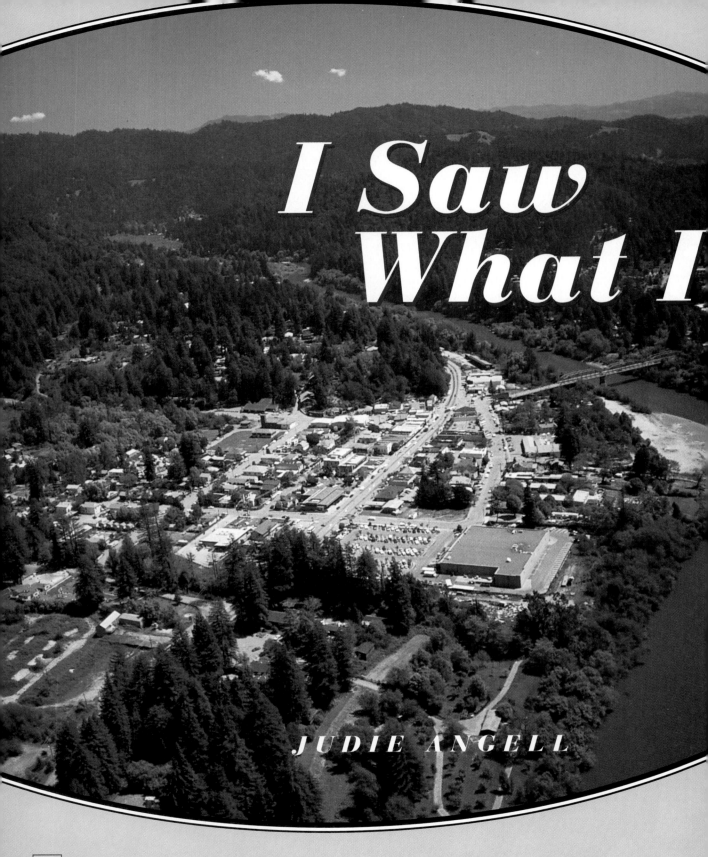

I Saw What I

JUDIE ANGELL

Yeah. Well. I'm not dumb. I don't lie, and I'm not one of those nuts, either. Ask anyone, anyone who's known me for the last twelve years, which is all the time I've been alive, if Ray Beane ever, I mean *ever* ran off at the mouth with stupid stuff nobody'd believe. I never did. I always tell it straight. My dad, before he died, that's the way he raised me. And my mom, she's the same way. *Be on the level with folks, Ray, and always look 'em in the eye.*

I live in Poma Valley, California. I was born here, like I said, twelve years ago, and I haven't hardly been anywhere else in all that time. Once, when I was nine—this was just before the Lord took my dad away with cancer—we went on a little trip south to San Francisco. It was just the three of us—my mom, my dad, and me—and we rode on the trolley car and saw some of the sights down there. But I guess that was about the only time I was out of Poma Valley. I have a grandpa from Ohio, but I have never visited him. He comes here sometimes to see us. See? I'm being as straight as I can be about everything, so nobody can say I lied or exaggerated or anything.

Poma Valley is a little town. Very rural, you'd call it. Only about five thousand people. And I go to school in a one-room schoolhouse, just like that old-fashioned program you see sometimes in reruns on TV. It's true. We have the sixth, seventh, and eighth grades all in one room. And there's only ten of us in all those classes. I get there by bus and it takes about forty-five minutes to an hour, depending on the roads and weather. Cross my heart. I know there are a lot of people who won't believe there are really places like that left in America, but there are, and I live in one. It's real, all right.

I know what's real.

I told you my name, but the whole of it is Raymond Earl Beane, Junior. I was named for my dad, and when I have a son of my own I'm going to name him Raymond Earle Beane the Third. My mom, she laughs and says I'd better have a wife who agrees with that choice, but I don't guess I'd marry somebody who didn't. Anyway, that's my name, and I said my age and mentioned everyone in my family except for some cousins who also live in Ohio, so that's it for my autobiography. We did autobiographies this year in seventh grade. Mine was pretty short.

I stand about five-two and weigh in at about one-hundred ten. I'm not very big but it doesn't bother me. I've got yellowish hair. It's straight and long, sort of, behind the ears. I like soccer and football and I like to listen to country music. Most of my friends like rock but I like country, and I don't care who knows it.

I have a dog. Maybe I should have mentioned him as part of my family, but I'll mention him now. He's part Lab and his name's Red. He's a black dog, but his name's Red and that's it.

I guess that's enough about me, but I wanted to tell the kind of person I am to help prove out what I say. Hope nobody minds.

The time I'm talking about now, it was six months ago in May. Just getting on to summer. What I wanted real bad was a team jacket. For soccer. I was on the team, and all the other kids had red jackets that said "Poma Valley Soccer" in white on the back with a picture of a soccer ball, and then you got your first name in white script writing put on the front on the left side. Boy, I wanted one, but we just couldn't afford it, Mom and me. See, I had a good jacket, so I didn't really need another one. This was just something I wanted. Around our house we can really just about deal with what we need. "Want" is something else.

So Mom said if I could raise the money over the summer, it'd be okay with her if I bought myself that jacket. And that's when it started.

Our main street, well, it's called Main Street and like you'd expect, it runs straight through town and then it turns into Route 34 and goes on to skirt by the farms. But there's a movie theater called the Poma on it, along with a pharmacy, a launderette, a Thom McAn shoe store, a hardware store, and a few other shops I can't remember. Oh, right, there's an army-navy store, too, and a diner on the corner. Out a ways in the other direction, there's an A&P and a bowling alley, too, and that's about it for Poma Valley.

The store I didn't mention is the little market between the launderette and the pharmacy. It sells groceries. It's called Meyer's.

I started out looking for work in the bowling alley. I wasn't sure what I could do, but I thought it would be fun to hang out there and maybe get to bowl a few frames every now and then, you know, improve my game. But no luck. So I moved on to the shoe store and the pharmacy (I skipped the launderette—doing the laundry at home is bad enough). I didn't have any luck there either and I finally ended up at Meyer's grocery store.

We never shopped at Meyer's. Mom says the little markets are always more expensive since they can't buy in bulk the way supermarkets can, so I had never met Mr. Meyer before. I guess I'd seen him some. I mean, you can't really miss anyone who lives in Poma Valley, but I never paid him any mind before that day. Funny thing was, he knew me.

"Ray Beane," he says when I come in. And he grins this big grin at me. I guess my jaw kind of drops and he laughs. His laugh is big and nice, not the kind of laugh where you think maybe he's making fun of you. "Sure I know you," he says. "I like to know who all the kids are."

I found out later that it was true he liked most of the kids, but he also wanted to keep an eye on us. There are plenty of kids who take stuff, rip it off, you know. And if he knew kids, called them by name and treated them nice, maybe they wouldn't do it so much to him. Take stuff, I mean.

He was a smart man, Mr. Meyer, but I didn't find any of this stuff out till later. Till I started working for him and getting to know him.

Yeah, he hired me. Minimum wage plus the tips I'd earn for deliveries. Part-time after school, and when school let out a few weeks later, full-time, ten till six. Sweep the place inside and out, dust the shelves, pack groceries, even wait on customers if he was busy, all the stuff you'd expect would be done in a small grocery store. What he didn't mention was he really wanted somebody to talk to. He talked a lot.

If that sounds as if I didn't like to hear him talk, then I said it wrong. I did like it.

Mr. Meyer's first name was Abe. Abraham. He was Jewish and spoke with an accent. He told me his age—sixty-seven. He was proud of it, he said, because he had been in a concentration camp[1] in the Second World War and any time he lived after that was "borrowed time." He laughed when he said it, but I knew he didn't think it was funny.

Except the thing is, he wasn't at all angry or anything, just grateful. He said he was grateful to have come out of such a dark and terrible time and be able to live in sunny California and run his own business, too.

He didn't have a family. He said they all died in the camp. He showed me two pictures, of a dark-haired woman and a little girl. The pictures were very old—they were black and white, and yellow around the edges, but he was proud of them and kept them in a gold frame in the back of the counter.

"My mother," he said. "And my sister." He told me their names,

1. **concentration camp:** place where the Nazis held, tortured, and killed Jewish people and others during World War II.

but I couldn't pronounce them. I know that the only time his eyes didn't laugh was when he looked at those two pictures.

The truth was that the store wasn't that busy most of the time. A lot of people must be like my mom and they shop at the A&P. Some folks'd come in for last-minute things like a newspaper or a carton of milk or bread or something, but not too much more. I may have made—tops—three deliveries all summer. But lunchtime was busy. Mr. Meyer made deli sandwiches, and the guys who worked on the roads and the truckers and local folks would come in for tuna salad, bologna, roast beef, whatever, and milk or a soda or beer. I guess that's where most of the money was made, the lunches. Anyway, he never complained about money, Mr. Meyer, so I guess he made enough for his needs. I didn't complain either, because so did I. And then some.

Except for lunchtime, we had time to kill, Mr. Meyer and me. We'd sit down behind the counter and he'd give me what he called his "philosophy of life."

"There's always someone worse off than you, Ray Beane," he'd say. He always called me Ray Beane, my whole name, like it was one word. "It's sad you have no papa, but a mama you have. There are boys who don't have both, you know. And not only that, your mama, she loves you very much, right?"

"Well, yeah . . ."

"Well, yeah, you say. Of course she loves you very much. To have someone to love you is a wonderful thing."

I wanted to ask him who he had to love *him*, except I thought it would be rude. Only he was one step ahead of me there.

"When I was young, I had a whole big family who loved me very much, so I know what it's like. Many people, they never know what it's like to be loved."

I looked at him.

"It's like the optimist and the pessimist, yes? The optimist has one glass of schnapps, he says it is half full. The pessimist has the same glass, he says it is half empty. You see the difference?"

I thought I did, except I didn't know what schnapps was.

"When you wake up in the morning, Ray Beane, what do you see?" he asked.

I thought for a second.

"Uh . . . my alarm clock . . . my closet door . . . Red, lots of times, he wakes me up."

"Do you see the sunlight streaming through your window?"

"Uh, yeah . . ."

"Uh, yeah. Does it make you feel good that another day is here? Another day when you can put on your clothes and your shoes and walk around, healthy, in the sunlight?"

"Uh, yeah . . ."

"Uh, yeah. Some vocabulary you got there, Ray Beane. We got to do something about that."

"I got an A in Vocabulary," I told him.

He smiled. "Only old men think about being lucky to wake up in the sunshine and walk around," he said. "Kids don't have to think about that. But it would be nice if they did. Just once in a while, Ray Beane. Think about it. It will make you a nicer person."

I didn't see how, but I liked him, so I decided to think about it. Once in a while.

"Did you know, Ray Beane, that ninety-nine percent of the things you worry about never, never happen?" he asked once.

"Huh?"

"It's true. Ninety-nine percent. A fact."

"Sometimes they do," I said.

"One percent. The odds are very good that worrying is a waste of time. And besides, worrying won't change what happens anyway, will it?"

I shook my head.

He shrugged this big shrug. His shoulders covered his ears. "So why worry?"

That was the kind of stuff he said, all the time. I told Mom about him and the things he said, and she said he sounded like a very wise man. She still doesn't shop there, though—she said everything in his place was at least a dime more than at the A&P.

Once my friend Frankie came in for candy. He was with his older brother and they were both acting wise. You know, kidding around, punching each other and ragging on us a little. Frankie was doing it because his brother Jim was there. Usually, he's pretty nice. But anyway, I saw Jim lift this Baby Ruth bar off the candy rack. I caught him in the big round magnifying mirror Mr. Meyer has at the front of the store, so you can see what's going on in the aisles. I didn't know what to do—I mean it. But still, there was Mr. Meyer and how nice he was to me and all—I mean, I always got to take stuff home at the end of the day and he was teaching me things—he made me learn a fact from the encyclopedia every single day and memorize it and tell it to him. He did.

I couldn't stand it. I turned red and my stomach hurt and then before I even knew it, Frankie and Jim were gone, outta there. My stomach hurt worse than before, but I still didn't say anything. And then I felt a hand on my shoulder.

"It's okay, Ray Beane. I knew they were your friends."

I felt like I was about to cry. Okay, I did cry.

"You're my friend too," I blubbered, feeling like a total wuss.

"A different kind," he said.

"Well, if you saw, how come you didn't say anything?" I asked, wiping my nose on my sleeve and feeling even stupider.

He didn't answer. I knew it was because he was waiting to see what I would do.

"I won't let it go again," I said, real softly.

"I won't put you in that position again," he said, even softer.

Later, after work, I found Frankie. I told him if he ever came in there with Jim again and ripped off Mr. Meyer, I'd personally break his face. I said *his*, not Jim's, because I couldn't take Jim. But I can take Frankie and he knows it, so it was a personal thing, between the two of us, and that way no one at school would have to know and Mr. Meyer wouldn't have to know and Frankie wouldn't let it happen again. I guessed. I hoped. I sort of worried about it every time Frankie came into the store with his brother, which wasn't that often, but neither of them even flicked a whisker, so Mr. Meyer was right about that—I worried for nothing.

It was what I *didn't* worry about that happened.

It was a Thursday. I know it was a Thursday. I woke up and thought about the sunshine that day. I was grinning all the way to work and I told Mr. Meyer about it and he grinned, too. And the day was bright and nice like it usually is, especially in summer. It was morning, before the lunch folks, so the store had its usual few customers. I remember Mrs. Lefton came in and bought cat food and Mrs. Crowley came in for orange juice and bread—she's the housekeeper for old Mr. Staley—and Willy Pelosi bought a paper, two doughnuts, and a black coffee. I remember all of that.

And I remember the truck. It was a red pickup and it pulled up right in front of the store, right there in the sunshine on Main Street, and one man jumped out of it. He was wearing a hat. And then it was fast and blurry and I don't like to talk about it, but this is the way it went.

The man had a gun and he pointed it right at us, Mr. Meyer and me. And he said he wanted money. He knew the old man kept a lot of it in a vault in the back and he wanted it, he wanted it. Mr. Meyer never said a word, but he was holding a can of bug spray—we were stacking them, the ant-and-roach-killer cans; he said they do pretty well in the summer—and suddenly he threw it, the can, he *threw* it right at the guy with the gun. He hit the guy and the guy dropped the gun, but not before it went off. And then Mr. Meyer, he picked up another spray can and sprayed the guy's face. The guy was yelling, because of the spray in his face, and I was so scared, I mean, I hope and pray never to be so scared again, but there was Mr. Meyer right next to me, saying, "It's okay, Ray Beane, get the gun, now before he can use it again, that's the boy, that's my boy, now hold it on him, I'm right here, we'll hold it on him, we'll do it together, just like we do things."

And he winked at me. He really did. Winked at me. I saw it.

Then I was holding the gun and hollering my head off. Outside I could hear the truck pulling away, grinding gears and blowing soot, and then Mr. Aiken from the pharmacy came in and he was with a whole bunch of people who heard the gun and the yelling and the truck and everything, and the police came and they took the gun away. He was still covering his face and crying or something from the spray in his eyes.

And then Mr. Aiken, he put his arm around my shoulders and he took me out of the store. Damned if I wasn't crying again, but I was shaking so bad I could hardly stand, I was still so scared.

"It's okay, Raymond. They've called your mom and she's on her way. It's all right, boy, it's all right," he kept saying.

And the crowd, I could hear the crowd. It was too early for the lunch folks, but they were there anyway—they just appeared, along with the rest of Poma Valley. I remember it all just perfectly, just like it was going on right this minute.

"Nothing like this *ever* happened before in the valley . . ."

"Did, too. Last year and the year before."

"That was the gas station got held up. And it was at night, no one was there."

"Was too there."

"Was not and there weren't no gun."

"One of 'em got away."

"Yeah, in a red pickup. They'll get him."

"Poor kid, poor Ray."

"Ray's the lucky one. Poor Meyer, that's who. Poor old guy."

That's when I stopped blubbering.

"What about Mr. Meyer?" I asked.

But instead of answering me, Mr. Aiken just kept patting and squeezing my shoulder. I moved quick then, and started to head back into the store, but Mr. Aiken and someone else grabbed me and held on to me and wouldn't let me go. So I *really* started hollering then, you bet, just yelling my fool head off for Mr. Meyer to come out. *"Come out! Mr. Meyer! Come out! Come out, Mr. Meyer!"*

But "Shh, boy" was all Mr. Aiken would say and everyone else just seemed to turn away from us, looking down at the sidewalk or up the street into the sun.

"He can't come out, Ray," Mrs. Lefton said. She took Mr. Aiken's place and pulled me away with her arm around my shoulder. "He can't come out, Ray, honey, he was shot. That shot everyone heard, it caught him, honey. You don't want to go back in there—"

But I did, and she couldn't hold me then. Nobody could. I raced past them, pushed past them. There wasn't anybody who could stop me then.

The paramedics from the volunteer ambulance corps were picking him up from where he'd been lying on the floor at the end of the shelf with all the bug sprays. They put him on a gurney,[2] and even though I knew he was dead, I still lost it when I saw them put the sheet over him.

They did catch the guy in the truck. His pal told them just where to find him. He also said how he heard "the old guy" had this safe in back of his store with all this money because Jews always have a lot of money they hoard, and how he knew the store was never busy that time of day, all kinds of stupid and weird stuff like that. I'm trying to

2. **gurney** [gėr′ nē]: stretcher or wheeled cot.

say how I remember it all and I do, anyone can see that, but it didn't come together for me until the police questioned me later. Actually, it was just Captain Ebsen, who sometimes takes my mother out, both of them being widowed. It was when he was asking me all those questions that everyone started looking at me funny.

See, the gun went off just once, and that's when Mr. Meyer had to have been shot. But it was *after* the gun went off that he sprayed the robber's face and told me to hold the gun on him and said we'd do it together, that he was with me. And winked at me.

But everyone said I was too upset to be rational. That's what they said. I wasn't rational, but it was understandable, they said, after what I went through.

Well, yeah, I guess I went through something. And I guess he'll always be with me, that old man and his old pictures and his "philosophy of life." And I don't guess I'll ever really get over what happened to him. I'll remember everything he said about being lucky and about worrying and about the sunshine and about the half-full glass, just like I know he'd want me to.

But after that shot went off, he was *there* next to me, calling me Ray Beane and telling me we'd do it together. And he winked at me.

I saw what I saw.

JUDIE ANGELL

Judie Angell was born in 1937 in New York City. She became an elementary school teacher before she began writing. She has said, "I think growing up heads the list of The Hardest Things to Do in Life. It's so hard, in fact, that some of us never get there." She tries, in her writing, to record memories, feelings, and imaginings in the hope that they will "help a little—make you laugh—make you feel you're not alone."

Angell is another user of pseudonyms. She has written for children under the name Maggie Twohill and as Fran Arrick for older readers. One of her novels for middle school readers (written as Judie Angell) is *Dear Lola, or How to Build Your Own Family.*

Asking Big Questions About the Literature

What does it mean to be a friend?

Theme

The main idea or message of a piece of literature is the **theme.** In this unit, one theme is *friends*. Think about how someone can be a friend. For example, in "The Chinese Checker Players," how can a six-year-old child and a ninety-three-year-old woman be friends? Are they friends simply because they play Chinese checkers? Choose two poems and write a paragraph to explain how each poem answers the question, "What does it mean to be a friend?" Before writing, use a cluster like the one shown to map out your ideas. (*See "Theme" on page 119.*)

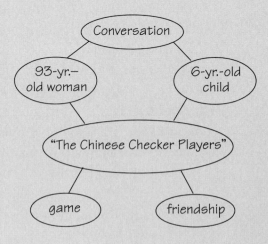

PERFORM a Conversation

With a partner, select two characters from one of the literature selections in this unit. Write the dialogue for a conversation these two characters might have about what it means to be a friend. Then perform the conversation for your class.

Define a Friend

In his book *How to Win Friends and Influence People*, Dale Carnegie says, "To make a friend, simply *be* one." Which character from the literature in this unit simply *is* a friend? Write a paragraph explaining why this character qualifies as a friend. Use examples from the literature to support your argument. Then display the quotation and your classmates' responses on a bulletin board.

What does it mean to have a friend?

Create a
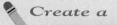
SURVEY

With your classmates, develop a questionnaire about friendship and distribute it to students in your school. Collect the surveys, tabulate the results, and use them as the basis of a news article: "Our Views About Having Friends." Submit your article to the school newspaper.

LITERATURE STUDY

Character

A **character** is a person or animal who participates in the action of a work of literature. As a reader, you get to know literary characters in much the same way that you get to know new friends—by how they look, what they say, how they act, and what others think of them. Which of the characters in this unit would you most like to have as a friend? To help you sort out your ideas, first complete a chart like this one. Write about the character and why he or she would make a good friend. Then share your thoughts with a partner. (*See "Character" on page 118.*)

	Detail 1	Detail 2	Detail 3	Detail 4
Appearance				
Speech				
Behavior				
Opinion of others				

RANK *Characters*

Rank the characters in the selections that you've read on the basis of the quality of their friendship. Use a range of 1 through 5, with 1=good friend and 5=poor friend. Compare rankings with a partner, and explain how you arrived at your decisions.

Asking Big Questions About the Literature

What are different kinds of friendship?

TELEVISION TALK SHOW

In a small group, develop a script for a talk show that stars characters from different literature selections. Brainstorm questions and answers about how the characters met, how their relationships developed, and how they'd describe the friendship. After rehearsing, present your talk show to the class.

LITERATURE STUDY

Character

In literature, **characters** can be described as either round or flat. A *round* character is one whose personality is well-developed. A *flat* character, on the other hand, may have only one or two character traits. In your journal, brainstorm a list of the characters from this unit that you would define as round. Then choose two of them and explain in two or more paragraphs why you would classify each one as a round character. (*See "Character" on page 118.*)

EXAMINE Connotations and Denotations

While all words have exact definitions, or **denotations**, they also have **connotations**—those positive or negative feelings people associate with words. For example, two words like *friend* and *pal* may be alike in meaning, but each conveys a different connotation. In a small group, brainstorm synonyms for *friend*. Then make a chart showing the denotation and connotations for each word. Discuss how the connotations suggest different kinds of friendships.

Word	Denotation	Connotations
pal	person one knows, likes, and trusts	buddy, super best friend

How can friendships change?

Write a
SCENE

With a partner, choose one of the selections in this unit. Write a scene that might happen if two of the characters met again ten years later. Based on what you know about the characters, construct a time line to plot out what's happened to them. Then perform your scene for your class and lead a discussion about how and why the characters' relationship may have changed. For example, the time line on this page describes what may have happened to Ruri and Laurie in "The Bracelet."

LITERATURE STUDY

Theme

Writers often wish to convey their insights about the world and human nature. This central idea, or insight, about a subject is the **theme** of a work. Choose one of the literature selections you've read and rewrite it in a simplified form for children. Your purpose is to teach a lesson about how friendships change. Collect your classmates' stories in an anthology and share it with students in a local elementary school. (*See "Theme" on page 119.*)

Ruri leaves camp in Utah —moves to San Francisco.	Laurie goes to college in New York City.	Ruri visits cousins in New York City.
3 years after story	5 years after story	8 years after story

Tell a Story

With a small group or in writing, tell a story about a change, for better or worse, that occurred in one of your friendships. Then discuss how the change you experienced is similar to one that occurred between two characters in a literature selection you've read.

NOW
Choose a Project!

Three projects involving friendship are described on the following pages. Which one is for you?

Writing Workshop

Unlike an autobiography, which is a connected story of your life that starts at the beginning, a *memoir* is a memory of a single experience and your thoughts about the meaning of that event. For this project, your **purpose** will be to write a memoir about an incident that involves a friend. Your memoir will give you the chance to relive an adventure and share it with an **audience** of people your age. Writing a memoir will also give you the chance to respond to the Big Questions in this unit: "What does it mean to be a friend?" and "What does it mean to have a friend?"

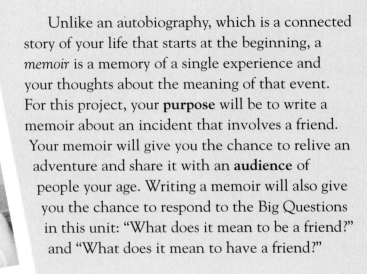

To help you recall incidents, try *clustering* your ideas by placing a friend's name in the center of a circle and branching your ideas out from there. Look at photo albums and school yearbooks to nudge your memory, or think of your life as a movie. Rerun possible scenes again and again until a picture emerges so vividly that it stops the reel. Whichever method you use, choose an incident that would interest an audience of your peers. What about the time you defended the underdog and won a friend—or the way a misunderstanding almost fractured the perfect friendship? Remember, an ordinary event can be as eye-opening and entertaining as a dramatic one.

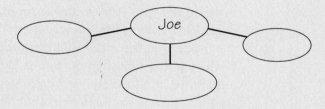

Prewriting

....

**MAKING
A PLAN**

Writing a memoir is like going on a trip. If you don't know where you're going, you may never reach a destination. A map will help to guide your way. This map may be as simple as filling out a chart with headings for *purpose, conflict, setting, characters, dialogue,* and *resolution* (or *who, what, where, when, how,* and *why*).

Purpose	Conflict	Setting	Characters	Dialogue	Resolution

Drafting
....
YOUR
MEMOIR

Once you've chosen an incident to write about, selected an audience, and mapped out ideas, you're ready to write your first draft. The following guidelines will help you draft your memoir.

Guidelines for Drafting a Memoir

Use the **first-person point of view** and the personal pronoun *I*. For example, Jennifer Haynes, a student writer, uses first-person pronouns to tell about a fishing experience on pages 110-111.

- Experiment with different kinds of introductions, such as providing background information, establishing the setting, introducing the characters through dialogue, or arousing curiosity with a question as Jennifer does in her introduction.

- The simplest way to write a memoir is to use **chronological order** to tell your story in the order that the events happened. In "Fishing for Friends," Jennifer relates the events of the incident in the order that they occurred. Some writers use **flashback** to establish important background information. For a dramatic impact, begin your memoir with the ending, then flash back to reveal the events that led up to it.

- Introduce **setting** early in your memoir. Use descriptive details or reveal the setting gradually through the action.

- Keep in mind the ways in which writers accomplish **characterization**. Make your characters believable.

- Remember that everyone has a unique way of talking. As you write the characters' **dialogue**, keep in mind that people ramble, interrupt each other, or stop abruptly. Read the dialogue aloud to yourself or to a partner to see if it sounds natural.

- Write a **conclusion** that will express what the incident meant to you. Jennifer closes her memoir with a comment about her teacher, who is the central figure in her writing.

- Write a **title** that attracts your readers' attention and arouses their curiosity. Make sure that the title suggests what your memoir is about. For example, Jennifer's title, "Fishing for Friends," arouses curiosity and suggests a fishing incident.

Revising
YOUR MEMOIR

As you read what you've written, ask yourself whether you've fulfilled your purpose. Have you expressed your feelings about a particular friendship? Does every detail, sentence, and paragraph clearly express what you want to say?

Look for ways of bringing your memoir to life. Would more dialogue move the action along and emphasize the conflict? Would adding more detail increase the suspense? If you get stuck at any point, go back to your prewriting notes.

You may want to test your memoir at this point by reading it aloud to a group of classmates. Their questions and reactions may pinpoint other areas that you need to work on. For example, if your classmates are confused about what happens when, you may need to add details or transitions to make the order of events clearer.

Editing
YOUR MEMOIR

After you've revised your memoir, exchange your work with a partner or other writing group members. Read and edit each other's work. Look carefully for errors in grammar, usage, spelling, and punctuation. Then correct the errors that have been pointed out. Pay special attention to punctuating and paragraphing dialogue correctly.

Publishing
YOUR MEMOIR

Once you've completed your memoir, you can share it with your classmates in a number of ways.

- Present it as a gift to the friend who is featured in it.
- Submit it to your school's literary magazine or to one of the national student writing publications.
- Turn it into a screenplay that you and several classmates can videotape.
- Publish a class anthology of memoirs and accompanying photographs that could be donated to the school or community library.

Fishing for Friends

a memoir by Jennifer Haynes, West Palm Beach, Florida

It was the first day of my summer vacation and where do you think I ended up? That's right—back at school! I had made a deal with my teacher, so there I was at 10:30 A.M. with my friend Tammi back in Mr. Tufts' classroom. The classroom was just as cluttered as we had left it the day before. The books were stacked a mile high ready to be packed away, and the posters were practically leaning off the walls screaming for our attention. When we entered the classroom, Mr. Tufts, my English teacher (some people call him Mr. T), was sitting at his desk.

"Hi! We're here," I said, as we leaned our fishing poles against the bulletin board. He didn't have to say a word. We knew our job and we knew our deal. Nonetheless, his military salute commanded us into action.

"Great! Right on time! Let's get busy. Take down the posters, pack the books, and pick up any papers on the floor. When you're done, we can post the sign: **Gone Fishing!**"

It was after lunch when Tammi and I finished the tasks. The once cluttered room looked quite empty now. Seeing that we had completed our part of the deal, Mr. Tufts herded us out of the classroom and posted his sign. "Now for my part of the deal," he said. "Pizza and fish!"

Tammi laughed and said, "Mr. Tufts, I do hope you don't mean we're going to use the fish we catch as topping for the pizza!"

Jokingly he replied, "Well, you'll have to wait and see!"

His response reminded me of how he would bait us like that and memories of a fun year flashed through my mind. As we walked toward the exit sign, I stopped myself just in time from tripping over Tammi's pole. Trying to hide my embarrassment, I just laughed with them.

When we reached the parking lot, Mr. Tufts' blue truck was not there! He had forgotten that his son had left him off at school and had borrowed the truck for the day. "So much for our fishing plans!" I thought. But luckily, we found a ride from another teacher, who pretended not to mind having our fishing poles hang out of her car window.

When we pulled up to Mr. Tufts' waterfront home, Tammi shyly asked, "Uh, Mr. T, would it be all right if I invited my friend, Mike, who lives nearby, to fish with us?"

"Sure," he said, "as long as he can catch a fish for pizza topping!" In an instant, Tammi was on the phone to Mike. Her invitation not only hooked Mike but also Adam!

After fishing unsuccessfully in front of Mr. T's place, we moved to the waterfront by Adam's grandparents' house. There our luck changed and all of us caught many fish. However, we didn't keep any of them. We simply threw the slimy things back into the water. I think deep down I just wanted to make sure we didn't have any to use as pizza topping—just in case Mr. T wasn't kidding!

By 6:30, the second part of Mr. T's promise came true. The pizza arrived. Leaving all fish behind, we went back to his deck and devoured our meal. It was delicious!

"We should do this again," I suggested.

"Maybe in another week," Mike blurted out.

That day I made two new friends, Mike and Adam, all because I helped my teacher clean up our classroom.

The day ended when my Mom picked up Tammi and me at Mr. T's home. It was a nice way to end my year as a seventh grader. I certainly have some great memories— thanks to a teacher who cared enough to take us fishing!

Cooperative Learning

ADVERTISING A FRIENDSHIP WEEK

Do particular television commercials stand out in your memory? How about magazine or newspaper advertisements? Can you think of other ways people sell products? With this project, you'll have the opportunity to develop and sell an idea called Friendship Week. First, you'll work with your class to list events for the week. Then you'll work in small groups to develop ways to advertise the events. Your end product will be an advertising campaign to let people know about Friendship Week.

The PROCESS

Imagine that you and your classmates are the producers of a local television station and you plan to sponsor a Friendship Week. The agenda for the week includes special television programs focusing on the importance of friendship. With your classmates, brainstorm a list of programs and activities on the chalkboard. Once you've agreed on your agenda, change roles and imagine that you're part of an advertising agency.

To be part of an advertising agency, you and your classmates will form small groups—each representing a different agency. First, decide on a name for your agency. Then decide how your advertising team will publicize Friendship Week for the local television station. Use the following three assignments to structure your ideas.

1. Make a poster.
2. Write and design a brochure.
3. Write and perform a commercial.

The PROCEDURE

Now decide how your group will complete its assignments. Depending on the size of your group, you may divide the tasks, or all of you may need to work on the tasks together. Whatever your approach, make a chart like the one below to help you keep track of who will do what, what materials you need, and how much time will be allowed to complete each task.

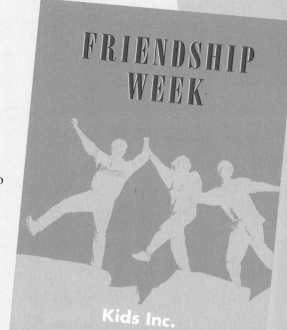

Task	Materials	Due Date	Person Responsible

The PRESENTATION

As a class, decide on a time and place for the presentations of the advertising campaigns for Friendship Week. Remember each group should display a poster, pass out a brochure (make copies if possible), and perform a commercial.

After each presentation, display the brochures and posters in the classroom. Then have a class discussion about the variety of ideas presented by each advertising agency.

PROJECT 3

Helping Your Community

A FRIEND-TO-MY-COMMUNITY DAY

One of the Big Questions in this unit asks, "What are different kinds of friendship?" In this project, you'll explore this question as you and your classmates develop and propose a plan for making community improvements during a Friend-to-My-Community Day.

Choosing A PLAN

With a partner or a small group, begin by brainstorming a list of ways you can be a friend to your community. Perhaps you know of an unsightly vacant lot that would make a wonderful community garden, or a neighborhood school that could use a litter patrol. Complete the statement below with one of the ideas from your brainstorming list.

• I'll become a friend to my community by_____.

Then develop your plan by using the following guidelines.

Laying THE GROUNDWORK

Depending on the community project you select, you may need permission and cooperation. For example, a *create-a-garden* plan may need the approval of the local authorities and the help of a garden club. To enlist the help of others, decide whether to write letters or to make personal visits.

Developing
YOUR PLAN

Now that you've thought out what you want to do and how to do it, it's time to develop and write your plan. Begin by explaining your purpose for having a Friend-to-My-Community Day.

Organizing
YOUR TASKS

Next form committees that will show volunteers what needs to be done. For example, you might set up separate committees for Publicity, Materials, and Donations. Make a list like the following one to organize your tasks and provide a deadline to indicate when the tasks should be completed.

Publicity Committee			
Person	**Task**	**Materials**	**Due Date**
Maria	Poster	Posterboard, markers	2/16
John	Poster		
Sarah			
Jesse			

Launching
YOUR PLAN

Use charts to present your plan. Be sure to include the details you've defined in the previous steps. Then present your plan for a Friend-to-My-Community Day to the class.

If it's not possible for your class to carry out the plan, send your plan to some organization that can make it a reality—the town council or a local charity. You too can make a difference.

Putting It All Together

How Have Your Ideas About Friendship Changed?

After meeting the characters in this unit, how have your ideas about friendship changed? Review the writing you did earlier in the unit, such as your journal responses to the Big Questions and your Writing Workshop. Has the meaning of friendship changed for you? With your classmates, share and discuss your thoughts on this topic. Then compose an essay or a poem that explains your definition of friendship.

CHANGING IDEAS ABOUT FRIENDSHIP

Prewriting and Drafting   To help you generate ideas for your essay or poem, think about the following questions. Which character from this unit best reflects your feelings about friendship? How would you define friendship? What are the qualities of true friendship? Don't forget to consider the poetry selections when you think about the literature in this unit.

Now draft an essay or poem that explains your definition of friendship. In your writing, explain how your perspective on friendship has broadened. Be sure to support your definition with specific references to the literature. Include two or more characters, incidents, or even quotations from the literature. You may even want to add examples from your own life.

Revising and Editing   First, review your own writing by reading it aloud to yourself. Make sure that you have expressed your main idea clearly, supported it with examples, and used vivid, colorful words. Next exchange papers with a classmate to check grammar, punctuation, and spelling. Then make any appropriate corrections.

Publishing   If you choose to share your essay with the whole class, you should now decide how the class's essays and poems should be organized. Then extend your creativity and design a cover for a collection of your classmates' writing called *Reflections on Friendship*. Share your collection with another class or display it in your school library.

Evaluating Your Work

With a partner, discuss the Big Questions on pages 10 and 11 and revisit the ideas you listed in your journal for *Now Think* on page 11. Compare your current ideas about friendship with your thoughts at the beginning of this unit.

Think Back About Your Work

Now that you've completed this unit, it's time to think about and evaluate your work. Think back about your journal responses, writing activities, and projects. Then, in a letter to a real or imaginary friend, try to capture what you have accomplished in this unit. Use the following questions to help you write your letter.

- Which literature selections changed your ideas about friendship?

- Which literature selections were most interesting? Least interesting? Why?

- What were your favorite and least favorite activities? Why?

- What did you learn as you worked on your project?

- What would you do differently if you worked on a similar project again?

- How would you rate your work in this unit? Use the following scale and explain why and how you chose this number.

1 = Outstanding	3 = Fair
2 = Good	4 = Not as good as it could have been

CHARACTER

What Is Character?   **Character** is the term for a person or animal that participates in the action of a work of literature. The characters in a work of literature can be divided into two categories: *main characters* and *minor characters*. *Main characters* are those people or animals that are the most important characters in a work of literature. For example, in the story "I Saw What I Saw," the main characters are the narrator, Ray Beane, and the grocer, Mr. Meyer. The *minor characters* are those who are not central to the action in a story. For example, in the story "I Saw What I Saw," some of the minor characters are Ray's mother, Frankie, Mr. Aiken, and the gunman.

Developing a Character   Make a list of the characters found in one of the literature selections that you've read in this unit. Then label each character as either *main* or *minor*. If you could develop one of the minor characters into a main character, which one would you choose? What changes would you make to this character, and how would these changes affect the outcome of the story? In a paragraph or two, explain the change or changes you would make to this minor character. Be sure to show how the outcome of the story would be affected. Share your writing with your classmates by creating a bulletin-board display with the title "Developing Characters."

Extending Your Vocabulary   What does the word *character* really mean? Sometimes you may hear, "Oh, what a *character* he is!" "Is she one of the *characters* in this production?" Obviously, there are many ways to use the word *character*. Look up in a dictionary the meanings listed for *character* and select three of them. Then write a paragraph explaining the meanings you have selected. Be sure to provide sentence examples, like the ones above, for each meaning you choose for the word *character*. Compare your selections with a partner.

What Is Theme?

Theme is the main idea of a work of literature. It is the underlying message, which a writer most often implies rather than states. For example, the short story that ends this unit, "I Saw What I Saw," is about an adolescent who gets a job in a small grocery store in order to earn some extra money. Yet underlying that is the theme that friendship can grow in the most surprising places. We see this in the bond that develops between Ray and Mr. Meyer, the grocery store owner. To help you fully understand the theme of a literary work, focus on two aspects of the selection. First, ask yourself in what ways the main character has changed. Then ask how the conflict in the story has been settled. The answers should give you a better understanding of the theme.

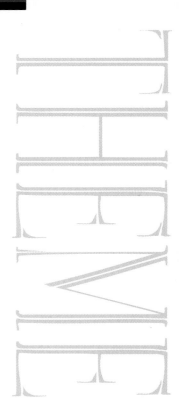

Writing to the Editor Suppose that the publishers of this unit contacted you about helping them with a revision of this book. Write a letter to the editor about which selections you would keep and explain why. Also suggest ideas you have for replacements. Make sure that your replacements fit in with the *theme* of this unit. Then design a book jacket with information about the book itself. Use your letters and book jackets for a bulletin-board display.

Creating a Theme Park Have you ever been to a theme park? In case you haven't, it's a park filled with amusement rides related to a theme. If the park were called "Storyland Park," the names of the rides would be linked to children's stories—for example, a roller coaster might be called the "Mad Hatter." With a partner or small group, brainstorm a list of ideas for a *Friendship Theme Park*. Think of some friendship stories, like *The Incredible Journey,* or some from this unit like "The Bracelet" for ideas. Then map out the park and label all the sections. Present your plan to your class.

GLOSSARY OF LITERARY TERMS

A

alliteration Repetition of the first sound—usually a consonant sound—in several words of a sentence or a line of poetry.

allusion An author's indirect reference to someone or something that is presumed to be familiar to the reader.

anecdote A short narrative about an interesting or a humorous event, usually in the life of a person.

antagonist The person or force opposing the protagonist, or main character in a literary work. [See also *protagonist*.]

autobiography A person's written account of his or her own life.

B

ballad A poem, often a song, that tells a story in simple verse.

biography An account of a person's life, written by another person.

blank verse Unrhymed poetry.

C

character A person or an animal that participates in the action of a work of literature. A *dynamic character* is one whose thoughts, feelings, and actions are changeable and lifelike; a *static character* always remains the same. [See also *protagonist, antagonist*.]

characterization The creation of characters through the characters' use of language and through descriptions of their appearance, thoughts, emotions, and actions. [See also *character*.]

chronology An arrangement of events in the order in which they happen.

cliché An overused expression that is trite rather than meaningful.

climax The highest point of tension in the plot of a work of literature. [See also *plot*.]

comedy An amusing play that has a happy ending.

conclusion The final part or ending of a piece of literature.

concrete poem A poem arranged on the page so that its punctuation, letters, and lines make the shape of the subject of the poem.

conflict A problem that confronts the characters in a piece of literature. The conflict may be *internal* (a character's struggle within himself or herself) or *external* (a character's struggle against nature, another person, or society). [See also *plot*.]

context The general sense of words that helps readers to understand the meaning of unfamiliar words and phrases in a piece of writing.

D

description An author's use of words to give the reader or listener a mental picture, an impression, or an understanding of a person, place, thing, event, or idea.

dialect A form of speech spoken by people in a particular group or geographical region that differs in vocabulary, grammar, and pronunciation from the standard language.

dialogue The spoken words and conversation of characters in a work of literature.

drama A play that is performed before an audience according to stage directions and using dialogue. Classical drama has two genres: *tragedy* and *comedy*. Modern drama includes *melodrama, satire, theater of the absurd,* and *pantomime*. [See also *comedy, play,* and *tragedy*.]

dramatic poetry A play written in the form of poetry.

E

epic A long narrative poem—written in a formal style and meant to be read aloud—that relates the adventures and

experiences of one or more great heroes or heroines.

essay   Personal nonfiction writing about a particular subject that is important to the writer.

excerpt   A passage from a larger work that has been taken out of its context to be used for a special purpose.

exposition   Writing that explains, analyzes, or defines.

extended metaphor   An elaborately drawn out metaphor. [See also *metaphor*.]

F

fable   A short, simple story whose purpose is to teach a lesson, usually with animal characters who talk and act like people.

fantasy   Imaginative fiction about unrealistic characters, places, and events.

fiction   Literature, including the short story and the novel, that tells about imaginary people and events.

figurative language   Language used to express ideas through figures of speech: descriptions that aren't meant to be taken literally. Types of figurative language include *simile, metaphor, extended metaphor, hyperbole,* and *personification*.

figure of speech   A type of figurative language, not meant to be taken literally, that expresses something in such a way that it brings the thing to life in the reader's or listener's imagination. [See also *figurative language*.]

flashback   A break in a story's action that relates a past happening in order to give the reader background information about a present action in the story.

folktale   A story that has been passed along from storyteller to storyteller for generations. Kinds of folktales include *tall tales, fairy tales, fables, legends,* and *myths*.

foreshadowing   The use of clues to create suspense by giving the reader or audience hints of events to come.

free verse   Poetry that has no formal rhyme scheme or metrical pattern.

G

genre   A major category of art. The three major literary genres are poetry, prose, and drama.

H

haiku   A three-line Japanese verse form. In most haiku, the first and third lines have five syllables, while the second line has seven. The

traditional haiku describes a complicated feeling or thought in simple language through a single image.

hero/heroine   The main character in a work of literature. In heroic literature, the hero or heroine is a particularly brave, noble, or clever person whose achievements are unusual and important. [See also *character*.]

heroic age   The historical period in western civilization—from about 800 B.C. through A.D. 200—during which most works of heroic literature, such as myths and epics, were created in ancient Greece and Rome.

hubris   Arrogance or excessive pride leading to mistakes; the character flaw in a hero of classical tragedy.

hyperbole   An obvious exaggeration used for emphasis. [See also *figurative language*.]

I

idiom   An expression whose meaning cannot be understood from the ordinary meaning of the words. For example, *It's raining cats and dogs*.

imagery   The words and phrases in writing that appeal to the senses of sight, hearing, taste, touch, and smell.

irony   An effect created by a sharp contrast between what is expected and what is real. An *ironic twist* in a plot is an event that is the complete opposite of what the characters have been hoping or expecting will happen. An *ironic statement* declares the opposite of the speaker's literal meaning.

J

jargon   Words and phrases used by a group of people who share the same profession or special interests in order to refer to technical things or processes with which they are familiar. In general, jargon is any terminology that sounds unclear, overused, or pretentious.

L

legend   A famous folktale about heroic actions, passed along by word of mouth from generation to generation. The legend may have begun as a factual account of real people and events but has become mostly or completely fictitious.

limerick   A form of light verse, or humorous poetry, written in one five-line stanza with a regular scheme of rhyme and meter.

literature   The branch of art that is expressed in written language and includes all written genres.

lyric poem   A short poem that expresses personal feelings and thoughts in a musical way. Originally, lyrics were the words of songs that were sung to music played on the lyre, a stringed instrument invented by the ancient Greeks.

M

metamorphosis   The transformation of one thing, or being, into another completely different thing or being, such as a caterpillar's change into a butterfly.

metaphor   Figurative language in which one thing is said to be another thing. [See also *figurative language.*]

meter   The pattern of rhythm in lines of poetry. The most common meter, in poetry written in English, is iambic pentameter, that is, a verse having five metrical feet, each foot of verse having two syllables, an unaccented one followed by an accented one.

mood   The feeling or atmosphere that a reader senses while reading or listening to a work of literature.

motivation   A character's reasons for doing, thinking, feeling, or saying something. Sometimes an author will make a character's motivation obvious from the beginning. In realistic fiction and drama, however, a character's motivation may be so complicated that the reader discovers it gradually, by studying the character's thoughts, feelings, and behavior.

myth   A story, passed along by word of mouth for generations, about the actions of gods and goddesses or superhuman heroes and heroines. Most myths were first told to explain the origins of natural things or to justify the social rules and customs of a particular society.

N

narration   The process of telling a story. For both fiction and nonfiction, there are two main kinds of narration, based on whether the story is told from a first-person or third-person point of view. [See also *point of view.*]

narrative poem   A poem that tells a story containing the basic literary ingredients of fiction: character, setting, and plot.

narrator   The person, or voice, that tells a story. [See also *point of view, voice.*]

nonfiction   Prose that is factually true and is about real people, events, and places.

nonstandard English
Versions of English, such as slang and dialects, that use pronunciation, vocabulary, idiomatic expressions, grammar, and punctuation that differ from the accepted "correct" constructions of English.

novel A long work of narrative prose fiction. A novel contains narration, a setting or settings, characters, dialogue, and a more complicated plot than a short story.

O

onomatopoeia The technique of using words that imitate the sounds they describe, such as *hiss*, *buzz*, and *splash*.

oral tradition Stories, poems, and songs that have been kept alive by being told, recited, and sung by people over many generations. Since the works were not originally written, they often have many different versions.

P

parable A brief story—similar to a fable, but about people— that describes an ordinary situation and concludes with a short moral or lesson to be learned.

personification Figurative language in which an animal, an object, or an idea is given human characteristics. [See also *figurative language*.]

persuasion A type of speech or writing whose purpose is to convince people that something is true or important.

play A work of dramatic literature written for performance by actors before an audience. In classical or traditional drama, a play is divided into five acts, each containing a number of scenes. Each act represents a distinct phase in the development of the plot. Modern plays often have only one act and one scene.

playwright The author of a play.

plot The sequence of actions and events in fiction or drama. A traditional plot has at least three parts: the *rising action*, leading up to a turning point that affects the main character; the *climax*, the turning point or moment of greatest intensity or interest; and the *falling action*, leading away from the conflict, or resolving it.

poetry Language selected and arranged in order to say something in a compressed or nonliteral way. Modern poetry may or may not use many of the traditional poetic techniques that include *meter*, *rhyme*, *alliteration*, *figurative language*, *symbolism*, and *specific verse forms*.

point of view The perspective from which a writer tells a story. *First-person* narrators tell the story from their own point of view, using pronouns such as *I* or *me*. *Third-person* narrators, using pronouns such as *he*, *she*, or *them*, may be *omniscient* (knowing everything about all characters), or *limited* (taking the point of view of one character). [See also *narration*.]

propaganda Information or ideas that may or may not be true, but are spread as though they are true, in order to persuade people to do or believe something.

prose The ordinary form of written and spoken language used to create fiction, nonfiction, and most drama.

protagonist The main character of a literary work. [See also *character* and *characterization*.]

R

refrain A line or group of lines that is repeated, usually at the end of each verse, in a poem or a song.

repetition The use of the same formal element more than once in a literary work, for emphasis or in order to achieve another desired effect.

resolution The falling action in fiction or drama,

including all of the developments that follow the climax and show that the story's conflict is over. [See also *plot*.]

rhyme scheme   A repeated pattern of similar sounds, usually found at the ends of lines of poetry or poetic drama.

rhythm   In poetry, the measured recurrence of accented and unaccented syllables in a particular pattern. [See also *meter*.]

S

scene   The time, place, and circumstances of a play or a story. In a play, a scene is a section of an act. [See also *play*.]

science fiction   Fantasy literature set in an imaginary future, with details and situations that are designed to seem scientifically possible.

setting   The time and place of a work of literature.

short story   Narrative prose fiction that is shorter and has a less complicated plot than a novel. A short story contains narration, at least one setting, at least one character, and usually some dialogue.

simile   Figurative language that compares two unlike things, introduced by the words "like" or "as." [See also *figurative language*.]

soliloquy   In a play, a short speech spoken by a single character when he or she is alone on the stage. A soliloquy usually expresses the character's innermost thoughts and feelings, when he or she thinks no other characters can hear.

sonnet   A poem written in one stanza, using fourteen lines of iambic pentameter. [See also *meter*.]

speaker   In poetry, the individual whose voice seems to be speaking the lines. [See also *narration, voice*.]

stage directions   The directions, written by the playwright, to tell the director, actors, and theater technicians how a play should be dramatized. Stage directions may specify such things as how the setting should appear in each scene, how the actors should deliver their lines, when the stage curtain should rise and fall, how stage lights should be used, where on the stage the actors should be during the action, and when sound effects should be used.

stanza   A group of lines in poetry set apart by blank lines before and after the group; a poetic verse.

style   The distinctive way in which an author composes a

work of literature in written or spoken language.

suspense   An effect created by authors of various types of fiction and drama, especially adventure and mystery to heighten interest in the story.

symbol   An image, person, place, or thing that is used to express the idea of something else.

T

tall tale   A kind of folk tale, or legend, that exaggerates the characteristics of its hero or heroine.

theme   The main idea or underlying subject of a work of literature.

tone   The attitude that a work of literature expresses to the reader through its style.

tragedy   In classical drama, a tragedy depicts a noble hero or heroine who makes a mistake of judgment that has disastrous consequences.

V

verse   A stanza in a poem. Also, a synonym for poetry as a genre. [See also *stanza*.]

voice   The narrator or the person who relates the action of a piece of literature. [See also *speaker*.]

ACKNOWLEDGMENTS

Grateful acknowledgment is made for permission to reprint the following copyrighted material.

"The Bracelet" by Yoshiko Uchida is reprinted by permission of the Estate of Yoshiko Uchida.

"A bald display of solidarity" is reprinted from *The Boston Globe*, December 5, 1992 by permission of the Associated Press.

"Our Good Day" from *The House on Mango Street* by Sandra Cisneros. Copyright © 1989 by Sandra Cisneros. Published in the United States by Vintage Books, a division of Random House, Inc., New York, and distributed in Canada by Random House of Canada Limited, Toronto. Originally published, in somewhat different form, by Arte Público Press in 1984 and revised in 1989. Reprinted by permission of Susan Bergholz Literary Services, New York.

"The Squirrel's Loan" by Partap Sharma is reprinted from *The Surangini Tales* by Partap Sharma published by Harcourt Brace Jovanovich, 1973. Permission granted by the author.

"Telephone Talk" by X. J. Kennedy. Reprinted with permission of Margaret L. McElderry Books, an imprint of Macmillan Publishing Company from *The Kite That Braved Old Orchard Beach* by X. J. Kennedy. Copyright © 1991 by X. J. Kennedy.

"A Time to Talk" by Robert Frost from *The Poetry of Robert Frost* edited by Edward Connery Lathem. Copyright 1944 by Robert Frost. Copyright 1916, © 1969 by Henry Holt and Company, Inc. Reprinted by permission of Henry Holt and Company, Inc.

"The Osage Orange Tree" by William Stafford is reprinted by permission of the author.

"Where Are You Now, William Shakespeare?" by M. E. Kerr from *Me Me Me Me Me*, copyright © 1983 by M. E. Kerr, a Charlotte Zolotow book. Reprinted by permission of HarperCollins Publisher.

"Thank You, M'am" by Langston Hughes from *The Langston Hughes Reader*, copyright © 1958 by Langston Hughes. Reprinted by permission of the Harold Ober Agency.

"Amigo Brothers" by Piri Thomas from *Stories From El Barrio*. Copyright © 1978 by Piri Thomas. Reprinted by permission of Alfred A. Knopf, Inc.

"Hannah Armstrong" by Edgar Lee Masters from *Spoon River Anthology* by Edgar Lee Masters, originally published by the Macmillan Co. Permission by Ellen C. Masters.

"Graduates hear some Clinton advice" from *The Boston Globe*, May 17, 1993 is reprinted by permission of the Associated Press.

"Lob's Girl" by Joan Aiken from *A Whisper in the Night*, copyright © 1981, 1982, 1983, 1984 by Joan Aiken Enterprises, Ltd. Reprinted by permission of Dell Publishing, a division of The Bantam Doubleday Dell Publishing Group, Inc.

"The Chinese Checker Players" by Richard Brautigan from *The Pill versus The Springhill Mine Disaster*, copyright © 1968 by Richard Brautigan is reproduced by permission of the Helen Brann Agency.

"Mr. Misenheimer's Garden" from *On The Road With Charles Kuralt* by Charles Kuralt. Reprinted by permission of The Putnam Publishing Group. Copyright © 1985 by CBS, Inc.

"I Saw What I Saw" by Judie Angell, copyright © 1992 by Judie Angell, from *Within Reach*, edited by Donald Gallo, copyright © 1993. By permission of HarperCollins Publisher.

ILLUSTRATION

26-27 Jennifer Hewitson; 32-37 Karen Watson; 40-47 R.J. Shay.

PHOTOGRAPHY

4 *l* Julie Bidwell/©D.C. Heath; *r* Skjold/The Image Works; 5 Courtesy Estate of Romare Bearden. Collection of Dr. and Mrs. Cyril J. Jones; 6 Sarah Putnam/©D.C. Heath; 8 Stephen Simpson/FPG International; 9 Erika Stone; 10 *t* Mary Kate Denny/PhotoEdit; *b* John Owens/©D.C. Heath; 11 *t* Mary Kate Denny/PhotoEdit; *b* Jim Whitmer/Stock Boston; 12, 15, 16, 17 Miné Okubo; 19 Photo by Deborah Storm/Courtesy of Macmillan Children's Book Group; 20-21 Karen Kerckhove; 22-23 National Museum of Modern Art, Paris/SCALA/Art Resource, NY. ©1995 ARS, NY/ADAGP, Paris; 25 AP/Wide World Photos; 28 Roy Lichtenstein. Courtesy of James Goodman Gallery, New York; 29 Dorothy M. Kennedy; 30 UPI/The Bettmann Archive; 30-31 Boston Public Library Print Department; 47 Photo by Zoe Kamitses; 48 The Howard University Gallery of Art, Permanent Collection, Washington, D.C.; 51 Courtesy Estate of Romare Bearden. Collection of Dr. and Mrs. Cyril J. Jones; 53 UPI/The Bettmann Archive; 54 Private Collection, California; 65 Alex Gotfrey; 66-67 *background* Peter Gridley/FPG International; 67 *t* Gift of Mr. and Mrs. William H. Lane and the Hayden Collection, by exchange. Courtesy, Museum of Fine Arts, Boston. 1990.376; *b* UPI/The Bettmann Archive; 68 Joe Sohn/Chromosohn/The Stock Market; 70-71 Karen Kasmauski/Woodfin Camp; 76 Adam Woolfitt/Woodfin Camp; 83 Photo by Rod Delroy. Courtesy of St. Martin's Press; 84-85 Louis K. Meisel Gallery, New York; 86-87, 88-89 Craig Hammell/The Stock Market; 89 CBS News; 90-91 Steve Proehl/The Image Bank; 94-95 David Hamilton/The Image Bank; 98 Susan Leavines/Photo Researchers; 101 Courtesy of Macmillan Children's Goup; 103 Nancy Sheehan/©D.C. Heath; 106 *t* Elizabeth Hamlin/Stock Boston; *b* Shawna Johnston; 110 Peter Fronk/Tony Stone Images; 112 Jean-Claude Lejeune/Stock Boston; 113 Nancy Sheehan/The Picture Cube; 114 *t* J. Sulley/The Image Works; 114 *b*-115 Courtesy of Wasatch Fish & Gardens, Salt Lake City, UT.

Back cover *t* Julie Bidwell/©D.C. Heath; *c* Sarah Putnam/©D.C. Heath; *b* John Owens/©D.C. Heath.

Full Pronunciation Key for Footnoted Words

(Each pronunciation and definition is adapted from *Scott, Foresman Advanced Dictionary* by E.L. Thorndike and Clarence L. Barnhart.)

The pronunciation of each footnoted word is shown just after the word, in this way: **abbreviate** [ə brē′ vē āt]. The letters and signs used are pronounced as in the words below. The mark ′ is placed after a syllable with primary or heavy accent, as in the example above. The mark ′ after a syllable shows a secondary or lighter accent, as in **abbreviation** [ə brē′ vē ā′ shən].

Some words, taken from foreign languages, are spoken with sounds that do not otherwise occur in English. Symbols for these sounds are given in the key as "foreign sounds."

a	hat, cap	j	jam, enjoy	u	cup, butter	**foreign sounds**	
ā	age, face	k	kind, seek	u̇	full, put		
ä	father, far	l	land, coal	ü	rule, move	Y as in French *du*.
		m	me, am	v	very, save	Pronounce (ē) with
b	bad, rob	n	no, in	w	will, woman	the lips rounded as
ch	child, much	ng	long, bring	y	young, yet	for (ü).
d	did, red			z	zero, breeze	
		o	hot, rock	zh	measure, seizure	à as in French *ami*.
e	let, best	ō	open, go			Pronounce (ä) with
ē	equal, be	ô	order, all	ə represents:		the lips spread and
ėr	term, learn	oi	oil, voice		a in about	held tense.
		ou	house, out		e in taken	
f	fat, if				i in pencil	œ as in French *peu*.
g	go, bag	p	paper, cup		o in lemon	Pronounce (ā) with the
h	he, how	r	run, try		u in circus	lips rounded as for (ō).
		s	say, yes			
i	it, pin	sh	she, rush			N as in French *bon*.
ī	ice, five	t	tell, it			The N is not pro-
		th	thin, both			nounced, but shows
		ŦH	then, smooth			that the vowel before
						it is nasal.

H as in German *ach*. Pronounce (k) without closing the breath passage.

Out of Tune

HEATH
MIDDLE LEVEL
LITERATURE

Heath
MIDDLE LEVEL
LITERATURE

Out of Tune

▼ THEME
CONFLICT RESOLUTION

A U T H O R S

Donna Alvermann
Linda Miller Cleary
Kenneth Donelson
Donald Gallo
Alice Haskins
J. Howard Johnston
John Lounsbury
Alleen Pace Nilsen
Robert Pavlik
Jewell Parker Rhodes
Alberto Alvaro Ríos
Sandra Schurr
Lyndon Searfoss
Julia Thomason
Max Thompson
Carl Zon

D.C. Heath and Company
Lexington, Massachusetts / Toronto, Ontario

STAFF CREDITS

EDITORIAL	Barbara A. Brennan, Helen Byers, Christopher Johnson, Kathleen Kennedy Kelley, Owen Shows, Rita M. Sullivan
	Proofreading: JoAnne B. Sgroi
CONTRIBUTING WRITERS	Nance Davidson, Florence Harris
SERIES DESIGN	Robin Herr
BOOK DESIGN	Caroline Bowden, Daniel Derdula, Susan Geer, Diana Maloney, Angela Sciaraffa, Bonnie Chayes Yousefian
	Art Editing: Carolyn Langley
PHOTOGRAPHY	*Series Photography Coordinator:* Carmen Johnson
	Photo Research Supervisor: Martha Friedman
	Photo Researchers: Wendy Enright, Linda Finigan, Po-yee McKenna, PhotoSearch, Inc., Gillian Speeth, Denise Theodores
	Assignment Photography Coordinators: Susan Doheny, Gayna Hoffman, Shawna Johnston
COMPUTER PREPRESS	Ricki Pappo, Kathy Meisl
	Richard Curran, Michele Locatelli
PERMISSIONS	Dorothy B. McLeod
PRODUCTION	Patrick Connolly

Cover: *Enigmatic Combat* Arshile Gorky; 1936-38, oil on canvas 35 3/4" x 48", San Francisco Museum of Modern Art, gift of Jeanne Reynal. **Cover Design:** Steve Snider

Published simultaneously in Canada

Printed in the United States of America

International Standard Book Number: 0-669-32100-1 (soft cover)
4 5 6 7 8 9 10-RRD-99 98

International Standard Book Number: 0-669-38170-5 (hard cover)
3 4 5 6 7 8 9 10-RRD-99 98 97 96 95

Middle Level Authors

Donna Alvermann, University of Georgia
Alice Haskins, Howard County Public Schools, Maryland
J. Howard Johnston, University of South Florida
John Lounsbury, Georgia College
Sandra Schurr, University of South Florida
Julia Thomason, Appalachian State University
Max Thompson, Appalachian State University
Carl Zon, California Assessment Collaborative

Literature and Language Arts Authors

Linda Miller Cleary, University of Minnesota
Kenneth Donelson, Arizona State University
Donald Gallo, Central Connecticut State University
Alleen Pace Nilsen, Arizona State University
Robert Pavlik, Cardinal Stritch College, Milwaukee
Jewell Parker Rhodes, Arizona State University
Alberto Alvaro Ríos, Arizona State University
Lyndon Searfoss, Arizona State University

Teacher Consultants

Suzanne Aubin, Patapsco Middle School, Ellicott City, Maryland
Judy Baxter, Newport News Public Schools, Newport News, Virginia
Saundra Bryn, Director of Research and Development, El Mirage, Arizona
Lorraine Gerhart, Elmbrook Middle School, Elm Grove, Wisconsin
Kathy Tuchman Glass, Burlingame Intermediate School, Burlingame, California
Lisa Mandelbaum, Crocker Middle School, Hillsborough, California
Lucretia Pannozzo, John Jay Middle School, Katonah, New York
Carol Schultz, Jerling Junior High, Orland Park, Illinois
Jeanne Siebenman, Grand Canyon University, Phoenix, Arizona
Gail Thompson, Garey High School, Pomona, California
Rufus Thompson, Grace Yokley School, Ontario, California
Tom Tufts, Conniston Middle School, West Palm Beach, Florida
Edna Turner, Harpers Choice Middle School, Columbia, Maryland
C. Anne Webb, Buerkle Junior High School, St. Louis, Missouri
Geri Yaccino, Thompson Junior High School, St. Charles, Illinois

CONTENTS

THE LITERATURE

ASKING BIG QUESTIONS ABOUT THE LITERATURE

P R O J E C T S

1 WRITING WORKSHOP

CONVINCE THEM WITH A LETTER   106-111

Persuade two opposing groups that there's a way to resolve their conflict.

2 COOPERATIVE LEARNING

A TV GUIDE FOR PARENTS   112-113

Make a TV guide that will help parents analyze TV sitcoms and evaluate which ones offer positive role models to young viewers.

3 HELPING YOUR COMMUNITY

WORDS OF ADVICE   114-115

How would you settle an argument with a friend? What's the best way to reach agreement in a group? Your conflict resolution manual can be just what others need.

Picture This

Imagine this predicament. You've been wanting to know a certain group of kids, but they've never seemed very friendly before. Now they've invited you to do something after school—but something you don't feel right about. You don't want to say yes, but if you say no, the group might not include you again. What do you feel? Conflict. What can you do? You can try to ignore your inner struggle. Or you can take steps to resolve it. No one likes conflict, but we all experience it at times. It can help to know there are different types of conflict—as well as strategies for trying to resolve them.

1
Pick a picture.

These photographs depict different sorts of conflict: people at odds with nature or with each other. Look at each picture carefully and speculate about what's happening in it. Then describe each picture in your journal as though you're watching its drama unfold. Describe how each conflict looks as well as how it feels to the person(s) experiencing it.

2

Discuss the conflict.

With a partner or a small group, compare notes about each photograph by discussing these questions:

- What might have caused this conflict?

- How does each person feel about his or her part in the conflict as it's happening? Afterward?

- What could be the immediate results of each party's actions? What might the later consequences be?

- What choices might each party have for dealing with the conflict?

3

Role-play the alternatives.

With your partner or small group, select one photograph and role-play the conflict and a possible resolution. Then dramatize it a second time, with another resolution. Discuss which option seems best to you, and why.

Asking Big Questions About the Theme

? What causes conflict?

In your journal, make a web like this one. Let your mind wander to words and phrases for things you consider to be causes of conflict between people. Write them inside circles around the central phrase. Then compare your web to a classmate's.

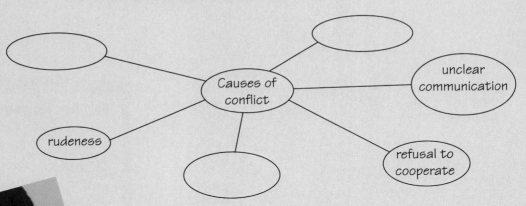

? What are the different kinds of conflict?

With the whole class, brainstorm different kinds of conflict. Then discuss each kind of conflict and classify it according to these categories: *person against person, person against nature, person against society,* or *person against self*.

How do individuals and groups resolve conflicts?

With a partner, collect newspaper and magazine articles about local, national, and international conflicts. Then fill out a chart like this one. Discuss patterns in conflict resolution that you notice.

Title of Article	People Involved	Conflict	Cause	Actions Taken	Result and Consequences

What can people learn from conflict?

Think of a past conflict you learned something from. In your journal, briefly summarize the conflict and write about what it taught you. Then explain how differently you might react to the same conflict if you experienced it today.

NOW Think!

Suppose you've been asked to serve on a conflict resolution committee at school. What kinds of skills and strategies do you need in order to help individuals and groups in conflict? As you read the literature selections in this unit, see whether your ideas about skills and strategies for conflict resolution grow and change.

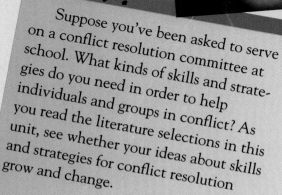

Amanda and the

Lithograph from *L'ordre des oiseaux*, Georges Braque

Wounded Birds

Colby Rodowsky

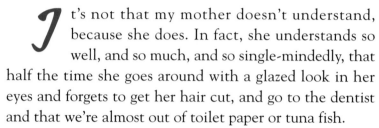

*I*t's not that my mother doesn't understand, because she does. In fact, she understands so well, and so much, and so single-mindedly, that half the time she goes around with a glazed look in her eyes and forgets to get her hair cut, and go to the dentist and that we're almost out of toilet paper or tuna fish.

She makes her living understanding, which may make more sense when I tell you that my mother is Dr. Emma Hart. Now, if that doesn't help, then probably, like me until my consciousness was raised, you've always thought of radio as the place to hear the Top 40 or sometimes the weather report when you're heading for the shore on a summer Friday afternoon. But just try twiddling the dial and you'll find her, way over to the left on the band, next to the country and western station.

Maybe what I should do is go back a little and explain. You see, my mother is a psychotherapist, which means that she counsels people and tries to help them find ways of dealing with their problems. She's also a widow. My father died when I was a baby, and sometimes I try to imagine what it must have been like for her, taking care of a baby alone and trying to establish a practice all at the same time. One thing I'm sure of is that knowing Mom, she handled it gracefully, and stoically,[1] and with that funny way she has of biting her lower lip so that for all her hanging-in-there attitude she still looks like a ten-year-old kid—the kind you want to do something for because she's

---

1. **stoically** [stō′ ə kəl lē]: calmly and without showing feelings.

not always whining or sniffling. I guess you'd have to say that as much as possible my mother is in charge of her own life, which is the way she tries to get the people who call in to her on the radio to be.

The way the radio program got started was that several years ago the producer was looking for something to put on in the late afternoon when people were mostly fixing dinner or driving carpool or just sitting with their feet up. It wasn't exactly prime time. Then he remembered how he'd heard Mom speak at a dinner once and had thought at the time that putting someone like her on radio would be a real public service. Besides, the ratings couldn't be any lower than they had been for the Handy Home Fixit show he'd had on before. Anyway, he tracked her down, arranged for a test, and then Mom was on the air.

I never will forget that first show. I mean, there was my mother's voice coming out of our kitchen radio, sounding slightly frantic and giving those first callers more than they bargained for: I guess she was afraid if she let them off the line there wouldn't *be* any more. That day even the producer called with a question. And the boy in the studio who went for coffee. But Mom hung in there, and calls continued to come in, and then they started backing up, and it wasn't long before people opened by saying, "I didn't think I'd *ever* get through to you." After only a month on the air the Emma Hart show went from one hour to two; and the way I figured it, a lot of people were eating dinner later than they ever had before. Including us.

Mom really cared about the people who telephoned her, and almost right from the beginning she was calling them her "wounded birds." Not on the air, of course, and *never* to anyone but me. I got used to her looking up in the middle of dinner or from watching the late news on TV and saying, "I hope my wounded bird with the abusive husband will get herself into counseling" or "The wounded bird with those children who walk all over her had better learn to assert herself before it's too late." And *I* sure learned not to joke around: once I referred to one of her callers as a fractured canary and almost started World War III.

Not long after this, things really started to happen. First, Mom's show was moved to a better time slot. Then it was syndicated, so that she wasn't just on the air here but in a bunch of other cities, too. The way "Doonesbury" and "Dick Tracy" are in a bunch of newspapers. Now, I have to say that for the most part my mother's pretty cool about things, but the day she found out that the Emma Hart show was being syndicated she just about flipped. She called me from the studio and told me to meet her at the Terrace Garden for dinner, to be sure and get spiffed up because we were going all out.

During dinner Mom spent a lot of time staring into the candlelight and smiling to herself. Finally she said, "Just think of all those people who'll be listening now." And let me tell you, I *was* thinking about them, and it worried me a lot. I mean the way I saw it, there were going to be even more problems: more victims who were downtrodden or misunderstood. More stories about people who had been abused or who had kids on drugs or dropping out, or ne'er-do-well relatives moving in. But when I tried to say that, Mom was suddenly all attention. "Don't be silly, Amanda. It's the same amount of time and the same number of calls—you'll hardly notice any difference. Only now I'll have wounded birds in Phoenix and Pittsburgh and Philadelphia."

In one way she was right: the show sounded pretty much the same. (Except that *I* found out that when your husband/lover/friend walks out on you it hurts as much in Peoria[2] as it does in Perth Amboy.[3])

In another way she was wrong: she was busier than she had ever been before, what with traveling and lecturing and doing guest shows from other cities. For a while there, it was as if I was spending as much time at my best friend Terri's as I was at my own house. Then eventually Mom decided I could stay at our place when she had to be out of town, as long as Terri stayed there with me, which wasn't as good or as bad as it sounds, because Terri lives right across the street and her mother has X-ray eyes. I mean we can hardly manage to reach for our favorite breakfast of Twinkies and Oreo ice cream with an orange juice chaser before her mother is on the telephone telling us to eat cornflakes instead—and to wash the dishes.

---

2. **Peoria** [pē ôr′ ē ə]: city in central Illinois.
3. **Perth Amboy** [pėrth am boy]: a seaport in New Jersey.

Sometimes I felt that life was nothing but a revolving door: Mom going out while I was coming in. I know there are some kids who would've thought I was lucky, but the thing about my mother is that she's okay. And I wanted to see more of her. Besides that, I needed to talk to her. I don't know why, but all of a sudden it seemed that things were piling up around me. No major crises, you understand. Nothing that would exactly stop traffic.

I'll give you an example.

Take my friend Terri. I have a terrible feeling that she has a secret crush on my boyfriend Josh. If she does, it would be a disaster, because how could we really be friends anymore? But then again how could Terri and I *not* be friends? I'm not sure *why* I think this, unless it's because she gets quiet and acts bored when I talk about him a lot—the way you do when you don't want to let on about liking someone. I mean she couldn't *really* be bored. Could she?

Then there's Miss Spellman, my English teacher, who has this really atrocious breath and is forever leaning into people as she reads poetry in class. Imagine somebody breathing garbage fumes on you as she recites Emily Dickinson. If something doesn't happen soon I may never like poetry again.

Now, maybe these aren't world problems, any more than the incident with the guidance counselor was, but it bugged me all the same. Our school has an obsession about students getting into *good* colleges a.s.a.p.[4] and knowing what they want to do with the rest of their lives (Terri and I call it the life-packaging syndrome). Anyway, this particular day I was coming out of gym on my way to study hall when Mr. Burnside, the guidance counselor, stopped me and started asking me all this stuff, like what my career goals were and had I decided what I wanted to major in in college.

What I said (only politer than it sounds here) was that how did I know what I wanted to major in when I didn't even know where I wanted to *go* to college. Mr. Burnside got a wild look in his eyes and started opening and closing his mouth so that all I could see was a shiny strand of spit running between his top and bottom teeth while he

4. **a.s.a.p.:** abbreviation for "as soon as possible."

Central ceiling panel in the room of Henry II the Louvre, Georges Braque, Paris

lectured me on how I was going about this whole college thing the wrong way. He said I should come into the guidance office someday and let him feed me into the computer—well, not me exactly, but stuff like my grades, extra curricular activities, and whether or not I needed financial aid.

"And what does your mother say?" he asked as he rooted in his pocket for a late pass to get me into study hall. "You'll certainly have it easier than anybody else in your class, or the school either for that matter—living with Dr. Emma Hart." He laughed that horselaugh of his and slapped me on the back. "She'll get right to the *Hart* of it." Another laugh. "Anybody else'd have to call her on the telephone." His laughter seemed to follow me all the way to study hall. I even heard it bouncing around in my head as I settled down to do my Spanish.

"Anybody else'd have to call her on the telephone," he had said.

W hy not? I thought as I was walking home from school. Why not? I asked myself when Josh and I were eating popcorn and playing Scrabble on the living room floor that night.

And pretty soon *why not?* changed to *when?* The answer to that one was easy though, because spring vacation was only a week and a half away and that would give me the perfect opportunity.

The funny thing was that once I'd decided to do it, I never worried about getting through. Maybe that was because I'd heard Mom say plenty of times that they always liked it when kids called into the show, and I guess I figured that unless everybody on spring vacation decided to call the Dr. Emma Hart Show, I wouldn't have any trouble. Besides, I practiced in the shower making my voice huskier than usual and just a little breathless, hoping that it would sound sincere and make an impression on Jordan, the guy who screens the calls and tries for just the right balance of men, women, and kids, with not too much emphasis on busted romances as opposed to anxiety attacks.

The next funny thing was that once I'd made up my mind to call Dr. Emma Hart, I began to feel like a wounded bird myself, and I was suddenly awfully glad that she cared about them the way she did. I had a little trouble deciding what I wanted to ask her on the show, and even before I could make up my mind I began to think of other things that bothered me too. Not problems, but stuff I'd like to talk over with Mom. Like Vietnam,[5] for example. I'd watched *Apocalypse Now*[6] on TV and there was a lot I didn't understand. And what about the sixties?—was Mom ever involved in sit-ins or walkouts or any of that? I somehow doubted it, but it would be important to know for sure. Finally it came to me: what I wanted to ask Dr. Hart about was not being able to talk to Mom because there she was all wrapped up with her wounded birds. Only the whole thing got confusing, one being the other and all.

Anyway, I did it. I put the call in just before eleven on the Monday morning of spring vacation and almost chickened out when Jordan answered. I had met him a couple of times down at the studio, and I could almost see him now, looking like some kind of an

5. **Vietnam** [vē et′ näm′]: country in Southeast Asia that was the scene of a war in which the United States was involved in the 1960s and 1970s.
6. *Apocalypse Now* [ə pok′ ə lips]: 1979 movie about the Vietnam War.

intense juggler who is trying to keep everything going at once. I heard my voice, as if it were coming from somewhere far away, giving my name as Claire (it's my middle name) and outlining my problem. When I got finished, Jordan said that he was putting me on hold and not to go away, that Dr. Hart would be with me shortly.

And all of a sudden she was. I mean, there I was talking to my own mother and telling her how I couldn't talk to my mother, and how the things I wanted to talk to her about weren't actually big deals anyway, but still—.

Dr. Hart let me go on for a while and then she broke in and said that it was important for me to know that my concerns were as real as anybody else's and it sounded as if my mother and I had a pretty good relationship that had just gotten a little off the track and what I had to do was be really up-front with her and let her know how I felt. Then she suggested that I make a date with my mother for lunch so that I could tell her (Mom) exactly what I'd told her (Dr. Emma Hart), and that I should be sure to call back and let her know how it worked out.

After that I said, "Okay," and "Thank you." Then I hung up.

The only trouble was that as soon as Mom got home that day I knew it wasn't going to work.

She was sort of coming unglued. It had been a bad day, she told me. One of her private patients was in the midst of a crisis; the producer of the show was having a fight with his wife and wanted to tell Mom all about it. She had a dinner speech to give Saturday night and didn't have a thought about what to say, and my uncle Alex had called from Scranton to ask Mom to try to talk some sense into his teenage son, who was driving them all crazy.

Then she looked at me and said, "Thank heavens you've got it all together."

Talk about guilt. Right away I knew I was going to break rule number one: I wasn't going to be able to be up-front.

The thing was, I knew I couldn't take what was already one rotten week for Mom and dump all my problems (which seemed to be getting bigger by the minute) on her. Even though I felt like I was going to explode.

By Friday I knew I needed another talk with Dr. Hart. After all, she'd said to call back, hadn't she?

Getting through Jordan was even easier the second time. All I had to say was that I'd spoken to Dr. Hart earlier in the week and that she'd said to let her know what happened.

"Oh, good, a success story," Jordan said right away, jumping to conclusions. I guess he knew what kind of a week it had been too. "Hold on; Dr. Hart will be with you soon," he said.

And there was Dr. Emma Hart again. And suddenly there I was, unloading about how what she had suggested wasn't going to work.

"Why not?" she wanted to know. "Did you try?"

"Yes—no," I said. Then I was going on again, all about Bad-Breath Spellman, the guidance counselor, and how maybe my best friend had a thing for my boyfriend. She kept steering me back to the subject of my mother and why I hadn't arranged to have lunch with her.

I said that my mother had had a bad week. That she was swamped, preoccupied, distracted, and running behind. And then it happened. I mean, I heard the words sliding off my lips and couldn't stop them. I said, "The thing about my mother is that she has all these wounded birds who have really important problems and they take all the time she has."

A silence ballooned up between us and was so loud I couldn't hear anything else—and if you know anything about radio, you know that the worst thing that can happen is silence. It lasted forever, and while it was going on I gave serious thought to running away from home, or at least hanging up.

When Mom finally spoke, her voice sounded choked, as if she had swallowed a gumball.

"We've been talking to Claire this morning, who is really Amanda," she said. "And one of the things we talk a lot about on this show is saying what you have to say—even if that's not always easy. Are you still there, Amanda?"

"Yes," I squeaked.

"If I know Amanda," my mother went on, "she would rather have run away, or hung up, but instead she did something harder. She hung on."

I gulped.

"Amanda is my daughter, and it seems we have some things to talk about, so what I'm going to do is to ask my assistant to make a reservation for lunch at the Terrace Garden." Then it sounded as though Mom had moved in closer to the microphone and was speaking just to me. "If you hurry, Amanda, I'll meet you at 1:30. So we can talk."

And we did: about Bad-Breath Spellman, and Terri, and how it's okay not to know now what I want to do with the rest of my life.

We talked about saving the whales, and our two weeks at the shore this summer, and how some day we're going to Ireland. About books and movies and the time in fourth grade when I got the chicken pox and Mom caught them from me.

And we talked about how we had missed talking to each other and what we could do about it.

We ate lunch slowly, and took ages deciding on dessert, and ages more eating it.

We sat there all afternoon, until the light streaking in the windows changed from yellow to a deep, burning gold and the busboys started setting the tables for dinner.

C O L B Y   R O D O W S K Y

Colby Rodowsky was born in Baltimore, Maryland. She lived in New York City and later in Washington, D.C., where she taught grade school. She later returned to Baltimore with her family.

Rodowsky's books are about teenagers who find themselves in serious situations. Some situations, such as the one in Rodowsky's book *P.S. Write Soon*, are the result of the character's choices or actions. Other situations, like the one in *A Summer's Worth of Shame*, are caused by forces beyond the character's control. Rodowsky's characters, such as Amanda in "Amanda and the Wounded Birds," have to work things out for themselves.

DANIELLE O'MARA

MEL GLENN

When my parents went away on a short vacation,
I stayed with my older sister, Madeline,
Who works for a real estate office downtown.
I simmered while she nagged me to
Wash the dishes, do the laundry, finish my homework.   5
Nothing I did was good enough for her.
Many evenings ended in heated arguments and slammed doors.
When she told me she was bringing a date home,
I decided to surprise her by making dinner.
I used the cookbook but,   10
The fish was raw,
The spaghetti limp,
The biscuits burnt,
And the poor guy staggered out the door, holding his stomach.
I thought my sister would fry me.   15
She looked at me and said,
"I didn't like him anyway."
We burst out giggling and hugged each other.

MEL GLENN

Mel Glenn was born in 1943 in Switzerland, but grew up in New York City. After college, Glenn became a journalist. During the 1960s, as a Peace Corps volunteer, he taught in West Africa, and continued teaching after he returned home.

Glenn's poetry and novels are based on his classroom experiences. "I write about what I know," he says. The basic idea for his first book, *Class Dismissed*, came from Edgar Lee Masters' *Spoon River Anthology*, in which people tell their own stories. "Danielle O'Mara" is from *Class Dismissed II: More High School Poems*.

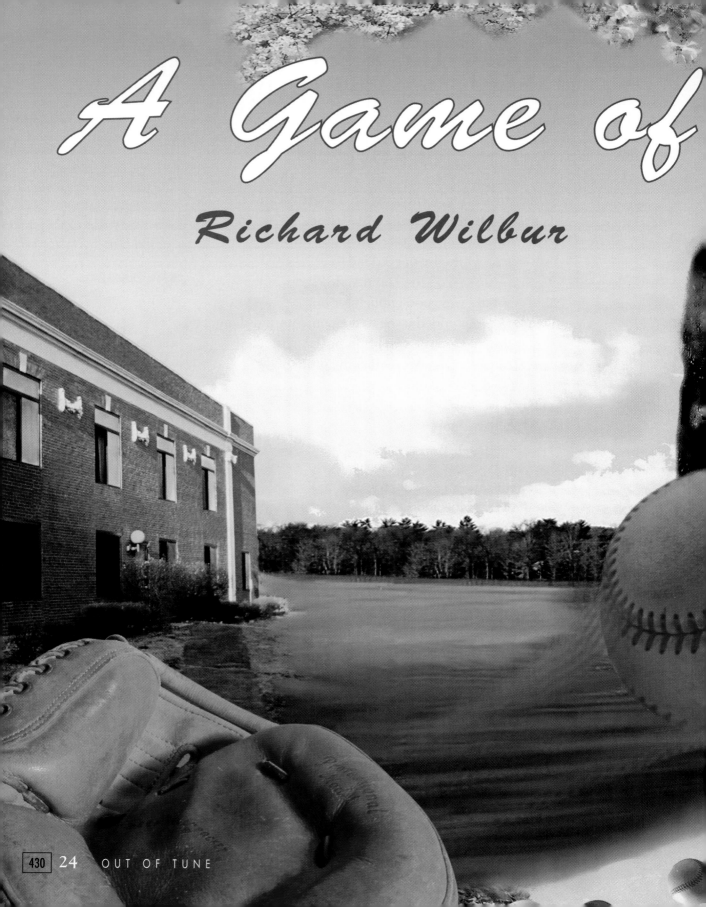

A Game of

Richard Wilbur

Catch

Monk and Glennie were playing catch on the side lawn of the firehouse when Scho caught sight of them. They were good at it, for seventh-graders, as anyone could see right away. Monk, wearing a catcher's mitt, would lean easily sidewise and back, with one leg lifted and his throwing hand almost down to the grass, and then lob the white ball straight up into the sunlight. Glennie would shield his eyes with his left hand and, just as the ball fell past him, snag it with a little dart of his glove. Then he would burn the ball straight toward Monk, and it would spank into the round mitt and sit, like a still-life apple on a plate, until Monk flipped it over into his right hand and, with a negligent flick of his hanging arm, gave Glennie a fast grounder.

They were going on and on like that, in a kind of slow, mannered, luxurious dance in the sun, their faces perfectly blank and entranced, when Glennie noticed Scho dawdling along the other side of the street and called hello to him. Scho crossed over and stood at the front edge of the lawn, near an apple tree, watching.

"Got your glove?" asked Glennie after a time. Scho obviously hadn't.

"You could give me some easy grounders," said Scho.

"But don't burn 'em."

"All right," Glennie said. He moved off a little, so the three of them formed a triangle, and they passed the ball around for about five minutes, Monk tossing easy grounders to Scho, Scho throwing to Glennie, and Glennie burning them in to Monk. After a while, Monk began to throw them back to Glennie once or twice before he let Scho have his grounder, and finally Monk gave Scho a fast, bumpy grounder that hopped over his shoulder and went into the brake on the other side of the street.

"Not so hard," called Scho as he ran across to get it.

"You should've had it," Monk shouted.

It took Scho a little while to find the ball among the ferns and dead leaves, and when he saw it, he grabbed it up and threw it toward Glennie. It struck the trunk of the apple tree, bounced back at an angle, and rolled steadily and stupidly onto the cement apron in front of the firehouse, where one of the trucks was parked. Scho ran hard and stopped it just before it rolled under the truck, and this time he carried it back to his former position on the lawn and threw it carefully to Glennie.

"I got an idea," said Glennie. "Why don't Monk and I catch for five minutes more, and then you can borrow one of our gloves?"

"That's all right with me," said Monk. He socked his fist into his mitt, and Glennie burned one in.

"All right," Scho said, and went over and sat under the tree. There in the shade he watched them resume their skillful play. They threw lazily fast or lazily slow— high, low, or wide—and always handsomely, their expressions serene,[1] changeless, and forgetful. When Monk missed a low backhand catch, he walked indolently[2] after the ball and, hardly even looking, flung it sidearm for an imaginary put-out.[3] After a good while of this, Scho said, "Isn't it five minutes yet?"

"One minute to go," said Monk, with a fraction of a grin.

Scho stood up and watched the ball slap back and forth for several minutes more, and then he turned and pulled himself up into the crotch of the tree.

1. **serene** [sə rēn′]: calm, peaceful.
2. **indolently** [in′ dl ənt lē]: lazily, idly.
3. **put-out** [pùt′ out′]: an action that puts the batter or base runner out of the game.

"Where you going?" Monk asked.

"Just up the tree," Scho said.

"I guess he doesn't want to catch," said Monk.

Scho went up and up through the fat light-gray branches until they grew slender and bright and gave under him. He found a place where several supple branches were knit to make a dangerous chair, and sat there with his head coming out of the leaves into the sunlight. He could see the two other boys down below, the ball going back and forth between them as if they were bowling on the grass, and Glennie's crew-cut head looking like a sea urchin.[4]

"I found a wonderful seat up here," Scho said loudly. "If I don't fall out." Monk and Glennie didn't look up or comment, and so he began jouncing gently in his chair of branches and singing "Yo-ho, heave ho" in an exaggerated way.

"Do you know what, Monk?" he announced in a few moments. "I can make you two guys do anything I want. Catch that ball, Monk! Now you catch it, Glennie!"

"I was going to catch it anyway," Monk suddenly said. "You're not making anybody do anything when they're already going to do it anyway."

"I made you say what you just said," Scho replied joyfully.

"No, you didn't," said Monk, still throwing and catching but now less serenely absorbed in the game.

"That's what I wanted you to say," Scho said.

The ball bounced off the rim of Monk's mitt and plowed into a gladiolus[5] bed beside the firehouse, and Monk ran to get it while Scho jounced in his treetop and sang, "I wanted you to miss that. Anything you do is what I wanted you to do."

"Let's quit for a minute," Glennie suggested.

"We might as well, until the peanut gallery[6] shuts up," Monk said.

---

4. **sea urchin:** a small, round sea animal with a spiny shell.
5. **gladiolus** [glad′ ē ō′ ləs]: a plant with sword-shaped leaves and spikes of large flowers in various colors.
6. **peanut gallery:** slang for people offering uninvited, insignificant comments or advice.

*T*hey went over and sat cross-legged in the shade of the tree. Scho looked down between his legs and saw them on the dim spotty ground, saying nothing to one another. Glennie soon began abstractedly spinning his glove between his palms; Monk pulled his nose and stared out across the lawn.

"I want you to mess around with your nose, Monk," said Scho, giggling. Monk withdrew his hand from his face.

"Do that with your glove, Glennie," Scho persisted. "Monk, I want you to pull up hunks of grass and chew on it."

Glennie looked up and saw a self-delighted, intense face staring down at him through the leaves. "Stop being a dope and come down and we'll catch for a few minutes," he said.

Scho hesitated, and then said, in a tentatively[7] mocking voice, "That's what I wanted you to say."

"All right, then, nuts to you," said Glennie.

"Why don't you keep quiet and stop bothering people?" Monk asked.

"I made you say that," Scho replied, softly.

"Shut up," Monk said.

"I made you say that, and I want you to be standing there looking sore. And I want you to climb up the tree! I'm making you do it!"

Monk was scrambling up through the branches, awkward in his haste, and getting snagged on twigs. His face was furious and foolish, and he kept telling Scho to shut up, shut up, shut up, while the other's exuberant[8] and panicky voice poured down upon his head.

"*Now* you shut up or you'll be sorry," Monk said, breathing hard as he reached up and threatened to shake the cradle of slight branches in which Scho was sitting.

"I *want*—" Scho screamed as he fell. Two lower branches broke his rustling, crackling fall, but he landed on his back with a deep thud and lay still, with a strangled look on his face and his eyes clenched. Glennie knelt down and asked breathlessly, "Are you

7. **tentatively** [ten′ tə tiv lē]: carefully, hesitatingly.
8. **exuberant** [eg zü′ bər ənt]: in high spirits, happy.

O.K., Scho? Are you O.K.?," while Monk swung down through the leaves crying that honestly he hadn't even touched him, the crazy guy just let go. Scho doubled up and turned over on his right side, and now both the other boys knelt beside him, pawing at his shoulder and begging to know how he was.

Then Scho rolled away from them and sat partly up, still struggling to get his wind but forcing a species[9] of smile onto his face.

"I'm sorry, Scho," Monk said. "I didn't mean to make you fall."

Scho's voice came out weak and gravelly, in gasps. "I meant—you to do it. You—had to. You can't do—anything—unless I want—you to."

Glennie and Monk looked helplessly at him as he sat there, breathing a bit more easily and smiling fixedly, with tears in his eyes. Then they picked up their gloves and the ball, walked over to the street, and went slowly away down the sidewalk, Monk punching his fist into the mitt, Glennie juggling the ball between glove and hand.

From under the apple tree, Scho, still bent over a little for lack of breath, croaked after them in triumph and misery, "I want you to do whatever you're going to do for the whole rest of your life!"

9. **species** [spē′ shēz]: kind, type.

RICHARD WILBUR

Richard Wilbur was born in 1921 and grew up in rural New England. He is best known as a poet whose poems often focus on nature. These subjects, Wilbur says, come from a childhood full of woods and cornfields, horses and haywagons. Two of his poetry collections are *Things of This World* and *The Beautiful Changes*.

Among his other achievements, Wilbur has become an expert on the life and works of the nineteenth-century American author, Edgar Allan Poe.

UMU MADU *in the* GOOD OLD DAYS

T. OBINKARAM ECHEWA

There was once a village called Umu Madu[1] where the people loved to have feasts. Every chance the villagers had, they called a feast to celebrate one thing or another.

"There is a new moon in the sky," the people of Umu Madu would say sometimes. "Let us have a feast to celebrate it."

"The moon is now full," the villagers might say a few weeks later. "Let us have a feast to celebrate the full moon."

At the beginning of the farming season, after they had planted their crops, the people of Umu Madu had a feast.

In the middle of the farming season, after the rains had started and the farms were green with growing crops, the people of Umu Madu held a feast.

At the end of the farming season, after the crops had been harvested and placed in the barns, the people of Umu Madu had a feast.

Sometimes even when nothing happened, the people of Umu Madu had a feast. If anyone asked them what the feast was for, they replied: "We are having this feast because nothing has happened."

Some of the feasts were small and some were big, but always there was a feast in the village of Umu Madu, and all the feasts were long and happy.

All the feasts were held under the big cottonwood tree in the middle of the market clearing at the center of the village of Umu Madu. The men killed the chickens or the goats or a cow, depending on how big the feast was. They also cut up the meat and cooked it in

1. **Umu Madu** [ü′ mü mä′ dü]

Raffia cloth Shoowa people, Kasai river area, Zaire, c. 1935, Museum of New Mexico

big iron pots, which they stirred with long sticks. The women cooked the soup and the stew as well as the rice and the fufu.[2] Children fetched water or firewood and darted here and there on errands for the adults.

When everything was ready, the elders of Umu Madu appointed four or five young men to divide the food so that every man, woman and child would get a share. Fufu and rice were piled high on everyone's plate. Big pieces of meat stuck out above the surface of everyone's stew and soup. However, the heart of the feast was the big lumps of meat which were spread out in long rows on banana leaves or raffia mats. From the oldest man to the youngest child, the people of Umu Madu chose their shares of meat according to their ages.

For as long as anyone could remember, the people of Umu Madu had always eaten their feasts on the ground. Some people squatted onto the ground. Some people knelt on the ground. Some people sat on the ground.

2. **fufu** [fü fü´]: dish comprised of bananas, squash, or yams.

Then one day a stranger arrived in the village of Umu Madu.

This was not the first time a stranger had come to Umu Madu. However, this stranger was very strange. No one had ever seen or heard anyone like him before. The villagers nicknamed the stranger No Skin because his skin had no color. No Skin had hair which looked like corn silk and eyes which shone like glass beads. At first everyone thought he had no toes, until he took off his shoes and allowed some of the villagers to count his toes. He had ten of them.

"Urupirisi. Urupirisi. Urupirisi," No Skin said to the villagers of Umu Madu. When someone was found who could understand No Skin's language, what he was saying was: "What have we here? Why are intelligent people like you eating their feast on the ground?"

"We have always eaten our feasts on the ground," the villagers replied. "Where do you want us to eat? On the treetops or in the sky?"

"Haven't you ever heard of tables?" No Skin asked.

"No," the villagers replied, surprised and a little ashamed. "We have never heard of tables. What are tables?"

No Skin began describing a table to the people of Umu Madu. He drew a picture of a table on the ground for them as he said: "My friends, these are modern times. If you want to be modern and up to date, you must stop eating on the ground and start eating on tables."

"Where can we find a table?" the villagers begged. "We do not want to be left behind by progress. We want to be modern and up to date."

"No problem," No Skin replied. "Send along four ablebodied men with me, and they will bring back a table to the village within a week."

Within a week, just as No Skin had promised, there was a table in the village of Umu Madu. It was big and long and heavy, and the villagers spent many hours admiring it, walking around it, rubbing their hands on it, and smiling at their reflections on its shiny top.

"This table is so good," the elders of the village said, "that we cannot wait until the next feast several weeks from now to try it. Let us have a feast at once and try the new table."

Everyone thought that was a good idea.

So a feast was called immediately. Two cows were killed. Fufu and rice were cooked in abundance. Everyone in the village came out to enjoy the big feast on the new table. No one bothered about raffia mats and banana leaves anymore.

However, as the young men who had been appointed by the elders began to divide the meat, they made a disturbing discovery. There was not enough space around the table for everyone.

"We have a problem here," one old man said. "How are we going to solve it?"

"Why don't the elders go into a conference with one another, as is our custom," someone suggested. "Let the elders tell us what to do about this problem."

"Yes, yes," everyone agreed. "Let the elders decide for us."

So the elders went into a conference. After a long time, they came back to the assembly and announced: "We cannot agree on how to satisfy everyone about the table. We cannot agree who should eat at the table and who should not. So we have decided instead to return the table to No Skin, so we can continue our unity and eat our feasts on the ground together, as we have always done. If we cannot find No Skin, we can put the table away, and he can take it back whenever he comes this way again."

"No-o-o-oh!" many members of the assembly shouted. There was a lot of murmuring and grumbling.

Then one young man said: "We now have the table, and everyone agrees it is a good thing. Would it not be foolish to let it sit idle? Would it not be even more foolish to give it back to No Skin? . . . All members of the assembly of Umu Madu who agree with me, please say Hay-ay-ay!"

"Hay-ay-ay!" everyone in the assembly seemed to shout.

The elders were surprised and disappointed. Not often did the community assembly fail to heed their advice. "All right," the elders said, "if that is the will of Umu Madu, then so be it. However, we will choose positions around the table according to age. Old people will choose first. People of Umu Madu, show that you agree with us by saying Hay-ay-ay!"

"Hay-ay-ay!" most voices shouted.

However, there were some voices which said "No!"

The village of Umu Madu liked to do things by having everyone agree. So the elders said, "If we cannot do it by age, how then shall we do it?"

One young man raised his hand and was given permission to speak.

"The times we live in are modern times," the young man said. "Modern times and modern things like the table are for the young. So I say, the young men should eat at the table. The elders can eat on the ground. Everyone who agrees with me say Hay-ay-ay!"

"Hay-ay-ay!" most of the young people shouted.

"No-o-o-oh!" most of the older people shouted.

The village of Umu Madu was faced with one of the sharpest disagreements its community assembly had ever seen. The elders looked at one another, shook their heads and scratched them. Then one elder cleared his throat and said:

"Perhaps we can do it by volunteering. Perhaps some people will volunteer to eat on the ground."

Everyone thought that was a good idea. However, when the elder said, "Who will volunteer to eat on the ground?" people began to answer: "Someone else."

"Who else?" the elders asked.

"Anyone else but me," everyone said.

At this point the elders decided to go into another conference. For a long time and after many debates they still could not agree on what to do. In the end they decided to settle the matter by drawing sticks. Anyone who drew a short stick would eat on the ground. Anyone who drew a long stick would eat at the table.

However, by the time the elders returned from their conference to announce their decision, the people were pushing, shoving, and fighting for places around the table.

"Shame!" the elders cried in dismay. "Shame, Umu Madu, shame!"

When the fighting stopped, the elders said, "All right, all right, if this is what we have been driven to, then let everyone keep the place he now has. Those of you who have occupied places around the table, keep your places. Those of you who are on the ground, stay on the ground. But please stop fighting like hyenas. We came here to feast, not to fight."

That was how the matter was settled for that day. However, it did not end there. Disunity had come to the feasts of Umu Madu, because when there was a feast some people ate at the table and some people on the ground. Envy had come to the feasts of Umu Madu. Those who ate on the ground looked enviously or rolled their eyes at those who ate at the table. Pride had come to the feasts of Umu Madu. Those who ate at the table stuck up their noses in the air and looked down on those who ate on the ground. Unhappiness had come to the feasts of Umu Madu. For the first time ever, everyone was not happy at the feasts.

Every feast that the people of Umu Madu held now ended in a fight. People came to the feasts not just to enjoy themselves but to fight for places around the table. Those who had eaten on the ground during the last feast thought it was their turn to eat at the table this time. However, those who had eaten at the table the last time thought they should do so again.

"Once a person has fought to get a place by the table," some of the villagers said, "he should keep it permanently."

Some villagers even felt that once a person had begun to eat at the table, his wives and children should also eat at the table, and even his children and his children's children, whenever they were born, should have the future right to eat at the table.

Some villagers became so angry at what was going on that they refused to attend any more feasts.

Then one day just before a very big feast, someone secretly sawed more than halfway through one of the table's legs. In the middle of the feast, when the meat and all other goodies had

been heaped on the table, the leg broke, the table tipped over, and all the meat fell to the ground.

Various people accused one another of the trick. A big free-for-all fight broke out. Pots were broken. Basins of rice were kicked over. The meat was trampled underfoot.

The day after the big fight, the elders called everyone together in the market clearing. "Umu Madu," the elders said, "the table which No Skin gave us has been nothing but trouble. There is only one way to solve our problem—destroy the table before it destroys us."

"Hay-ay-ay!" the whole assembly responded in unison. "Let us destroy the table before it destroys us!"

The men, women, and children of Umu Madu went home and got their axes, machetes,[3] clubs, and pestles[4] and set upon the table and smashed it to pieces.

"Now we can be one again," one elder said after the task was done.

"Yes," another elder replied. "We can eat our feasts in unity and harmony once again."

"Yes," someone else in the assembly said. "Let us call a feast immediately to celebrate our freedom from the table."

"Yes, yes," everyone agreed.

A date was set for the special feast. Three cows were killed. Banana leaves and clean raffia mats were laid out on the swept ground, as in the old days. This was going to be the biggest and happiest feast Umu Madu had ever had.

However, just as the feast was about to start, someone pointed out that a few villagers had brought their own little, private tables to the feast.

"Why?" the elders asked. "Did we not agree to eat together on the ground as we used to do before No Skin brought us the table?"

"We agreed! Yes, we agreed!" a majority of the assembly replied.

"Why then have some people brought tables?" the elders asked.

---

3. **machetes** [mə shet′ ēs]: large, heavy knives used for cutting brush.
4. **pestles** [pes′ əlz]: club-shaped tools for pounding substances into powder.

"I now like tables," one table owner said. "I found No Skin, and he said I can have my own table if I wish. So, since I enjoy eating at a table, why shouldn't I be able to do so?"

"Me, too," another table owner said. "I not only like tables, but I have become so used to them that I can no longer bear to eat my meals on the ground."

Other table owners gave similar answers.

"You must destroy the tables," the elders commanded, "so that we can have harmony and unity as of old."

"My table is mine to do with as I please," one table owner said in an insulting voice. "It cost me plenty of money. No one can destroy it."

Another table owner agreed with the first one. He said: "If I cannot eat *my* part of the feast on *my* table, then I will not share in the feast at all!"

So the big feast which was supposed to bring back peace and harmony to Umu Madu instead brought disharmony and discord. There was first a long argument and then a big fight, during which many bones were broken. Since that day harmony and unity left the village and have not returned.

T. OBINKARAM ECHEWA

T. Obinkaram Echewa was born in 1940 in Nigeria, Africa. Echewa came to the United States when he was 21. He graduated from the University of Notre Dame and went on to Columbia University and the University of Pennsylvania.

While doing graduate work, Echewa not only taught English but wrote his first book—a novel. "I have been side-stepping along in my career looking for an outlet," Echewa said at that time. "Perhaps I will find it in writing serious fiction." Since then, Echewa has rediscovered the value of tales and humorous anecdotes from "the good old days" in his home country.

THE CLEARING

Night Firing of Tobacco Thomas Hart Benton, 1943
oil and tempera on canvas, 20" x 31", United Missouri
Bank, Kansas City

JESSE STUART

Finn and I were pruning the plum trees around our garden when a rock came cracking among the branches of the tree I was pruning.

"Where did that come from?" I asked Finn, who was on the ground below piling the branches.

"I don't know," he said.

Then we heard the Hinton boys laughing on the other side of the valley. I went back to pruning. In less than a minute, a rock hit the limb above my head and another rock hit at Finn's feet. Then I came down from the tree. Finn and I started throwing rocks. In a few minutes rocks were falling like hailstones around them and around us. The land was rocky on both sides of the valley and there were plenty of rocks to throw.

One of their rocks hit Finn on the foot and one of our rocks peeled the largest Hinton boy's head.

"Think of it," Finn said. "We fight before we know each other's names! What will it be as time goes on?"

We fought all afternoon with rocks. At sunset the Hinton boys took off up the path and over the hill. We went home. When Pa asked why we hadn't finished pruning the trees, we told him.

"I told you," he said to Mom. "You'll see whether we can live apart or not."

"Wait until we know them and they know us," Mom said.

"But how are we ever goin' to know people like them?" Pa asked.

"Oh, something will happen," she replied calmly. "You'll see."

Next day Mort Hinton was with his boys. They climbed higher on the hill, cutting the briers¹ and brush and tree laps and stacking them neatly into piles. Finn and I pruned our trees.

---

1. **briers** [brī′ərz]: bushes that have prickly stems, such as the blackberry plant or wild rose.

"I'll say one thing for the Hintons," Mom said. "They're good workers."

"When they don't throw rocks," Finn said.

My guineas[2] flew across the valley where the Hintons were clearing land, on the fourth day.

"Get these back on your side the valley," Mort Hinton yelled. "Get 'em back where they belong."

I didn't want to put my guineas in the henhouse. But I had to. I knew Mort Hinton would kill them. I wanted to tell him that they would help his land. They'd rid it of insects that might destroy his crop. But I was afraid to tell him anything.

A week had passed before my guineas got out and flew across the valley.

"If you don't keep your guineas on your side of the valley," Morton Hinton hollered to me, "I'll wring their infernal necks."

That night I put my guineas up again. I fixed the henhouse so they couldn't get out and roam the hills as they had always done. While Finn, Pa and I cleared land on one side of the valley, the Hintons cleared on the other side.

Though we'd never been close enough to the Hintons to talk with them and we didn't want to get that close, we found ourselves trying to do more work than the four of them. Each day, that early March, rain or sunshine, four Hintons worked on their side of the valley, and Pa, Finn and I worked on our side. One day a Hinton boy hollered at us, "You can't clear as much land as we can."

"Don't answer him," Pa said.

The next day Mrs. Hinton came to the clearing and worked with them. Mom watched her using a sprouting hoe, a mattock,[3] brier scythe[4] and an ax.

"She works like a man," Mom said, as she watched her from the window. "Poor woman. I feel sorry for her. Out working like that!"

2. **guineas** [gin′ ēz]: large, dark, speckled birds, similar to pheasants, which are often raised for food.
3. **mattock** [mat′ ək]: a large tool with a steel head and a flat blade, used for loosening soil and cutting roots.
4. **scythe** [sīth]: a long, curved blade on a long handle used for cutting grass.

"Other women work," Pa snapped. "You work, don't you?"

"When I'm pregnant, I don't get out in the cold March wind and clear ground," Mom said.

"I didn't know she was pregnant," Pa said.

"Well, she is," Mom answered.

When April came and the Hintons had finished clearing the hill, and had burned the brush, Mort Hinton brought a skinny mule hitched to a cutter plow and started plowing the newground. He plowed slowly the first day. The second day my guineas got out again and flew across the valley to the plowed ground. Mort Hinton caught two of them, twisted their necks and threw them down into the valley. The others flew back home when he tried to catch them. Then he yelled across to where we were plowing our newground and told us what he had done.

"I feel like taking a shotgun and sprinkling him," I said.

"Your guineas were on his land," Mom said. "He'd told you to put them up."

Mort Hinton plowed his newground by working from daylight until dusk, while Mrs. Hinton and the boys carried armloads of roots from the field and stacked them in great heaps. By the first of May they had made this rooty newground soil like a garden. Then came a rainy season in early May and they carried baskets of tobacco plants and set them in the straight-furrowed[5] rows.

"They're workers, all right," Pa said, agreeing with Mom. "But I don't understand how a man can let his wife get out there and drop tobacco plants when she is so near to being a mother again."

"Maybe they have to work to live," Mom said.

"Not like that," Pa said.

On a dark night about a week later I watched from my upstairs window a moving light. It came from the direction of Hintons', over the hill and down into the valley below our house. In a few minutes I heard footsteps on the porch. Then a loud knock on our door. I heard Pa get out of bed and open the door.

5. **straight-furrowed** [fèr′ ōd]: cut in long, narrow grooves by a plow.

Detail from **Night Firing of Tobacco**,
Thomas Hart Benton

"I'm Mort Hinton," a voice said. "My wife sent for your wife."

I heard Mom getting out of bed.

"I'll be ready in a minute," she called out.

Neither Pa nor Mort said another word.

"I'll be back when everything is all right," Mom told Pa as she hurried away.

I watched the lantern fade from sight as Mort Hinton and Mom went down the path into the deep valley below the house. In two minutes or more it flashed into sight again when they reached Hinton's tobacco field. The light moved swiftly up and over the hill. Next morning Pa cooked breakfast for us. He quarreled about Hintons as he stood near the hot stove frying eggs.

"Yeah, when they need something over there," Pa grumbled and muttered.

"Dollie Hinton's got a pretty girl baby over there," were Mom's first words as she sat down for a cup of coffee.

"What did they name the baby?" Glenna asked.

"They've not named her yet," Mom said. "Think they plan to call her Ethel. They're tickled to death. Six boys and now a girl!"

"What kind of people are they, anyway?" Pa asked.

"Like other people," Mom said. "They don't have much furniture in their house. They're working hard to pay for their farm."

"Will they be any better neighbors?" Pa asked.

"I think so," Mom said. "That hill over there is not a fence between us any longer."

"There's more than a hill between us," I said. "What about my guineas Mort Hinton killed? Did he say anything about 'em last night?"

"And what about the Hinton boy that hit me on the foot with a rock?" Finn said. "I'd like to meet up with him sometime."

By the time we had finished our breakfast, Mort Hinton was plowing the young tobacco. His three sons were hoeing the tender plants with long-handled gooseneck hoes.

"Looks like Mr. Hinton would be sleepy," Mom said. "He never went to bed last night. And the boys slept on the hay in the barn loft."

Pa, Finn and I didn't have too much sympathy for the Hintons. Through the dining-room window we could look across the valley and watch Mort keep the plow moving steadily. We watched his boys dig with their hoes, never looking up from the ground.

"This will be a dry, sunny day," Pa said. "We'll burn the brush piles on the rest of our clearing."

We gathered our pitch-forks, hoes and rakes and went to the hill where we had cleared ground all spring. There were hundreds of brush piles on our twenty acres of cleared ground. The wind was still. The sun had dried the dew from the leaves and tufts of broom sage that carpeted the ground between the brush piles.

"It's the right time to burn," Pa said, holding up his hand. "I can't feel any wind. The brush has seasoned in these piles until it is as dry as powder."

Pa struck a match to the brush pile at the bottom of the clearing. The fire started with

Detail from **Night Firing of Tobacco**, Thomas Hart Benton

little leaps over the leaf-carpeted ground. Finn, Pa and I fired along the bottom of the clearing until we had a continuous line of fire going up the slope. Then a wind sprang from nowhere. And when flames leaped from brush pile to brush pile, Pa looked at me.

"This is out of control," Pa said. "Grab a hoe and start raking a ring."

"I'm afraid we can't stop it," Finn said. "We'll have to work fast if we save the orchards."

"Shut up and run to the house and get Sall and Glenna," Pa yelled.

"Look, Pa," Finn said, pointing down the hill.

Mort Hinton was in front. He was running up the hill. His three sons were running behind him, each with a hoe across his shoulder.

"It's out of control," Pa shouted to Mort before he reached us.

"We've come to help," Mort said.

"Can we keep it from the orchards?" Pa asked.

"Let's run to the top of the hill and fire against it," Mort said. "I've burnt hundreds of acres of clearing on hillsides and I always fire the top first and let it burn down! I fire the bottom last. Maybe we'll not be too late to save the orchards!"

Mort ran up the hill and we followed. Finn and I didn't speak to his boys and they didn't speak to us. But when we started raking a ring side by side, we started talking to the Hintons. We forgot about the rock fight. Now wasn't the time to remember it, when flames down under the hill were shooting twenty to thirty feet high. In no time we raked the ring across the top of the clearing. And the fire Mort Hinton set along the ring burned fiercely down the hill and made the ring wider and wider. Only once fire blew across the ring, and Pa stopped it then.

As soon as we had this spot under control, we raked a ring down the west side near the peach orchard. Mort set a line of fire along this ring and let it burn toward the middle of the clearing. Then we raked a ring on the east side and fired against the fire that was approaching our plum trees and our house. Soon the leaping flames met in the clearing. We had the fire under control. Our clearing was burned clean as a whistle.

"How much do I owe you?" Pa asked Mort Hinton.

"You don't owe me anything, Mick," Mort said. "We're just paying you back for the help your wife gave us last night."

"Then let's go to the house for dinner," Pa said.

"Some other time," Mort said. "We must go home and see about Dollie and the baby."

As we went down the hill, Finn and I talked with Big Adger, Al and Little Mort about squirrel hunting and wild-bee trees, while Pa and Mort laughed and talked about weather and crops.

JESSE STUART

Jesse Stuart [1906-1984] was born in a one-room log cabin in Greenup County, Kentucky, so far in the hills that he was fifteen before he saw an electric light or a telephone. Stuart often had to leave school to help support the family. Because he had missed so much elementary school, high school was a struggle. He succeeded because he loved to read.

Stuart worked his way through college and began teaching school in his home county, writing in his spare time. During the 1960s, he worked as a lecturer for the U.S. Information Service, traveling all over the world. Eventually he published more than fifty books—fiction, nonfiction, and poetry—nearly all to do with Appalachian country life. One of his best known books, *The Thread That Runs So True*, tells of his years teaching in Greenup County.

The Long Way Around

JEAN McCORD

I hadn't spoken to my stepmother in three days. I was absorbed by an inner grief and anger because she had given away my mother's dresses to the Salvation Army.

I could still feel my mother around the house. Sometimes I'd come bursting in from school with some important piece of news that I wanted to share immediately, and coming through the door, I'd shout, "Mother, I'm home. Where are you?" and instantly, before the echo had died, I'd remember, too late.

My stepmother had answered once, the first time, coming out from her bedroom with a smile on her face, thinking I was calling her, saying "Yes, Patty, what is it?" But my face was set in a frozen scowl, and I was standing there rigid, unyielding and furious at myself for such a mistake. She understood and turning away without pressing me any further, she went back into her room and closed her door.

My mother had died two years before when I was twelve, and even though I knew better, sometimes in the middle of the night, I'd awake in a terrible fear and to comfort myself back to sleep I'd whisper into the pillow, "She's only gone away on a trip. And she'll be back." In the morning I had to face my own lie.

My father had married again last year and though my two little brothers, Jason and Scott, called this new woman "Mother," my father had told me I didn't have to do so. I called her Alice even though sometimes it felt strange to call a grown woman by her first name. This Alice wasn't anything at all like my own mother. For one thing, she couldn't cook. My mother had been the best cook in the whole neighborhood. Even the other mothers around us used to say that and would come over for coffee and butter scones and things that my mother would just whip up on a moment's notice. This Alice . . . well, sometimes our whole supper ended up in the garbage can, and my father would take us out to a restaurant. I thought it was pretty stupid and expensive, but of course Jason and Scott loved it.

To make things even worse, so it seemed to me, my father had taken a new job, and we had moved away from the town and the neighborhood where I'd spent my whole life with kids I knew and had grown up with and gone to school with and graduated with.

Now I was in Jr. High with a whole new batch of kids and I didn't like any of them. They didn't like me, either. I kept my distance and when school was over, I walked home alone, carrying my books with my head down and hurrying by the groups of girls laughing and giggling over some private joke. I could feel them looking at my back and the talk always hushed a little until I was by, then they'd break out into silly, stifled snickers when I was down the street aways.

Actually I hated them all. I hated the teachers and the new school and my new stepmother and my father who seemed a new person too. Even my little brothers seemed to deserve a good slap for the way they had forgotten and called this Alice "Mother" as if they had never had a mother of their own.

The only one who hadn't changed, who was still the way he had always been, was Rufus, our old Samoyed.[1] Rufus is as old as I am, and

1. **Samoyed** [sam′ ə yəd′]: a Russian breed of medium-sized husky dogs that have long, thick, white fur.

in his way he understood. After my mother died, he'd lain on his braided rag rug and refused to move for over two weeks. He wouldn't eat because he was used to my mother fixing him up a strange mixture of dog food with raw egg and bacon drippings, and nobody else seemed to know just how to do it. Finally I tried and after a while he ate while looking at me from the corner of his eyes and seeming to apologize for it. I sat down beside him and cried into his neck, and he stopped eating long enough to lick my face which only made me cry harder.

Now the only reason I had for getting up in the morning was to greet Rufus and give him an egg. After school the only reason I came home was to take Rufus for a walk and together we had covered most of this new town. The only trouble was that the town stayed new. Somehow no matter how often we walked down the same streets, the houses always seemed strange. Rufus would plod along at my side, his head just at the reach of my hand. He stumbled once in a while over a curb, but that was because his eyesight wasn't too good any more. My own eyesight seemed slightly affected too because there was a gray film between me and everything I looked at.

We walked all over town after school, my feet just leading the two of us. Finally I knew we had tromped over every square inch of all the streets, but still nothing looked familiar. Sometimes returning home, I woudn't even know we had reached the end of the walk until Rufus turned off the sidewalk and went up our front steps.

One Saturday morning I woke up very early. This was about a month ago, I think, or maybe two months. I had lain awake a long time that night watching the shadow patterns change on the ceiling when the wind tossed the big snowball bush outside my window. It seemed like the night was trying to tell me something, but I couldn't quite make out what it was. Out in the kitchen I could hear that Rufus was awake, too, because every time he left his rug and walked across the floor, his toenails clicked on the linoleum. He seemed to be pacing the floor as if he wanted to go out into the night. Maybe he sensed something waiting out there for him. If my mother had been here, she'd know . . . she would have known . . .

Somewhere there in the middle of the night, I must have made up my mind what I was going to do. When the dawn came, I just rose and dressed and without even consciously thinking about it, I packed my small overnight case, putting in my parents' wedding picture which I had retrieved from a trunk in the attic, all the socks I had, two books from the library which were due in three days, one book of my own, and a little stuffed felt doll which I had given to Jason and then taken back from him. I rolled up my printed-rose quilt and tied it in several places with my belts. Then in blue jeans and a ski jacket I tiptoed out to the kitchen with my belongings and looked down at Rufus who thumped his tail hard against the floor and got up. He stood with his chin over his dish waiting for me to break his egg into it. I saw then that I couldn't leave him behind so while he slurped his egg I rolled his rug around the outside of my quilt. Now it was a big sloppy bundle but I didn't care.

Just as I was easing open the kitchen door I remembered I had no money, so I had to carefully put everything down and return to my bedroom. I had had a dollar put away for a long time because there was nothing I wanted to spend it on. Outside in the snowball bush the birds were beginning to cheep and call with a tremendous clatter. They were so noisy I wondered how anyone could sleep through that, and I knew I had to get away quickly.

Rufus was waiting with his head leaning against the kitchen door. He knew we were going for a walk. I wanted to take his dish, but didn't see how I could carry everything. We'd manage somehow. I stepped out into the cool grayness with those birds still clattering and the eastern sky beginning to flag out in streaks of red. It was going to be a warm day, and I knew I wouldn't need the ski jacket. Still, I thought . . . at night . . .

Rufus and I headed towards what I hoped was south. This was vaguely the direction where our old town and old friends were. I had looked at it often enough on the map, but I wasn't sure of just what road to go along. And besides I wanted to stay off the roads. I could picture my father driving along looking for us soon enough, right about breakfast time, I thought, when they would first miss me. But they wouldn't know anything for sure, I told myself, until I remembered I was carrying Rufus' rug.

"That was very stupid of you," I told Rufus severely, "to let me take your old rug when you knew it would give us away."

I walked a few swift steps ahead of him.

"Just for that, I ought to make you go back alone. Without me. Serve you right."

I was very angry. Rufus was hanging his head. The tone of my voice told him he'd done something really bad, but I finally had to forgive him. After all, it had been my own idea.

We used the road only far enough to get us out of town, then I decided we'd better strike across country even though it would be harder traveling, and we would have to climb a lot of fences. It would be safer that way. I soon found out I was right about one thing; it was a lot harder going. We walked through pasture where the ground was spongy and wet and my shoes became waterlogged. We fought our way through brush that kept trying to tear my bundles away from me, and by this time, they really felt heavy. I gave Rufus a sour look, wishing he could carry his own rug at least. We puffed up hills that gave me a stitch in the side, and I noticed that Rufus wasn't holding up too well. He was panting and beginning to lag behind.

By the time the sun was high, I was starving to death. Rufus, at least, had eaten an egg for breakfast, but I hadn't had a bite. And of course by now, I had lost my sense of direction completely. I had no idea which way was south although I had been keeping my eyes open looking for the moss that is supposed to grow on the north side of trees. I hadn't found any.

Every once in a while we would come close to a farmhouse and there was always trouble. Farmers must keep the meanest dogs in the world. At each place a big shrieking dog would come bounding out at us, and try to pick a fight with Rufus just because we were walking nearby. Rufus would say, "Urrgghh," and show all his teeth with his black lips drawn so far back he looked like a snarling wolf and the farm dogs would back off towards home, but never shut up. I was afraid the farmers might call the police, so we would hurry on.

It was a long time before I saw a country road which I figured was safe enough to walk on. In a couple of miles we came up to a crossroads and a store with one red gas pump squatting to one side and looking like it never had any customers.

I dropped my bundles outside and went into darkness and unfamiliar smells and there was this old farmer-type man dressed in striped overalls sitting on a sack of something. I didn't know what I wanted to buy, but anything would do. He had a small candy counter, so I bought three chocolate bars. I decided that canned dog food

would keep the best for Rufus, so I got seven cans which took all the rest of my money.

"Stranger round here, aren't you, Miss?" the storekeeper said.

I mumbled something and waved backwards, because my mouth was full of stale-tasting candy. He put the cans in a sack and I left, but he followed me to the door and watched very slyly as I had to pick up my suitcase and rolled quilt which left me no way to carry the dog food. I struggled to force it under my arm, but the sack broke and the cans rolled all over the ground. In desperation I knelt and shoved them into my suitcase and Rufus and I marched down the road with the striped overalls watching us all the way.

I could just almost hear him on the telephone, if he had such a thing, saying, "Sheriff, there's a strange gal going down the road with a big old dog and a suitcase full of dog food. Looks mighty suspicious to me." So there was no choice; we had to leave the road and go back to the pastures and farmhouses.

In the middle of the day I knew I couldn't carry that terribly heavy suitcase any further, so I said to Rufus,

"You are going to carry some of your own food inside of you."

We sat down in the shade of some bushes, and I opened the suitcase to get out a couple of the cans. Then I broke into tears from sheer rage. I had forgotten to bring along a can opener.

I cried a long time while Rufus looked at me sadly, laying his heavy head on my knee, and banging his tail, which was full of burrs and briars, against the stony ground.

My vaguely formed idea when we first started out was that we'd make our way back to our old town and maybe one of the old neighbors or even my favorite teacher, Miss Virginia Townsend, would take us in and keep us both if I worked for our board and room. Now I saw clearly that we weren't going to make it. It was over two hundred miles back there, and without even a can opener, well. . . .

We rested for an hour or so while I talked it over with Rufus who was a good listener and always agreed with me.

"You knew it was a long ways when you started out with me, didn't you?"

He thumped his tail once. I guess he was too tired to argue.

"I always understood that dogs knew their own way back to their old homes. Why didn't you lead?"

He looked away down the hill as if he was searching for the right direction.

"If we go back, you know what it means, don't you? They'll all be against us, and you'll certainly have to mind your P's and Q's from here on in!"

He hung his head in shame, but how could you ask a fourteen-year-old dog to walk two hundred miles when he was all worn out from doing about ten?

We stood up and looked out over a valley that faded into a blue haze in the far distance. I picked up the luggage, and we went back down the hill towards the country store. By the time we got there Rufus was limping.

I went into that dim interior again, and the man was back on his sack, just resting and waiting with his legs crossed.

"Thought you'd be back," he said with a snort of choked laughter.

"Could I please use your telephone?" I asked with great dignity.

"In the back there. Ask the Missus." He jerked his head.

I had to go into their living quarters. It seems they lived right there surrounded by all those groceries and hardware and chicken feed and medicine for cows and horses. His Missus was a pleasant, stumpy woman with square glasses, and afer I'd called home, she gave me a glass of lemonade. I had to ask her where we were, and she took the telephone to give my father directions. He was really boiling mad and hollered over the phone at me, "Swanson's Corner! Where in hell is that?"

I went outside to call Rufus, and she let him come into the kitchen for a drink of cold water. While we waited for my father, I tried to think of how to explain all those cans of dog food and the quilt and Rufus' rug, but there didn't seem to be any way. When my father drove up we climbed in and rode all the way home in guilty silence. My stepmother, Alice, must have told him not to say a word.

When we got home my little brothers looked at me fearfully and my father said with a glint in his eye, "Go to your room and stay there. I'll deal with you later."

Nothing more ever came of it which surprised me no end because I waited all week for punishment.

So now it was a month later, or maybe more.

I still kept to myself at school and if a person talked to me, I just turned away because I had nothing to say to any of them.

On the 5th of November it was my birthday. I woke up with poison in my heart and an ache in my throat that I had to keep swallowing because I was remembering my twelfth birthday when my mother had made a dress for me and also bought me *Tales of Robin Hood* which I don't read anymore, but it was the book I had taken with me when Rufus and I ran away.

Breakfast seemed strangely quiet, all the more so because nobody said a thing, not even "Happy Birthday." I knew they had forgotten.

At school, like always, I answered if I was called on, but not otherwise. I ate my lunch by myself and passed most of the day thinking of how many birthdays I would have to live through before Rufus and I could leave again for good. About four more, I decided, then knew with a deep sorrow that Rufus wouldn't last to be eighteen.

When school was out, I turned in the wrong direction from home and headed for a park up on a high bluff. It was pleasant and empty. The trees were dropping their leaves in little piles and a couple of squirrels chased each other around tree trunks like they were on a merry-go-round. I wanted to stay there forever. I wanted the leaves to cover me like little Hansel and Gretel when they were lost in the woods. I wondered if they had had a stepmother who drove them off, and then I said aloud, "No, that isn't fair. You know it isn't Alice's fault. I don't know whose fault it is for feeling so left out of things."

I looked again at the fallen leaves and thought that my family was like the strong tree that would survive the winter, but I was probably one of the lost leaves.

"I didn't expect them to give me any presents," I kicked at the leaves. I propped my chin on my knees and sat for a long time, thinking and because it was getting late, I read my next day's history lesson. Finally it was too hard to read and looking up, I saw it was almost dark and it was a long way home.

I walked home like I always walked, neither slow nor hurrying. It was just too bad if I was late for supper. I didn't want any anyhow.

When I opened the door the house felt strange. My father was sitting in the front room behind his paper which he put aside for a moment, looked at me and said, "Humph!"

Jason came dancing up to me and grabbed me by the hand pulling me to the dining room.

"Where you been, Patty?" he said. "Everybody waited and waited."

Rufus rushed out from the kitchen to greet me as always, but he was wearing a silly little paper hat tied under his chin. I stood in the brightly lighted room and looked around confused. There had obviously been a party. Used paper plates lay all over and the remains of a big frosted cake was crumpled in the center of the table which had a good linen cloth on it. A pile of wrapped presents lay on the sideboard. In the kitchen I could hear Scott chattering to Alice like a little parakeet and Jason, still clutching my hand, was trying to tell me something.

"All your classmates, Patty," he was saying. "All of them. When you dint come home, we had to have the party without you. Your presents are here."

He tried to drag me towards them, but I shucked him off and rushed to my room.

I was pretty shamefaced when Alice came in to see if I wanted supper.

She sat beside me on the bed and patted me on the back.

"It was my fault," she said. "I shouldn't have tried to surprise you. Anyway, come on out and feed Rufus. I think he's going to be sick from all that cake he was given."

So that's how matters stand now.

Nothing is going to change very much. I don't feel quite so mad at the whole world, and I notice my actions towards Alice are a lot friendlier. It doesn't bother me any when the boys call her "Mother." Maybe, sometime, a long time from now, I might start calling her that myself. Maybe, by spring or so, I might start growing myself back on that family tree.

JEAN McCORD
....

Jean McCord was born in 1924. She lost her parents when she was twelve, and her love of books provided steadiness in a life that was constantly changing. McCord attended sixteen different schools before graduating from high school at fifteen. After college she had, by her own count, at least forty-five different occupations.

Much of McCord's story-writing is based on her memories of the restless years of her growing up. "The Long Way Around" comes from her book *Deep Where the Octopi Lie*.

I HAVE A DREAM

MARTIN LUTHER KING, JR.

I am happy to join with you today in what will go down in history as the greatest demonstration for freedom in the history of our nation.

Fivescore[1] years ago, a great American, in whose symbolic shadow we stand today, signed the Emancipation Proclamation. This momentous decree came as a great beacon light of hope to millions of Negro slaves who had been seared in the flames of withering injustice. It came as a joyous daybreak to end the long night of their captivity.

But one hundred years later, the Negro is still not free; one hundred years later, the life of the Negro is still sadly crippled by the manacles[2] of segregation and the chains of discrimination; one hundred years later, the Negro lives on a lonely island of poverty in the midst of a vast ocean of material prosperity; one hundred years later,

1. **fivescore** [fīv skōr′]: one hundred; one score is a group of twenty.
2. **manacles** [man′ ə kəlz]: restraints.

the Negro is still languished³ in the corners of American society and finds himself in exile in his own land.

So we've come here today to dramatize a shameful condition. In a sense we've come to our nation's capital to cash a check. When the architects of our republic wrote the magnificent words of the Constitution and the Declaration of Independence, they were signing a promissory note⁴ to which every American was to fall heir. This note was the promise that all men, yes, black men as well as white men, would be guaranteed the unalienable⁵ rights of life, liberty, and the pursuit of happiness.

It is obvious today that America has defaulted on this promissory note in so far as her citizens of color are concerned. Instead of

3. **languished** [lang′ gwishd]: suffering in sadness and neglect.
4. **promissory note** [prom′ ə sôr′ ē]: a written promise.
5. **unalienable** [un ā′ lyə nə bəl]: that cannot be given or taken away.

honoring this sacred obligation, America has given the Negro people a bad check; a check which has come back marked "insufficient funds." We refuse to believe that there are insufficient funds in the great vaults of opportunity of this nation. And so we've come to cash this check, a check that will give us upon demand the riches of freedom and the security of justice.

We have also come to this hallowed[6] spot to remind America of the fierce urgency of now. This is no time to engage in the luxury of cooling off or to take the tranquilizing drug of gradualism. Now is the time to make real the promises of democracy; now is the time to rise from the dark and desolate valley of segregation to the sunlit path of racial justice; now is the time to lift our nation from the quicksands of racial injustice to the solid rock of brotherhood; now is the time to make justice a reality for all God's children. It would be fatal for the nation to overlook the urgency of the moment. This sweltering summer of the Negro's legitimate discontent will not pass until there is an invigorating autumn of freedom and equality.

Nineteen sixty-three is not an end, but a beginning. And those who hope that the Negro needed to blow off steam and will now be content, will have a rude awakening if the nation returns to business as usual.

There will be neither rest nor tranquility in America until the Negro is granted his citizenship rights. The whirlwinds of revolt will continue to shake the foundations of our nation until the bright day of justice emerges.

But there is something that I must say to my people who stand on the warm threshold which leads into the palace of justice. In the process of gaining our rightful place we must not be guilty of wrongful deeds.

Let us not seek to satisfy our thirst for freedom by drinking from the cup of bitterness and hatred. We must forever conduct our struggle on the high plane of dignity and discipline. We must not allow our creative protest to degenerate into physical violence. Again and again we must rise to the majestic heights of meeting physical force with soul force.

---

6. **hallowed** [hal′ ōd]: holy, sacred.

The marvelous new militancy which has engulfed the Negro community must not lead us to a distrust of all white people, for many of our white brothers, as evidenced by their presence here today, have come to realize that their destiny is tied up with our destiny and they have come to realize that their freedom is inextricably bound to our freedom. This offense we share mounted to storm the battlements of injustice must be carried forth by a biracial army. We cannot walk alone.

And as we walk, we must make the pledge that we shall always march ahead. We cannot turn back. There are those who are asking the devotees of civil rights, "When will you be satisfied?" We can never be satisfied as long as the Negro is the victim of the unspeakable horrors of police brutality.

We can never be satisfied as long as our bodies, heavy with fatigue of travel, cannot gain lodging in the motels of the highways and the hotels of the cities. We cannot be satisfied as long as the Negro's basic mobility is from a smaller ghetto to a larger one.

We can never be satisfied as long as our children are stripped of their selfhood and robbed of their dignity by signs stating "for whites only." We cannot be satisfied as long as a Negro in Mississippi cannot vote and a Negro in New York believes he has nothing for which to vote. No, we are not satisfied, and we will not be satisfied until justice rolls down like waters and righteousness like a mighty stream.

I am not unmindful that some of you come here out of excessive trials and tribulation. Some of you have come fresh from narrow jail cells. Some of you have come from areas where your quest for freedom left you battered by the storms of persecution and staggered by the winds of police brutality. You have been the veterans of creative suffering. Continue to work with the faith that unearned suffering is redemptive.

Go back to Mississippi; go back to Alabama; go back to South Carolina; go back to Georgia; go back to Louisiana; go back to the slums and ghettos of the northern cities, knowing that somehow this situation can, and will be changed. Let us not wallow in the valley of despair.

So I say to you, my friends, that even though we must face the difficulties of today and tomorrow, I still have a dream. It is a dream deeply rooted in the American dream that one day this nation will rise up and live out the true meaning of its creed—we hold these truths to be self-evident, that all men are created equal.

I have a dream that one day on the red hills of Georgia, sons of former slaves and sons of former slave-owners will be able to sit down together at the table of brotherhood.

I have a dream that one day, even the state of Mississippi, a state sweltering with the heat of injustice, sweltering with the heat of oppression, will be transformed into an oasis of freedom and justice.

I have a dream my four little children will one day live in a nation where they will not be judged by the color of their skin but by the content of their character. I have a dream today!

I have a dream that one day, down in Alabama, with its vicious racists, with its governor[7] having his lips dripping with the words of interposition[8] and nullification,[9] that one day, right there in Alabama, little black boys and black girls will be able to join hands with little white boys and white girls as sisters and brothers. I have a dream today!

I have a dream that one day every valley shall be exalted, every hill and mountain shall be made low, the rough places shall be made plain, and the crooked places shall be made straight and the glory of the Lord will be revealed and all flesh shall see it together.

This is our hope. This is the faith that I go back to the South with.

With this faith we will be able to hew out of the mountain of despair a stone of hope. With this faith we will be able to transform the jangling discords of our nation into a beautiful symphony of brotherhood.

With this faith we will be able to work together, to pray together, to struggle together, to go to jail together, to stand up for freedom together, knowing that we will be free one day. This will be the day when all of God's children will be able to sing with new meaning—"my country 'tis of thee; sweet land of liberty; of thee I sing; land where my fathers died, land of the pilgrim's pride; from

---

7. **governor:** reference to George Wallace, governor of Alabama, who in 1963 opposed school integration.
8. **interposition** [in tər pə zish′ ən]: interruption, interference.
9. **nullification** [nul′ ə fə kā′ shən]: act of causing something to cease to exist.

every mountainside, let freedom ring"—and if America is to be a great nation, this must become true.

So let freedom ring from the prodigious hilltops of New Hampshire.

Let freedom ring from the mighty mountains of New York.

Let freedom ring from the heightening Alleghenies of Pennsylvania.

Let freedom ring from the snow-capped Rockies of Colorado.

Let freedom ring from the curvaceous slopes of California.

But not only that.

Let freedom ring from Stone Mountain of Georgia.

Let freedom ring from Lookout Mountain of Tennessee.

Let freedom ring from every hill and molehill of Mississippi, from every mountainside, let freedom ring.

And when we allow freedom to ring, when we let it ring from every village and hamlet, from every state and city, we will be able to speed up that day when all of God's children—black men and white men, Jews and Gentiles, Catholics and Protestants—will be able to join hands and sing in the words of the old Negro spiritual, "Free at last, free at last; thank God Almighty, we are free at last."

MARTIN LUTHER KING, JR.

Martin Luther King, Jr. [1928-1968], was born in Atlanta, Georgia. He skipped ninth and twelfth grades and entered college when he was only 15 years old. He became a Baptist minister and later earned a Ph.D. in theology. King became a national figure during the civil rights movement of the 1960s. Advocating nonviolent protest he led many of the demonstrations for equal rights that helped to end segregation. In Birmingham, Alabama, where violence flared against the demonstrators, King was jailed for his role as leader.

After the Civil Rights Act passed, King was awarded the Nobel Peace Prize. Four years later, his assassination stunned the world.

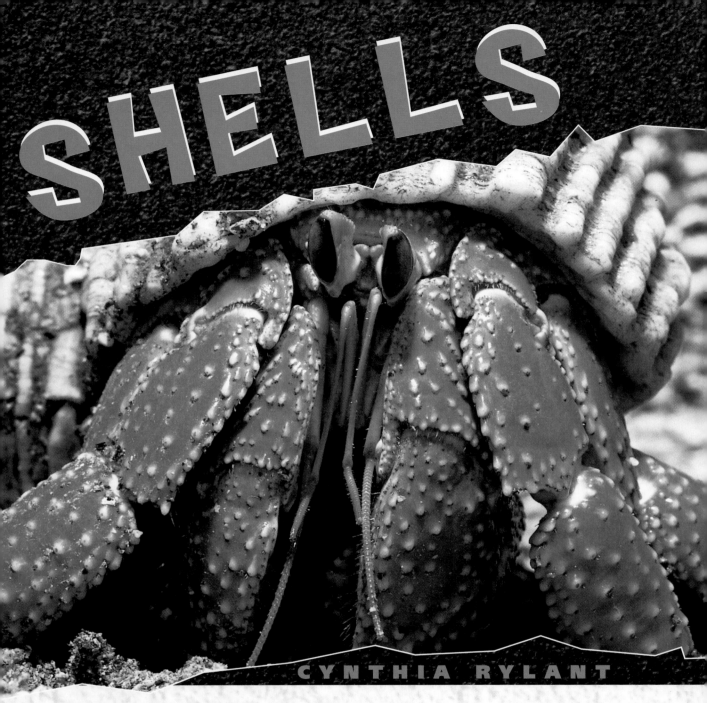

SHELLS

CYNTHIA RYLANT

"You *hate* living here."

Michael looked at the woman speaking to him.

"No, Aunt Esther. I don't." He said it dully, sliding his milk glass back and forth on the table. "I don't hate it here."

Esther removed the last pan from the dishwasher and hung it above the oven.

"You hate it here," she said, "and you hate me."

"I don't!" Michael yelled. "It's not *you!*"

The woman turned to face him in the kitchen.

"Don't yell at me!" she yelled. "I'll not have it in my home. I can't make you happy, Michael. You just refuse to be happy here. And you punish me every day for it."

"*Punish* you?" Michael gawked[1] at her. "I don't punish you! I don't care about you! I don't care what you eat or how you dress or where you go or what you think. Can't you just leave me alone?"

He slammed down the glass, scraped his chair back from the table and ran out the door.

"Michael!" yelled Esther.

They had been living together, the two of them, for six months. Michael's parents had died and only Esther could take him in—or, only she had offered to. Michael's other relatives could not imagine dealing with a fourteen-year-old boy. They wanted peaceful lives.

Esther lived in a condominium in a wealthy section of Detroit. Most of the area's residents were older (like her) and afraid of the world they lived in (like her). They stayed indoors much of the time. They trusted few people.

Esther liked living alone. She had never married or had children. She had never lived anywhere but Detroit. She liked her condominium.

But she was fiercely loyal to her family, and when her only sister had died, Esther insisted she be allowed to care for Michael. And Michael, afraid of going anywhere else, had accepted.

Oh, he was lonely. Even six months after their deaths, he still expected to see his parents—sitting on the couch as he walked into Esther's living room, waiting for the bathroom as he came out of the shower, coming in the door late at night. He still smelled his father's Old Spice somewhere, his mother's talc.

Sometimes he was so sure one of them was *somewhere* around him that he thought maybe he was going crazy. His heart hurt him. He wondered if he would ever get better.

And though he denied it, he did hate Esther. She was so different from his mother and father. Prejudiced—she admired only those who

---

1. **gawked** [gôkd]: stared idly or rudely.

were white and Presbyterian.[2] Selfish—she wouldn't allow him to use her phone. Complaining—she always had a headache or a backache or a stomachache.

He didn't want to, but he hated her. And he didn't know what to do except lie about it.

Michael hadn't made any friends at his new school, and his teachers barely noticed him. He came home alone every day and usually found Esther on the phone. She kept in close touch with several other women in nearby condominiums.

Esther told her friends she didn't understand Michael. She said she knew he must grieve for his parents, but why punish her? She said she thought she might send him away if he couldn't be nicer. She said she didn't deserve this.

But when Michael came in the door, she always quickly changed the subject.

One day after school Michael came home with a hermit crab.[3] He had gone into a pet store, looking for some small, living thing, and hermit crabs were selling for just a few dollars. He'd bought one, and a bowl.

Esther, for a change, was not on the phone when he arrived home. She was having tea and a crescent roll and seemed cheerful. Michael wanted badly to show someone what he had bought. So he showed her.

Esther surprised him. She picked up the shell and poked the long, shiny nail of her little finger at the crab's claws.

"Where is he?" she asked.

Michael showed her the crab's eyes peering through the small opening of the shell.

"Well, for heaven's sake, come out of there!" she said to the crab, and she turned the shell upside down and shook it.

"Aunt Esther!" Michael grabbed for the shell.

"All right, all right." She turned it right side up. "Well," she said, "what does he do?"

2. **Presbyterian** [prez′ bə tir′ ē ən]: belonging to the Presbyterian Church, a Protestant Christian church denomination.
3. **hermit crab:** a crab with a soft body; often lives in the empty shells of snails for protection.

Michael grinned and shrugged his shoulders.

"I don't know," he answered. "Just grows, I guess."

His aunt looked at him.

"An attraction to a crab is something I cannot identify with. However, it's fine with me if you keep him, as long as I can be assured he won't grow out of that bowl." She gave him a hard stare.

"He won't," Michael answered. "I promise."

The hermit crab moved into the condominium. Michael named him Sluggo and kept the bowl beside his bed. Michael had to watch the bowl for very long periods of time to catch Sluggo with his head poking out of his shell, moving around. Bedtime seemed to be Sluggo's liveliest part of the day, and Michael found it easy to lie and watch the busy crab as sleep slowly came on.

One day Michael arrived home to find Esther sitting on the edge of his bed, looking at the bowl. Esther usually did not intrude in Michael's room, and seeing her there disturbed him. But he stood at the doorway and said nothing.

Esther seemed perfectly comfortable, although she looked over at him with a frown on her face.

"I think he needs a companion," she said.

"What?" Michael's eyebrows went up as his jaw dropped down.

Esther sniffed.

"I think Sluggo needs a girl friend." She stood up. "Where is that pet store?"

Michael took her. In the store was a huge tank full of hermit crabs.

"Oh my!" Esther grabbed the rim of the tank and craned her neck over the side. "Look at them!"

Michael was looking more at his Aunt Esther than at the crabs. He couldn't believe it.

"Oh, look at those shells. You say they grow out of them? We must stock up with several sizes. See the pink in that one? Michael, look! He's got his little head out!"

Esther was so dramatic—leaning into the tank, her bangle bracelets clanking, earrings swinging, red pumps clicking on the linoleum—that she attracted the attention of everyone in the store. Michael pretended not to know her well.

He and Esther returned to the condominium with a thirty-gallon tank and twenty hermit crabs.

Michael figured he'd have a heart attack before he got the heavy tank into their living room. He figured he'd die and Aunt Esther would inherit twenty-one crabs and funeral expenses.

But he made it. Esther carried the box of crabs.

"Won't Sluggo be surprised?" she asked happily. "Oh, I do hope we'll be able to tell him apart from the rest. He's their founding father!"

Michael, in a stupor[4] over his Aunt Esther and the phenomenon[5] of twenty-one hermit crabs, wiped out the tank, arranged it with gravel and sticks (as well as the plastic scuba diver Aunt Esther insisted on buying) and assisted her in loading it up, one by one, with the new residents. The crabs were as overwhelmed as Michael. Not one showed its face.

4. **stupor** [stü′ pər]: a dazed condition.
5. **phenomenon** [fə nom′ ə non]: an extraordinary occurrence.

Before moving Sluggo from his bowl, Aunt Esther marked his shell with some red fingernail polish so she could distinguish him from the rest. Then she flopped down on the couch beside Michael.

"Oh, what would your mother *think*, Michael, if she could see this mess we've gotten ourselves into!"

She looked at Michael with a broad smile, but it quickly disappeared. The boy's eyes were full of pain.

"Oh, my," she whispered. "I'm sorry."

Michael turned his head away.

Aunt Esther, who had not embraced anyone in years, gently put her arm about his shoulders.

"I am so sorry, Michael. Oh, you must hate me."

Michael sensed a familiar smell then. His mother's talc.

He looked at his aunt.

"No, Aunt Esther." He shook his head solemnly. "I don't hate you."

Esther's mouth trembled and her bangles clanked as she patted his arm. She took a deep, strong breath.

"Well, let's look in on our friend Sluggo," she said.

They leaned their heads over the tank and found him. The crab, finished with the old home that no longer fit, was coming out of his shell.

CYNTHIA RYLANT

Cynthia Rylant was born in 1954 in Hopewell, Virginia, and spent much of her childhood with her grandparents in West Virginia. "With my grandparents," Rylant says, "there was some poverty, but mostly a very rich existence." The rest of her childhood was spent with her mother in the small town of Beaver, West Virginia. The town had no library, and Rylant had little to read. In college, she discovered that she wanted to be a writer.

"It took me about seven books to feel like a writer," Rylant has said. "But I know now that's what I am." Two of her books for young people are *A Blue-Eyed Daisy* and *A Fine White Dust*.

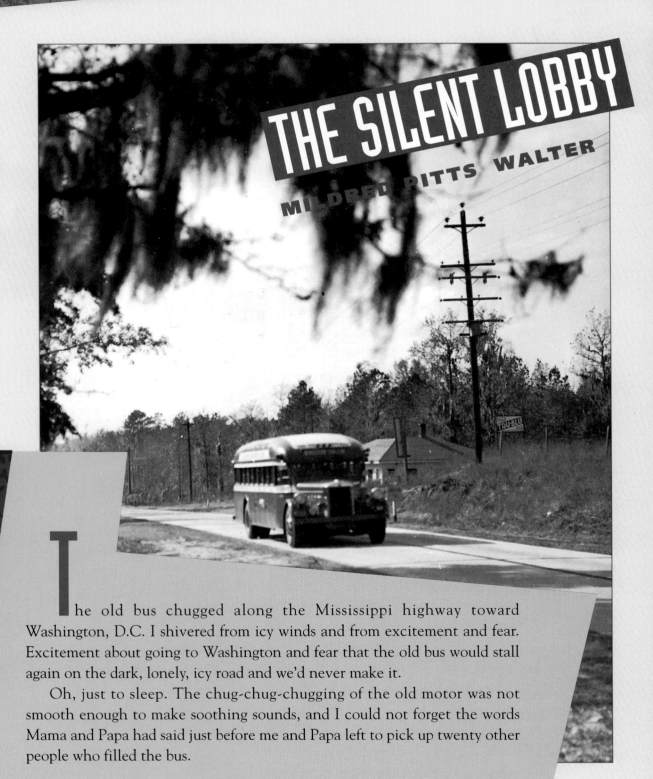

THE SILENT LOBBY

MILDRED PITTS WALTER

The old bus chugged along the Mississippi highway toward Washington, D.C. I shivered from icy winds and from excitement and fear. Excitement about going to Washington and fear that the old bus would stall again on the dark, lonely, icy road and we'd never make it.

Oh, just to sleep. The chug-chug-chugging of the old motor was not smooth enough to make soothing sounds, and I could not forget the words Mama and Papa had said just before me and Papa left to pick up twenty other people who filled the bus.

"It's too dangerous," Mama had said. "They just might bomb that bus."

"They could bomb this house for that matter," Papa said.

"I know," Mama went on. "That's why I don't want you to go. Why can't you just forget about this voting business and let us live in peace?"

"There can be no peace without freedom," Papa said.

"And you think someone is going to give you freedom?" Mama asked with heat in her voice. "Instead of going to Washington, you should be getting a gun to protect us."

"There are ways to win a struggle without bombs and guns. I'm going to Washington and Craig is going with me."

"Craig is too young."

"He's eleven. That's old enough to know what this is all about," Papa insisted.

I knew. It had all started two years ago, in 1963. Papa was getting ready to go into town to register to vote. Just as he was leaving, Mr. Clem, Papa's boss, came and warned Papa that he should not try to register.

"I intend to register," Papa said.

"If you do, I'll have to fire you." Mr. Clem drove away in a cloud of dust.

"You ought not go," Mama said, alarmed. "You know that people have been arrested and beaten for going down there."

"I'm going," Papa insisted.

"Let me go with you, Papa." I was scared, too, and wanted to be with him if he needed help.

"No, you stay and look after your mama and the house till I get back."

Day turned to night, and Papa had not returned. Mama paced the floor. Was Papa in jail? Had he been beaten. We waited, afraid. Finally, I said, "Mama, I'll go find him."

"Oh, no!" she cried. Her fear scared me more, and I felt angry because I couldn't do anything.

At last we heard Papa's footsteps. The look on his face let us know right away that something was mighty wrong.

"What happened, Sylvester?" Mama asked.

"I paid the poll tax,[1] passed the literacy test, but I didn't interpret the state constitution the way they wanted. So they wouldn't register me."

Feeling a sense of sad relief, I said, "Now you won't lose your job."

"Oh, but I will. I tried to register."

Even losing his job didn't stop Papa from wanting to vote. One day he heard about Mrs. Fannie Lou Hamer and the Mississippi Freedom Democratic Party. The Freedom Party registered people without charging a poll tax, without a literacy test, and without people having to tell what the Mississippi Constitution was about.

On election day in 1964, Papa proudly voted for Mrs. Hamer, Mrs. Victoria Grey, and Mrs. Annie Devine to represent the people of the Second Congressional District of Mississippi. Eighty-three thousand other black men and women voted that day, too. Great victory celebrations were held in homes and churches. But the Governor of Mississippi, Paul B. Johnson, declared all of those eighty-three thousand votes of black people illegal. He gave certificates of election to three white men—William Colmer, John Williams, and a Mr. Whittier—to represent the mostly black Second Congressional District.

Members of the Freedom Party were like Papa—they didn't give up. They got busy when the governor threw out their votes. Lawyers from all over the country came to help. People signed affidavits[2] saying that when they tried to register they lost their jobs, they were beaten, and their homes were burned and churches bombed. More than ten thousand people signed petitions to the governor asking him to count their votes. There was never a word from the governor.

My mind returned to the sound of the old bus slowly grinding along. Suddenly the bus stopped. Not again! We'd never make it now. Papa got out in the cold wind and icy drizzling rain and raised the hood. While he worked, we sang and clapped our hands to keep

1. **poll tax** [pōl taks]: a tax paid (prior to 1964) by every adult citizen in order to be able to vote.
2. **affidavits** [af′ ə dā′ vitz]: statements written down and sworn to be true.

warm. I could hear Sister Phyllis praying with all her might for our safety. After a while we were moving along again.

I must have finally fallen asleep, for a policeman's voice woke me. "You can't stop here near the Capitol," he shouted.

"Our bus won't go," Papa said.

"If you made it from Mississippi all the way to D.C., you'll make it from here," the policeman barked.

At first the loud voice frightened me. Then, wide awake, sensing the policeman's impatience, I wondered why Papa didn't let him know that we would go as soon as the motor started. But Papa, knowing that old bus, said nothing. He stepped on the starter. The old motor growled and died. Again the policeman shouted, "I said get out of here."

"We'll have to push it," Papa said.

Everyone got off the bus and pushed. Passersby stopped and stared. Finally we were safe on a side street, away from the Capitol with a crowd gathered around us.

"You mean they came all the way from Mississippi in that?" someone in the crowd asked.

Suddenly the old bus looked shabby. I lowered my head and became aware of my clothes: my faded coat too small; my cotton pants too thin. With a feeling of shame, I wished those people would go away.

"What brings you all to the District?" a man called to us.

"We've come to see about seating the people we voted for and elected," Papa answered. "Down home they say our votes don't count, and up here they've gone ahead and seated men who don't represent us. We've come to talk about that."

"So you've come to lobby," a woman shouted. The crowd laughed.

Why were they laughing? I knew that to lobby meant to try to get someone to decide for or against something. Yes, that was why we had come. I wished I could have said to those people who stood gawking at us that the suffering that brought us here was surely nothing to laugh about.

The laughter from the crowd quieted when another woman shouted, "You're too late to lobby. The House of Representatives will vote on that issue this morning."

Too late. That's what had worried me when the old bus kept breaking down. Had we come so far in this cold for nothing? Was it really too late to talk to members of the House of Representatives to persuade them to seat our representatives elected by the Freedom Party, *not* the ones chosen by the governor?

Just then rain began to fall. The crowd quickly left, and we climbed onto our bus. Papa and the others started to talk. What would we do now? Finally, Papa said, "We can't turn back now. We've done too much and come too far."

After more talk we all agreed that we must try to do what we had come to do. Icy rain pelted us as we rushed against cold wind back to the Capitol.

A doorman stopped us on the steps. "May I have your passes?"

"We don't have any," Papa replied.

"Sorry, you have to have passes for seats in the gallery." The doorman blocked the way.

"We're cold in this rain. Let us in," Sister Phyllis cried.

"Maybe we should just go on back home," someone suggested.

"Yes. We can't talk to the legislators now, anyway," another woman said impatiently.

"No," Papa said. "We must stay if we do no more than let them see that we have come all this way."

"But we're getting soaking wet. We can't stand out here much longer," another protested.

"Can't you just let us in out of this cold?" Papa pleaded with the doorman.

"Not without passes." The doorman still blocked the way. Then he said, "There's a tunnel underneath this building. You can go there to get out of the rain."

We crowded into the tunnel and lined up along the sides. My chilled body and hands came to life pressed against the warm walls. Then footsteps and voices echoed through the tunnel. Police. This tunnel . . . a trap! Would they do something to us for trying to get in without passes? I wanted to cry out to Papa, but I could not speak.

The footsteps came closer. Then many people began to walk by.

When they came upon us, they suddenly stopped talking. Only the sound of their feet echoed in the tunnel. Where had they come from? What did they do? "Who are they, Papa?" I whispered.

"Congressmen and women." Papa spoke so softly, I hardly heard him, even in the silence.

They wore warm coats, some trimmed with fur. Their shoes gleamed. Some of them frowned at us. Others glared. Some sighed quickly as they walked by. Others looked at us, then turned their eyes to their shoes. I could tell by a sudden lift of the head and a certain look that some were surprised and scared. And there were a few whose friendly smiles seemed to say, Right on!

I glanced at Papa. How poor he and our friends looked beside those well-dressed people. Their clothes were damp, threadbare, and wrinkled; their shoes were worn and mud stained. But they all stood straight and tall.

My heart pounded. I wanted to call out to those men and women, "Count my papa's vote! Let my people help make laws, too." But I didn't dare speak in that silence.

Could they hear my heart beating? Did they know what was on my mind? "Lord," I prayed, "let them hear us in this silence."

Then two congressmen stopped in front of Papa. I was frightened until I saw smiles on their faces.

"I'm Congressman Ryan from New York," one of them said. Then he introduced a black man: "This is Congressman Hawkins from California."

"I'm Sylvester Saunders. We are here from Mississippi," Papa said.

"We expected you much earlier," Congressman Ryan said.

"Our old bus and bad weather delayed us," Papa explained.

"That's unfortunate. You could've helped us a lot. We worked late into the night lobbying to get votes on your side. But maybe I should say on *our* side." Mr. Ryan smiled.

"And we didn't do very well," Congressman Hawkins said.

"We'll be lucky if we get fifty votes on our side today," Congressman Ryan informed us. "Maybe you would like to come in and see us at work."

"We don't have passes," I said, surprised at my voice.

"We'll see about getting all of you in," Congressman Hawkins promised.

A little later, as we found seats in the gallery, Congressman Gerald Ford from the state of Michigan was speaking. He did not want Mrs. Hamer and other fairly elected members of the Freedom Party seated in the House. He asked his fellow congressmen to stick to the rule of letting only those with credentials from their states be seated in Congress. The new civil rights act[3] would, in time, undo wrongs done to black Americans. But for now, Congress should let the men chosen by Governor Johnson keep their seats and get on with other business.

Then Congressman Ryan rose to speak. How could Congress stick to rules that denied blacks their right to vote in the state of Mississippi? The rule of letting only those with credentials from a segregated state have seats in the House could not *justly* apply here.

I looked down on those men and few women and wondered if they were listening. Did they know about the petitions? I remembered what Congressman Ryan had said: "We'll be lucky if we get fifty. . . ." Only 50 out of 435 elected to the House.

Finally the time came for Congress to vote. Those who wanted to seat Mrs. Hamer and members of the Freedom Democratic Party were to say, yes. Those who didn't want to seat Mrs. Hamer were to say, no.

At every yes vote I could hardly keep from clapping my hands and shouting, "Yea! Yea!" But I kept quiet, counting: thirty, then forty, forty-eight . . . only two more. We would lose badly.

Then something strange happened. Congressmen and congresswomen kept saying "Yes. Yes. Yes." On and on, "Yes." My heart pounded. Could we win? I sat on my hands to keep from clapping. I looked at Papa and the others who had come with us. They all sat on the edge of their seats. They looked as if they could hardly keep from shouting out, too, as more yes votes rang from the floor.

When the voting was over, 148 votes had been cast in our favor.

3. **civil rights act:** a federal law of 1964 that authorized federal action against segregation in employment and in public places.

What had happened? Why had so many changed their minds?

Later, Papa introduced me to Congressman Hawkins. The congressman asked me, "How did you all know that some of us walk through that tunnel from our offices?"

"We didn't know," I answered. "We were sent there out of the rain."

"That's strange," the congressman said. "Your standing there silently made a difference in the vote. Even though we lost this time, some of them now know that we'll keep on lobbying until we win."

I felt proud. Papa had been right when he said to Mama, "There are ways to win a struggle without bombs and guns." We had lobbied in silence and we had been *heard*.

MILDRED PITTS WALTER

Mildred Pitts Walter was born in 1922 in Sweetville, Louisiana. Walter's parents brought her up to believe in herself, despite poverty and the everyday discrimination that they and other African Americans faced in those days. "I always knew that I could do any kind of work," she once said. "And if I set my mind to it, I could do anything I wanted."

Walter worked her way through college, moved to Los Angeles, and became active in the civil rights movement of the 1960s. Later, she began teaching and writing for children and young people. Her books *The Girl on the Outside* and *Because We Are* tell of the civil rights struggle. Another book, *Have a Happy . . .* , celebrates aspects of African American heritage that Walter learned during a trip to Africa.

The

onald leaned into the car trunk to find the box holding the giveaways. He had to pay for each letter opener, shoehorn, and vegetable brush, money out of his own commission,[1] but it was worth it. Why else would people listen to his sales spiel if it wasn't because they felt indebted the second they reached for a sample?

What a mess, he thought, getting grease on his hand. Ever since Mom stopped driving. Ever since she . . .

Fuller Brush Man

GLORIA D. MIKLOWITZ

Well, there was no use dwelling on that. When he had time he'd try to get rid of some of the junk. He dropped a dozen plastic shoehorns into his sample case, snapped the lock, and glanced at his watch.

Man, he was hungry. He'd been working steadily since right after school, four hours. All he'd eaten was a doughnut left in the breadbox at home, running out the door with Ava calling after him to get a glass of milk first.

He'd sold enough brushes to call it

quits for the day, but maybe he'd work another hour. If he went home now, even though it would mean a real meal, not McDonald's, Ava would be there. Their newest housekeeper, she'd sit there at the kitchen table, arms folded, watching him, and she'd go into her usual song and dance.

"Go in to your mother. Just for a minute. Say hello. Say *something*."

"Later."

"*Now*. She'll be asleep later."

"Why? She can't talk. She probably doesn't even know who I am. What difference does it make?"

"Donnie, Donnie. You love her. I know you do. Do it for you, if not for her."

"Leave me alone."

He'd get this picture in his head of Mom, the way she had become lately. Bloated face, dull eyes that followed him without seeming to see, a stomach as if she was pregnant. And her arms skinny, all bones. *Why? How could she do that to him, to them?*

---

1. **commission** [kə mish′ ən]: a percentage of the amount of money earned by a business deal, paid to the agent who does the business.

No. He'd just get a bite nearby and go home later. He could maybe make five more sales. More money for the college fund. And with what Dad was putting out in medical bills and nursing care, every cent counted.

He crossed the street and was nearly knocked down by a kid on a two-wheeler, shooting out of a driveway, wobbling his way down the road. When had *he* learned to ride a bike? Eight, nine years ago? Yes. In the Apperson Street schoolyard, late afternoons. He could hear the crickets chirping even now, and for a second he felt the same surge of fear and exultation[2] he'd felt then gripping the handlebars.

"I can't! I can't! I'm falling! Mom, Mom! Help me!"

"You can! You can! Keep going! That's right! You're doing it!"

Running alongside, face sweating and flushed, red hair flying about her eyes and cheeks, she was laughing with joy. And when he finally managed to stop she threw her arms around him and cried, "See? You did it! I knew you could!"

He swallowed a lump in his throat and marched briskly up the walk to the door of a small, wooden house. He rang the bell and waited, peering through the screen door into a living room with a worn couch, a TV flickering against one wall, and a small child sitting in front of it.

"*If you don't behave, you'll have to watch TV,*" his mother would say when he was that age, as if watching TV was punishment. Maybe that's why he hardly watched even now.

When *he* was little, this was the time of day he loved most. Right after supper and before bedtime. He'd climb up on the couch to sit beside Mom. Bonnie would take her place on Mom's other side and for a half hour it was "weed books" time.

He felt an overwhelming hunger for those times, for Mom's arm around him and her warm voice reading. He wiped a hand across his eyes as a woman, holding a baby, came to the door.

"Fuller brush man! Good evening, missus. Would you like a sample?" Donald held out a brush, a letter opener, and a shoehorn. With but a second's hesitation the woman unlatched the door and stepped forward, eyeing the samples greedily. She took the brush.

"Good choice," Donald said. "They're great for scrubbing vegetables. Now, would you like to see our specials?" He held the catalog open to the specials page, but the light was fading.

---

2. **exultation** [eg′ zul tā′ shən]: a great rejoicing, triumph.

"I don't need any . . ."

"Then maybe you'd like to try our new tile-cleaning foam. See?" He plucked a can from his case and showed her the cap with its stiff bristles for the "hard-to-clean places between the tiles."

"I have Formica."[3]

"Sally? Sally? Who the devil is that?"

"Just a brush salesman, honey!"

"Well, tell him you don't need any!"

The woman gave him a sheepish grin, backed away, and said, "Sorry." She closed the screen door and latched it again.

He used to take rejection hard, getting a pain in his stomach that grew with each door shut in his face, each disgusted "Don't bother me." He still withdrew inside when people turned him away, although he wouldn't show it now, keeping his voice pleasant and a smile on his face. If anyone asked, he'd say he hated the job even though he was learning a lot about human nature and keeping books, and it did pay well.

"**S**ell door to door?" his mother had asked when he first proposed the idea. "Absolutely not!"

"Why not? I could save what I make for college!"

"No!"

"Why? That's not fair!"

"Because." He watched her struggle to find words for what she hadn't thought out. "Because it's not safe, knocking on strange people's doors. The world is full of crazies. Because I don't want you to have to get doors slammed in your face. Because it will be summer soon and too hot to work outdoors. If you want a job, find one where it's air-conditioned."

"Let him try," Dad said. "One day of it and he'll quit."

"*Please*, Mom?"

"Oh, all right," she conceded, but only because that morning he'd accused her of still treating him like a baby. "But only to try it. *One* day!"

It was three months now. She must have been sick even then, because after that first day when he'd come home triumphant with having made fifty-four dollars in only six hours, he didn't hear anything more about quitting. It was about then that she went into the hospital for the first time and his whole life began to change.

"**W**hen he finished another block, he circled back to the car, a dog barking at his heels. One of the hazards of selling things in strange neighborhoods was the dogs. He

3. **Formica** [fôr mī′ kə]: plastic, used on kitchen and furniture surfaces, that resists water, heat, and most chemicals.

carried Mace[4] but hated using it. He found that if he stood his ground and shouted "No," most dogs would go through their ferocious act and run off when they figured they'd done their duty.

In the dim light of the car he looked over his orders and decided to drive down to the boulevard for something to eat. Maybe he'd phone Shannon afterwards, drop by for a few minutes before going home. He started the engine, turned on the headlights, and drove down the hill.

"How's your Mom?" Shannon asked when he reached her from the phone in the parking lot. There was so much traffic noise he had to press the receiver tight against his ear.

"What are you doing?" he asked in response. "I can be by in ten minutes. We could go for a walk."

"When are you going to talk about it?" Shannon asked. "Bonnie says she's worse. It's awful how you're acting. It's not her fault."

For a second he considered not answering at all, but finally he said, "Stop bugging me. Everyone's after me about it. It's *my* mom. It's my business. If that's all you want to talk about, forget it."

"But, Donnie! You can't put it off much longer."

He hung up without answering and ran back to the car.

Slamming the door, he slumped in the driver's seat and stared out at the ribbon of lights on the freeway. If he let himself think about what Shannon said, he'd just start blubbering like a baby. Better to work. He'd get at the orders for the week. They were due to be toted up and recorded on the big order sheet by tomorrow. Usually he'd work on it at home, spreading the papers out on his desk and marking how many of this or that he'd sold that week. But if he went home now, they'd *all* be there: Dad, Bonnie, and Ava. All accusing. Bonnie with her *Please, Donnie's*. Ava with her *Why don't you's*. And Dad with his sad silence, worse than words.

But worst of all was knowing that Mom lay in the next room wasting away, dying, not even fighting anymore. He felt that if he was forced to go in there, all he'd do is scream at her. "Don't you care? Try! You always told us never to give up! You're not trying!" And he'd want to strike out at her. Well, maybe not at her, but at something!

There wasn't a moment in the day that he didn't think about her. It was as if they were joined by an invisible wire

---

4. **Mace** [mās]: a chemical spray containing tear gas.

and he felt everything she did. And he felt now that she was slipping away. He couldn't stop it. He couldn't do a thing about it. There was nothing to say, nothing! Everything he thought of saying sounded false or stupid.

Well, all right! If that's what he had to do, he'd do it. He'd *go* home. He'd go into her room. He'd look at that woman who was and wasn't his mother anymore and he'd say *something*. Whatever came into his head, no matter how mean or dumb. *All right!* If that's what they all wanted, that's what he'd do.

He turned the key in the ignition and gunned the car out of the parking lot and into the street. He drove above the speed limit, mouth clenched in a tight line, totally intent on the road, mind empty except for the determination to get home fast.

He parked the car in the drive and ran into the house. Suddenly he was terribly afraid. What if it was too late? He almost felt in his gut that he'd waited too long.

"Donnie?" Dad called from the family room. "That you?"

He made some kind of guttural response and ran past the room, not even nodding. He had a fleeting sense that Dad was there reading the paper, that Bonnie was doing homework. His heart hammered loudly in his ears. An electrical pulse ran down his arms to his legs as he reached his mother's bedroom door and put a hand on the knob.

And then he stopped. For a long moment he stood waiting for his legs to quit trembling, for his heart to slow down. And then he closed his eyes, took a deep breath, and straightened his shoulders. Fixing a smile on his face, he knocked. "Fuller brush man!" he called, lightly opening the door.

GLORIA D. MIKLOWITZ

Gloria D. Miklowitz was born in 1927 in New York City. Before she began writing for young people, she says, she wrote documentary films on rockets and torpedoes for the Navy.

Miklowitz says she enjoys writing because it lets her "live hundreds of different lives . . . . On paper . . . I enter lives I can never really live and try to bring to my readers compassion and understanding for those lives."

Miklowitz has written more than thirty books about problems young adults face. Her books have been translated into many languages. Two of her books are *Anything to Win* and *The Emerson High Vigilantes*.

BROWN VS. BOARD OF EDUCATION

WALTER DEAN MYERS

Thurgood Marshall as a young man

There was a time when the meaning of freedom was easily understood. For an African crouched in the darkness of a tossing ship, wrists chained, men with guns standing on the decks above him, freedom was a physical thing, the ability to move away from his captors, to follow the dictates of his own heart, to listen to the voices within him that defined his values and showed him the truth of his own path. The plantation owners wanted to make the Africans feel helpless, inferior. They denied them images of themselves as Africans and told them that they were without beauty. They segregated them and told them they were without value.

Slowly, surely, the meaning of freedom changed to an elusive thing that even the strongest people could not hold in their hands. There were no chains on black wrists, but there were the shadows of chains, stretching for hundreds of years back through time, across black minds.

From the end of the Civil War in 1865 to the early 1950's, many public schools in both the North and South were segregated. Segregation was different in the different sections of the country. In the North most of the schools were segregated *de facto;*[1] that is, the law allowed blacks and whites to go to school together, but they did not actually always attend the same schools. Since a school is generally attended by children living in its neighborhood, wherever there were predominantly African-American neighborhoods there were, "in fact," segregated schools. In many parts of the country, however, and especially in the South, the segregation was *de jure,*[2] meaning that there were laws which forbade blacks to attend the same schools as whites.

The states with segregated schools relied upon the ruling of the Supreme Court in the 1896 *Plessy vs. Ferguson* case for legal justification: Facilities that were "separate but equal" were legal.

In the early 1950's the National Association for the Advancement of Colored People (N.A.A.C.P.) sponsored five cases that eventually reached the Supreme Court. One of the cases involved the school board of Topeka, Kansas.

Thirteen families sued the Topeka school board, claiming that to segregate the children was harmful to the children and, therefore, a violation of the equal protection clause of the Fourteenth Amendment.[3] The names on the Topeka case were listed in alphabetical order, with the father of seven-year-old Linda Brown listed first.

---

1. *de facto* [di fak′ tō]: in fact, in reality.
2. *de jure* [dē jùr′ ē]: by right, according to law.
3. **Fourteenth Amendment:** the constitutional amendment (1868) guaranteeing equal protection under the law for all those born or naturalized in the United States, including former slaves.

I didn't understand why I couldn't go to school with my playmates. I lived in an integrated neighborhood and played with children of all nationalities, but when school started they went to a school only four blocks from my home and I was sent to school across town,

she says.

For young Linda the case was one of convenience and of being made to feel different, but for African-American parents it had been a long, hard struggle to get a good education for their children. It was also a struggle waged by lawyers who had worked for years to overcome segregation. The head of the legal team who presented the school cases was Thurgood Marshall.[4]

The city was Baltimore, Maryland, and the year was 1921. Thirteen-year-old Thurgood Marshall struggled to balance the packages he was carrying with one hand while he tried to get his bus fare out of his pocket with the other. It was almost Easter, and the part-time job he had would provide money for flowers for his mother. Suddenly he felt a violent tug at his right arm that spun him around, sending his packages sprawling over the floor of the bus.

"Nigguh, don't you never push in front of no white lady again!" an angry voice spat in his ear.

Thurgood turned and threw a punch into the face of the name caller. The man charged into Thurgood, throwing punches that mostly missed, and tried to wrestle the slim boy to the ground. A policeman broke up the fight, grabbing Thurgood with one huge black hand and pushing him against the side of the bus. Within minutes they were in the local courthouse.

Thurgood was not the first of his family to get into a good fight. His father's father had joined the Union Army during the Civil War, taking the names Thorough Good to add to the one name he had in bondage. His grandfather on his mother's side was a man brought

4. **Thurgood Marshall** [thėr′ gůd mär shǝl]: (1908-1993) African American civil rights leader, chief legal counsel for the NAACP, and a Supreme Court justice.

from Africa and, according to Marshall's biography, "so ornery that his owner wouldn't sell him out of pity for the people who might buy him, but gave him his freedom instead and told him to clear out of the county."

Thurgood's frequent scrapes earned him a reputation as a young boy who couldn't be trusted to get along with white folks.

Thurgood Marshall's parents

His father, Will Marshall, was a steward at the Gibson Island Yacht Club near Baltimore, and his mother, Norma, taught in a segregated school. The elder Marshall felt he could have done more with his life if his education had been better, but there had been few opportunities available for African Americans when he had been a young man. When it was time for the Marshall boys to go to college, he was more than willing to make the sacrifices necessary to send them.

Young people of color from all over the world came to the United States to study at Lincoln University, a predominantly black institution in southeastern Pennsylvania. Here Marshall majored in pre-dentistry, which he found boring, and joined the Debating Club, which he found interesting. By the time he was graduated at the age of twenty-one, he had decided to give up dentistry for the law. Three years later he was graduated, first in his class, from Howard University Law School.

At Howard there was a law professor, Charles Hamilton Houston, who would affect the lives of many African-American lawyers and who would influence the legal aspects of the civil rights movement. Houston was a great teacher, one who demanded that his students be not just good lawyers but great lawyers. If they were going

Thurgood Marshall with Central High School students from Little Rock, Arkansas, September, 1957

to help their people—and for Houston the only reason for African Americans to become lawyers was to do just that—they would have to have absolute understanding of the law, and be diligent in the preparation of their cases. At the time, Houston was an attorney for the N.A.A.C.P. and fought against discrimination in housing and in jobs.

After graduation, Thurgood Marshall began to do some work for the N.A.A.C.P., trying the difficult civil rights cases. He not only knew about the effects of discrimination by reading about it, he was still living it when he was graduated from law school in 1933. In 1936 Marshall began working full-time for the N.A.A.C.P., and in 1940 became its chief counsel.

It was Thurgood Marshall and a battery of N.A.A.C.P. attorneys who began to challenge segregation throughout the country. These men and women were warriors in the cause of freedom for African Americans, taking their battles into courtrooms across the country. They understood the process of American justice and the power of the Constitution.

In *Brown vs. Board of Education of Topeka*, Marshall argued that segregation was a violation of the Fourteenth Amendment—that even if the facilities and all other "tangibles"[5] were equal, which was the heart of the case in *Plessy vs. Ferguson*, a violation still existed. There were intangible factors, he argued, that made the education unequal.

Everyone involved understood the significance of the case: that it was much more than whether black children could go to school with white children. If segregation in the schools was declared unconstitutional, then *all* segregation in public places could be declared unconstitutional.

5. **tangibles** [tan′ jə bəlz]: whatever is real and can be touched, such as property and money.

Southerners who argued against ending school segregation were caught up, as then-Congressman Brooks Hays of Arkansas put it, in "a lifetime of adventures in that gap between law and custom." The law was one thing, but most Southern whites felt just as strongly about their customs as they did the law.

Dr. Kenneth B. Clark, an African-American psychologist, testified for the N.A.A.C.P. He presented clear evidence that the effect of segregation was harmful to African-American children. Describing studies conducted by black and white psychologists over a twenty-year period, he showed that black children felt inferior to white children. In a particularly dramatic study that he had supervised, four dolls, two white and two black, were presented to African-American children. From the responses of the children to the dolls, identical in every way except color, it was clear that the children were rejecting the black dolls. African-American children did not just feel separated from white children, they felt that the separation was based on their inferiority.

Dr. Clark understood fully the principles and ideas of those people who had held Africans in bondage and had tried to make slaves of captives. By isolating people of African descent, by barring them from certain actions or places, they could make them feel inferior. The social scientists who testified at *Brown vs. Board of Education* showed that children who felt inferior also performed poorly.

The Justice Department argued that racial segregation was objectionable to the Eisenhower Administration and hurt our relationships with other nations.

On May 17, 1954, after deliberating for nearly a year and a half, the Supreme Court made its ruling. The Court stated that it could not use the intentions of 1868, when the Fourteenth Amendment was passed, as a guide to its ruling, or even those of 1896, when the decision in *Plessy vs. Ferguson* was handed down. Chief Justice Earl Warren wrote:

We must consider public education in the light of its full development and its present place in American life throughout the nation. We must look

Thurgood Marshall,
Supreme Court Justice

instead to the effect of segregation itself on public education.

The Court went on to say that "modern authority" supported the idea that segregation deprived African Americans of equal opportunity. "Modern authority" referred to Dr. Kenneth B. Clark and the weight of evidence that he and the other social scientists had presented.

The high court's decision in *Brown vs. Board of Education* signaled an important change in the struggle for civil rights. It signaled clearly that the legal prohibitions that oppressed African Americans would have to fall. Equally important was the idea that the nature of the fight for equality would change. Ibrahima,[6] Cinqué,[7] Nat Turner,[8] and George Latimer[9] had struggled for freedom by fighting against their captors or fleeing from them. The 54th[10] had fought for African freedom on the battlefields of the Civil War. Ida B. Wells[11] had fought for equality with her pen.

6. **Ibrahima** [ē brä hē mä]: (1762-1829) African prince who became a slave, later obtained his freedom, and returned to West Africa.
7. **Cinqué** [singk ā′]: African slave, sold in 1839, who took command of a slave ship, was captured, tried in Connecticut, and freed; he later returned to West Africa.
8. **Nat Turner:** a slave of the early 1800s who led the only effective slave revolt in the United States; he was captured and hanged in 1831.
9. **George Latimer:** African slave who escaped in Boston in 1842 and led the first of several fugitive slave uprisings.
10. **54th:** African American regiment from Massachusetts during the War Between the States.
11. **Ida B. Wells:** African American woman, editor of the Memphis newspaper *Free Speech*, who worked for civil rights from the late 1800s until her death in 1931.

Lewis H. Latimer[12] and Meta Vaux Warrick[13] had tried to earn equality with their work. In *Brown vs. Board of Education* Thurgood Marshall, Kenneth B. Clark, and the lawyers and social scientists, both black and white, who helped them had won for African Americans a victory that would bring them closer to full equality than they had ever been in North America. There would still be legal battles to be won, but the major struggle would be in the hearts and minds of people and "in that gap between law and custom."

In 1967 Thurgood Marshall was appointed by President Lyndon B. Johnson as an associate justice of the U.S. Supreme Court. He retired in 1991.

"I didn't think of my father or the other parents as being heroic at the time," Linda Brown says. "I was only seven. But as I grew older and realized how far-reaching the case was and how it changed the complexion of the history of this country, I was just thrilled that my father and the others here in Topeka were involved."

12. **Lewis H. Latimer:** African American, son of an escaped slave, who invented the carbon filament for the incandescent lamp, patented in 1881; he was also a poet, painter, and civil rights worker.
13. **Meta Vaux Warrick** [me′ tə vō wô′ rik]: African American woman artist of the late 1800s and early 1900s who studied art in Paris.

WALTER DEAN MYERS

Walter Dean Myers was born in 1937 in Martinsburg, West Virginia, but grew up on the streets of Harlem in New York City. In high school, Myers found that literature offered a "connection with things and events that I was not part of in 'real' life."

Since his family couldn't afford to send him to college, Myers went into the Army. Later he took various jobs to get by until he could support himself as a full-time writer. Myers is best known for novels such as *The Young Landlords* and *The Outside Shot*. His nonfiction books include *Now Is Your Time: The African American Struggle for Freedom* and *The World of Work: A Guide to Choosing a Career*.

GET UP and BAR THE DOOR

ANONYMOUS

It fell about the Martinmas[1] time,
    And a gay time it was then,
When our goodwife got puddings to make,
    And she's boiled them in the pan.

The wind so cold blew south and north,   5
    And blew into the floor;
Quoth our goodman to our goodwife,
    "Get up and bar the door."

"My hand is in my household work,
    Goodman, as ye may see;   10
And it will not be barred for a hundred years,
    If it's to be barred by me!"

They made a pact between them both,
    They made it firm and sure,
That whosoe'er should speak the first,   15
    Should rise and bar the door.

Then by there came two gentlemen,
    At twelve o'clock at night,
And they could see neither house nor hall,
    Nor coal nor candlelight.   20

1. **Martinmas** [märʹ tn məs]: a Roman
Catholic feast day, celebrated
November 11, to honor Saint Martin
(1250-1300).

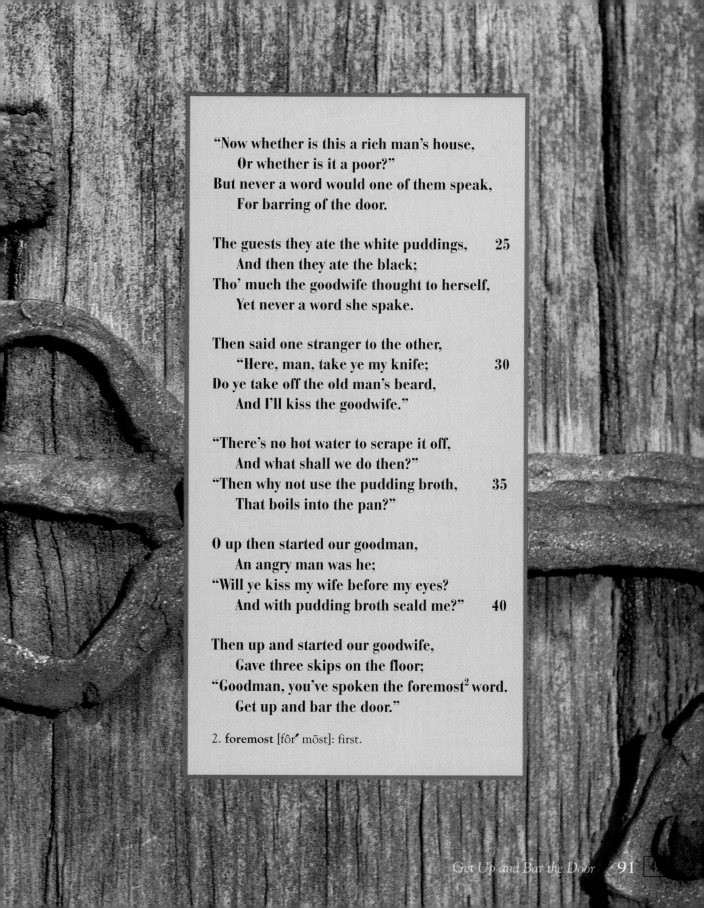

"Now whether is this a rich man's house,
　　Or whether is it a poor?"
But never a word would one of them speak,
　　For barring of the door.

The guests they ate the white puddings,　25
　　And then they ate the black;
Tho' much the goodwife thought to herself,
　　Yet never a word she spake.

Then said one stranger to the other,
　　"Here, man, take ye my knife;　30
Do ye take off the old man's beard,
　　And I'll kiss the goodwife."

"There's no hot water to scrape it off,
　　And what shall we do then?"
"Then why not use the pudding broth,　35
　　That boils into the pan?"

O up then started our goodman,
　　An angry man was he;
"Will ye kiss my wife before my eyes?
　　And with pudding broth scald me?"　40

Then up and started our goodwife,
　　Gave three skips on the floor;
"Goodman, you've spoken the foremost[2] word.
　　Get up and bar the door."

2. foremost [fôr′ mōst]: first.

The Necklace

Boulevard Montmartre on a Winter Day Camille Jacob Pissarro, 1897, oil on canvas, 25 ½" x 32", Metropolitan Museum of Art, New York   (Detail on page 96)

GUY DE MAUPASSANT

She was one of those pretty, charming young ladies born, as if through an error of destiny, into a family of clerks. She had no dowry, no hopes, no means of becoming known, appreciated, loved, and married by a man either rich or distinguished; and she allowed herself to marry a petty clerk in the office of the Board of Education.

She was simple, not being able to adorn herself; but she was unhappy, as one out of her class; for women belong to no caste, no race; their grace, their beauty, and their charm serving them in the place of birth and family. Their inborn finesse, their instinctive elegance, their suppleness of wit are their only aristocracy, making some daughters of the people the equal of great ladies.

She suffered incessantly, feeling herself born for all delicacies and luxuries. She suffered from the poverty of her apartment, the shabby walls, the worn chairs, and the faded stuffs. All these things, which another woman of her station would not have noticed, tortured and angered her. The sight of the little Breton, who made this humble home, awoke in her sad regrets and desperate dreams. She thought of quiet antechambers[1], with their Oriental hangings, lighted by high, bronze torches, and of the two great footmen in short trousers who sleep in the large armchairs, made sleepy by the heavy air from the heating apparatus. She thought of large drawingrooms, hung in old silks, of graceful pieces of furniture carrying bric-à-brac[2] of inestimable value, and of the little perfumed coquettish[3] apartments, made for five o'clock chats with most intimate friends, men known and sought after, whose attention all women envied and desired.

When she seated herself for dinner, before the round table where the tablecloth had been used three days, opposite her husband who uncovered the tureen with a delighted air, saying: "Oh! the good potpie! I know nothing better than that—" she would think of the elegant dinners, of the shining silver, of the tapestries peopling the walls with ancient personages and rare birds in the midst of fairy forests; she thought of the exquisite food served on marvelous dishes, of the whispered gallantries, listened to with the smile of the sphinx, while eating the rose-colored flesh of the trout or a chicken's wing.

She had neither frocks nor jewels, nothing. And she loved only those things. She felt that she was made for them. She had such a desire to please, to be sought after, to be clever, and courted.

She had a rich friend, a schoolmate at the convent whom she did not like to visit, she suffered so much when she returned. And

1. **antechambers** [an′ ti chām′ bərz]: small waiting rooms.
2. **bric-à-brac** [brik′ ə brak′]: curious decorative ornaments, such as vases or china.
3. **coquettish** [kō ket′ ish]: attracting attention.

The Necklace 93 499

she wept for whole days from chagrin, from regret, from despair, and disappointment.

One evening her husband returned elated, bearing in his hand a large envelope.

"Here," said he, "here is something for you."

She quickly tore open the wrapper and drew out a printed card on which were inscribed these words:

"The Minister of Public Instruction and Madame George Ramponneau[4] ask the honor of Mr. and Mrs. Loisel's[5] company Monday evening, January 18, at the Minister's residence."

Instead of being delighted, as her husband had hoped, she threw the invitation spitefully upon the table murmuring:

"What do you suppose I want with that?"

"But, my dearie, I thought it would make you happy. You never go out, and this is an occasion, and a fine one! I had a great deal of trouble to get it. Everybody wishes one, and it is very select; not many are given to employees. You will see the whole official world there."

4. **Ramponneau** [räM pô nō´]
5. **Loisel** [lwä zel´]

She looked at him with an irritated eye and declared impatiently:

"What do you suppose I have to wear to such a thing as that?"

He had not thought of that; he stammered:

"Why, the dress you wear when we go to the theater. It seems very pretty to me—"

He was silent, stupefied, in dismay, at the sight of his wife weeping. Two great tears fell slowly from the corners of his eyes toward the corners of his mouth; he stammered:

"What is the matter? What is the matter?"

By a violent effort, she had controlled her vexation and responded in a calm voice, wiping her moist cheeks:

"Nothing. Only I have no dress and consequently I cannot go to this affair. Give your card to some colleague whose wife is better fitted out than I."

He was grieved, but answered:

"Let us see, Matilda. How much would a suitable costume cost, something that would serve for other occasions, something very simple?"

She reflected for some seconds, making estimates and thinking of a sum that she could ask for without bringing with it an immediate refusal and a frightened exclamation from the economical clerk.

Finally she said, in a hesitating voice:

"I cannot tell exactly, but it seems to me that four hundred francs ought to cover it."

He turned a little pale, for he had saved just this sum to buy a gun that he might be able to join some hunting parties the next summer, on the plains at Nanterre, with some friends who went to shoot larks up there on Sunday. Nevertheless, he answered:

"Very well. I will give you four hundred francs. But try to have a pretty dress."

The day of the ball approached and Mme. Loisel seemed sad, disturbed, anxious. Nevertheless, her dress was nearly ready. Her husband said to her one evening:

"What is the matter with you? You have acted strangely for two or three days."

And she responded: "I am vexed not to have a jewel, not one stone, nothing to adorn myself with. I shall have such a poverty-laden look. I would prefer not to go to this party."

He replied: "You can wear some natural flowers. At this season they look very chic. For ten francs you can have two or three magnificent roses."

She was not convinced. "No," she replied, "there is nothing more humiliating than to have a shabby air in the midst of rich women."

Then her husband cried out: "How stupid we are! Go and find your friend Mrs. Forestier and ask her to lend you her jewels. You are well enough acquainted with her to do this."

She uttered a cry of joy: "It is true!" she said. "I had not thought of that."

The next day she took herself to her friend's house and related her story of distress. Mrs. Forestier went to her closet with the glass doors, took out a large jewel-case, brought it, opened it, and said: "Choose, my dear."

She saw at first some bracelets, then a collar of pearls, then a Venetian cross of gold and jewels and of admirable workmanship. She tried the jewels before the glass, hesitated, but could neither decide to take them nor leave them. Then she asked:

"Have you nothing more?"

"Why, yes. Look for yourself. I do not know what will please you."

Suddenly she discovered, in a black satin box, a supurb necklace of diamonds, and her heart beat fast with an immoderate desire. Her hands trembled as she took them up. She placed them about her throat against her dress, and remained in ecstasy before them. Then she asked, in a hesitating voice, full of anxiety:

"Could you lend me this? Only this?"

"Why, yes, certainly."

She fell upon the neck of her friend, embraced her with passion, then went away with her treasure.

The day of the ball arrived. Mme Loisel was a great success. She was the prettiest of all, elegant, gracious, smiling, and full of joy. All the men noticed her, asked her name, and wanted to be presented. All the members of the Cabinet wished to waltz with her. The Minister of Education paid her some attention.

She danced with enthusiasm, with passion, intoxicated with pleasure, thinking of nothing, in the triumph of her beauty, in the glory of her success, in a kind of cloud of happiness that came of all this homage, and all this admiration, of all these awakened desires, and this victory so complete and sweet to the heart of woman.

She went home toward four o'clock in the morning. Her husband had been half asleep in one of the little salons since midnight, with three other gentlemen whose wives were enjoying themselves very much.

He threw around her shoulders the wraps they had carried for the coming home, modest garments of everyday wear, whose poverty clashed with the elegance of the ball costume. She felt this and wished to hurry away in order not to be noticed by the other women who were wrapping themselves in rich furs.

Loisel retained her: "Wait," said he. "You will catch cold out there. I am going to call a cab."

But she would not listen and descended the steps rapidly. When they were in the street, they found no carriage; and they began to seek one, hailing the coachmen whom they saw at a distance.

They walked along toward the Seine,[6] hopeless and shivering. Finally they found on the dock one of those old, nocturnal coupés[7] that one sees in Paris after nightfall, as if they were ashamed of their misery by day.

6. **Seine** [sān]: a river that flows from Eastern France to the English Channel.

7. **coupés** [kü pāz´]: closed, horse-drawn carriages holding passengers inside and the driver outside.

It took them as far as their door in Martyr street, and they went wearily up to their apartment. It was all over for her. And on his part, he remembered that he would have to be at the office by ten o'clock.

She removed the wraps from her shoulders before the glass, for a final view of herself in her glory. Suddenly she uttered a cry. Her necklace was not around her neck.

Her husband, already half undressed, asked: "What is the matter?"

She turned toward him excitedly:

"I have—I have—I no longer have Mrs. Forestier's necklace."

He arose in dismay: "What! How is that? It is not possible."

And they looked in the folds of the dress, in the folds of the mantle, in the pockets, everywhere. They could not find it.

He asked: "You are sure you still had it when we left the house?"

"Yes, I felt it in the vestibule[8] as we came out."

"But if you had lost it in the street, we should have heard it fall. It must be in the cab."

"Yes. It is probable. Did you take the number?"

"No. And you, did you notice what it was?"

"No."

They looked at each other utterly cast down. Finally, Loisel dressed himself again.

"I am going," said he, "over the track where we went on foot, to see if I can find it."

And he went. She remained in her evening gown, not having the force to go to bed, stretched upon a chair, without ambition or thoughts.

Toward seven o'clock her husband returned. He had found nothing.

He went to the police and to the cab offices, and put an advertisement in the newspapers, offering a reward; he did everything that afforded them a suspicion of hope.

She waited all day in a state of bewilderment before this frightful disaster. Loisel returned at evening with his face harrowed and pale; he had discovered nothing.

"It will be necessary," said he, "to write to your friend that you have broken the clasp of the necklace and that you will have it repaired. That will give us time to turn around."

She wrote as he dictated.

At the end of a week, they had lost all hope. And Loisel, older by five years, declared:

"We must take measures to replace this jewel."

---

8. **vestibule** [ves′ tə byül]: a hall between the outer door and the inside of a building.

The next day they took the box which had inclosed it, to the jeweler whose name was on the inside. He consulted his books:

"It is not I, Madame," said he, "who sold this necklace; I only furnished the casket."

Then they went from jeweler to jeweler seeking a necklace like the other one, consulting their memories, and ill, both of them, with chagrin and anxiety.

In a shop of the Palais-Royal, they found a chaplet[9] of diamonds which seemed to them exactly like the one they had lost. It was valued at forty thousand francs. They could get it for thirty-six thousand.

They begged the jeweler not to sell it for three days. And they made an arrangement by which they might return it for thirty-four thousand francs if they found the other one before the end of February.

Loisel possessed eighteen thousand francs which his father had left him. He borrowed the rest.

He borrowed it, asking for a thousand francs of one, five hundred of another, five louis[10] of this one, and three louis of that one. He gave notes, made ruinous promises, took money of usurers and the whole race of lenders. He compromised his whole existence, in fact, risked his signature, without even knowing whether he could make it good or not, and, harassed by anxiety for the future, by the black misery which surrounded him, and by the prospect of all physical privations and moral torture, he went to get the new necklace, depositing on the merchant's counter thirty-six thousand francs.

When Mrs. Loisel took back the jewels to Mrs. Forestier, the latter said to her in a frigid tone:

"You should have returned them to me sooner, for I might have needed them."

She did open the jewel-box as her friend feared she would. If she should perceive the substitution, what would she think? What should she say? Would she take her for a robber?

Mrs. Loisel now knew the horrible life of necessity. She did her part, however, completely, heroically. It was necessary to pay this frightful debt. She would pay it. They sent away the maid; they changed her

9. **chaplet** [chap′ lit]: a string of jewels.
10. **louis** [lü′ ē]: a former French gold coin, worth 20 francs.

lodgings; they rented some rooms under a mansard[11] roof.

She learned the heavy cares of a household, the odious work of a kitchen. She washed the dishes, using her rosy nails upon the greasy pots and the bottoms of the stewpans. She washed the soiled linen, the chemises[12] and dishcloths, which she hung on the line to dry; she took down the refuse to the street each morning and brought up the water, stopping at each landing to breathe. And, clothed like a woman of the people, she went to the grocer's, the butcher's, and the fruiterer's, with her basket on her arm, shopping, haggling, defending to the last sou[13] her miserable money.

Every month it was necessary to renew some notes, thus obtaining time, and to pay others.

The husband worked evenings, putting the books of some merchants in order, and nights he often did copying at five sous a page.

And this life lasted for ten years.

At the end of ten years, they had restored all, all, with interest of the usurer, and accumulated interest besides.

Mrs. Loisel seemed old now. She had become a strong, hard woman, the crude woman of the poor household. Her hair badly dressed, her skirts awry, her hands red, she spoke in a loud tone, and washed the floors in large pails of water. But sometimes, when her husband was at the office, she would seat herself before the window and think of that evening party of former times, of that ball where she was so beautiful and so flattered.

How would it have been if she had not lost that necklace? Who knows? Who knows? How singular is life, and how full of changes! How small a thing will ruin or save one!

One Sunday, as she was taking a walk in the Champs-Elysèe[14] to rid herself of the cares of the week, she suddenly perceived a woman walking with a child. It was Mrs. Forestier, still young, still

a11. **mansard** [man′särd]: a roof with two slopes on each side, named after the seventeenth-century French architect François Mansard.

12. **chemises** [shə mēz′ əz]: shirtlike undergarments for women and girls.

13. **sou** [sü]: a former French coin, worth 1/20 of a franc.

14. **Champs-Elysèe** [shäNs ā lē zē′]

In the Dining Room   Berthe Morisot, 1886, oil on canvas, 24 1/8" x 19 3/4", National Gallery of Art, Washington, D. C.   (Detail on page 99)

pretty, still attractive. Mrs. Loisel was affected. Should she speak to her? Yes, certainly. And now that she had paid, she would tell her all. Why not?

She approached her. "Good morning, Jeanne."

Her friend did not recognize her and was astonished to be so familiarly addressed by this common personage. She stammered:

"But, Madame—I do not know—You must be mistaken—"

"No, I am Matilda Loisel."

Her friend uttered a cry of astonishment: "Oh! my poor Matilda! How you have changed—"

"Yes, I have had some hard days

since I saw you; and some miserable ones—and all because of you—"

"Because of me? How is that?"

"You recall the diamond necklace that you loaned me to wear to the Commissioner's ball?"

"Yes, very well."

"Well, I lost it."

"How is that, since you returned it to me?"

"I returned another to you exactly like it. And it has taken us ten years to pay for it. You can understand that it was not easy for us who have nothing. But it is finished and I am decently content."

Madame Forestier stopped short. She said:

"You say that you bought a diamond necklace to replace mine?"

"Yes. You did not perceive it then? They were just alike."

And she smiled with a proud and simple joy. Madame Forestier was touched and took both her hands as she replied:

"Oh! my poor Matilda! Mine were false. They were not worth over five hundred francs!"

GUY DE MAUPASSANT

Guy de Maupassant (gē də mō pä säN′) (1850-1893) was born near Dieppe, in Normandy, France, and grew up in an unhappy home. His parents fought constantly and separated when he was twelve years old. The boy's interest in literature attracted the attention of a family friend, the author Gustave Flaubert, who advised the young writer all his life.

In 1870 the Franco-Prussian War began. By then de Maupassant was studying law in Paris, but rushed off to enlist. The devastating end of the war and the bitter civil war that followed had a strong influence on his writing. He took a tedious job he hated, but spent more and more time writing. Much of his work—the short stories for which he is famous—was published in magazines and newspapers of the time. Many of his stories, like "The Necklace," are famous for the twist in their endings.

Asking Big Questions About the Literature

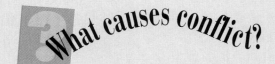

What causes conflict?

COMPARE Causes

Choose a literature selection from this unit. Then write a dialogue in which several characters from the selection debate the causes of the conflict. Have each individual state and defend a position on what has caused the conflict. Invite some classmates to perform your dialogue for your class.

LITERATURE STUDY

Plot

In stories, plays, and some poems, the **plot** is the actions and events of the story. Most plots have three main parts—*rising action, climax,* and *falling action.* The writer usually develops the conflict in the rising action.

For each story that you read in this unit, make a list of the plot events that reveal the conflict. List them in the order in which they happen. (*See "Plot" on page 119.*)

PLOT A LITERARY PLOT

The diagram on this page shows the rising action, climax, and falling action of "The Clearing." Select another story from this unit and diagram its plot. Mark the story's main events where they happen along the plot line.

Climax

Mother helps Mrs. Hinton give birth.

Boys have rock fight.

Rising Action

Falling Action

Hintons help put out fire.

The families become friends.

What are the different kinds of conflict?

LITERATURE STUDY

Conflict

In literature, the struggle of the characters is called **conflict**. *External conflict* is caused by forces outside a character, such as another person, nature, or society. *Internal conflict* occurs when the character struggles with some inner feeling or quality, such as fear or aggression.

Conflict in a nonfiction account can also be internal or external. With a partner, select one of the nonfiction selections that you read in this unit and discuss whether the conflict it describes is internal, external, or a combination of both. (*See "Conflict" on page 118.*)

Investigate Idioms

With a small group, brainstorm expressions that describe conflict, such as *to hold a grudge* or *to be between a rock and a hard place*. Collect your expressions in a booklet for a classroom library resource. Then discuss which idioms could describe experiences in the literature selections that you read in this unit. For example, some readers might say that Scho in "A Game of Catch" has *a chip on his shoulder*.

Chart the Conflicts

In a small group, classify the conflict in each of the literature selections that you read in this unit by making a chart like this one. Then write a short explanation of why each selection belongs in its particular category.

| Character against ... | | | |
Character	Society	Nature	Self
"Get Up and Bar the Door"	"I Have a Dream"		

Asking Big Questions About the Literature

How do individuals and groups resolve conflicts?

Find Out WHAT HAPPENED

Choose a conflict from one of the non-fiction selections that you've read. Then do some research to discover how people have continued trying to resolve this conflict. For example, have any parts of Martin Luther King, Jr.'s dream come true? If so, where? How fully? Keep track of your facts by making note cards like the one below. Then present your findings to the class as a special report.

Reference title: _____
Author's name: _____
Subject: Integration laws passed since 1963
_____
Events: 1. _____
_____
2. _____
_____
3. _____

LITERATURE STUDY

Conflict

In a work of literature, how a character resolves a **conflict** reveals the character's identity. Choose one of the stories you've read in this unit and write an essay about the main character's efforts to resolve the conflict. Explain the character's options for resolving the conflict, what the character decides to do, and what this choice reveals about him or her. (*See "Conflict" on page 118.*)

ROLE-PLAY
Resolutions

With a group, think of a real-life conflict that resembles a conflict in a literature selection in this unit. For example, perhaps a new coach at your school has introduced changes, creating a conflict comparable to the one in "Umu Madu in the Good Old Days." Then role-play confrontations and resolutions between the two sides. Vote on which method best resolved the conflict.

What can people learn from conflict?

COMPARE & CONTRAST

Compare and contrast how two individuals your age have resolved a similar personal struggle. One should be a character from a literature selection in this unit. The other can be you or someone you know. Use a chart like the one below to help you write several paragraphs about the characters' similarities and differences.

Conflict	Character: Amanda	Me
Type	Internal (self against self)	Internal (self against self)
Subject	Wants to spend more time with mother.	Wants to spend more time with sister.
Causes	Mother is too busy.	Sister has boyfriend.
Resolution		

LITERATURE STUDY

Plot

Choose one of the stories you've read in this unit. Now imagine the story if one of the events of the **plot** was changed. Rewrite the plot in outline form to show how this change would affect the story. *(See "Plot" on page 119.)*

Hold A PANEL DISCUSSION

In a small group, let each member role-play a character from one of the literature selections in this unit. Each character should summarize his or her conflict. The class can then ask the characters questions about what they learned and what they might have done differently.

NOW Choose a Project!

Three projects that deal with conflict and resolution are described on the following pages. Choose the one that's right for you.

Writing Workshop

CONVINCE THEM WITH A LETTER

Wouldn't it be great to persuade two individuals or groups to resolve their conflict? This writing project will give you the chance to write a persuasive letter that will help others overcome their differences. The **purpose** of your persuasive letter will be to influence the opinions and actions of your **audience**, the people who are involved in this conflict. When you've sent your letter, you may find out how influential your words and ideas can really be.

Prewriting
THINK OF A CONFLICT

Read some letters to the editor in newspapers and magazines to give you ideas for local, national or international conflicts you'd like to write about. You'll soon get an idea of the kind of topics and issues that everyone is discussing.

When you have chosen a topic, ask yourself these questions.

- Is this a topic I have strong ideas about?
- Does this topic have more than one side?
- Can I find enough evidence to support my position?

Put yourself in your readers' place. Are your readers likely to agree or to disagree with your position? How well informed are they? Will you need to provide background information? What kind of evidence will convince them to agree with your position?

5207 Los Almos
San Jose, NM 96341

January 20, 199—

Sarah Brown
Sun Times
1234 Main Street
Sunnyvale, NM 82970

Dear Ms. Brown,

It bothers me that...

Anita Chavez
5207 Los Almos
San Jose, NM 96341

Sarah Brown Editor
Sun Times
1234 Main Street
Sunnyvale, NM 82970

Prewriting

DECIDE ON YOUR POSITION

Begin planning your persuasive letter by taking a stand. Write a clear thesis statement that states your main point and suggests a solution to the conflict.

In addition, summarize the main point of the opposing argument. Identifying the opposition's argument will show your readers that you've considered all sides of the issue.

The next step is to gather evidence that will support your position. Research to collect facts that will help make your argument convincing.

Finally map out your argument by making an informal outline. List the points you want to make, and be sure each one supports your thesis statement. Then list at least one piece of supporting evidence for each idea, like this:

Thesis statement: _____

Point 1: _____

Supporting evidence: _____

Point 2: _____

Supporting evidence: _____

Point 3: _____

Supporting evidence: _____

Drafting
YOUR LETTER

Your outline will help you plan the basic structure of your argument. Be sure it includes the three essential parts—introduction, body, and conclusion.

- The introduction should explain the conflict, state your position, and suggest a resolution. Emily Johnson, a student writer, introduces her persuasive letter with a strong, clear thesis statement that states her position on gun control, "America needs stricter gun control laws . . ."

- The body should consist of one or more paragraphs that lead the reader logically through your main points. Be sure to support each point with evidence. For example, Emily presents statistics to show the low numbers of handgun murders in countries that have strict gun control laws. Her evidence adds support to her main point.

- Present the arguments of the opposition, to show that you have considered both sides of the issue. For example, Emily considers the argument that guns are necessary to defend the home. She then rejects this argument by presenting statistics showing that keeping a gun at home actually increases the possibility of murder.

- Write a conclusion that sums up your position and suggests a course of action. Emily, for example, ends her letter by calling for "stricter gun control laws, a waiting period for buying a gun, and more effective punishments for illegal gun suppliers."

Read Emily's argument on pages 110-111 for an example of a persuasive letter.

Revising YOUR LETTER

Now test the persuasiveness of your letter on several classmates. Their responses to questions such as these will help you polish your argument.

- Does the introduction present my position clearly?
- Is my argument clear and well supported?
- Which evidence is most convincing? Which is least convincing?
- Are there any opposing arguments I haven't mentioned?
- Did my argument persuade you?

Editing YOUR LETTER

After you've revised your draft, work with a partner to edit your persuasive letter. Read one another's letters and check for errors in spelling, grammar, and punctuation. Mistakes could make your readers doubt the authority of your argument or the care of your research. Correct your errors and make a publishable copy of your letter.

Publishing YOUR LETTER

Send your letter to those involved in the specific conflict, if possible, or send it to the editor of a local newspaper or magazine. You might read the letter at school, or elsewhere, as a speech—or even as part of a political campaign.

136 Old Mill Road
Framingham, MA 01701
March 3, 1994

Ms. Sarah Siddons
Editor
Daily Times
976 Main Street
Framingham, MA 01701

Dear Ms. Siddons:

America needs stricter gun control laws, such as a waiting period for buying guns to allow the police enough time to check the purchaser's criminal record. At the moment, Americans have easy access to these weapons. Many handgun owners, though, do not know how to use a gun properly. Nor do they know to keep guns away from children.

Opponents of gun control argue that "guns don't kill people—people kill people." This may be true, but a gun makes it much easier to kill someone. A gun may be a harmless object in itself, but when people use it to kill or hurt, shouldn't its use be controlled?

Opponents of gun control argue that guns are necessary to defend one's home against armed intruders. The truth is that having a gun in the house makes the possibility of killing someone who lives there three times greater. Gun supporters also argue that if the right to buy a gun is reduced or taken away, only criminals will have guns, purchased on the black market. Although some criminals do get guns on the black market, many don't need to when they can buy guns legally in a store. Making stricter regulations and punishments involving illegal selling of guns is a beginning to the solution of this many-sided problem.

Many people say that it is a question of freedom and argue that gun control is an attack on our constitutional rights. However, gun control is not the same as making all guns illegal and does not challenge our constitutional right to own a firearm. Gun control is not a violation of our rights—it is a moderation of them.

The statistics in favor of gun control are overwhelming. In males aged 17-24, handgun murder is the second most common cause of death. If guns were taken off the street, wouldn't it reduce the number of drive-by shootings? Controlling distribution of guns puts us one step closer to solving the problem of youth violence.

The following list reveals the number of handgun murders in countries with strict gun control laws compared to the handgun murder rate in the United States during 1990: Australia—10 deaths; Sweden—18; Great Britain—22; Canada—68; Japan—87; Switzerland—91; The UNITED STATES—10,567. These numbers are evidence of our country's problem.

How can we ignore the obvious? The arguments against guns far outweigh the arguments in favor of them. We need stricter gun control laws, a waiting period for buying a gun, and more effective punishments for illegal gun suppliers. When the number of guns on the street is reduced, maybe we can feel safer in our cities, our towns, and our homes.

Sincerely,

Emily Johnson

Emily Johnson

Cooperative Learning

Situation comedies on TV are mostly about the assorted struggles people experience in daily life. Viewers can observe the characters dealing with ordinary problems week after week and surviving with spirit and humor.

All "sitcoms" aren't instructive in positive ways, though. Some show characters coasting in and out of conflict through negative behavior such as deception. These programs may not offer good role models for younger children. That's where you can help. You and your small group will develop a TV guide for parents of elementary students who want to supervise their kids' TV watching.

good

TV Viewing
for
Elementary School
Kids

The RATING PROCESS

Use a weekly TV guide to make a list of prime-time situation comedies in your area. Each person in your group should then choose two or three shows to watch and evaluate. To be fair in making your evaluations, track each show over several weeks with the help of the evaluation sheet on the facing page.

T V Show		Dates
Plot	• Summarize the plot of a typical episode. • What types of conflict does the show usually depict? Who or what causes them? • What sort of thing tends to happen in the last scene?	
Characters	• Are the characters types, or are they like real people? • What strategies do the characters use to solve their problems? • Do the characters learn from their conflicts, or do they make similar choices and mistakes each week?	
Theme	• What do the writers of this program seem to believe about people? What lessons or values does their show express?	
Conclusions	• What did you like and dislike about the program? • Does this show provide positive or negative role models?	
Recommendation	• Do you recommend this program for young children?	

The PUBLICATION

Now assign the roles of Secretary, Copy Writer, Designers, Editor, and Proofreader to the members of your group. The Secretary will collect everyone's evaluation sheets and order them according to the times on the TV schedule. The Copy Writer will write an introduction that explains the purpose and standards of the guide. Then the Editor will check for errors in usage, punctuation, and spelling. Next the Secretary can type or neatly rewrite the pages. While Designers create a cover, the Proofreader can check the pages for errors.

The PRESENTATION

With your teacher's help, arrange a time to present your TV guide to an elementary school principal or teacher for distribution to parents. Make as many copies of the guide as you need, and staple or put them in folders. Then get ready to be thanked for all your guidance and hard work!

Helping Your Community

Since people are individuals with different experiences, values, and beliefs, we can't reasonably hope to eliminate all conflict from the planet. But you and a small group can make a difference on a smaller scale. By teaching conflict management skills in a specially developed manual, you can help others—such as two groups of people in your town—develop the skills they need for settling disagreements peacefully.

Designing
PART ONE

For this first section of your conflict resolution manual, brainstorm with your group all the general behavior strategies that help people solve disputes. Consider your own experiences as well as those of characters in the literature selections for this unit. Think of strategies people need in all kinds of conflict situations, from a playground scuffle to a parent-teenager argument over a curfew. Keep in mind that readers will need many strategies in order to resolve different kinds of conflict and that the resolution of a single conflict often requires several strategies. List your strategies under big headings such as *Speaking*, *Listening*, and *Negotiating*.

"Couldn't we try mediation?"

Next, work with your group to write explanations and examples to go with each strategy on your lists. For instance, to help people avoid blaming each other, you might explain that wording statements about wants and needs with "I…" rather than "You…" can prevent the other party from feeling blamed or accused. Keep your explanations and examples brief, clear, and as useful in real life as possible.

Designing PART TWO

In the second part of your conflict resolution manual, focus on a specific community issue that your group can help resolve. For example, merchants and chalk artists in your town may be at odds over who can decorate the sidewalk, or a neighborhood may say it needs a park that the city says it can't afford. As you write this section, be sure not to take sides on the issue. Fairly summarize both sides, and suggest possible compromises. Where it might help, refer your readers to conflict resolution methods in Part One, suggesting how certain methods can be used in this case.

Publishing YOUR MANUAL

Whether you produce your manual by handwriting or by typing doesn't really matter, but a neat, error-free guide does. Once you've polished and proofread, supply copies to the local groups you targeted in Part Two. You could also offer your work to the school, the town council, or any other group needing conflict mediation.

Putting It All Together

What Have You Learned About the Theme?

Now that you've read *Out of Tune*, completed the activities, and created a project, think about what you've learned. Review all the writing you've done for this unit. Then—to see whether your ideas about conflict resolution have changed— write an essay comparing and contrasting how you resolved a conflict in the past with how you'd resolve it today.

PAST AND PRESENT

Prewriting   Think of a conflict you once needed to resolve, such as a disagreement with someone you cared about or a hard decision. It doesn't matter whether the result was positive or negative, as long as you remember the details. Then think about how you would resolve the same problem today. If necessary, make a Venn diagram to sort out the similarities and differences.

Drafting   Begin by summarizing the conflict. Don't try to narrate the entire thing; just explain the issue, the cause of the conflict, the methods you used to resolve it, and the outcome. In a second paragraph, explain how you'd deal with the same situation now. Then write a concluding paragraph about why you think your past and present methods for resolving the conflict are different. Did you learn anything new about conflict resolution from a particular literature selection or an activity in this unit? If your methods haven't changed, explain what literature or projects in this unit reinforced your ideas about how to resolve conflict.

Now go back and write a topic sentence and an introduction to your essay.

Revising, Proofreading, and Publishing
As you revise your essay, be sure that it supports the major point expressed in your topic sentence. Your summary of the original conflict, your explanation of how you'd resolve it today, and the conclusion you draw should support and clarify this main idea. Once you've proofread for errors in grammar, usage, punctuation, and spelling, give copies of your essay to the members of a group that you worked with in this unit.

Evaluating Your Work

Think Back About the Big Questions

With a partner, discuss the Big Questions on pages 10-11. Do you have trouble answering any of these questions now? Write some sentences about how your answers to the Big Questions have changed as a result of your work in this unit.

Think Back About Your Work

Now evaluate your work, including your reading, your writing, your activities, and your projects. On another page, answer the following questions. Add your name. Then give your evaluation to your teacher.

- How have your ideas about conflict resolution changed? What literature selections or activities in this unit contributed to the change? If your ideas stayed the same, what parts of the unit reinforced them?

- Which literature selections would you recommend to your friends? Explain.

- What were your favorite activities? Why?

- What part of your project did you enjoy most?

- What kind of activity or project would you have liked to see in the unit? Explain.

- In one sentence, sum up the importance of conflict resolution.

- How do you rate your work in this unit? (Be honest and fair to yourself.) Use the following scale. Then explain why you chose that number.

  1=Outstanding   3=Fair

  2=Good   4=Not as good as it could have been

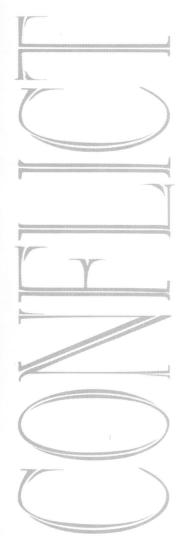

What Is Conflict?

Conflict in a piece of literature is a dramatic struggle between opposites. The conflict is said to be *internal* when it occurs within someone; for example, when the protagonist both does and does not want to do something that will hurt someone else. In some literature, the main character may struggle against things in the outer world: natural forces, another character, or society. Then the conflict is called *external*. In drama or fiction, the audience's interest or reader's interest in the story is mostly focused on how the protagonist's conflict will develop, become increasingly complicated, and eventually be resolved.

Requesting and Offering Advice   Imagine that you are someone facing some kind of conflict. This conflict could be internal or external. Then write a letter to the advice column of a newspaper, explaining the conflict. Address the letter to yourself. Then switch roles and imagine you are the advice columnist. Write a response to your first letter, suggesting ways of resolving the conflict.

Role-Playing a Solution   With a partner, select two characters from a short story selection in this unit whose conflict you found especially interesting. Then imagine a different kind of conflict that these two characters might experience. Discuss how the characters might resolve this conflict. It might help your discussion if you remember how these characters dealt with their conflict in the story. Was it easy or difficult for them to resolve their problem? Role-play their interaction for your class, beginning with their conflict and ending with the conflict's resolution.

experiences of one or more great heroes or heroines.

essay   Personal nonfiction writing about a particular subject that is important to the writer.

excerpt   A passage from a larger work that has been taken out of its context to be used for a special purpose.

exposition   Writing that explains, analyzes, or defines.

extended metaphor   An elaborately drawn out metaphor. [See also *metaphor*.]

F

fable   A short, simple story whose purpose is to teach a lesson, usually with animal characters who talk and act like people.

fantasy   Imaginative fiction about unrealistic characters, places, and events.

fiction   Literature, including the short story and the novel, that tells about imaginary people and events.

figurative language Language used to express ideas through figures of speech: descriptions that aren't meant to be taken literally. Types of figurative language include *simile*, *metaphor*, *extended metaphor*, *hyperbole*, and *personification*.

figure of speech   A type of figurative language, not meant to be taken literally, that expresses something in such a way that it brings the thing to life in the reader's or listener's imagination. [See also *figurative language*.]

flashback   A break in a story's action that relates a past happening in order to give the reader background information about a present action in the story.

folktale   A story that has been passed along from storyteller to storyteller for generations. Kinds of folktales include *tall tales*, *fairy tales*, *fables*, *legends*, and *myths*.

foreshadowing   The use of clues to create suspense by giving the reader or audience hints of events to come.

free verse   Poetry that has no formal rhyme scheme or metrical pattern.

G

genre   A major category of art. The three major literary genres are poetry, prose, and drama.

H

haiku   A three-line Japanese verse form. In most haiku, the first and third lines have five syllables, while the second line has seven. The traditional haiku describes a complicated feeling or thought in simple language through a single image.

hero/heroine   The main character in a work of literature. In heroic literature, the hero or heroine is a particularly brave, noble, or clever person whose achievements are unusual and important. [See also *character*.]

heroic age   The historical period in western civilization—from about 800 B.C. through A.D. 200—during which most works of heroic literature, such as myths and epics, were created in ancient Greece and Rome.

hubris   Arrogance or excessive pride leading to mistakes; the character flaw in a hero of classical tragedy.

hyperbole   An obvious exaggeration used for emphasis. [See also *figurative language*.]

I

idiom   An expression whose meaning cannot be understood from the ordinary meaning of the words. For example, *It's raining cats and dogs*.

imagery   The words and phrases in writing that appeal to the senses of sight, hearing, taste, touch, and smell.

irony   An effect created by a sharp contrast between what is expected and what is real. An *ironic twist* in a plot is an event that is the complete opposite of what the characters have been hoping or expecting will happen. An *ironic statement* declares the opposite of the speaker's literal meaning.

J

jargon   Words and phrases used by a group of people who share the same profession or special interests in order to refer to technical things or processes with which they are familiar. In general, jargon is any terminology that sounds unclear, overused, or pretentious.

L

legend   A famous folktale about heroic actions, passed along by word of mouth from generation to generation. The legend may have begun as a factual account of real people and events but has become mostly or completely fictitious.

limerick   A form of light verse, or humorous poetry, written in one five-line stanza with a regular scheme of rhyme and meter.

literature   The branch of art that is expressed in written language and includes all written genres.

lyric poem   A short poem that expresses personal feelings and thoughts in a musical way. Originally, lyrics were the words of songs that were sung to music played on the lyre, a stringed instrument invented by the ancient Greeks.

M

metamorphosis   The transformation of one thing, or being, into another completely different thing or being, such as a caterpillar's change into a butterfly.

metaphor   Figurative language in which one thing is said to be another thing. [See also *figurative language*.]

meter   The pattern of rhythm in lines of poetry. The most common meter, in poetry written in English, is iambic pentameter, that is, a verse having five metrical feet, each foot of verse having two syllables, an unaccented one followed by an accented one.

mood   The feeling or atmosphere that a reader senses while reading or listening to a work of literature.

motivation   A character's reasons for doing, thinking, feeling, or saying something. Sometimes an author will make a character's motivation obvious from the beginning. In realistic fiction and drama, however, a character's motivation may be so complicated that the reader discovers it gradually, by studying the character's thoughts, feelings, and behavior.

myth   A story, passed along by word of mouth for generations, about the actions of gods and goddesses or superhuman heroes and heroines. Most myths were first told to explain the origins of natural things or to justify the social rules and customs of a particular society.

N

narration   The process of telling a story. For both fiction and nonfiction, there are two main kinds of narration, based on whether the story is told from a first-person or third-person point of view. [See also *point of view*.]

narrative poem   A poem that tells a story containing the basic literary ingredients of fiction: character, setting, and plot.

narrator   The person, or voice, that tells a story. [See also *point of view, voice*.]

nonfiction   Prose that is factually true and is about real people, events, and places.

nonstandard English
Versions of English, such as slang and dialects, that use pronunciation, vocabulary, idiomatic expressions, grammar, and punctuation that differ from the accepted "correct" constructions of English.

novel   A long work of narrative prose fiction. A novel contains narration, a setting or settings, characters, dialogue, and a more complicated plot than a short story.

O

onomatopoeia   The technique of using words that imitate the sounds they describe, such as *hiss*, *buzz*, and *splash*.

oral tradition   Stories, poems, and songs that have been kept alive by being told, recited, and sung by people over many generations. Since the works were not originally written, they often have many different versions.

P

parable   A brief story—similar to a fable, but about people—that describes an ordinary situation and concludes with a short moral or lesson to be learned.

personification   Figurative language in which an animal, an object, or an idea is given human characteristics. [See also *figurative language*.]

persuasion   A type of speech or writing whose purpose is to convince people that something is true or important.

play   A work of dramatic literature written for performance by actors before an audience. In classical or traditional drama, a play is divided into five acts, each containing a number of scenes. Each act represents a distinct phase in the development of the plot. Modern plays often have only one act and one scene.

playwright   The author of a play.

plot   The sequence of actions and events in fiction or drama. A traditional plot has at least three parts: the *rising action*, leading up to a turning point that affects the main character; the *climax*, the turning point or moment of greatest intensity or interest; and the *falling action*, leading away from the conflict, or resolving it.

poetry   Language selected and arranged in order to say something in a compressed or nonliteral way. Modern poetry may or may not use many of the traditional poetic techniques that include *meter*, *rhyme*, *alliteration*, *figurative language*, *symbolism*, and *specific verse forms*.

point of view   The perspective from which a writer tells a story. *First-person* narrators tell the story from their own point of view, using pronouns such as *I* or *me*. *Third-person* narrators, using pronouns such as *he*, *she*, or *them*, may be *omniscient* (knowing everything about all characters), or *limited* (taking the point of view of one character). [See also *narration*.]

propaganda   Information or ideas that may or may not be true, but are spread as though they are true, in order to persuade people to do or believe something.

prose   The ordinary form of written and spoken language used to create fiction, nonfiction, and most drama.

protagonist   The main character of a literary work. [See also *character* and *characterization*.]

R

refrain   A line or group of lines that is repeated, usually at the end of each verse, in a poem or a song.

repetition   The use of the same formal element more than once in a literary work, for emphasis or in order to achieve another desired effect.

resolution   The falling action in fiction or drama,

including all of the developments that follow the climax and show that the story's conflict is over. [See also *plot*.]

rhyme scheme   A repeated pattern of similar sounds, usually found at the ends of lines of poetry or poetic drama.

rhythm   In poetry, the measured recurrence of accented and unaccented syllables in a particular pattern. [See also *meter*.]

S

scene   The time, place, and circumstances of a play or a story. In a play, a scene is a section of an act. [See also *play*.]

science fiction   Fantasy literature set in an imaginary future, with details and situations that are designed to seem scientifically possible.

setting   The time and place of a work of literature.

short story   Narrative prose fiction that is shorter and has a less complicated plot than a novel. A short story contains narration, at least one setting, at least one character, and usually some dialogue.

simile   Figurative language that compares two unlike things, introduced by the words "like" or "as." [See also *figurative language*.]

soliloquy   In a play, a short speech spoken by a single character when he or she is alone on the stage. A soliloquy usually expresses the character's innermost thoughts and feelings, when he or she thinks no other characters can hear.

sonnet   A poem written in one stanza, using fourteen lines of iambic pentameter. [See also *meter*.]

speaker   In poetry, the individual whose voice seems to be speaking the lines. [See also *narration*, *voice*.]

stage directions   The directions, written by the playwright, to tell the director, actors, and theater technicians how a play should be dramatized. Stage directions may specify such things as how the setting should appear in each scene, how the actors should deliver their lines, when the stage curtain should rise and fall, how stage lights should be used, where on the stage the actors should be during the action, and when sound effects should be used.

stanza   A group of lines in poetry set apart by blank lines before and after the group; a poetic verse.

style   The distinctive way in which an author composes a work of literature in written or spoken language.

suspense   An effect created by authors of various types of fiction and drama, especially adventure and mystery, to heighten interest in the story.

symbol   An image, person, place, or thing that is used to express the idea of something else.

T

tall tale   A kind of folk tale, or legend, that exaggerates the characteristics of its hero or heroine.

theme   The main idea or underlying subject of a work of literature.

tone   The attitude that a work of literature expresses to the reader through its style.

tragedy   In classical drama, a tragedy depicts a noble hero or heroine who makes a mistake of judgment that has disastrous consequences.

V

verse   A stanza in a poem. Also, a synonym for poetry as a genre. [See also *stanza*.]

voice   The narrator or the person who relates the action of a piece of literature. [See also *speaker*.]

ACKNOWLEDGMENTS

Grateful acknowledgment is made for permission to reprint the following copyrighted material.

"Amanda and the Wounded Birds" by Colby Rodowsky, copyright © 1987 by Colby Rodowsky, from *Visions* by Donald R. Gallo, Editor. Used by permission of Dell Books, a division of Bantam Doubleday Dell Publishing Group, Inc.

"Danielle O'Mara" from *Class Dismissed II* by Mel Glenn. Text copyright © 1986 by Mel Glenn. Reprinted by permission of Clarion Books/Houghton Mifflin Co. All rights reserved.

"A Game of Catch" by Richard Wilbur is reprinted by permission from *Stories From The New Yorker 1950-1960*, copyright © 1960 by the *New Yorker Magazine, Inc.* Published by Simon and Schuster.

"Umu Madu in the Good Old Days" from *How Tables Came to Umu Madu* by T. Obinkaram Echewa. Reprinted by permission of the author.

"The Clearing" by Jesse Stuart. "The Clearing" by Jesse Stuart appeared originally in Ladies' Home Journal. Copyright 1954 by Jesse Stuart. Copyright © renewed 1982 Jesse Stuart Foundation. Reprinted by permission of the Jesse Stuart Foundation, P.O. Box 391, Ashland KY 41114.

"The Long Way Around" by Jean McCord from *Deep Where the Octopi Lie*, copyright © 1968 by Jean McCord. Reprinted by permission of the author.

"I Have a Dream" by Martin Luther King, Jr., is reprinted by arrangement with The Heirs to the Estate of Martin Luther King, Jr., c/o Joan Daves Agency as agent for the proprietor.
Copyright © 1963 by Martin Luther King, Jr., copyright renewed 1991 by Coretta Scott King.

"Shells" by Cynthia Rylant. Reprinted with the permission of Bradbury Press, an Affiliate of Macmillan, Inc. from *Every Living Thing* by Cynthia Rylant. Copyright © 1985 by Cynthia Rylant.

"The Silent Lobby" by Mildred Pitts Walter. Copyright © 1990 by Mildred Pitts Walter. Reprinted by permission of the author.

"The Fuller Brush Man" by Gloria D. Miklowitz, copyright © 1987 by Gloria D. Miklowitz, from *Visions* by Donald R. Gallo, Editor. Used by permission of Dell Books, a division of Bantam Doubleday Dell Publishing Group, Inc.

"Brown vs. Board of Education" by Walter Dean Myers from *Now Is Your Time! : The African-American Struggle for Freedom*, copyright © 1991 by Walter Dean Myers. Reprinted by permission of HarperCollins Publishers.

PHOTOGRAPHY

4 *l* John Owens/©D.C. Heath; *r* Sandy Roessler/The Stock Market; **5** Lois Schlowsky Computer Imagery. Photo of Martin Luther King, Jr., by Bob Adelman/Magnum Photos, Inc.; **6** Richard Haynes/©D.C. Heath; **8** *t* Robert Brenner/PhotoEdit; *b* Pamela Schuyler/Stock Boston; **9** *t* John Eastcott/Stock Boston; *b* Alan Oddie/PhotoEdit; **10** *t* Sarah Putnam/©D.C. Heath; *b* Julie Bidwell/©D.C. Heath; **11** *t* Skjold/The Image Works; *c* Jim Whitmer/Stock Boston; *b* Tony Freeman/PhotoEdit; **12-13** Rare Books Division, Library of Congress; **17** ©Photo R.M.N. ©SPADEM Paris/Artists Rights Society, New York, 1994; **21** Photo by Sally Foster. Courtesy of Farrar, Straus and Giroux, Inc.; **22** Harriet Gans/The Image Works; **23** Courtesy of Clarion Books; **24-27** Lois Schlowsky Computer Imagery. Photos of tree and baseball player by Gayna Hoffman; **29** Photo by Constance Stuart Larrabee. Courtesy of Harcourt Brace and Company; **30-37** *border* From the Girard Foundation Collection in the Museum of International Folk Art, a unit of the Museum of New Mexico. Photo by Michel Montaux; **31** Sally Mayman/Tony Stone Images; **34-35** Bruno Barbey/Magnum Photos; **38-39, 40-41** *detail*, **43** *detail* United Missouri Bank, Kansas City. ©Thomas Hart Benton/VAGA, NY, 1995. Photo by Robert Newcombe; **45** The Jesse Stuart Foundation; **46-52** Ralph Mercer Photography/©D.C. Heath; **56-57** Lois Schlowsky Computer Imagery. Photo of children by David Young-Wolff/PhotoEdit. Photo of Martin Luther King, Jr., by Bob Adelman/Magnum Photos, Inc.; **61** Howard Frank/Personality Photos; **62** José Luis Grande/Photo Researchers; **65, 66-67** *t* Tom McHugh/Allstock; **67** *b* Courtesy of Macmillan Children's Book Group; **68** The Bettmann Archive; **70-71** *background* The Bettman Archive; **74-75** UPI/Bettmann; **75** *b* Courtesy of Macmillan Children's Book Group; **76-81** R.P. Kingston/Stock Boston; **81** *inset* Sandy Weiner. Courtesy of Bantam Doubleday Dell; **82, 85** Collection of Michael D. Davis; **86** UPI/Bettmann; **88** Collection of the Supreme Court of the United States; **89** Courtesy of HarperCollins Publishers; **90-91** ©Terje Rakke/The Image Bank; **92, 96** *detail* The Metropolitan Museum of Art. Gift of Katrin S. Vietor, in loving memory of Ernest G. Vietor, 1960. (60.174); **99** *detail*, **100** Chester Dale Collection. ©1993 National Gallery of Art, Washington; **103** Nancy Sheehan/©DC Heath; **106** *t* Elizabeth Hamlin/Stock Boston; *b* Ken O'Donoghue/©D.C. Heath; **108** Peanuts cartoon reprinted by permission of UFS, Inc.; **112** Jean-Claude Lejeune/Stock Boston; **114** *t* © J. Sulley/The Image Works; *b* ©1993 Peter Steiner and the Cartoon Bank, Inc.
Back cover *t* Sarah Putnam/©D.C. Heath; *c* John Owens/©D.C. Heath; *b* Julie Bidwell/©D.C. Heath.

Full Pronunciation Key for Footnoted Words

(Each pronunciation and definition is adapted from *Scott, Foresman Advanced Dictionary* by E.L. Thorndike and Clarence L. Barnhart.)

The pronunciation of each footnoted word is shown just after the word, in this way: **abbreviate** [ə brē′ vē āt]. The letters and signs used are pronounced as in the words below. The mark ′ is placed after a syllable with primary or heavy accent, as in the example above. The mark ′ after a syllable shows a secondary or lighter accent, as in **abbreviation** [ə brē′ vē ā′ shən].

Some words, taken from foreign languages, are spoken with sounds that do not otherwise occur in English. Symbols for these sounds are given in the key as "foreign sounds."

a	hat, cap	j	jam, enjoy	u	cup, butter		
ā	age, face	k	kind, seek	ů	full, put		
ä	father, far	l	land, coal	ü	rule, move		
		m	me, am	v	very, save		
b	bad, rob	n	no, in	w	will, woman		
ch	child, much	ng	long, bring	y	young, yet		
d	did, red			z	zero, breeze		
		o	hot, rock	zh	measure, seizure		
e	let, best	ō	open, go				
ē	equal, be	ô	order, all	ə represents:			
ėr	term, learn	oi	oil, voice	a in about			
		ou	house, out	e in taken			
f	fat, if			i in pencil			
g	go, bag	p	paper, cup	o in lemon			
h	he, how	r	run, try	u in circus			
		s	say, yes				
i	it, pin	sh	she, rush				
ī	ice, five	t	tell, it				
		th	thin, both				
		ŦH	then, smooth				

foreign sounds

Y as in French *du*. Pronounce (ē) with the lips rounded as for (ü).

à as in French *ami*. Pronounce (ä) with the lips spread and held tense.

œ as in French *peu*. Pronounce (ā) with the lips rounded as for (ō).

N as in French *bon*. The N is not pronounced, but shows that the vowel before it is nasal.

H as in German *ach*. Pronounce (k) without closing the breath passage.

Just imagine

H E A T H
MIDDLELEVEL
LITERATURE

Just Imagine

T H E M E
MYSTERY AND THE IMAGINATION

A U T H O R S

Donna Alvermann
Linda Miller Cleary
Kenneth Donelson
Donald Gallo
Alice Haskins
J. Howard Johnston
John Lounsbury
Alleen Pace Nilsen
Robert Pavlik
Jewell Parker Rhodes
Alberto Alvaro Ríos
Sandra Schurr
Lyndon Searfoss
Julia Thomason
Max Thompson
Carl Zon

D.C. Heath and Company
Lexington, Massachusetts / Toronto, Ontario
HEATH

STAFF CREDITS

EDITORIAL Barbara A. Brennan, Helen Byers, Christopher Johnson, Kathleen Kennedy Kelley, Owen Shows, Rita M. Sullivan

Proofreading: JoAnne B. Sgroi

CONTRIBUTING WRITERS Nance Davidson, Florence Harris

SERIES DESIGN Robin Herr

BOOK DESIGN Caroline Bowden, Daniel Derdula, Susan Geer, Diana Maloney, Angela Sciaraffa, Bonnie Chayes Yousefian

Art Editing: Carolyn Langley

PHOTOGRAPHY *Series Photography Coordinator:* Carmen Johnson

Photo Research Supervisor: Martha Friedman

Photo Researchers: Wendy Enright, Linda Finigan, Po-yee McKenna, PhotoSearch, Inc., Gillian Speeth, Denise Theodores

Assignment Photography Coordinators: Susan Doheny, Gayna Hoffman, Shawna Johnston

COMPUTER PREPRESS Ricki Pappo, Kathy Meisl

Richard Curran, Michele Locatelli

PERMISSIONS Dorothy B. McLeod

PRODUCTION Patrick Connolly

Middle Level Authors

Donna Alvermann, University of Georgia
Alice Haskins, Howard County Public Schools, Maryland
J. Howard Johnston, University of South Florida
John Lounsbury, Georgia College
Sandra Schurr, University of South Florida
Julia Thomason, Appalachian State University
Max Thompson, Appalachian State University
Carl Zon, California Assessment Collaborative

Literature and Language Arts Authors

Linda Miller Cleary, University of Minnesota
Kenneth Donelson, Arizona State University
Donald Gallo, Central Connecticut State University
Alleen Pace Nilsen, Arizona State University
Robert Pavlik, Cardinal Stritch College, Milwaukee
Jewell Parker Rhodes, Arizona State University
Alberto Alvaro Ríos, Arizona State University
Lyndon Searfoss, Arizona State University

Teacher Consultants

Suzanne Aubin, Patapsco Middle School, Ellicott City, Maryland
Judy Baxter, Newport News Public Schools, Newport News, Virginia
Saundra Bryn, Director of Research and Development, El Mirage, Arizona
Lorraine Gerhart, Elmbrook Middle School, Elm Grove, Wisconsin
Kathy Tuchman Glass, Burlingame Intermediate School, Burlingame, California
Lisa Mandelbaum, Crocker Middle School, Hillsborough, California
Lucretia Pannozzo, John Jay Middle School, Katonah, New York
Carol Schultz, Jerling Junior High, Orland Park, Illinois
Jeanne Siebenman, Grand Canyon University, Phoenix, Arizona
Gail Thompson, Garey High School, Pomona, California
Rufus Thompson, Grace Yokley School, Ontario, California
Tom Tufts, Conniston Middle School, West Palm Beach, Florida
Edna Turner, Harpers Choice Middle School, Columbia, Maryland
C. Anne Webb, Buerkle Junior High School, St. Louis, Missouri
Geri Yaccino, Thompson Junior High School, St. Charles, Illinois

CONTENTS

Detail from **Real Ripe Mango**, Alison Chapman-Andrews

ASKING BIG QUESTIONS ABOUT THE LITERATURE

How do people respond to strange and unusual stories? 102-103

How do writers make strange and unusual stories work?   104-105

PROJECTS

1 WRITING WORKSHOP

WRITING A REVIEW   106-111

Have you ever wanted to be a critic? Here's your chance!

2 COOPERATIVE LEARNING

MAKING A BOARD GAME   112-113

Work with a team to design and build a board game.

3 HELPING YOUR COMMUNITY

A STORYTELLING PERFORMANCE   114-115

Organize a storytelling performance for your school or community center.

CREATE A WEIRD STORY

Just imagine! You're driving cross-country, and no matter how far you go, you keep passing the same hitch-hiker. Weird? Unreal? Sure. But wouldn't it make a good story? In fact, it's exactly what happens in one of the selections in this unit!

What creepy, strange, or mysterious ideas can you come up with? Work with classmates to create and tell a weird story.

1 Imagine what's happening.

Imagine that this picture was handed to a book publisher by a writer who disappeared mysteriously, leaving the picture without an accompanying story. Now it's up to you and a group of classmates to put the picture's strange, mysterious story into words. Then you can tell it to others in your class or school.

Working with a group, concentrate on the picture as you invent a caption and a title. Examine *all* the details. List them in your journal.

Choose someone to be timekeeper. For exactly one minute, discuss the details and what they might mean. Don't be afraid of exploring strange possibilities or unreal ideas. Say whatever comes to mind.

Listen as each classmate speaks in turn. Jot down good ideas.

Detail from **Chris Van Allsburg's** *The Mysteries of Harris Burdick,* Houghton Mifflin, 1984.

2 Put your ideas together.

Discuss the ideas you've come up with. Which ideas are wonderfully weird, and which are just silly? Which ideas might help explain the picture? Discuss how to construct a story that will keep an audience spellbound. How can you build suspense? What surprise or twist in the plot can you come up with? What will make the characters interesting?

Agree on the outline of a story by filling out a Story Staircase like the one shown. Write it in your journal.

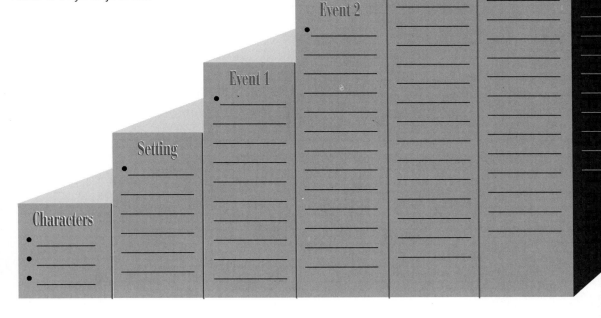

Characters

Setting

Event 1

Event 2

Event 3

Climax, "twist"

Resolution

3 Tell your story.

Who in the group would like to tell the story, complete with gestures and in the voices of different characters? Who might like to pantomime, or act out the events silently, as the story is told? Who might want to make story boards, signs, or props, or supply sound effects or background music? Agree on who will do what. Then rehearse until the group is ready to perform.

Asking Big Questions About the Theme

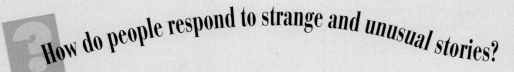

How do people respond to strange and unusual stories?

A Storytelling Circle In a group, take turns telling mysterious, creepy, or startling stories. As you listen, keep a listener's journal. Write what you think and feel.

How did you respond to the different stories? Draw an outline of your head and fill it with your responses. Decorate it if you like.

A Talk Show With three classmates, discuss these questions.

What makes a story weird? Creepy? Startling?
Why is it fun to imagine strange events?
Why do people like unusual stories?
How do weird stories affect you?

Now, in front of your class audience, pretend to be a panel of experts on a talk show called "Why Weird Stories?" Decide who'll be the host. Then start talking.

A Class Story Begin a weird story by writing the following sentence on a sheet of paper: "It was nearly dusk." Then let the person sitting next to you continue the story by writing a sentence of his or her own. Take turns adding sentences to the story until everyone has contributed. Then ask a volunteer to read the story out loud.

How do writers make strange and unusual stories work?

A Weird Story List With a group, make a list of weird movies or television shows that you have seen. Then discuss how each of the following techniques was used to make these weird stories work.

1. suspense: anticipation about the outcome of the plot
2. exaggeration: a description that magnifies and distorts the quality of something
3. surprise twist: an unexpected plot development
4. mood: the feeling or atmosphere of a work of literature

Beside each weird story, write the name of the technique or techniques that made the story work.

Surprise Twists In your journal, list five ordinary situations, such as *a girl crosses the street, a cloud hides the sun*, and so on. Then, with a partner, come up with a strange twist for each event. Use a map like the one below to record your ideas.

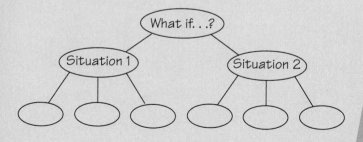

Then present one situation to the class in the form of a picture, poem, or song.

NOW *Think!*

With one or more classmates, think of other questions about weird stories. Write them in your journal. Ask yourself these questions and the two Big Questions as you go through the unit. How does each selection, activity, and project help you find answers?

Cartouche rug Iran, early 16th century, detail, silk, wool, 16'4" x 11'2", Metropolitan Museum of Art, New York

THE WISH

ROALD DAHL

Under the palm of one hand the child became aware of the scab of an old cut on his knee-cap. He bent forward to examine it closely. A scab was always a fascinating thing; it presented a special challenge he was never able to resist.

Yes, he thought, I will pick it off, even if it isn't ready, even if the middle of it sticks, even if it hurts like anything.

With a fingernail he began to explore cautiously around the edges of the scab. He got the nail underneath it, and when he raised it, but ever so slightly, it suddenly came off, the whole hard brown scab came off beautifully, leaving an interesting little circle of smooth red skin.

Nice. Very nice indeed. He rubbed the circle and it didn't hurt. He picked up the scab, put it on his thigh and flipped it with a finger so that it flew away and landed on the edge of the carpet, the enormous red and black and yellow carpet that stretched the whole length of the hall from the stairs on which he sat to the front door in the distance. A tremendous carpet. Bigger than the tennis lawn. Much bigger than that. He regarded it gravely, settling his eyes upon it with mild pleasure. He had never really noticed it before, but now, all of a sudden, the colours[1] seemed to brighten mysteriously and spring out at him in a most dazzling way.

You see, he told himself, I know how it is. The red parts of the carpet are red-hot lumps of coal. What I must do is this: I must walk all the way along it to the front door without touching them. If I touch the red I will be burnt. As a matter of fact, I will be burnt up completely.

---

1. **colours** [kul′ ərz]: British spelling of "colors."

And the black parts of the carpet . . . yes, the black parts are snakes, poisonous snakes, adders[2] mostly, and cobras, thick like tree-trunks round the middle, and if I touch one of *them*, I'll be bitten and I'll die before tea time. And if I get across safely, without being burnt and without being bitten, I will be given a puppy for my birthday tomorrow.

He got to his feet and climbed higher up the stairs to obtain a better view of this vast tapestry of colour and death. Was it possible? Was there enough yellow? Yellow was the only colour he was allowed to walk on. Could it be done? This was not a journey to be undertaken lightly; the risks were too great for that. The child's face—a fringe of white-gold hair, two large blue eyes, a small pointed chin—peered down anxiously over the banisters. The yellow was a bit thin in places and there were one or two widish gaps, but it did seem to go all the way along to the other end. For someone who had only yesterday triumphantly travelled the whole length of the brick path from the stables to the summer-house without touching the cracks, this carpet thing should not be too difficult. Except for the snakes. The mere thought of snakes sent a fine electricity of fear running like pins down the backs of his legs and under the soles of his feet.

He came slowly down the stairs and advanced to the edge of the carpet. He extended one small sandaled foot and placed it cautiously upon a patch of yellow. Then he brought the other foot up, and there was just enough room for him to stand with the two feet together. There! He had started! His bright oval face was curiously intent, a shade whiter perhaps than before, and he was holding his arms out sideways to assist his balance. He took another step, lifting his foot high over a patch of black, aiming carefully with his toe for a narrow channel of yellow on the other side. When he had completed the second step he paused to rest, standing very stiff and still. The narrow channel of yellow ran forward unbroken for at least five yards and he advanced gingerly along it, bit by bit, as though walking a tight-rope. Where it finally curled off sideways, he had to take another long

2. **adders** [ad′ ərz]: small, poisonous snakes.

stride, this time over a vicious looking mixture of black and red. Halfway across he began to wobble. He waved his arms around wildly, windmill fashion, to keep his balance, and he got across safely and rested again on the other side. He was quite breathless now, and so tense he stood high on his toes all the time, arms out sideways, fists clenched. He was on a big safe island of yellow. There was lots of room on it, he couldn't possibly fall off, and he stood there resting, hesitating, waiting, wishing he could stay forever on this big safe yellow island. But the fear of not getting the puppy compelled him to go on.

Step by step, he edged further ahead, and between each one he paused to decide exactly where next he should put his foot. Once, he had a choice of ways, either to left or right, and he chose the left because although it seemed the more difficult, there was not so much black in that direction. The black was what made him nervous. He glanced quickly over his shoulder to see how far he had come. Nearly halfway. There could be no turning back now. He was in the middle and he couldn't turn back and he couldn't jump off sideways either because it was too far, and when he looked at all the red and all the black that lay ahead of him, he felt that old sudden sickening surge of panic in his chest—like last Easter time, that afternoon when he got lost all alone in the darkest part of Piper's Wood.

He took another step, placing his foot carefully upon the only little piece of yellow within reach, and this time the point of the foot came within a centimetre[3] of some black. It wasn't touching the black, he could see it wasn't touching, he could see the small line of yellow separating the toe of his sandal from the black; but the snake stirred as though sensing the nearness, and raised its head and gazed at the foot with bright beady eyes, watching to see if it was going to touch.

3. **centimetre** [sen′ tə mē′ tər]: British spelling of "centimeter": unit of length; one inch equals 2.54 centimeters.

"*I'm not touching you! You mustn't bite me! You know I'm not touching you!*"

Another snake slid up noiselessly beside the first, raised its head, two heads now, two pairs of eyes staring at the foot, gazing at a little naked place just below the sandal strap where the skin showed through. The child went high up on his toes and stayed there, frozen stiff with terror. It was minutes before he dared to move again.

The next step would have to be a really long one. There was this deep curling river of black that ran clear across the width of the carpet, and he was forced by his position to cross it at its widest part. He thought first of trying to jump it, but decided he couldn't be sure of landing accurately on the narrow band of yellow on the other side. He took a deep breath, lifted one foot, and inch by inch he pushed it out in front of him, far far out, then down and down until at last the tip of his sandal was across and resting safely on the edge of the yellow. He leaned forward, transferring his weight to this front foot.

Then he tried to bring the back foot up as well. He strained and pulled and jerked his body, but the legs were too wide apart and he couldn't make it. He tried to get back again. He couldn't do that either. He was doing the splits and he was properly stuck. He glanced down and saw this deep curling river of black underneath him. Parts of it were stirring now, and uncoiling and sliding and beginning to shine with a dreadful oily glister.[4] He wobbled, waved his arms frantically to keep his balance, but that seemed to make it worse. He was starting to go over. He was going over to the right, quite slowly he was going over, then faster and faster, and at the last moment, instinctively he put out a hand to break the fall and the next thing he saw was this bare hand of his going right into the middle of a great glistening mass of black and he gave one piercing cry of terror as it touched.

Outside in the sunshine, far away behind the house, the mother was looking for her son.

4. **glister** [glis′ tər]: shine, glitter.

ROALD DAHL
....

Roald Dahl [1916-1990] was born in Llandaff, South Wales. Energetic and mischievous as a boy, Dahl did poorly at school and refused college. He dreamed of going to "wonderful faraway places like Africa or China." As an adult, he took a job that sent him to Tanzania, Africa. Dahl said that he loved the "roasting heat and the crocodiles and the snakes and safaries."

Dahl's imagination relished fantasy, and someone suggested he try writing fiction. He did—and horror stories for adults made him famous. When he became a father, his bedtime tales became children's books. *Charlie and the Chocolate Factory* became a classic, and people also love Dahl's autobiography, *Boy: Tales of Childhood*. Although he wrote many books, Dahl once said, "becoming a writer was pure fluke. Without being asked to, I doubt if I'd ever [have] thought of it."

THE ADVENTURE OF THE

SPECKLED BAND

ARTHUR CONAN DOYLE

On glancing over my notes of the seventy odd cases in which I have during the last eight years studied the methods of my friend Sherlock Holmes, I find many tragic, some comic, a large number merely strange, but none commonplace; for, working as he did rather for the love of his art than for the acquirement of wealth, he refused to associate himself with any investigation which did not tend towards the unusual, and even the fantastic. Of all these varied cases, however, I cannot recall any which presented more singular features than that which was associated with the well-known Surrey family of the Roylotts of Stoke Moran. The events in question occurred in the early days of my association with Holmes when we were sharing rooms as bachelors in Baker Street. It is possible that I might have placed them upon record before but a promise of secrecy was made at the time, from which I have only been freed during the last month by the untimely death of the lady to whom the pledge was given. It is perhaps as well that the facts should now come to light, for I have reasons to know that there are widespread rumors as to the death of Dr. Grimesby Roylott which tend to make the matter even more terrible than the truth.

It was early in April in the year 1883 that I woke one morning to find Sherlock Holmes standing, fully dressed, by the side of my bed. He was a late riser, as a rule, and as the clock on the mantelpiece showed me that it was only a quarter past seven, I blinked up at him in some surprise, and perhaps just a little resentment, for I was myself regular in my habits.

"Very sorry to wake you up, Watson," said he, "but it's the common lot this morning. Mrs. Hudson has been awakened, she retorted upon me, and I on you."

"What is it, then—a fire?"

"No; a client. It seems that a young lady has arrived in a considerable state of excitement who insists upon seeing me. She is waiting now in the sitting room. Now, when young ladies wander about the metropolis[1] at this hour of the morning, and get sleepy people up out of their beds, I presume that it is something very pressing which they have to communicate. Should it prove to be an interesting case, you would, I am sure, wish to follow it from the outset. I thought, at any rate, that I should call you and give you the chance."

"My dear fellow, I would not miss it for anything."

I had no keener pleasure than in following Holmes in his professional investigations, and in admiring the rapid deductions,[2] as swift as intuitions,[3] and yet always founded on a logical basis, with which he unraveled the problems which were submitted to him. I rapidly threw on my clothes and was ready in a few minutes to accompany my friend down to the sitting room. A lady dressed in black and heavily veiled, who had been sitting in the window, rose as we entered.

"Good morning, madam," said Holmes cheerily. "My name is Sherlock Holmes. This is my intimate friend and associate, Dr. Watson, before whom you can speak as freely as before myself. Ha! I am glad to see that Mrs. Hudson has had the good sense to light the fire. Pray draw up to it, and I shall order you a cup of hot coffee, for I observe that you are shivering."

---

1. **metropolis** [mə trop′ ə lis]: the capital or chief city of a country or region.
2. **deductions** [di duk′ shənz]: answers found by reasoning.
3. **intuitions** [in′ tü ish′ ənz]: insights gained without reasoning.

"It is not cold which makes me shiver," said the woman in a low voice, changing her seat as requested.

"What, then?"

"It is fear, Mr. Holmes. It is terror." She raised her veil as she spoke, and we could see that she was indeed in a pitiable state of agitation, her face all drawn and gray, with restless, frightened eyes, like those of some hunted animal. Her features and figure were those of a woman of thirty, but her hair was shot with premature gray, and her expression was weary and haggard. Sherlock Holmes ran her over with one of his quick, all-comprehensive glances.

"You must not fear," said he soothingly, bending forward and patting her forearm. "We shall soon set matters right, I have no doubt. You have come in by train this morning, I see."

"You know me, then?"

"No, but I observe the second half of a return ticket in the palm of your left glove. You must have started early, and yet you had a good drive in a dogcart[4] along heavy roads, before you reached the station."

The lady gave a violent start and stared in bewilderment at my companion.

"There is no mystery, my dear madam," said he, smiling. "The left arm of your jacket is spattered with mud in no less than seven places. The marks are perfectly fresh. There is no vehicle save a dogcart which throws up mud in that way, and then only when you sit on the left-hand side of the driver."

"Whatever your reasons may be, you are perfectly correct," said she. "I started from home before six, reached Leatherhead at twenty past, and came in by the first train to Waterloo. Sir, I can stand this

4. **dogcart:** a small, open, horse-drawn carriage with two seats placed back to back.

strain no longer; I shall go mad if it continues, I have no one to turn to—none, save only one, who cares for me, and he, poor fellow, can be of little aid. I have heard of you, Mr. Holmes, I have heard of you from Mrs. Farintosh, whom you helped in the hour of her sore need. It was from her that I had your address. Oh, sir, do you not think that you could help me, too, and at least throw a little light through the dense darkness which surrounds me? At present it is out of my power to reward you for your service, but in a month or six weeks I shall be married, with the control of my own income, and then at least you shall not find me ungrateful."

Holmes turned to his desk and, unlocking it, drew out a small case book, which he consulted.

"Farintosh," said he. "Ah yes, I recall the case; it was concerned with an opal tiara.[5] I think it was before your time, Watson. I can only say, madam, that I shall be happy to devote the same care to your case as I did to that of your friend. As to reward, my profession is its own reward; but you are at liberty to defray whatever expenses I may be put to, at the time which suits you best. And now I beg that you will lay before us everything that may help us in forming an opinion upon the matter."

"Alas!" replied our visitor, "the very horror of my situation lies in the fact that my fears are so vague, and my suspicions depend so entirely upon small points, which might seem trivial to another, that even he to whom of all others I have a right to look for help and advice looks upon all that I tell him about it as fancy. He does not say so, but I can read it from his soothing answers and averted eyes. But I have heard, Mr. Holmes, that you can see deeply into the manifold[6] wickedness of the human heart. You may advise me how to walk amid the dangers which encompass me."

"I am all attention, madam."

"My name is Helen Stoner, and I am living with my stepfather,

5. **tiara** [tē är´ ə]: a band of gold, jewels, or flowers worn around the head as an ornament.
6. **manifold** [man´ ə fōld]: many and varied.

who is the last survivor of one of the oldest Saxon families in England; the Roylotts of Stoke Moran, on the western border of Surrey."

Holmes nodded his head. "The name is familiar to me," said he.

"The family was at one time among the richest in England, and the estates extended over the borders into Berkshire in the north, and Hampshire in the west. In the last century, however, four successive heirs were of a dissolute[7] and wasteful disposition,[8] and the family ruin was eventually completed by a gambler in the days of the Regency. Nothing was left save a few acres of ground, and the two-hundred-year-old house, which is itself crushed under a heavy mortgage. The last squire dragged out his existence there, living the horrible life of an aristocratic pauper;[9] but his only son, my stepfather, seeing that he must adapt himself to the new conditions, obtained an advance from a relative, which enabled him to take a medical degree and went out to Calcutta, where, by his professional skill and his force of character, he established a large practice. In a fit of anger, however, caused by some robberies which had been perpetrated in the house, he beat his native butler to death and narrowly escaped a capital sentence. As it was, he suffered a long term of imprisonment and afterwards returned to England a morose and disappointed man.

"When Dr. Roylott was in India he married my mother, Mrs. Stoner, the young widow of Major-General Stoner, of the Bengal Artillery. My sister Julia and I were twins, and we were only two years old at the time of my mother's remarriage. She had a considerable sum of money—not less than £1000 a year[10]—and this she bequeathed to Dr. Roylott entirely while we resided with him, with a provision that a certain annual sum should be allowed to each of us in the event of our marriage. Shortly after our return to England my mother died—she was killed eight years ago in a railway accident

---

7. **dissolute** [disʹ ə lüt]: living an immoral life.
8. **disposition** [disʹ pə zishʹ ən]: nature, way of acting.
9. **aristocratic pauper** [ə risʹ tə kratʹ ik pôʹ pər]: a noble poor person.
10. **£1000 a year:** 1,000 pounds; a pound is a unit of British money.

near Crewe. Dr. Roylott then abandoned his attempts to establish himself in practice in London and took us to live with him in the old ancestral house at Stoke Moran. The money which my mother had left was enough for all our wants, and there seemed to be no obstacle to our happiness.

"But a terrible change came over our stepfather about this time. Instead of making friends and exchanging visits with our neighbors, who had at first been overjoyed to see a Roylott of Stoke Moran back in the old family seat, he shut himself up in his house and seldom came out save to indulge in ferocious quarrels with whoever might cross his path. Violence of temper approaching to mania has been hereditary in the men of the family, and in my stepfather's case it had, I believe, been intensified by his long residence in the tropics. A series of disgraceful brawls took place, two of which ended in the police court, until at last he became the terror of the village, and the folks would fly at his approach, for he is a man of immense strength, and absolutely uncontrollable in his anger.

"Last week he hurled the local blacksmith over a parapet[11] into a stream, and it was only by paying over all the money which I could gather together that I was able to avert another public exposure. He had no friends at all save the wandering gypsies, and he would give these vagabonds leave to encamp upon the few acres of bramble-covered land which represent the family estate, and would accept in return the hospitality of their tents, wandering away with them sometimes for weeks on end. He has a passion also for Indian animals, which are sent over to him by a correspondent, and he has at this moment a cheetah and a baboon, which wander freely over his grounds and are feared by the villagers almost as much as is their master.

"You can imagine from what I say that my poor sister Julia and I had no great pleasure in our lives. No servant would stay with us, and for a long time we did all the work of the house. She was but thirty at the time of her death, and yet her hair had already begun to whiten, even as mine has."

11. **parapet** [par´ ə pət]: a low wall or barrier at the edge of a balcony, roof, or bridge.

"Your sister is dead, then?"

"She died just two years ago, and it is of her death that I wish to speak to you. You can understand that, living the life which I have described, we were little likely to see anyone of our own age and position. We had, however, an aunt, my mother's maiden sister, Miss Honoria Westphail, who lives near Harrow, and we were occasionally allowed to pay short visits at this lady's house. Julia went there at Christmas two years ago, and met there a major in the Marines, to whom she became engaged. My stepfather learned of the engagement when my sister returned and offered no objection to the marriage; but within a fortnight[12] of the day which had been fixed for the wedding, the terrible event occurred which has deprived me of my only companion."

Sherlock Holmes had been leaning back in his chair with his eyes closed and his head sunk in a cushion, but he half opened his lids now and glanced across at his visitor.

"Pray be precise as to details," said he.

"It is easy for me to be so, for every event of that dreadful time is seared into my memory. The manor house is, as I have already said, very old, and only one wing is now inhabited. The bedrooms in this wing are on the ground floor, the sitting rooms being in the central block of the buildings. Of these bedrooms the first is Dr. Roylott's, the second my sister's, and the third my own. There is no communication between them, but they all open out into the same corridor. Do I make myself plain?"

"Perfectly so."

"The windows of the three rooms open out upon the lawn. That fatal night Dr. Roylott had gone to his room early, though we knew that he had not retired to rest, for my sister was troubled by the smell of the strong Indian cigars which it was his custom to smoke. She left her room, therefore, and came into mine, where she sat for some time, chatting about her approaching wedding. At eleven o'clock she rose to leave me, but she paused at the door and looked back.

12. **fortnight** [fôrt′ nīt]: two weeks.

" 'Tell me, Helen,' said she, 'have you ever heard anyone whistle in the dead of the night?'

" 'Never,' said I.

" 'I suppose that you could not possibly whistle, yourself, in your sleep?'

" 'Certainly not. But why?'

" 'Because during the last few nights I have always, about three in the morning, heard a low, clear whistle. I am a light sleeper, and it has awakened me. I cannot tell where it came from— perhaps from the next room, perhaps from the lawn. I thought that I would just ask you whether you had heard it.'

" 'No, I have not. It must be the gypsies in the plantation.'

" 'Very likely. And yet if it were on the lawn, I wonder that you did not hear it also.'

" 'Ah, but I sleep more heavily than you.'

" 'Well, it is of no great consequence, at any rate.' She smiled back at me, closed my door, and a few moments later I heard her key turn in the lock."

"Indeed," said Holmes. "Was it your custom always to lock yourselves in at night?"

"Always."

"And why?"

"I think that I mentioned to you that the doctor kept a cheetah and a baboon. We had no feeling of security unless our doors were locked."

"Quite so. Pray proceed with your statement."

"I could not sleep that night. A vague feeling of impending misfortune impressed me. My sister and I, you will recollect, were

twins, and you know how subtle are the links which bind two souls which are so closely allied. It was a wild night. The wind was howling outside, and the rain was beating and splashing against the windows. Suddenly, amid all the hubbub of the gale, there burst forth the wild scream of a terrified woman. I knew that it was my sister's voice. I sprang from my bed, wrapped a shawl round me, and rushed into the corridor. As I opened my door I seemed to hear a low whistle, such as my sister described, and a few moments later a clanging sound, as if a mass of metal had fallen. As I ran down the passage, my sister's door was unlocked, and revolved slowly upon its hinges. I stared at it horror-stricken, not knowing what was about to issue from it. By the light of the corridor lamp I saw my sister appear at the opening, her face blanched with terror, her hands groping for help, her whole figure swaying to and fro like that of a drunkard. I ran to her and threw my arms round her, but at that moment her knees seemed to give way and she fell to the ground. She writhed as one who is in terrible pain, and her limbs were dreadfully convulsed. At first I thought that she had not recognized me, but as I bent over her she suddenly shrieked out in a voice which I shall never forget. 'Oh, Helen! It was the band! The speckled band!' There was something else which she would fain[13] have said, and she stabbed with her finger into the air in the direction of the doctor's room, but a fresh convulsion seized her and choked her words. I rushed out, calling loudly for my stepfather, and I met him hastening from his room in his dressing gown. When he reached my sister's side she was unconscious, and though he poured brandy down her throat and sent for medical aid from the village, all efforts were in vain, for she slowly sank and died without having recovered her consciousness. Such was the dreadful end of my beloved sister."

"One moment," said Holmes; "are you sure about this whistle and metallic sound? Could you swear to it?"

"That was what the county coroner asked me at the inquiry. It is my strong impression that I heard it, and yet, among the crash of the

13. **fain** [fān]: willingly.

gale and the creaking of an old house, I may possibly have been deceived."

"Was your sister dressed?"

"No, she was in her nightdress. In her right hand was found the charred stump of a match, and in her left a matchbox."

"Showing that she had struck a light and looked about her when the alarm took place. That is important. And what conclusions did the coroner come to?"

"He investigated the case with great care, for Dr. Roylott's conduct had long been notorious in the county, but he was unable to find any satisfactory cause of death. My evidence showed that the door had been fastened upon the inner side, and the windows were blocked by old-fashioned shutters with broad iron bars, which were secured every night. The walls were carefully sounded, and were shown to be quite solid all round, and the flooring was also thoroughly examined, with the same result. The chimney is wide, but is barred up by four large staples. It is certain, therefore, that my sister was quite alone when she met her end. Besides, there were no marks of any violence upon her."

"How about poison?"

"The doctors examined her for it, but without success."

"What do you think that this unfortunate lady died of, then?"

"It is my belief that she died of pure fear and nervous shock, though what it was that frightened her I cannot imagine."

"Were there gypsies in the plantation at the time?"

"Yes, there are nearly always some there."

"Ah, and what did you gather from this allusion to a band—a speckled band?"

"Sometimes I have thought that it was merely the wild talk of delirium, sometimes that it may have referred to some band of people, perhaps to these very gypsies in the plantation. I do not know whether the spotted handkerchiefs which so many of them wear over their heads might have suggested the strange adjective which she used."

Holmes shook his head like a man who is far from being satisfied.

"These are very deep waters," said he; "pray go on with your narrative."

"Two years have passed since then, and my life has been until lately lonelier than ever. A month ago, however, a dear friend, whom I have known for many years, has done me the honour to ask my hand in marriage. His name is Armitage—Percy Armitage—the second son of Mr. Armitage, of Crane Water, near Reading. My step-father has offered no opposition to the match, and we are to be married in the course of the spring. Two days ago some repairs were started in the west wing of the building, and my bedroom wall has been pierced, so that I have had to move into the chamber in which my sister died, and to sleep in the very bed in which she slept. Imagine, then, my thrill of terror when last night, as I lay awake, thinking over her terrible fate, I suddenly heard in the silence of the night the low whistle which had been the herald of her own death. I sprang up and lit the lamp, but nothing was to be seen in the room. I was too shaken to go to bed again, however, so I dressed, and as soon as it was daylight I slipped down, got a dogcart at the Crown Inn, which is opposite, and drove to Leatherhead, from whence I have come on this morning with the one object of seeing you and asking your advice."

"You have done wisely," said my friend. "But have you told me all?"

"Yes, all."

"Miss Roylott, you have not. You are screening your stepfather."

"Why, what do you mean?"

For answer Holmes pushed back the frill of black lace which fringed the hand that lay upon our visitor's knee. Five little livid spots, the marks of four fingers and a thumb, were printed upon the white wrist.

"You have been cruelly used," said Holmes.

The lady colored deeply and covered over her injured wrist. "He is a hard man," she said, "and perhaps he hardly knows his own strength."

There was a long silence, during which Holmes leaned his chin upon his hands and stared into the crackling fire.

"This is a very deep business," he said at last. "There are a thousand details which I should desire to know before I decide upon our course of action. Yet we have not a moment to lose. If we were to come to Stoke Moran today, would it be possible for us to look over these rooms without the knowledge of your stepfather?"

"As it happens, he spoke of coming into town today upon some most important business. It is probable that he will be away all day, and that there would be nothing to disturb you. We have a housekeeper now, but I could easily get her out of the way."

"Excellent. You are not averse to this trip, Watson?"

"By no means."

"Then we shall both come. What are you going to do yourself?"

"I have one or two things which I would wish to do now that I am in town. But I shall return by the twelve o'clock train, so as to be there in time for your coming."

"And you may expect us early in the afternoon. I have myself some small business matters to attend to. Will you not wait and breakfast?"

"No, I must go. My heart is lightened already since I have confided my trouble to you. I shall look forward to seeing you again this afternoon." She dropped her thick black veil over her face and glided from the room.

"And what do you think of it all, Watson?" asked Sherlock Holmes, leaning back in his chair.

"It seems to me to be a most dark and sinister business."

"Dark enough and sinister enough."

"Yet if the lady is correct in saying that the flooring and walls are sound, and that the door, window, and chimney are impassable, then her sister must have been undoubtedly alone when she met her mysterious end."

"What becomes, then, of these nocturnal[14] whistles, and what of the very peculiar words of the dying woman?"

"I cannot think."

---

14. **nocturnal** [nok tėr´ nl]: of the night.

"When you combine the ideas of whistles at night, the presence of a band of gypsies who are on intimate terms with this old doctor, the fact that we have every reason to believe that the doctor has an interest in preventing his stepdaughter's marriage, the dying allusion to a band, and, finally, the fact that Miss Helen Stoner heard a metallic clang, which might have been caused by one of those metal bars that secured the shutters falling back into its place, I think that there is good ground to think that the mystery may be cleared along those lines."

"But what, then, did the gypsies do?"

"I cannot imagine."

"I see many objections to any such theory."

"And so do I. It is precisely for that reason that we are going to Stoke Moran this day. I want to see whether the objections are fatal, or if they may be explained away. But what in the name of the devil!"

The ejaculation had been drawn from my companion by the fact that our door had been suddenly dashed open, and that a huge man had framed himself in the aperture.[15] His costume was a peculiar mixture of the professional and of the agricultural, having a black top hat, a long frock coat, and a pair of high gaiters,[16] with a hunting crop swinging in his hand. So tall was he that his hat actually brushed the crossbar of the doorway, and his breadth seemed to span it across from side to side. A large face, seared with a thousand wrinkles burned yellow with the sun, and marked with every evil passion, was turned from one to the other of us, while his deep-set, bile-shot eyes, and his high, thin, fleshless nose, gave him somewhat the resemblance to a fierce old bird of prey.

"Which of you is Holmes?" asked this apparition.

"My name, sir; but you have the advantage of me," said my companion quietly.

"I am Dr. Grimesby Roylott, of Stoke Moran."

"Indeed, Doctor," said Holmes blandly. "Pray take a seat."

15. **aperture** [ap′ ər chúr]: an opening.
16. **gaiters** [gā′ tərz]: coverings for the lower leg or ankle, made of cloth or leather, for walking outdoors.

"I will do nothing of the kind. My stepdaughter has been here. I have traced her. What has she been saying to you?"

"It is a little cold for the time of the year," said Holmes.

"What has she been saying to you?" screamed the old man furiously.

"But I have heard that the crocuses promise well," continued my companion imperturbably.

"Ha! You put me off, do you?" said our new visitor, taking a step forward and shaking his hunting crop. "I know you, you scoundrel! I have heard of you before. You are Holmes, the meddler."

My friend smiled.

"Holmes, the busybody!"

His smile broadened.

"Holmes, the Scotland Yard Jack-in-office!"

Holmes chuckled heartily. "Your conversation is most entertaining," said he. "When you go out close the door, for there is a decided draft."

"I will go when I have said my say. Don't you dare to meddle with my affairs. I know that Miss Stoner has been here. I traced her! I am a dangerous man to fall foul of! See here." He stepped swiftly forward, seized the poker, and bent it into a curve with his huge brown hands.

"See that you keep yourself out of my grip," he snarled, and hurling the twisted poker into the fireplace he strode out of the room.

"He seems a very amiable person," said Holmes, laughing. "I am not quite so bulky, but if he had remained I might have shown him that my grip was not much more feeble than his own." As he spoke he picked up the steel poker and, with a sudden effort, straightened it out again.

"Fancy his having the insolence to confound me with[17] the official detective force! This incident gives zest to our investigation, however, and I only trust that our little friend will not suffer from her imprudence in allowing this brute to trace her. And now, Watson, we shall order breakfast, and afterwards I shall walk down to Doctors' Commons, where I hope to get some data which may help us in this matter."

17. **insolence to confound me with:** daring to mistake me for.

It was nearly one o'clock when Sherlock Holmes returned from his excursion. He held in his hand a sheet of blue paper, scrawled over with notes and figures.

"I have seen the will of the deceased wife," said he. "To determine its exact meaning I have been obliged to work out the present prices of the investments with which it is concerned. The total income, which at the time of the wife's death was little short of £1100, is now, through the fall in agricultural prices, not more than £750. Each daughter can claim an income of £250, in case of marriage. It is evident, therefore, that if both girls had married, this beauty would have had a mere pittance,[18] while even one of them would cripple him to a very serious extent. My morning's work has not been wasted, since it has proved that he has the very strongest motives for standing in the way of anything of the sort. And now, Watson, this is too serious for dawdling, especially as the old man is aware that we are interesting ourselves in his affairs; so if you are ready, we shall call a cab and drive to Waterloo. I should be very much obliged if you would slip your revolver into your pocket. An Eley's No. 2 is an excellent argument with gentlemen who can twist steel pokers into knots. That and a toothbrush are, I think, all that we need."

At Waterloo we were fortunate in catching a train for Leatherhead, where we hired a trap[19] at the station inn and drove for four or five miles through the lovely Surrey lanes. It was a perfect day, with a bright sun and a few fleecy clouds in the heavens. The trees and wayside hedges were just throwing out their first green shoots, and the air was full of the pleasant smell of the moist earth. To me at least there was a strange contrast between the sweet promise of the spring and this sinister quest upon which we were engaged. My companion

18. **pittance** [pitˊns]: a small amount.
19. **trap** [trap]: a light, two-wheeled horse-drawn carriage.

sat in the front of the trap, his arms folded, his hat pulled down over his eyes, and his chin sunk upon his breast, buried in the deepest thought. Suddenly, however, he started, tapped me on the shoulder, and pointed over the meadows.

"Look there!" said he.

A heavily timbered park stretched up in a gentle slope, thickening into a grove at the highest point. From amid the branches there jutted out the gray gables and high rooftop of a very old mansion.

"Stoke Moran?" said he.

"Yes, sir, that be the house of Dr. Grimesby Roylott," remarked the driver.

"There is some building going on there," said Holmes; "that is where we are going."

"There's the village," said the driver, pointing to a cluster of roofs some distance to the left; "but if you want to get to the house, you'll find it shorter to get over this stile,[20] and so by the footpath over the fields. There it is, where the lady is walking."

"And the lady, I fancy, is Miss Stoner," observed Holmes, shading his eyes. "Yes, I think we had better do as you suggest."

We got off, paid our fare, and the trap rattled back on its way to Leatherhead.

"I thought it as well," said Holmes as we climbed the stile, "that this fellow should think we had come here as architects, or on some definite business. It may stop his gossip. Good afternoon, Miss Stoner. You see that we have been as good as our word."

Our client of the morning had hurried forward to meet us with a face which spoke her joy. "I have been waiting so eagerly for you," she cried, shaking hands with us warmly. "All has turned out splendidly. Dr. Roylott has gone to town, and it is unlikely that he will be back before evening."

20. **stile** [stīl]: a step or steps for getting over a fence or wall.

"We have had the pleasure of making the doctor's acquaintance," said Holmes, and in a few words he sketched out what had occurred. Miss Stoner turned white to the lips as she listened.

"Good heavens!" she cried, "he has followed me, then."

"So it appears."

"He is so cunning that I never know when I am safe from him. What will he say when he returns?"

"He must guard himself, for he may find that there is someone more cunning than himself upon his track. You must lock yourself up from him tonight. If he is violent, we shall take you away to your aunt's at Harrow. Now, we must make the best use of our time, so kindly take us at once to the rooms which we are to examine."

The building was of gray, lichen-blotched[21] stone, with a high central portion and two curving wings, like the claws of a crab, thrown out on each side. In one of these wings the windows were broken and blocked with wooden boards, while the roof was partly caved in, a picture of ruin. The central portion was in little better repair, but the right-hand block was comparatively modern, and the blinds in the windows, with the blue smoke curling up from the chimneys, showed that this was where the family resided. Some scaffolding had been erected against the end wall, and the stonework had been broken into, but there were no signs of any workmen at the moment of our visit. Holmes walked slowly up and down the ill-trimmed lawn and examined with deep attention the outsides of the windows.

"This, I take it, belongs to the room in which you used to sleep, the center one to your sister's, and the one next to the main building to Dr. Roylott's chamber?"

"Exactly so. But I am now sleeping in the middle one."

"Pending the alterations, as I understand. By the way, there does not seem to be any very pressing need for repairs at that end wall."

"There were none. I believe that it was an excuse to move me from my room."

21. **lichen-blotched** [lī′ kən blochd]: stained with lichen: moss-like, flowerless plants that grow on trees, rocks, and walls.

"Ah! That is suggestive. Now, on the other side of this narrow wing runs the corridor from which these three rooms open. There are windows in it, of course?"

"Yes, but very small ones. Too narrow for anyone to pass through."

"As you both locked your doors at night, your rooms were unapproachable from that side. Now, would you have the kindness to go into your room and bar your shutters?"

Miss Stoner did so, and Holmes, after a careful examination through the open window, endeavored in every way to force the shutter open, but without success. There was no slit through which a knife could be passed to raise the bar. Then with his lens he tested the hinges, but they were of solid iron, built firmly into the massive masonry. "Hum!" said he, scratching his chin in some perplexity, "My theory certainly presents some difficulties. No one could pass through these shutters if they were bolted. Well, we shall see if the inside throws any light upon the matter."

A small side door led into the whitewashed corridor from which the three bedrooms opened. Holmes refused to examine the third chamber, so we passed at once to the second, that in which Miss Stoner was now sleeping, and in which her sister had met with her fate. It was a homely little room, with a low ceiling and a gaping fireplace, after the fashion of old country houses. A brown chest of drawers stood in one corner, a narrow white-counterpaned bed in another, and a dressing table on the left-hand side of the window. These articles, with two small wickerwork chairs, made up all the furniture in the room save for a square of Wilton carpet in the center. The boards round and the paneling of the walls were of brown, worm-eaten oak, so old and discolored that it may have dated from the original building of the house. Holmes drew one of the chairs into a corner and sat silent, while his eyes traveled round and round and up and down, taking in every detail of the apartment.

"Where does that bell communicate with?" he asked at last, pointing to a thick bell-rope which hung down beside the bed, the tassel actually lying upon the pillow.

"It goes to the housekeeper's room."

"It looks newer than the other things?"

"Yes, it was only put there a couple of years ago."

"Your sister asked for it, I suppose?"

"No, I never heard of her using it. We used always to get what we wanted for ourselves."

"Indeed, it seemed unnecessary to put so nice a bell-pull there. You will excuse me for a few minutes while I satisfy myself as to this floor." He threw himself down upon his face with his lens in his hand and crawled swiftly backward and forward, examining minutely the cracks between the boards. Then he did the same with the woodwork with which the chamber was paneled. Finally he walked over to the bed and spent some time in staring at it and in running his eye up and down the wall. Finally he took the bell-rope in his hand and gave it a brisk tug.

"Why, it's a dummy," said he.

"Won't it ring?"

"No, it is not even attached to a wire. This is very interesting. You can see now that it is fastened to a hook just above where the little opening for the ventilator is."

"How very absurd! I never noticed that before!"

"Very strange!" muttered Holmes, pulling at the rope. "There are one or two very singular points about this room. For example, what a fool a builder must be to open a ventilator into another room, when, with the same trouble, he might have communicated with the outside air!"

"That is also quite modern," said the lady.

"Done about the same time as the bell-rope?" remarked Holmes.

"Yes, there were several little changes carried out about that time."

"They seem to have been of a most interesting character—dummy bell-ropes, and ventilators which do not ventilate. With your permission, Miss Stoner, we shall now carry our researches into the inner apartment."

Dr. Grimesby Roylott's chamber was larger than that of his step-daughter, but was as plainly furnished. A camp bed, a small wooden

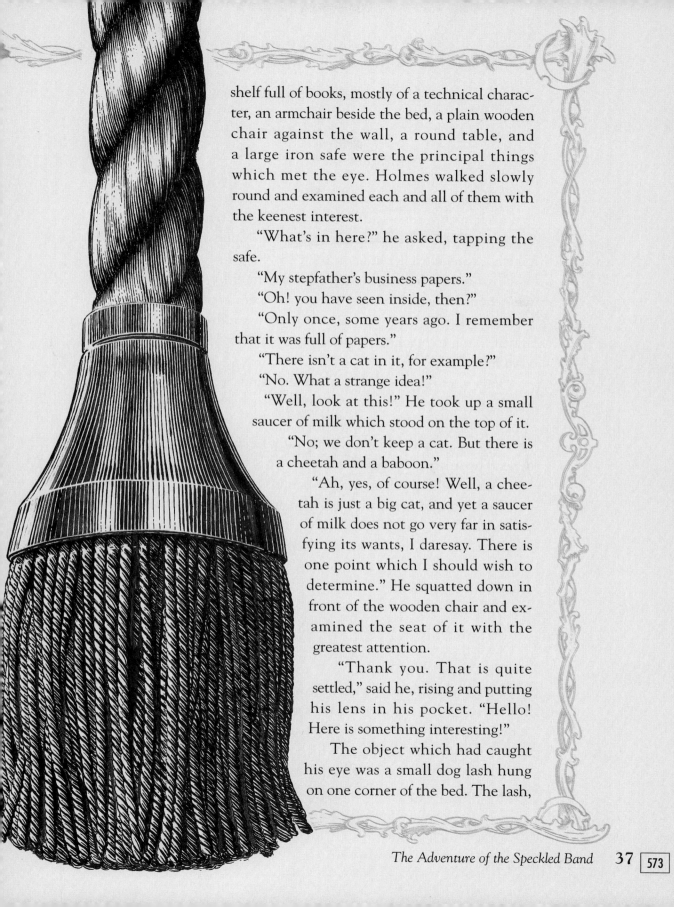

shelf full of books, mostly of a technical character, an armchair beside the bed, a plain wooden
chair against the wall, a round table, and
a large iron safe were the principal things
which met the eye. Holmes walked slowly
round and examined each and all of them with
the keenest interest.

"What's in here?" he asked, tapping the
safe.

"My stepfather's business papers."

"Oh! you have seen inside, then?"

"Only once, some years ago. I remember
that it was full of papers."

"There isn't a cat in it, for example?"

"No. What a strange idea!"

"Well, look at this!" He took up a small
saucer of milk which stood on the top of it.

"No; we don't keep a cat. But there is
a cheetah and a baboon."

"Ah, yes, of course! Well, a cheetah is just a big cat, and yet a saucer
of milk does not go very far in satisfying its wants, I daresay. There is
one point which I should wish to
determine." He squatted down in
front of the wooden chair and examined the seat of it with the
greatest attention.

"Thank you. That is quite
settled," said he, rising and putting
his lens in his pocket. "Hello!
Here is something interesting!"

The object which had caught
his eye was a small dog lash hung
on one corner of the bed. The lash,

however, was curled upon itself and tied so as to make a loop of whip-cord.

"What do you make of that, Watson?"

"It's a common enough lash. But I don't know why it should be tied."

"That is not quite so common, is it? Ah, me! it's a wicked world, and when a clever man turns his brains to crime it is the worst of all. I think that I have seen enough now, Miss Stoner, and with your permission we shall walk out upon the lawn."

I had never seen my friend's face so grim or his brow so dark as it was when we turned from the scene of this investigation. We had walked several times up and down the lawn, neither Miss Stoner nor myself liking to break in upon his thoughts before he roused himself from his reverie.

"It is very essential, Miss Stoner," said he, "that you should absolutely follow my advice in every respect."

"I shall most certainly do so."

"The matter is too serious for any hesitation. Your life may depend upon your compliance."[22]

"I assure you that I am in your hands."

"In the first place, both my friend and I must spend the night in your room."

Both Miss Stoner and I gazed at him in astonishment.

"Yes, it must be so. Let me explain. I believe that that is the village inn over there?"

"Yes, that is the Crown."

"Very good. Your windows would be visible from there?"

"Certainly."

"You must confine yourself to your room, on pretense of a headache, when your stepfather comes back. Then when you hear him retire for the night, you must open the shutters of your window, undo the hasp, put your lamp there as a signal to us, and then withdraw quietly with everything which you are likely to want into the

22. **compliance** [kəm plī′ əns]: doing as another wishes.

room which you used to occupy. I have no doubt that, in spite of the repairs, you could manage there for one night."

"Oh, yes, easily."

"The rest you will leave in our hands."

"But what will you do?"

"We shall spend the night in your room, and we shall investigate the cause of this noise which has disturbed you."

"I believe, Mr. Holmes, that you have already made up your mind," said Miss Stoner, laying her hand upon my companion's sleeve.

"Perhaps I have."

"Then for pity's sake, tell me what was the cause of my sister's death."

"I should prefer to have clearer proofs before I speak."

"You can at least tell me whether my own thought is correct, and if she died from some sudden fright."

"No, I do not think so. I think that there was probably some more tangible cause. And now, Miss Stoner, we must leave you, for if Dr. Roylott returned and saw us our journey would be in vain. Goodbye, and be brave, for if you will do what I have told you, you may rest assured that we shall soon drive away the dangers that threaten you."

Sherlock Holmes and I had no difficulty in engaging a bedroom and sitting room at the Crown Inn. They were on the upper floor, and from our window we could command a view of the avenue gate, and of the inhabited wing of Stoke Moran Manor House. At dusk we saw Dr. Grimesby Roylott drive past, his huge form looming up beside the little figure of the lad who drove him. The boy had some slight difficulty in undoing the heavy iron gates, and we heard the hoarse roar of the doctor's voice and saw the fury with which he shook his clinched fists at him. The trap drove on, and a few minutes later we saw a sudden light spring up among the trees as the lamp was lit in one of the sitting rooms.

"Do you know, Watson," said Holmes as we sat together in the gathering darkness, "I have really some scruples as to taking you tonight. There is a distinct element of danger."

"Can I be of assistance?"

"Your presence might be invaluable."

"Then I shall certainly come."

"It is very kind of you."

"You speak of danger. You have evidently seen more in these rooms than was visible to me."

"No, but I fancy that I may have deduced a little more. I imagine that you saw all that I did."

"I saw nothing remarkable save the bell-rope, and what purpose that could answer I confess is more than I can imagine."

"You saw the ventilator, too?"

"Yes, but I do not think that it is such a very unusual thing to have a small opening between two rooms. It was so small that a rat could hardly pass through."

"I knew that we should find a ventilator before ever we came to Stoke Moran."

"My dear Holmes!"

"Oh, yes, I did. You remember in her statement she said that her sister could smell Dr. Roylott's cigar. Now, of course that suggested at once that there must be a communication between the two rooms. It could only be a small one, or it would have been remarked upon at the coroner's inquiry. I deduced a ventilator."

"But what harm can there be in that?"

"Well, there is at least a curious coincidence of dates. A ventilator is made, a cord is hung, and a lady who sleeps in the bed dies. Does not that strike you?"

"I cannot as yet see any connection."

"Did you observe anything very peculiar about that bed?"

"No."

"It was clamped to the floor. Did you ever see a bed fastened like that before?"

"I cannot say that I have."

"The lady could not move her bed. It must always be in the same relative position to the ventilator and to the rope—or so we may call it, since it was clearly never meant for a bell-pull."

"Holmes," I cried, "I seem to see dimly what you are hinting at. We are only just in time to prevent some subtle and horrible crime."

"Subtle enough and horrible enough. When a doctor does go wrong he is the first of criminals. He has nerve and he has knowledge. Palmer and Pritchard were among the heads of their profession. This man strikes even deeper, but I think, Watson, that we shall be able to strike deeper still. But we shall have horrors enough before the night is over; for goodness' sake let us have a quiet pipe and turn our minds for a few hours to something more cheerful."

About nine o'clock the light among the trees was extinguished, and all was dark in the direction of the Manor House. Two hours passed slowly away, and then, suddenly, just at the stroke of eleven, a single bright light shone out right in front of us.

"That is our signal," said Holmes, springing to his feet; "it comes from the middle window."

As we passed out he exchanged a few words with the landlord, explaining that we were going on a late visit to an acquaintance, and that it was possible that we might spend the night there. A moment later we were out on the dark road, a chill wind blowing in our faces, and one yellow light twinkling in front of us through the gloom to guide us on our somber errand.

There was little difficulty in entering the grounds, for unrepaired breaches gaped in the old park wall. Making our way among the trees, we reached the lawn, crossed it, and were about to enter through the window when out from a clump of laurel bushes there darted what seemed to be a hideous and distorted child, who threw itself upon the grass with writhing limbs and then ran swiftly across the lawn into the darkness.

"My God!" I whispered; "did you see it?"

Holmes was for the moment as startled as I. His hand closed like a vise[23] upon my wrist in his agitation. Then he broke into a low laugh and put his lips to my ear.

"It is a nice household," he murmured. "That is the baboon."

23. **vise** [vīs]: a tool for holding work in a very strong grip.

I had forgotten the strange pets which the doctor affected. There was a cheetah, too; perhaps we might find it upon our shoulders at any moment. I confess that I felt easier in my mind when, after following Holmes's example and slipping off my shoes, I found myself inside the bedroom. My companion noiselessly closed the shutters, moved the lamp onto the table, and cast his eyes round the room. All was as we had seen it in the daytime. Then creeping up to me and making a trumpet of his hand, he whispered into my ear again so gently that it was all that I could do to distinguish the words:

"The least sound would be fatal to our plans."

I nodded to show that I had heard.

"We must sit without light. He would see it through the ventilator."

I nodded again.

"Do not go asleep; your very life may depend upon it. Have your pistol ready in case we should need it. I will sit on the side of the bed, and you in that chair."

I took out my revolver and laid it on the corner of the table.

Holmes had brought up a long thin cane, and this he placed upon the bed beside him. By it he laid the box of matches and the stump of a candle. Then he turned down the lamp, and we were left in darkness.

How shall I ever forget that dreadful vigil? I could not hear a sound, not even the drawing of a breath, and yet I knew that my companion sat open-eyed, within a few feet of me, in the same state of nervous tension in which I was myself. The shutters cut off the least ray of light, and we waited in absolute darkness. From outside came the occasional cry of a night bird, and once at our very window a long-drawn catlike whine, which told us that the cheetah was indeed at liberty. Far away we could hear the deep tones of the parish clock, which boomed out every quarter of an hour. How long they seemed, those quarters! Twelve struck, and one and two and three, and still we sat waiting silently for whatever might befall.

Suddenly there was the momentary gleam of a light up in the direction of the ventilator, which vanished immediately, but was succeeded by a strong smell of burning oil and heated metal. Someone in the next room had lit a dark lantern.[24] I heard a gentle sound of movement, and then all was silent once more, though the smell grew stronger. For half an hour I sat with straining ears. Then suddenly another sound became audible—a very gentle, soothing sound like that of a small jet of steam escaping continually from a kettle. The instant that we heard it, Holmes sprang from the bed, struck a match, and lashed furiously with his cane at the bell-pull.

"You see it, Watson?" he yelled. "You see it?"

But I saw nothing. At the moment when Holmes struck the light I heard a low, clear whistle, but the sudden glare flashing into my weary eyes made it impossible for me to tell what it was at which my friend lashed so savagely. I could, however, see that his face was deadly pale and filled with horror and loathing.

He had ceased to strike and was gazing up at the ventilator when suddenly there broke from the silence of the night the most horrible cry to which I have ever listened. It swelled up louder and louder, a hoarse yell of pain and fear and anger all mingled in the one dreadful shriek. They say that away down in the village, and even in the distant parsonage, that cry raised the sleepers from their beds. It struck

24. **dark lantern:** a lantern with a shutter to hide the light.

cold to our hearts, and I stood gazing at Holmes, and he at me, until the last echoes of it had died away into the silence from which it rose.

"What can it mean?" I gasped.

"It means that it is all over," Holmes answered. "And perhaps, after all, it is for the best. Take your pistol, and we will enter Dr. Roylott's room."

With a grave face he lit the lamp and led the way down the corridor. Twice he struck at the chamber door without any reply from within. Then he turned the handle and entered, I at his heels, with the cocked pistol in my hand.

It was a singular sight which met our eyes. On the table stood a dark lantern with the shutter half open, throwing a brilliant beam of light upon the iron safe, the door of which was ajar. Beside this table, on the wooden chair, sat Dr. Grimesby Roylott, clad in a long gray dressing gown, his bare ankles protruding beneath, and his feet thrust into red heelless Turkish slippers. Across his lap lay the short stock with the long lash which we had noticed during the day. His chin was cocked upward and his eyes were fixed in a dreadful, rigid stare at the corner of the ceiling. Round his brow he had a peculiar yellow band, with brownish speckles, which seemed to be bound tightly round his head. As we entered he made neither sound nor motion.

"The band! the speckled band!" whispered Holmes.

I took a step forward. In an instant his strange headgear began to move, and there reared itself from among his hair the squat diamond-shaped head and puffed neck of a loathsome serpent.

"It is a swamp adder!" cried Holmes; "the deadliest snake in India. He has died within ten seconds of being bitten. Violence does, in truth, recoil upon the violent, and the schemer falls into the pit which he digs for another. Let us thrust this creature back into its den, and we can then remove Miss Stoner to some place of shelter and let the county police know what has happened."

As he spoke he drew the dog whip swiftly from the dead man's lap, and throwing the noose round the reptile's neck he drew it from its horrid perch and, carrying it at arm's length, threw it into the iron safe, which he closed upon it.

Such are the true facts of the death of Dr. Grimesby Roylott, of Stoke Moran. It is not necessary that I should prolong a narrative which has already run to too great a length by telling how we broke the sad news to the terrified girl, how we conveyed her by the morning train to the care of her good aunt at Harrow, of how the slow process of official inquiry came to the conclusion that the doctor met his fate while indiscreetly playing with a dangerous pet. The little which I had yet to learn of the case was told me by Sherlock Holmes as we traveled back next day.

"I had," said he, "come to an entirely erroneous conclusion which shows, my dear Watson, how dangerous it always is to reason from insufficient data. The presence of the gypsies, and the use of the word *band*, which was used by the poor girl, no doubt to explain the appearance which she had caught a hurried glimpse of by the light of her match, were sufficient to put me upon an entirely wrong scent. I can only claim the merit that I instantly reconsidered my position when, however, it became clear to me that whatever danger threatened an occupant of the room could not come either from the window or the door. My attention was speedily drawn, as I have already remarked to you, to this ventilator, and to the bell-rope which hung down to the bed. The discovery that this was a dummy, and that the bed was clamped to the floor, instantly gave rise to the suspicion that the rope was there as a bridge for something passing through the hole and coming to the bed. The idea of a snake instantly occurred to me, and when I coupled it with my knowledge that the doctor was furnished with a supply of creatures from India, I felt that I was probably on the right track. The idea of using a form of poison which could not possibly be discovered by any chemical test was just such a one as would occur to a clever and ruthless man who had had an Eastern training. The rapidity with which such a poison would take effect would also, from his point of view, be an advantage. It would be a sharp-eyed coroner, indeed, who could distinguish the two little dark punctures which would show where the poison fangs had done their work. Then I thought of the whistle. Of course he must recall the snake before the morning light revealed it to the victim. He had trained it, probably by the use of the milk which we saw, to return to him when summoned. He would put it through this ventilator at the hour that he thought best, with the certainty that it would crawl down the rope and land on the bed. It might or might not bite the occupant, perhaps she might escape every night for a week, but sooner or later she must fall a victim.

"I had come to these conclusions before ever I had entered his room. An inspection of his chair showed me that he had been in the habit of standing on it, which of course would be necessary in order that he should reach the ventilator. The sight of the safe, the saucer of milk, and the loop of whipcord were enough to finally dispel any doubts which may have remained. The metallic clang heard by Miss Stoner was obviously caused by her stepfather hastily closing the door of his safe upon its terrible occupant. Having once made up my mind, you know the steps which I took in order to put the matter to the proof. I heard the creature hiss as I have no doubt that you did also, and I instantly lit the light and attacked it."

"With the result of driving it through the ventilator."

"And also with the result of causing it to turn upon its master at the other side. Some of the blows of my cane came home and roused its snakish temper, so that it flew upon the first person it saw. In this way I am no doubt indirectly responsible for Dr. Grimesby Roylott's death, and I cannot say that it is likely to weigh very heavily upon my conscience."

ARTHUR CONAN DOYLE

Arthur Conan Doyle [1859-1930] was born in Edinburgh, Scotland. As a young man, Doyle studied medicine and spent several adventurous years as a ship's doctor. Afterwards, in England, he opened a practice but had so few patients he began writing to earn money. Doyle modeled his detective Sherlock Holmes on a professor he'd known in medical school. The Sherlock Holmes stories became so popular that Doyle gave up medicine and turned to writing full time. His notebooks and diaries provided useful material.

Doyle wrote all the time. He tried everything: detective stories, historical novels, science fiction, horror, humor, sports, plays, and poetry. However, Doyle was proudest of his nonfiction writing. He would have been happier if his fame had not been due entirely to Sherlock Holmes!

The Fear

Robert Frost

A lantern light from deeper in the barn
Shone on a man and woman in the door
And threw their lurching shadows on a house
Nearby, all dark in every glossy window.
A horse's hoof pawed once the hollow floor,   5
And the back of the gig[1] they stood beside
Moved in a little. The man grasped a wheel,
The woman spoke out sharply, 'Whoa, stand still!
I saw it just as plain as a white plate,'
She said, 'as the light on the dashboard ran   10
Along the bushes at the roadside—a man's face.
You *must* have seen it too.'
                                    'I didn't see it.
Are you sure—'
                        'Yes, I'm sure!'   15
                                '—it was a face?'

---

1. **gig** [gig]: a light, open, two-wheeled carriage drawn by one horse.

Moonlight Walk John Atkinson Grimshaw, mid–19th century, oil on canvas, Private collection

'Joel, I'll have to look. I can't go in,
I can't, and leave a thing like that unsettled.
Doors locked and curtains drawn will make no difference.
I always have felt strange when we came home   20
To the dark house after so long an absence,
And the key rattled loudly into place
Seemed to warn someone to be getting out
At one door as we entered at another.
What if I'm right, and someone all the time   25
Don't hold my arm!'
                              'I say it's someone passing.'

'You speak as if this were a traveled road.
You forget where we are. What is beyond
That he'd be going to or coming from   30
At such an hour of night, and on foot too?
What was he standing still for in the bushes?'

'It's not so very late—it's only dark.
There's more in it than you're inclined to say.
Did he look like—?'   45   35
                              'He looked like anyone.
I'll never rest tonight unless I know.
Give me the lantern.'

                              'You don't want the lantern.'

She pushed past him and got it for herself.   40

'You're not to come,' she said. 'This is my business.
If the time's come to face it, I'm the one
To put it the right way. He'd never dare—
Listen! He kicked a stone. Hear that, hear that!
He's coming towards us. Joel, *go* in—please.   45
Hark!—I don't hear him now. But please go in.'

In the first place you can't make me believe it's

It is—or someone else he's sent to watch.
And now's the time to have it out with him
While we know definitely where he is.   50
Let him get off and he'll be everywhere
Around us, looking out of trees and bushes
Till I sha'n't dare to set a foot outdoors.
And I can't stand it. Joel, let me go!'

But it's nonsense to think he'd care enough.'   55

You mean you couldn't understand his caring.
Oh, but you see he hadn't had enough—
Joel, I won't—I won't—I promise you.
We mustn't say hard things. You mustn't either.'

I'll be the one, if anybody goes!   60
But you give him the advantage with this light.
What couldn't he do to us standing here!
And if to see was what he wanted, why,
He has seen all there was to see and gone.'

He appeared to forget to keep his hold,   65
But advanced with her as she crossed the grass.

What do you want?' she cried to all the dark.
She stretched up tall to overlook the light
That hung in both hands hot against her skirt.

There's no one; so you're wrong,' he said.   70

                    'There is.—
What do you want?' she cried, and then herself
Was startled when an answer really came.

'Nothing.' It came from well along the road.

She reached a hand to Joel for support:
The smell of scorching woolen made her faint.   75

'What are you doing round this house at night?'

'Nothing.' A pause: there seemed no more to say.

And then the voice again: 'You seem afraid.
I saw by the way you whipped up the horse.
I'll just come forward in the lantern light   80
And let you see.'

        'Yes, do. — Joel, go back!'

She stood her ground against the noisy steps
That came on, but her body rocked a little.

'You see,' the voice said.   85

         'Oh.' She looked and looked.

'You don't see — I've a child here by the hand.
A robber wouldn't have his family with him.'

'What's a child doing at this time of night — ?'

'Out walking. Every child should have the memory   90
Of at least one long-after-bedtime walk.
What, son?'

'Then I should think you'd try to find
Somewhere to walk —'

'The highway, as it happens— 95
We're stopping for the fortnight[2] down at Dean's.'

'But if that's all—Joel—you realize—
You won't think anything. You understand?
You understand that we have to be careful.
This is a very, very lonely place.   100
Joel!' She spoke as if she couldn't turn.
The swinging lantern lengthened to the ground,
It touched, it struck, it clattered and went out.

2. **fortnight** [fôrt′ nīt]: two weeks.

ROBERT FROST

Robert Frost [1874-1963] was born in San Francisco. Frost's father died when he was ten years old, and he and his mother moved east, to Lawrence, Massachusetts. By the time he was fifteen, Frost knew that poetry would be his life's work.

Later, when his writing was ignored in the United States, Frost moved with his wife and children to England. His poems—with their New England country settings and voices—made him famous abroad. When he and his family moved home to a farm in New Hampshire, Frost's new fame moved home with them. He became known as a great New England poet.

Among Frost's many honors, perhaps the most memorable was his taking part in the inauguration ceremonies of President John F. Kennedy.

AUGUST HEAT

WILLIAM FRYER HARVEY

Three Spheres II M.C. Escher, 1946, lithograph, 10^5/$_8$" x 18^1/$_4$"

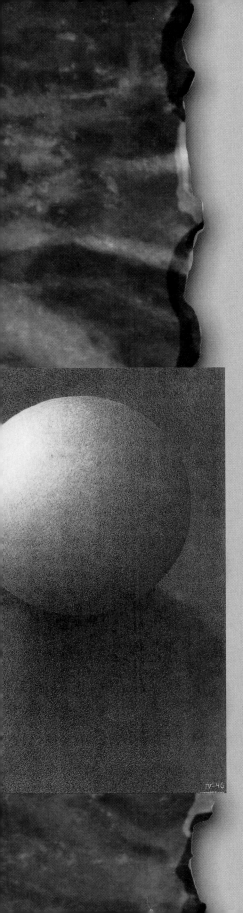

PENISTONE ROAD, CLAPHAM
20th August, 190—.

I have had what I believe to be the most remarkable day in my life, and while the events are still fresh in my mind, I wish to put them down on paper as clearly as possible.

Let me say at the outset that my name is James Clarence Withencroft.

I am forty years old, in perfect health, never having known a day's illness.

By profession I am an artist, not a very successful one, but I earn enough money by my black-and-white work to satisfy my necessary wants.

My only near relative, a sister, died five years ago, so that I am independent.

I breakfasted this morning at nine, and after glancing through the morning paper I lighted my pipe and proceeded to let my mind wander in the hope that I might chance upon some subject for my pencil.

The room, though door and windows were open, was oppressively hot, and I had just made up my mind that the coolest and most comfortable place in the neighborhood would be the deep end of the public swimming-bath, when the idea came.

I began to draw. So intent was I on my work that I left my lunch untouched, only stopping work when the clock of St. Jude's struck four.

The final result, for a hurried sketch, was, I felt sure, the best thing I had done.

It showed a criminal in the dock immediately after the judge had pronounced sentence. The man was fat—enormously fat. The flesh hung in rolls about his chin; it creased his huge, stumpy neck. He was clean-shaven (perhaps I should say a few days before he must have been clean shaven) and almost bald. He stood in the dock, his short, clumsy fingers clasping the rail, looking straight in front of him. The feeling that his expression conveyed was not so much one of horror as of utter, absolute collapse.

There seemed nothing in the man strong enough to sustain that mountain of flesh.

I rolled up the sketch, and without quite knowing why, placed it in my pocket. Then with the rare sense of happiness which the knowledge of a good thing well done gives, I left the house.

I believe that I set out with the idea of calling upon Trenton, for I remember walking along Lytton Street and turning to the right along Gilchrist Road at the bottom of the hill where the men were at work on the new tram lines.

From there onwards I have only the vaguest recollection of where I went. The one thing of which I was fully conscious was the awful heat, that came up from the dusty asphalt pavement as an almost palpable[1] wave. I longed for the thunder promised by the great banks of copper-coloured cloud that hung low over the western sky.

I must have walked five or six miles, when a small boy roused me from my reverie by asking the time.

It was twenty minutes to seven.

When he left me I began to take stock of my bearings. I found myself standing before a gate that led into a yard bordered by a strip of thirsty earth, where there were flowers, purple stock and scarlet geranium. Above the entrance was a board with the inscription:

CHS. ATKINSON. MONUMENTAL MASON.[2]
WORKER IN ENGLISH AND ITALIAN MARBLES.

---

1. **palpable** [pal′ pə bəl]: can be touched or felt.
2. **Monumental Mason** [mon′ yə men′ tl   mā′ sn]: person who makes stone monuments or tombstones.

From the yard itself came a cheery whistle, the noise of hammer blows, and the cold sound of steel meeting stone.

A sudden impulse made me enter.

A man was sitting with his back toward me, busy at work on a slab of curiously veined marble. He turned round as he heard my steps and stopped short.

It was the man I had been drawing, whose portrait lay in my pocket.

He sat there, huge and elephantine, the sweat pouring from his scalp, which he wiped with a red silk handkerchief. But though the face was the same, the expression was absolutely different.

He greeted me smiling, as if we were old friends, and shook my hand.

I apologized for my intrusion.

'Everything is hot and glary outside,' I said. 'This seems an oasis in the wilderness.'

'I don't know about the oasis,' he replied, 'but it certainly is hot, as hot as hell. Take a seat, sir!'

He pointed to the end of the gravestone on which he was at work, and I sat down.

'That's a beautiful piece of stone you've got hold of,' I said.

He shook his head. 'In a way it is,' he answered; 'the surface here is as fine as anything you could wish, but there's a big flaw at the back, though I don't expect you'd ever notice it. I could never make really a good job of a bit of marble like that. It would be all right in the summer like this; it wouldn't mind the blasted heat. But wait till the winter comes. There's nothing quite like frost to find out the weak points in stone.'

'Then what's it for?' I asked.

The man burst out laughing.

'You'd hardly believe me if I was to tell you it's for an exhibition, but it's the truth. Artists have exhibitions, so do grocers and butchers; we have them too. All the latest little things in headstones, you know.'

He went on to talk of marbles, which sort best withstood wind and rain, and which were easiest to work; then of his garden and a new sort of carnation he had bought. At the end of every other minute he would drop his tools, wipe his shining head, and curse the heat.

I said little, for I felt uneasy. There was something unnatural, uncanny, in meeting this man.

I tried at first to persuade myself that I had seen him before, that his face, unknown to me, had found a place in some out-of-the-way corner of my memory, but I knew that I was practicing little more than a plausible[3] piece of self-deception.

Mr. Atkinson finished his work, spat on the ground, and got up with a sigh of relief.

3. **plausible** [plô′ zə bəl]: believable.

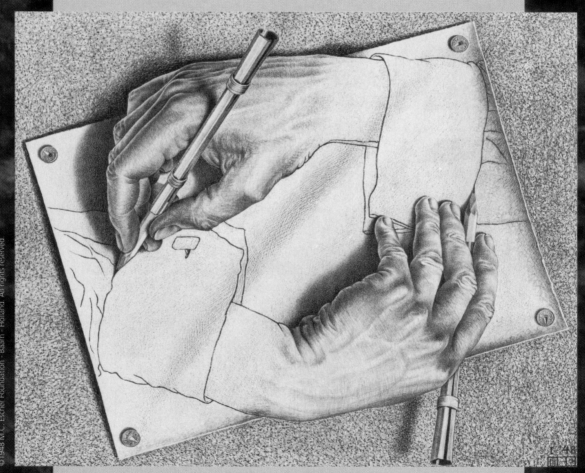

Drawing Hands M.C. Escher, 1948, lithograph, 11 1/8" x 13 1/8"

'There! What do you think of that?' he said, with an air of evident pride.

The inscription which I read for the first time was this:

SACRED TO THE MEMORY
OF
JAMES CLARENCE WITHENCROFT.
BORN JAN. 18TH, 1860.
HE PASSED AWAY VERY SUDDENLY
ON AUGUST 20TH, 190—
'In the midst of life we are in death'

For some time I sat in silence. Then a cold shudder ran down my spine. I asked him where he had seen the name.

'Oh, I didn't see it anywhere,' replied Mr. Atkinson. 'I wanted some name, and I put down the first that came into my head. Why do you want to know?'

'It's a strange coincidence, but it happens to be mine.'

He gave a long, low whistle.

'And the dates?'

'I can only answer for one of them, and that's correct.'

'It's a rum go!' he said.

But he knew less than I did. I told him of my morning's work. I took the sketch from my pocket and showed it to him. As he looked, the expression of his face altered until it became more and more like that of the man I had drawn.

'And it was only the day before yesterday,' he said, 'that I told Maria there were no such things as ghosts!'

Neither of us had seen a ghost, but I knew what he meant.

'You probably heard my name,' I said.

'And you must have seen me somewhere and have forgotten it! Were you at Clacton-on-Sea last July?'

I had never been to Clacton in my life. We were silent for some time. We were both looking at the same thing, the two dates on the gravestone, and one was right.

'Come inside and have some supper,' said Mr. Atkinson.

His wife is a cheerful little woman, with the flaky red cheeks of the country-bred. Her husband introduced me as a friend of his who was an artist. The result was unfortunate, for after the sardines and watercress had been removed, she brought out a Doré Bible, and I had to sit and express my admiration for nearly half an hour.

I went outside, and found Atkinson sitting on the gravestone smoking.

We resumed the conversation at the point we had left off.

'You must excuse my asking,' I said, 'but do you know of anything you've done for which you could be put on trial?'

He shook his head.

'I'm not a bankrupt, the business is prosperous enough. Three years ago I gave turkeys to some of the guardians at Christmas, but that's all I can think of. And they were small ones, too,' he added as an afterthought.

He got up, fetched a can from the porch, and began to water the flowers. 'Twice a day regular in the hot weather,' he said, 'and then the heat sometimes gets the better of the delicate ones. And ferns, good Lord! They could never stand it. Where do you live?'

I told him my address. It would take an hour's quick walk to get back home.

'It's like this,' he said. 'We'll look at the matter straight. If you go back home to-night, you take your chance of accidents. A cart may run over you, and there's always banana skins and orange peel, to say nothing of falling ladders.'

He spoke of the improbable with an intense seriousness that would have been laughable six hours before. But I did not laugh.

'The best thing we can do,' he continued, 'is for you to stay here till twelve o'clock. We'll go upstairs and smoke; it may be cooler inside.'

To my surprise I agreed.

We were sitting now in a long, low room beneath the eaves. Atkinson has sent his wife to bed. He himself is busy sharpening some tools at a little oilstone, smoking one of my cigars the while.

The air seems charged with thunder. I am writing this at a shaky table before the open window. The leg is cracked, and Atkinson, who seems a handy man with his tools, is going to mend it as soon as he has finished putting an edge on his chisel.

It is after eleven now. I shall be gone in less than an hour.

But the heat is stifling.

It is enough to send a man mad.

WILLIAM FRYER HARVEY

William Fryer Harvey [1885-1937] was born in Yorkshire, England. His family belonged to the Religious Society of Friends and sent him to Quaker schools. Harvey went on to Oxford University and then studied medicine. During World War I, he served in the Royal Navy as a surgeon-lieutenant and received a medal "for gallantry in saving life at sea."

Harvey was known to his friends as a kind, gentle man. It was a mystery to them how such a person could excel in writing hair-raising ghost stories and tales of horror—but so he did. Harvey's books include *Midnight House*, *Moods and Tenses*, and *The Beast with Five Fingers*, which was made into a movie during the 1940s.

I Used to Live Here Once

Jean Rhys

She was standing by the river looking at the stepping stones and remembering each one. There was the round unsteady stone, the pointed one, the flat one in the middle—the safe stone where you could stand and look round. The next

Real Ripe Mango Alison Chapman-Andrews, 1982, acrylic, 34" x 34", Art Collection Foundation, Barbados

wasn't so safe for when the river was full the water flowed over it and even when it showed dry it was slippery. But after that it was easy and soon she was standing on the other side.

The road was much wider than it used to be but the work had been done carelessly. The felled trees had not been cleared away and the bushes looked trampled. Yet it was the same road and she walked along feeling extraordinarily happy.

It was a fine day, a blue day. The only thing was that the sky had a glassy look that she didn't remember. That was the only word she could think of. Glassy. She turned the corner, saw that what had been the old *pavé*[1] had been taken up, and there too the road was much wider, but it had the same unfinished look.

She came to the worn stone steps that led up to the house and her heart began to beat. The screw pine was gone, so was the mock summer house called the *ajoupa*,[2] but the clove tree was still there and at the top of the steps the rough lawn stretched away, just as she remembered it. She stopped and looked towards the house that had been added

1. *pavé* [pä vā′]: pavement.
2. *ajoupa* [ä zhü′ pä]

Detail from ***Real Ripe Mango***
Alison Chapman-Andrews

to and painted white. It was strange to see a car standing in front of it.

There were two children under the big mango tree, a boy and a little girl, and she waved to them and called 'Hello' but they didn't answer her or turn their heads. Very fair children, as Europeans born in the West Indies[3] so often are: as if the white blood is asserting it-self against all odds.

The grass was yellow in the hot sunlight as she walked towards them. When she was quite close she called again shyly: 'Hello.' Then, 'I used to live here once,' she said.

Still they didn't answer. When she said for the third time 'Hello' she was quite near them. Her arms went out instinctively with the longing to touch them.

It was the boy who turned. His grey eyes looked straight into hers. His expression didn't change. He said: 'Hasn't it gone cold all of a sudden. D'you notice? Let's go in.' 'Yes let's,' said the girl.

Her arms fell to her sides as she watched them running across the grass to the house. That was the first time she knew.

3. **West Indies:** long chain of islands between Florida and South America, including Greater Antilles, Lesser Antilles, and the Bahamas.

JEAN RHYS

Jean Rhys [1890-1979] was born in Dominica, West Indies. Rhys had a lonely childhood, for her older siblings were away at school and she had few friends. She felt "alone except for books" and voices in her head that "wanted to be written down." She wrote them down.

At sixteen, Rhys was sent to live with an aunt in England. Used to the West Indies, she felt like an outsider. Wanting to be an actress but lacking money for drama school, she joined the chorus of a musical comedy team that toured England during World War I. Later, living in Paris, Rhys began to write. Her first book of stories was published in 1927. Much of her writing—including "I Used to Live Here Once"—was based on her West Indies childhood.

Those Three Wishes

Judith Gorog

No one ever said that Melinda Alice was nice. That wasn't the word used. No, she was clever, even witty. She was called—never to her face, however—Melinda Malice. Melinda Alice was clever and cruel. Her mother, when she thought about it at all, hoped Melinda would grow out of it. To her father, Melinda's very good grades mattered.

It was Melinda Alice, back in the eighth grade, who had labeled the shy, myopic[1] new girl "Contamination" and was the first to pretend that anything or anyone touched by the new girl had to be cleaned, inoculated,[2] or avoided. High school had merely given Melinda Alice greater scope for her talents.

The surprising thing about Melinda Alice was her power; no one trusted her, but no one avoided her either. She was always included, always in the middle. If you had seen her, pretty and witty, in the center of a group of students walking past your house, you'd have thought, "There goes a natural leader."

Melinda Alice had left for school early. She wanted to study alone in a quiet spot she had because there was going to be a big math test, and Melinda Alice was not prepared. That A mattered; so

1. **myopic** [mī op′ ik]: near-sighted.
2. **inoculated** [in ok′ yə lāt əd]: injected with a material made of germs in order to prevent disease.

Melinda Alice walked to school alone, planning her studies. She didn't usually notice nature much, so she nearly stepped on a beautiful snail that was making its way across the sidewalk.

"Ugh. Yucky thing," thought Melinda Alice, then stopped. Not wanting to step on the snail accidentally was one thing, but now she lifted her shoe to crush it.

"Please don't," said the snail.

"Why not?" retorted Melinda Alice.

"I'll give you three wishes," replied the snail evenly.

"Agreed," said Melinda Alice. "My first wish is that my next," she paused a split second, "my next thousand wishes come true." She smiled triumphantly and opened her bag to take out a small notebook and pencil to keep track.

Melinda Alice was sure she heard the snail say, "What a clever girl," as it made it to the safety of an ivy bed beside the sidewalk.

During the rest of the walk to school, Melinda was occupied with wonderful ideas. She would have beautiful clothes. "Wish number two, that I will always be perfectly dressed," and she was just that. True, her new outfit was not a lot different from the one she had worn leaving the house, but that only meant Melinda Alice liked her own taste.

After thinking awhile, she wrote, "Wish number three. I wish for pierced ears and small gold earrings." Her father had not allowed Melinda to have pierced ears, but now she had them anyway. She felt her new earrings and shook her beautiful hair in delight. "I can have anything: stereo, tapes, TV videodisc, moped, car, anything! All my life!" She hugged her books to herself in delight.

By the time she reached school, Melinda was almost an altruist;[3] she could wish for peace. Then she wondered, "Is the snail that powerful?" She felt her ears, looked at her perfect blouse, skirt, jacket, shoes. "I could make ugly people beautiful, cure cripples . . ." She

3. **altruist** [al′ trü ist]: a person who helps others without expecting anything in return.

stopped. The wave of altruism had washed past. "I could pay people back who deserve it!" Melinda Alice looked at the school, at all the kids. She had an enormous sense of power. "They all have to do what *I* want now." She walked down the crowded halls to her locker. Melinda Alice could be sweet; she could be witty. She could—The bell rang for homeroom. Melinda Alice stashed her books, slammed the locker shut, and just made it to her seat.

"Hey, Melinda Alice," whispered Fred. "You know that big math test next period?"

"Oh, no," grimaced Melinda Alice. Her thoughts raced; "That damned snail made me late, and I forgot to study."

"I'll blow it," she groaned aloud. "I wish I were dead."

JUDITH GOROG

Judith Gorog was born in Madison, Wisconsin, in 1938. Gorog attended college in California but later went east to live in Princeton, New Jersey. Gorog's imagination has traveled too.

One of Gorog's books retells the story of Sheherazade, the Mideastern storyteller. Gorog had read the tale long ago. She told it as she remembered it to her students and then reread the original. "I was surprised to notice how greatly I had changed the story…" she said. From that realization came her own version, *Winning Sheherazade*.

"Those Three Wishes" is from Gorog's book, *A Taste for Quiet and Other Disquieting Tales*. For more disquieting tales, try another of her books: *Three Dreams and a Nightmare*.

The Hitch-Hiker

Lucille Fletcher

Characters

RONALD ADAMS

MRS. ADAMS

THE HITCH-HIKER

FILLING STATION MAN

ROAD STAND PROPRIETOR

PROPRIETOR'S WIFE

GIRL HITCH-HIKER

LOCAL GALLUP OPERATOR

LONG DISTANCE OPERATOR

NEW YORK OPERATOR

ALBUQUERQUE OPERATOR

MRS. WHITNEY

(Music: *Opening chords, dark and ominous. A piano may be used, or a brief passage from some orchestral record. The selection will depend on the Director's individual taste, but its major effect should consist of a strong, terrifying opening, followed by a kind of monotonous[1] eeriness. The eerie part of the music continues throughout following speech, but faded down so that the words are audible.[2]*)

[Scene: *As curtains part, we see a stage set up for a radio broadcast. Central microphone, at which Ronald Adams is standing. A semicircle of chairs, rear, on which entire cast is seated. Sound-effects and music grouped wherever their level will complement and bolster the voice, but not overbalance it. Relative sound-levels are vitally important in this production, and should be carefully studied for maximum effectiveness.*]

RONALD ADAMS: I am in a trailer camp on Route Sixty-six just west of Gallup, New Mexico. If I tell it, perhaps it will help me. It will keep me from going mad. But I must tell this quickly. I am not mad now. I feel perfectly well, except that I am running a slight temperature. My name is Ronald Adams. I am thirty-six years of age, unmarried, tall, dark, with a black mustache. I drive a Buick, license number YO-6091. I was born in Brooklyn.[3] All this I know. I know that I am at this moment perfectly sane. That it is not me who has gone mad—but something else—something utterly beyond my control. But I must speak quickly. At any moment the link may break. This may be the last thing I ever tell on earth . . . the last night I ever see the stars . . . (*Pause. Music fades out.*) [Scene: *Mrs. Adams rises from chair, rear, and comes forward to microphone.*] Six days ago I left Brooklyn, to drive to California.

MRS. ADAMS: Good-bye, son. Good luck to you, my boy.

ADAMS: Good-bye, Mother. Here—give me a kiss, and then I'll go.

MRS. ADAMS: I'll come out with you to the car.

ADAMS: No. It's raining. Stay here at the door. Hey—what's this? Tears? I thought you promised me you wouldn't cry.

---

1. **monotonous** [mə not′ n əs]: not changing tone or pitch.
2. **audible** [ô′ də bəl]: loud enough to be heard.
3. **Brooklyn** [brük′ lən]: section of New York City on Long Island.

MRS. ADAMS: I know, dear. I'm sorry. But I—do hate to see you go.

ADAMS: I'll be back. I'll only be on the Coast three months.

MRS. ADAMS: Oh—it isn't that. It's just—the trip. Ronald—I wish you weren't driving.

ADAMS: Oh, Mother. There you go again. People do it every day.

MRS. ADAMS: I know. But you'll be careful, won't you? Promise me you'll be extra careful. Don't fall asleep—or drive fast—or pick up any strangers on the road.

ADAMS: Gosh—no. You'd think I was still seventeen to hear you talk.

MRS. ADAMS: And wire me as soon as you get to Hollywood, won't you, son?

ADAMS: Of course I will. Now, don't you worry. There isn't anything going to happen. It's just eight days of perfectly simple driving on smooth civilized roads. (Manual Sound: *Slam of car door.* Sound Recording: *Car starts. Sound of car motor running.*) With a motel or a hamburger stand every ten miles. . . . (*He chuckles slightly.*) (Sound Recording: *Automobile in motion full.*) (*Calling.*) G'bye, Mom—

[*Scene: Mrs. Adams leaves microphone, returning to row of chairs at rear stage.*] (*Sound recording of automobile continues behind following.*) I was in excellent spirits. The drive ahead of me, even the loneliness, seemed like a lark. But I reckoned—without—him. (Music: *Dark opening chords, followed by theme of eerie quality. Continue faded down as before, mingling with sound of car motor running.*) Crossing Brooklyn Bridge that morning in the rain, I saw a man leaning against the cables. He seemed to be waiting for a lift. There were spots of fresh rain on his shoulders. He was carrying a cheap overnight bag in one hand. He was thin, nondescript, with a cap pulled down over his eyes. . . . (*Music fades out. Sound of auto continues.*) I would have forgotten him completely, except that just an hour later, while crossing the Pulaski Skyway over the Jersey flats, I saw him again. At least he looked like the same person. He was standing now, with one thumb pointing west. I couldn't figure out how he'd got there, but I thought probably one of those fast trucks had picked him up, beaten me to the Skyway, and let him off. I didn't stop for him. Then—late that night—I saw him again. (Music: *Dark ominous chords, followed by eerie theme. Continue through following speech.*) It was on the Pennsylvania Turnpike between Harrisburg and Pittsburgh. I was just slowing down for one of the tunnels, when I saw him—standing under an arc light by the side of the road. I could see him quite distinctly. The bag, the cap, even the spots of fresh rain spattered over his shoulders. (*Music stops.*) He hailed me this time.

HITCH-HIKER (*off-stage, through megaphone, hollowly*): Hallooo. . . . (*Slightly closer.*) Hall . . . llooo. . . . (Sound Recording: *Automobile running faster.*)

ADAMS: I stepped on the gas like a shot. That's lonely country through the Alleghenies,[4] and I had no intention of stopping. Besides, the coincidence, or whatever it was, gave me the willies. (Sound Recording: *Automobile out.*) I stopped at the next gas station. (Manual Sound: *Nervous honking of horn.*) [Scene: *The filling station man leaves chair and advances to microphone.*]

FILLING STATION MAN: Yes, sir.

ADAMS: Fill her up.

FILLING STATION MAN: Certainly, sir. Check your oil, sir?

ADAMS: No, thanks. (Manual Sound: *Clank of hose. Sound of insertion into gas tank. Tinkle of bell at regular intervals as though from filling station pump. This continues behind following conversation.*)

FILLING STATION MAN: Nice night, isn't it?

ADAMS: Yes. It hasn't been raining here recently, has it?

FILLING STATION MAN: Not a drop of rain all week.

ADAMS: H'm. I suppose that hasn't done your business any harm?

FILLING STATION MAN: Oh—people drive through here all kinds of weather. Mostly business, you know. There aren't many pleasure cars on the Turnpike this season of the year.

ADAMS: I suppose not. (*Casually.*) What about hitch-hikers?

FILLING STATION MAN: Hitch-hikers—here? (Manual Sound:

4. **Alleghenies** [al′ ə gā′ nēz]: Allegheny Mountains, range of the Appalachian Mountains in Pennsylvania, Maryland, Virginia, and West Virginia.

Tinkling bell stops. Sound of hose being detached.)

ADAMS: What's the matter? Don't you ever see any?

FILLING STATION MAN: Not much. If we did, it'd be a sight for sore eyes. *(Manual sound stops.)*

ADAMS: Why?

FILLING STATION MAN: A guy'd be a fool who started out to hitch rides on this road. Look at it.

ADAMS: Then you've never seen anybody?

FILLING STATION MAN: Nope. Mebbe they get the lift before the Turnpike starts—I mean—you know—just before the tollhouse—but then it'd be a mighty long ride. Most cars wouldn't want to pick up a guy for that long a ride. This is pretty lonesome country here—mountains and woods. . . . You ain't seen anybody like that, have you?

ADAMS: No. *(Quickly.)* Oh, no, not at all. It was—just a technical question.

FILLING STATION MAN: I see. Well— that'll be just five dollars—with the tax. . . . *[Scene: Filling Station Man steps back from microphone,*

and returns to seat at rear of stage, as:] (Sound recording fades in automobile starting, motor hum. Continue through following:)

ADAMS: The thing gradually passed from my mind, as sheer coincidence. I had a good night's sleep in Pittsburgh. I didn't think about the man all next day—until just outside of Zanesville, Ohio, I saw him again. *(Music: Dark chords, followed by eeriness. Continue through following: Sound recording of auto motor fade down behind music and words, but continue quietly.)* It was a bright sunshiny afternoon. The peaceful Ohio fields, brown with the autumn stubble, lay dreaming in the golden light. I was driving slowly, drinking it in, when the road suddenly ended in a detour. In front of the barrier—he was standing. *(Sound Recording: Motor hum fades out. Music continues.)* Let me explain about his appearance before I go on. I repeat. There was nothing sinister about him. He was as drab as a mud fence. Nor was his attitude menacing. He merely stood there, waiting, almost drooping a little, the cheap overnight bag in his hand. He looked as though he had been waiting there for hours. Then he looked up— (*Music stops.*) He hailed me. He started to walk forward. . . .

HITCH-HIKER (*off-stage, through megaphone, hollowly*): Hallooo. . . . Hallo . . . ooo. . . . (*Manual Sound: Starter button. Sound of gears jamming. Through megaphone off-stage, closer.*) Hall-ooo. . . . (*Manual sound continues. Clash of gears. Dead starter.*)

ADAMS (*panicky*): No—not just now. Sorry. . . .

HITCH-HIKER (*through megaphone off-stage*): Going to Cal-i-fornia . . . a. . .?

ADAMS (*panicky*): No. Not today. The other way. Going to New York. Sorry. . . . (*Sound Recording: Automobile starts noisily. Wildly.*) Sorry . . . ! (*Sound Recording: Automobile hum continuing through following:*) After I got the car back onto the road again, I felt like a fool. Yet the thought of picking him up, of having him sit beside me was somehow unbearable. Yet at the same time, I felt more than ever, unspeakably alone. . . . (*Music: Just the eerie section fades in above sound of*

automobile hum. *It continues through following:*) Hour after hour went by. The fields, the towns, ticked off one by one. The light changed. I knew now that I was going to see him again. And though I dreaded the sight, I caught myself searching the side of the road, waiting for him to appear. . . . (*Music and sound recording out. Manual Recording: Horn honk two or three times. Pause. Nervous honk again.*) [*Scene: Roadside Stand Proprietor,[5] elderly rural[6] type, comes forward to microphone.*] (*Manual Sound Two: Creak of squeaky door.*)

PROPRIETOR (*querulous,[7] mountain voice*): Yep? What is it? What do you want?

ADAMS (*breathless*): You sell sandwiches and pop here, don't you?

PROPRIETOR (*cranky*): Yep. We do. In the daytime. But we're closed up now for the night.

ADAMS: I know. But—I was wondering if you could possibly let me have a cup of coffee—black coffee.

PROPRIETOR: Not at this time of

---

5. **proprietor** [prə pri′ ə tər]: owner.
6. **rural** [rur′ əl]: in or of the country.
7. **querulous** [kwer′ ə ləs]: complaining.

night, mister. My wife's the cook, and she's in bed. Mebbe further down the road, at the Honeysuckle Rest. (Manual Sound: *Creak of door closing.*)

ADAMS: No—no—don't shut the door. Listen—just a minute ago, there was a man standing here—right beside this stand—a suspicious-looking man. . . . [Scene: *Proprietor's Wife stands up, calling from chair at rear of stage, not moving forward.*]

PROPRIETOR'S WIFE (*a quavery, whiny voice*): Hen-ry? Who is it, Hen-ry?

PROPRIETOR: It's nobuddy, Mother. Just a feller thinks he wants a cup of coffee. Go back into bed. [Scene: *Wife stands beside chair, listening, then slowly begins creeping forward.*]

ADAMS: I don't mean to disturb you. But you see, I was driving along—when I just happened to look—and there he was. . . .

PROPRIETOR: What was he doing?

ADAMS: Nothing. He ran off—when I stopped the car.

PROPRIETOR: Then what of it? That's nothing to wake a man in the middle of his sleep about. . . .

WIFE: Mebbe he's been drinkin', Henry. . . . (*Calling.*)

PROPRIETOR (*sternly*): Young man. I've got a good mind to turn you over to the sheriff—

ADAMS: But—I—

PROPRIETOR: You've been taking a nip, that's what you've been doing. And you haven't got anything better to do than to wake decent folk out of their hard-earned sleep. Get going. Go on.

WIFE (*calling*): Jes' shet the door on him, Henry—

ADAMS: But he looked as though he were going to rob you.

HENRY: I ain't got nothin' in this stand to lose. (Manual Sound: *Door creaking closed.*) Now—on your way before I call out Sheriff Oakes. (*Door slams shut. Bolted.*) [Scene: *Proprietor and his wife return to their seats at rear of stage.*] (Sound Recording: *Auto starting.*)

ADAMS: I got into the car again, and drove on slowly. I was beginning to hate the car. If I could have found a place to stop . . . to rest a little. But I was in the Ozark Mountains[8] of Missouri now.

8. **Ozark Mountains** [ō′ zärk]: low mountain range in southern Missouri, northern Arkansas, and eastern Oklahoma.

The few resort places there were closed. Only an occasional log cabin, seemingly deserted, broke the monotony of the wild wooded landscape. I *had* seen him at that roadside stand. I knew I would see him again—perhaps at the next turn of the road. I knew that when I saw him next—I would run him down. (Music: *Dark chords, followed by eerie melody.*) But I did not see him again until late next afternoon. *(Music continues eerily.* Manual Sound: *The tinkling of signal bell at railroad crossroads. Continue through following:)* I had stopped the car at a sleepy little junction just across the border into Oklahoma . . . to let a train pass by—when he appeared across the tracks, leaning against a telephone pole. . . . *(Music and manual sound continuing. Very tense.)* It was a perfectly airless, dry day. The red clay of Oklahoma was baking under the southwestern sun. Yet there were spots of fresh rain on his shoulders. . . . *(Music stops.)* I couldn't stand that. Without thinking, blindly, I started the car across the tracks. (Sound Recording: *Distant, very faint cry of train whistle approaching. Manual sound of bell continuing.*) He didn't even look up at me. He was staring at the ground. I stepped on the gas hard, veering the wheel sharply toward him. (Sound Recording: *Train whistle closer. Chugging of wheel fading in.*) I could hear the train in the distance now. But I didn't care. (*Manual Sound One continues signal bell.* Manual Sound Two: Jamming of gears. Clash of metal.) Then—something went wrong with the car. (Manual Sound Two: *Gears jamming. Starter button dead.* Sound Recording: *Train chugging up, louder.*) The train was coming closer. I could hear the cry of its whistle. (Sound Recording: *Train chugging. Cry of whistle closer. All this should be a cacophony[9] of sound blended together, almost overriding Adams' voice, which tries to rise above it, almost hysterical with panic.)* Still he stood there. And now—I knew that he was beckoning—beckoning me to my death. . . . (Sound Recording: *Full train chugging topped by wild cry of train whistle overpowering all other sound, full, then dying away slowly to silence. Music fades in with the eerie part of*

---

9. *cacophony* [kə kof′ ə nē]: harsh clashing sound.

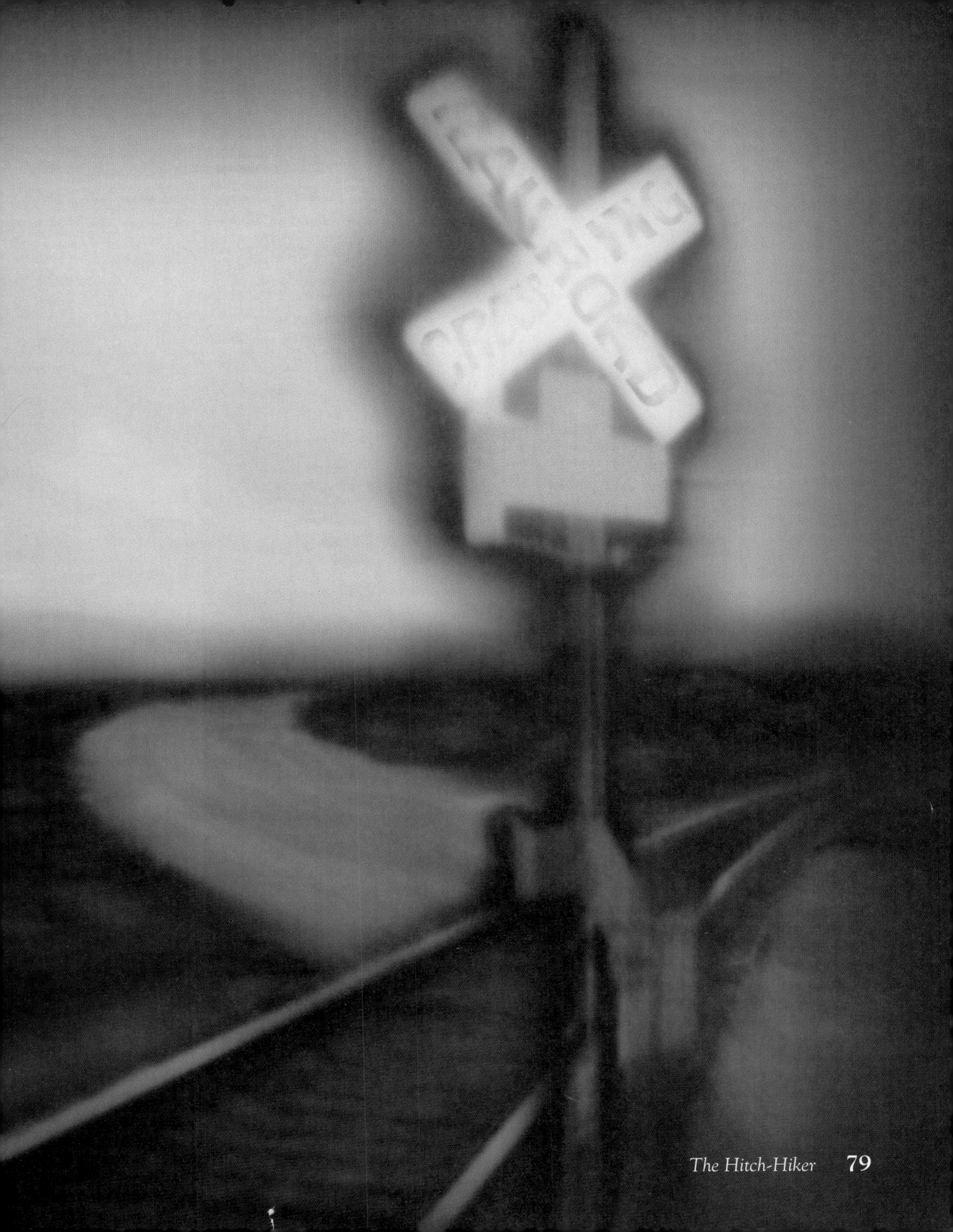

the theme. *We hear this a second or two, then Adams says breathlessly, quietly:)* Well—I frustrated him that time. The starter worked at last. I managed to back up. But when the train passed, he was gone. I was all alone, in the hot dry afternoon. *(Music continuing. Sound Recording: Fade in auto hum.)* After that, I knew I had to do something. I didn't know who this man was, or what he wanted of me. I only knew that from now on, I must not let myself be alone on the road for one moment. *(Music and sound recording of auto out.)* [Scene: *Girl Hitch-Hiker comes forward to microphone.*] (Manual Recording: *Honk of horn.*) Hello, there. Like a ride?

GIRL: What do you think? How far you going?

ADAMS: Where do you want to go?

GIRL: Amarillo, Texas. (Manual Sound: *Car door opening.*)

ADAMS: I'll drive you there.

GIRL: Gee! (Manual Sound: *Car door slams. Sound Recording: Auto starting up, hum. It continues through following.*) Mind if I take off my shoes? My dogs are killing me.

ADAMS: Go right ahead.

GIRL: Gee, what a break this is. A swell car, a decent guy, and driving all the way to Amarillo. All I been getting so far is trucks.

ADAMS: Hitch-hike much?

GIRL: Sure. Only it's tough sometimes, in these great open spaces, to get the breaks.

ADAMS: I should think it would be. Though I'll bet if you get a good pick-up in a fast car, you can get to places faster than, say, another person in another car.

GIRL: I don't get you?

ADAMS: Well, take me, for instance. Suppose I'm driving across the country, say, at a nice steady clip of about fifty miles an hour. Couldn't a girl like you, just standing beside the road, waiting for lifts, beat me to town after town—provided she got picked up every time in a car doing from sixty-five to seventy miles an hour?

GIRL: I dunno. What difference does it make?

ADAMS: Oh—no difference. It's just a—crazy idea I had sitting here in the car.

GIRL (*laughing*): Imagine spending your time in a swell car, and thinking of things like that.

ADAMS: What would you do instead?

GIRL (*admiringly*): What would I do? If I was a good-looking fellow like yourself? Why—I'd just *enjoy* myself—every minute of the time. I'd sit back and relax, and if I saw a good-looking girl along the side of the road . . . (*Sharply.*) Hey—look out! (Sound Recording: *Auto hum continuing.*)

ADAMS (*breathlessly*): Did you see him, too?

GIRL: See who?

ADAMS: That man. Standing beside the barbed-wire fence.

GIRL: I didn't see—nobody. There wasn't nothing but a bunch of steer—and the wire fence. What did you think you was doing? Trying to run into the barbed-wire fence? (Sound Recording: *Auto motor continuing.*)

ADAMS: There was a man there, I tell you . . . a thin gray man, with an overnight bag in his hand. And I was trying to run him down.

GIRL: Run him down? You mean—kill him?

ADAMS: But—(*desperately*) you say you didn't see him back there? You're sure?

GIRL (*queerly*): I didn't see a soul. As as far as I'm concerned, mister . . .

ADAMS: Watch for him the next time then. Keep watching. Keep your eyes peeled on the road. He'll turn up again—maybe any minute now. (*Excitedly.*) There! Look there. . . . (Manual Recording: *Car skidding. Screech. A crash of metal as of car going into barbed-wire fence. Girl screams.* Manual Recording: *A bump.* Manual Recording Two: *Sound of door handle of car turning.*)

GIRL: How does this door work? I—I'm gettin' out of here.

ADAMS: Did you see him that time?

GIRL (*sharply, choked*): No. I didn't see him that time. And personally, mister, I don't expect never to see him. All I want to do is go on living—and I don't see how I will very long, driving with you.

ADAMS: I'm sorry. I—I don't know what came over me. (*Frightened.*) Please . . . don't go. . . .

GIRL: So if you'll excuse me, mister.

ADAMS: You can't go. Listen, how would you like to go to

California? I'll drive you to California.

GIRL: Seeing pink elephants all the way? No, thanks. (Manual Sound: *Door handle turning.*)

ADAMS: Listen. Please. For just one moment——

GIRL: You know what I think you need, big boy? Not a girl friend. Just a dose of good sleep. There. I got it now. . . . (Manual Sound: *Door opens. Slams. Metallic.*)

ADAMS: No. You can't go.

GIRL (*wildly*): Leave your hands offa me, do you hear? Leave your— (Manual Sound: *Sharp slap.* Second Manual Sound: *Footsteps over gravel, running. They die away. A pause.*)

ADAMS: She ran from me, as though I were a monster. A few minutes later, I saw a passing truck pick her up. I knew then that I was utterly alone. (Manual Sound: *Imitation of low mooing of steer, or sound recording of same.*) I was in the heart of the great Texas prairies. There wasn't a car on the road after the truck went by. I tried to figure out what to do, how to get hold of myself. If I could find a place to rest. Or even if I could sleep right there in the car for a few hours, along the side of the road. (Music: *The eerie theme stealing in softly.*) I was getting my winter overcoat out of the back seat to use as a blanket, when I saw him coming toward me, emerging from the herd of moving steer. . . . (Sound: *Mooing of steer, low. Out of it emerges voice of:*)

HITCH-HIKER (*hollowly off-stage through megaphone*): Hall . . . ooo. . . . Hall . . . ooo. . . . (Sound Recording: *Auto starting. Auto hum steady up. Music continuing.*)

ADAMS: Perhaps I should have spoken to him then, fought it out then and there. For now he began to be everywhere. Wherever I stopped, even for a moment— for gas, oil, for a can of beer, a cup of coffee, a sandwich—he was there. (*Music continuing. Auto sound continuing. More tense and rapid.*) I saw him standing outside the motel in Amarillo, that night, when I dared to slow down. He was sitting near the drinking fountain in a little camping spot just inside the border of New Mexico. . . . (*Music steady. Rapid, more breathless.*) He was waiting for me outside the Navajo Reservation where I stopped to check my tires. I saw him in Albuquerque, where I bought twenty gallons of gas. I was afraid now, afraid to stop. I began to drive faster and faster. I was in lunar landscape now— the great arid mesa[10] country of New Mexico. I drove through it with the indifference of a fly crawling over the face of the moon. . . . (*Auto hum up. Music more and more eerie. More desperately.*) But now he didn't even wait for me to stop. Unless I drove at eighty-five miles an hour over those endless roads, he waited for me at every other mile. I would see his figure, shadowless, flitting before me, still in its same attitude, over the cold lifeless ground, flitting over dried-up rivers, over broken stones cast up by old glacial upheavals, flitting in the pure and cloudless air. . . . (*Music reaches eerie climax. Stops. Sound recording of auto hum stops. A low voice in the silence.*) I was beside myself when I finally reached Gallup, New Mexico, this morning. There is a trailer camp west of the city . . . cold, almost deserted at this time of year. I went inside and asked if there was a telephone. . . . (Manual Recording: *Sound of footsteps on wood, heavy, echoing.*) I had the feeling that if only I could speak to someone familiar, someone I loved, I could pull myself together. [Scene: *First Operator rises, comes forward to microphone.*] (Manual Sound: *Dime put into phone.*)

OPERATOR: Number, please?

ADAMS: Long distance.

OPERATOR: Thank you. [Scene: *Long Distance Operator comes forward to microphone.*] (Manual Sound: *Return of dime. Buzz.*)

LONG DISTANCE: This is Long Distance.

ADAMS: I'd like to put in a call to my home in Brooklyn, New York. I'm Ronald Adams. The number is Beechwood 2-0828, area code 212.

LONG DISTANCE: Thank you. What is your number? [*A mechanical tone.*]

ADAMS: My number . . . Mesa 6-3121. [Scene: *Third Operator rises from chair, remaining at rear stage.*] (Manual Sound: *A buzz.*)

10. **mesa** [mā′ sə]: a small, high plateau with a flat top and steep sides.

THIRD OPERATOR (*from distance*): Albuquerque.

LONG DISTANCE OPERATOR: New York for Gallup. [Scene: *Fourth Operator rises, stands beside chair at rear stage.*]

FOURTH OPERATOR: New York.

LONG DISTANCE: Gallup, New Mexico, calling Beechwood 2-0828. [Scene: *Fourth Operator steps back a little distance from microphone during following.*]

ADAMS: I had read somewhere that love could banish demons. It was the middle of the morning. I knew Mother would be home. I pictured her tall, white-haired, in her crisp house dress, going about her tasks. It would be enough, I thought, merely to hear the even calmness of her voice.

LONG DISTANCE: Will you please deposit one dollar and seventy cents for the first three minutes. (Sound: *Clunk of money as through telephone.*) Ready with Brooklyn—go ahead, please. [Scene: *Long Distance steps back little farther toward rear, as Mrs. Whitney comes forward.*]

ADAMS: Hello.

MRS. WHITNEY: Mrs. Adams' residence.

ADAMS: Hello. Hello—Mother?

MRS. WHITNEY (*very flat and proper*): This is Mrs. Adams' residence. Who is it you wished to speak to, please?

ADAMS: Why—who's this?

MRS. WHITNEY: This is Mrs. Whitney.

ADAMS: Mrs. Whitney? I don't know any Mrs. Whitney. Is this Beechwood 2-0828?

MRS. WHITNEY: Yes.

ADAMS: Where's my mother? Where's Mrs. Adams?

MRS. WHITNEY: Mrs. Adams is not at home. She is still in the hospital.

ADAMS: The hospital?

MRS. WHITNEY: Yes. Who is this calling, please? Is it a member of the family?

ADAMS: What's she in the hospital for?

MRS. WHITNEY: She's been prostrated for five days. Nervous breakdown. But who is this calling?

ADAMS: Nervous breakdown? But— my mother was never nervous.

MRS. WHITNEY: It's all taken place since the death of her oldest son, Ronald.

ADAMS: Death of her oldest son, Ronald . . . ? Hey—what is this? What number is this?

MRS. WHITNEY: This is Beechwood 2-0828. It's all been very sudden. He was killed just six days ago in an automobile accident on the Brooklyn Bridge. *[Scene: Long Distance Operator comes forward.]*

LONG DISTANCE: Your three minutes are up, sir. *(Pause.)* Your three minutes are up, sir. . . . *[Scene: Long Distance Operator and Mrs. Whitney back away, as Adams stands there.]* Sir—your three minutes are up. . . . *[Scene: Long Distance Operator and Mrs. Whitney sit down.]* Your three minutes are up, sir. . . . *(Softly. A pause.* Music: *Fade in eerie theme softly.)*

ADAMS *(a strange voice):* And so, I am sitting here in this deserted trailer camp in Gallup, New Mexico. I am trying to think. I am trying to get hold of myself. Otherwise I shall go mad. . . . Outside it is night—the vast, soulless night of New Mexico. A million stars are in the sky. Ahead of me stretch a thousand miles of empty mesa, mountains, prairies, desert. Somewhere, among them, he is waiting for me. . . . *[Scene: He turns slowly from microphone, looking off-stage, in direction of Hitch-Hiker's voice.]* Somewhere I shall know who he is—and who . . . I am. . . . *(Music continues to an eerie climax.)* *[Scene: Adams walks slowly away from microphone, and off-stage, as CURTAIN FALLS.]*

LUCILLE FLETCHER

Lucille Fletcher was born in 1912 in Brooklyn, New York. She graduated from Vassar College.

Fletcher is best known for her radio and television plays— especially the famous chiller, *Sorry, Wrong Number*, which has had several lives as a movie, a play, a television drama, and a novel. Fletcher has also written short stories and mysteries.

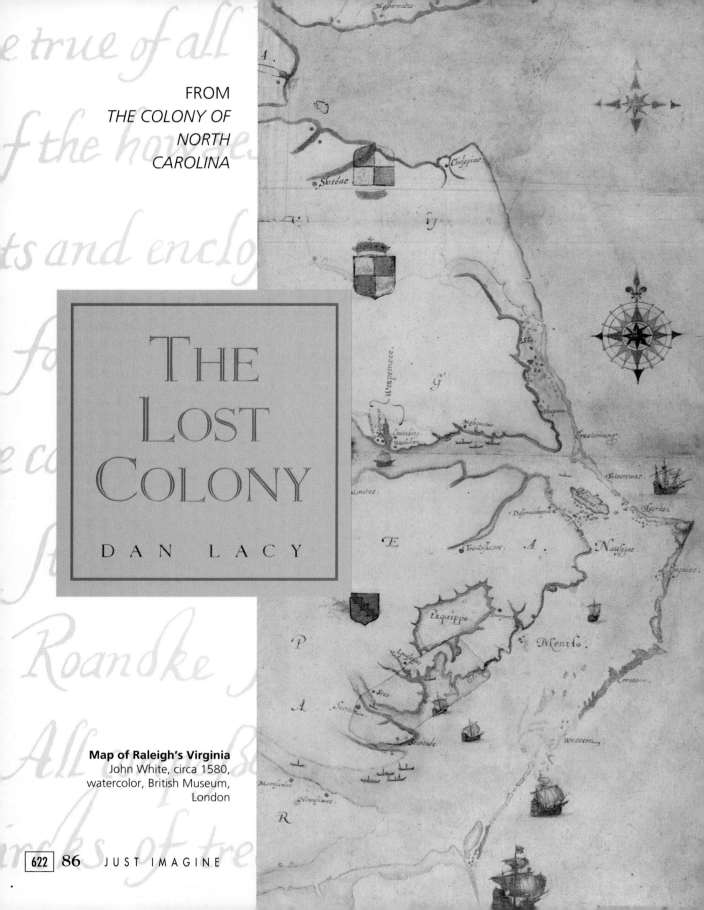

FROM
*THE COLONY OF
NORTH
CAROLINA*

THE
LOST
COLONY

DAN LACY

Map of Raleigh's Virginia
John White, circa 1580,
watercolor, British Museum,
London

Roanoke Island is small, flat, and sandy—about twelve miles long and three miles wide. It lies between Pamlico and Albemarle sounds,[1] hidden from the Atlantic Ocean by a long chain of narrow islands, really little more than sand dunes, known as the Outer Banks of North Carolina. Even today only very small ships can reach the sounds by threading their way through narrow inlets in the Outer Banks, inlets that may change with every storm.

Hundreds of years ago, in the summer of 1587, a small band of men, women, and children landed on Roanoke Island and began to clear the trees and build huts. They had sailed from England in three tiny ships, a journey that had lasted for weeks. They came with food and tools and supplies to build homes and establish a permanent colony in the New World.

Englishmen had been on Roanoke Island before this group. Since Columbus's landing in America nearly a century before, expeditions from Spain had conquered and settled Florida, Mexico, the Pacific coast of South America, and most of the larger islands in the Caribbean.[2] Fortunes were made for Spain from the gold and silver mines in Mexico and Peru. An ocean current called the Gulf Stream flows northward from Florida to North Carolina along the coast of what is now the United States. Every year fleets of large, slow Spanish galleons[3] made their way along the coast, following the Gulf Stream until they could strike out east across the Atlantic, laden with American treasure for the king of Spain.

England was then a relatively poor country, far less wealthy and powerful than Spain. But Englishmen were eager to share in the treasures of the New World. They wanted an English empire in America and they wanted a chance to capture Spanish treasure ships and seize their cargoes of gold and silver.

1. **Pamlico and Albemarle sounds** [pam′ lə kō, al′ bə märl]: narrow, shallow bodies of water on the coast of North Carolina.
2. **Caribbean** [kar′ ə bē′ ən]: sea bordered by Central America, the West Indies, and South America.
3. **galleons** [gal′ ē ənz]: large sailing ships used in the 1400s and 1500s.

Roanoke Island gave them a chance to do both. It could be their first foothold on the new continent. And light, swift English ships could slip out through the inlets and seize unsuspecting Spanish treasure ships, then retreat back through the same inlets where large Spanish ships of war could not follow.

Sir Walter Raleigh, a wealthy knight and favorite of Queen Elizabeth I, was given the right to explore and settle the coast of what is now the southern United States. In 1584 he sent an expedition that picked Roanoke Island as the best place for a first colony. The following year a large group of soldiers was sent to the island to build a fort. They used up all their supplies, and before a relief ship came they abandoned the fort and returned to England on ships commanded by Sir Francis Drake,[4] who by good fortune had stopped at Roanoke Island on his way back from the Caribbean.

When the English settlers landed in 1587 ready to found their colony, they expected to find more than a dozen men who had been left to hold the island over the winter of 1586-87. But all they found was one bare skeleton and the ruins of a destroyed fort. From friendly Indians they learned the story. A band of hostile Indians had attacked the little fort and killed most of the men. The rest had fled in a boat and had never been seen again.

In spite of this warning of the dangers around them, the colonists set out to make their new homes. The fort was restored. Dirt-floored huts were built to provide shelter. A palisade[5] of tree trunks sunk deep in the ground was erected as a wall around the little settlement. Fields were cleared to plant crops. The colonists knew, however, that they did not have sufficient supplies to last them until crops could be harvested the following year. They urged John White, governor of the colony, to return to England so that he could persuade Sir Walter Raleigh to send an immediate relief expedition with more supplies.

Before White left at the end of August 1587, two important things happened—the first children of English parents were born in

4. **Sir Francis Drake:** (circa 1540-1596) English navigator of the sixteenth century who was the first English voyager to sail around the world.
5. **palisade** [pal′ ə sād′]: a strong fence of large, wooden stakes set close together to enclose or defend.

America. One of the settlers was Governor White's daughter, Eleanor, who made the journey with her husband, Ananias Dare. She had left England knowing she would bear a child in the New World. On August 18 the baby was born, a little girl who was christened Virginia. And before a week passed a second baby was born in the colony, a boy to Dyonis and Margery Harvey.

White sailed from a happy and hopeful colony. But when he reached England, he found the country full of preparations for war with Spain. It was too dangerous to try the stormy Atlantic in winter, and with the arrival of spring 1588, England's one thought was to defend itself against an enormous Spanish fleet that had been formed for an invasion. Neither ship nor man could be spared for any other purpose. The great battle with the Armada, as the Spanish fleet was called, took place in the summer of 1588. Helped by a violent storm, the smaller English fleet won a complete victory. But Raleigh was left without money or time to organize a relief expedition that year, and in 1589 a relief ship was turned back by storms and a Spanish attack.

Not until 1590 did White have a chance to get back to Roanoke Island. His ship made it through the narrow inlet and anchored in the sound. White and a few sailors launched a small boat and rowed to the site of the colony but it was nighttime, and too dark to go on shore. The men played English tunes on a trumpet and loudly sang English songs, so that the colonists they hoped to find on shore would not think they were attacking Indians or Spaniards and fire at them.

There was no answer, but White felt sure that the colonists were safe, for he thought he saw a fire burning on shore. Next morning he eagerly hurried up the beach, hoping to see his daughter and granddaughter, who would have just turned three.

But when John White reached the palisade around the little village, his heart sank. The gate hung open, and on one of the gateposts were carved the letters C R O. Inside all was abandoned. The huts

stood empty. Pumpkins grew on the dirt floors and vines twined through the windows. The only sound came from deer scampering away from the newcomers. A trench had been opened, in which trunks and boxes had been buried. Books, papers, and pieces of armor, some of them White's own that he had left, were scattered about, mildewed and rusted by the rain. The settlers were gone, leaving nothing of value except the buried chests and a few bars of iron and lead too heavy to carry.

They were gone, but where? On a tree was carved the full word CROATOAN. White had agreed with the colonists when he left three years before that if they moved, they would carve on a tree the name of the place to which they were going. If they were in serious trouble, they were to carve a cross above the name. There was no cross, and White was cheered by this. He knew of a friendly Indian village called Croatan near Cape Hatteras.[6] One of their chiefs, Manteo, had gone back to England with one of the earlier expeditions and had returned with White's colonists. He spoke English and had been very helpful. No doubt the colonists had sought shelter in his village when they ran short of food or were pressed[7] by the hostile Indians of the mainland. White was encouraged by the fact that there was no evidence of fighting on Roanoke Island.

He hoped to leave the next day for Croatan. But a severe storm arose that left the British ships battered and unable to sail to the village. The captain of the little fleet had to put out to sea and was not willing to bring his damaged ships back to the stormy Outer Banks. John White never got back to Roanoke, and no white man ever saw the settlers again. They had become the Lost Colony.

Nobody knows what happened to them. Apparently they stayed at Roanoke Island for a year or two and then left, but not because of

6. **Cape Hatteras** [hat′ ər əs]: a chain of islands off the east coast of North Carolina where there have been many shipwrecks.

7. **pressed:** repeatedly attacked.

Indian Village of Pomeiock John White, 1587, watercolor, British Museum, London

an Indian attack. They probably ran out of food and went to Croatan, as their carving said, hoping to live on fish and oysters and such food as they could get from Manteo's friendly tribe. They may have built a ship or used a small pinnace[8] left with them in an effort to return to England, and may have been lost at sea. Twenty years later the English settled Jamestown in Virginia and sent out explorers to try to learn the fate of the lost colonists. They heard many rumors, but most of them said that Powhatan, the Indian ruler of the whole area, had wiped out the colony because it had become allied with other tribes that warred with Powhatan. Other rumors said that some of the settlers had survived and lived among the Indians, intermarrying with them but still speaking the English language and living in houses built in the English manner. But no such survivors, if there were any, were ever found. Whatever their fate, they live in memory as the first English men and women to cross the ocean intending to make their homes and their children's homes forever in the New World.

8. **pinnace** [pin′ is]: a light boat.

DAN LACY

Dan Lacy was born in 1914 in Newport News, Virginia. As he grew up, Lacy was fascinated by early American history, and especially by the story of the Lost Colony at nearby Roanoke. After college, Lacy began a survey of historical records in Washington, D.C. He went on to work at the U.S. National Archives and the Library of Congress, and later started a new career in publishing.

One of Lacy's best known books is *The Meaning of the American Revolution*, which has been translated into Spanish, Arabic, and Chinese.

The tooth was lying on the sidewalk, camouflaged against the erratic[1] pattern of embedded[2] oyster shells. But Troy had caught its alien shape. Curious, he bent down to pick it up.

It seemed real enough. A big molar[3] with long roots, the enamel clean and white. Gingerly he sniffed at it, expecting a synthetic smell to signal that it was a fake, but braced for the reek of decay. There was no odor at all. He shrugged and put it into his pocket, wondering idly if finding a tooth meant good luck, like finding a penny.

When he got to school, Lida was standing right there on the

---

1. **erratic** [ə rat′ ik]: not steady, irregular.
2. **embedded** [em bed′ əd]: fastened firmly.
3. **molar** [mō′ lər]: back tooth with a broad surface for grinding food.

TEETH

PATRICIA WINDSOR

steps. Troy's heart began its beat-skipping tricks, and as usual he tensed up, torn between fierce hope for a kind word or glance and resignation to the fact she didn't know he was alive.

"Hi, Troy," she said.

He walked right on past, head down as if waiting for a blow; it took that long for her words to sink in. When they did, he twisted around and almost fell.

"Hi . . ." he said uncertainly. "How're you doing, Lida?" It was amazing that he could speak.

"I'm doing just fine," she replied, brown eyes twinkling. "How 'bout you?"

"Fine," he mumbled, and trudged away. She was only playing with him.

At lunchtime in the cafeteria, as he was gazing down at the selection of wilted salads and curled cheese sandwiches, his best friend, Willie, came up behind him and put her arm around his shoulder. "Hey, Troy, what's this I hear about Lida being mad at you?"

Troy, reaching for a salad, paused in disbelief. "She's *mad* at me?"

Willie nodded, a crooked smile on her face. "She's telling everybody how you snubbed her this morning." Willie peered at him. "You feeling all right, Troy? I mean, you *snubbed* Lida? After all this time trying to get her to notice you?"

Troy was about to explain to Willie that it was a mistake; he hadn't meant to rebuff Lida, he'd just been too shy and uncertain to respond. Then an unfamiliar but favorable feeling of power swept through him. If Lida was angry with him, he had some kind of upper hand. "Yeah," he told Willie, swinging his tray off the rails. "Who does she think she is, anyway?"

Willie followed him to a table. "Way to go, Troy," she said, laughing. "Playing hard to get, right?"

Troy laughed with her. "Maybe." He felt so good. He didn't even bother to look around the room to find Lida in the crowd of students. Let her suffer.

But by evening the feeling of triumph had worn off. He hadn't heard anything more from Lida. He was right back where he started. Willie might have been wrong. Lida didn't care spit about him. He wished he knew what to do next. He phoned Willie for advice.

"Call her up or something," Willie said.

Troy felt a nervous chill. "You mean on the phone?"

"That's how it's usually done."

"I couldn't . . ."

"It's real simple, Troy. Just like you're talking to me right now."

"That's different. Talking to you is like . . ."

Willie sighed. "Yeah, I know, like talking to yourself."

Something in Willie's voice made him pause. "What's wrong? Now are you mad at me too?"

"Of course not. Call Lida, Troy. Get it over with."

He would, in a minute. When he got in the right mood. He

drank a can of soda. He put a tape on. He flipped through his note-book and pretended to do some homework. The hands on the clock kept moving. Soon it would be too late to phone.

All at once he just did it. No need to look up her number; he'd had it memorized for months. Punched in the digits quickly, before he could change his mind. Two rings and she picked it up herself.

"Hi, Lida?"

"Who is this?"

"Me, Troy."

"You've got to be kidding." She made a derisive sound, half laugh, half snort, and hung up on him.

The next morning he kept rubbing his jaw. His mother wanted to know what was the matter.

"Nothing, just feels sore."

"Grinding your teeth in your sleep again, I bet."

He remembered the tooth. Got it out of his pocket and tossed it onto his bureau with the other junk. So much for good luck.

That afternoon he found another one. Coming back from the playing field, he saw it lying on the ground. Might have easily missed it. The shape caught his eye, looking incongruous there on the grass. He picked the tooth up, wondering how it could be here instead of home in his room. Then realized he was an idiot—it wasn't the same tooth. This one was slightly less dazzling. A little yellow around the edges, maybe the beginning of a cavity on the side. *Okay*, he thought, *let's see if this one brings better luck*. Of course he wasn't serious.

Lida was standing in the hall when he came out of the locker room. "Hey, Troy," she said. Her voice was softer than he had ever heard it. Vulnerable—was that the word?

"I'm sorry I hung up on you," she said, brown eyes melting into his. "It's just . . . I was hurt, you know?"

"Hurt?"

She lowered her lashes. His legs were turning into syrup. Gosh, she was beautiful.

"I thought you didn't like me anymore," she said.

"Like you? Lida, I . . ." He swallowed. He wanted to believe what was happening, that this was no cruel joke. "I could never be mad at you, Lida."

Her face lit up. She glanced around, then pecked a quick kiss on his face, missing his cheek, her lips glancing off his chin. "Troy, I'm so glad!"

He watched her walk away. His fingers caressed the spot she'd kissed. Had it really happened?

In math class he felt the soreness in his jaw again. He rubbed at it. Funny. As if Lida's lips had left the pain. He liked that. He could suffer through any pain she wanted to inflict on him. He was used to it.

His mother made him go to the dentist.

"Looks like a wisdom tooth coming in," the dentist said. "Nothing to worry about. You'll feel like a li'l ole baby for a few days." The dentist chuckled heartily. "But think of all those smarts that are coming in!"

Troy swabbed the sore gum with Anbesol and forgot the pain. It was nothing compared with how Lida was making him feel. She hadn't talked to him since yesterday. Acted as if nothing had happened between them. Troy was confused. Did she like him or not?

"She's trifling with me," he told Willie as they walked home together. It was hot for April. The newly bloomed azaleas hung their heads; the sun pushed through the shading of Spanish moss on the live oak trees; the air was hazy. Willie's upper lip was beaded with perspiration.

She shook her head. "It's the way the game is played, Troy. Romance is like that." Her voice was plaintive,[4] somehow sad.

"Like a cat worrying a mouse," Troy said. "If this is romance, it's no fun."

But he felt mildly encouraged. He trusted Willie. If this was the way it was done, all right, he could take it. But he was afraid to phone Lida again in case she hung up. He locked himself in his room and lay on the bed. He'd been doing that a lot these last few

4. **plaintive** [plān′ tiv]: sorrowful.

days, neglecting his homework and chores. He put his finger into his mouth. The wisdom tooth had come in fast. Now another one was cutting through on the other side. What a joke, teething at his age.

Teeth. The second molar he'd found was there on top of his dresser with the first one. A crazy idea titillated his mind. What if he found another tooth? Would it make Lida talk to him again?

Troy searched the streets the next morning on his way to school, half serious, half as a joke. As if teeth would be lying around all over the place. He didn't find any.

"Visualization," Willie said at lunch, licking spaghetti sauce off her chin. "That's the way to get what you want."

Troy had been telling her his problem. On again, off again Lida. "How do you mean?"

"Make a picture of what you want in your mind. Visualize Lida saying she loves you."

"If she just agrees to go out with me, it's enough. Will it really work?"

Willie shrugged. "Some people believe it. My sister, for one. She's busy visualizing an engagement ring. Don't look so darn serious, Troy!"

She giggled, and Troy knew she was humoring him. Still, secretly he thought it was worth a try. He would visualize finding another tooth. It was weird, probably dumb, but he had to believe the teeth brought him luck with Lida. Well, maybe it wasn't so weird. It was like a rabbit's foot. He shut his eyes, saw himself walking home from school, saw the oyster-shell sidewalk glistening in the afternoon sun, saw the tooth lying there, saw himself bending down to pick it up.

"Earth to Troy, you still with us?" Willie was asking.

"Huh? Sure, just thinking," Troy said sheepishly.

"You were a thousand miles away."

The third tooth he found had a bad odor, like stale breath. It was dingier, too, and had a definite brown hole where a cavity had been, where maybe a filling had fallen out. Troy put it in his pocket. He felt a shiver go through him. A goblin pain of anticipation gripped his stomach.

That evening Lida phoned. She was nicer than she had ever been. Encouraged, he asked her out. She didn't exactly say yes, but then she didn't refuse either.

By morning another wisdom tooth had appeared in his mouth. Funny how they grew so fast.

When Troy found a fourth molar—this one had a hole where a filling had fallen out—his final wisdom tooth cut through. Probably coincidence, but Lida was suddenly warmer, more affectionate. The trouble was, it didn't last. One minute she was squeezing his hand, the next minute she was cold as ice. So he had to look for another tooth, crazy as it seemed. Anything to make her smile at him again.

After he found the fifth molar—stained, smellier, more decayed—Troy noticed something in the roof of his mouth. A strange sort of bump. A few days later a tooth pushed through. He looked at it in the bathroom, craning his neck awkwardly as he held his mother's makeup mirror. He was scared at the bizarre sight of it; teeth didn't belong in the roof of your mouth! He said nothing to his mother, not wanting another visit to the dentist. He felt somehow ashamed.

But this time Lida's attitude really changed. The attention she paid to him was not so short-lived. She actually walked part of the way home with him. Troy was aware that Willie straggled behind. He wished she wasn't there.

He began avoiding Willie. She had become an inconvenience; he was too busy with Lida. When Willie phoned, he told his mother to say he was out. Anyway, it hurt to talk on the phone so much. Especially at night, the extra teeth hurt. Sometimes he woke up just before morning, bathed in sweat, thinking he really should do something about it. Go to the dentist and have them all pulled out. But then he'd find another tooth on the street and Lida would be waiting for him on the school steps, smiling that special smile, eyes only for him, and he was afraid to do anything that might break the spell.

He was looking for teeth all the time now. "I've got to stop this," he told himself, and then went out and searched the sidewalks anyway. The collection of molars was growing. He hid them in his closet at first, but the smell was so bad, he had to take them outside and put them in the back of the tool shed.

By June nine new teeth crowded the roof of his mouth, and a tenth was breaking through under his tongue. It was really hard to talk now. He mumbled about dental surgery when the kids at school or the teachers gave him funny looks. It was a strain to keep his lips tightly closed around his overfilled mouth. Willie commented on his new reticence. That is, she spoke to him when she managed to catch up with him, or grab him unawares. He took different routes home; he sneaked through the lanes and other people's gardens to keep out of her way. But sometimes, in those early-morning panics, it was Willie he thought of. He loved Lida, but it was Willie who came to mind when he felt most scared.

Willie stopped him in the corridor one day, her grasp on his arm determined, almost fierce. "You don't talk to me anymore, Troy," she said, and worry creased her brow. He was tempted to reply, to tell her everything. But he couldn't find the words. Even if he could figure out what to say, he wouldn't be able to say it. That strange, shameful feeling welled inside him. And then there was Lida, coming down the hall, calling to him. Willie's face closed up.

"True love," she said, giving Lida a slit-eyed glance. "Smile, Troy, don't work so hard at it."

Smiles were a thing of the past. It was hard to smile without opening your mouth. His mouth felt like it was full of rocks. It was getting harder to eat.

"He has no appetite," his mother said. "I'm worried."

"He's probably in love," said his father, winking at Troy over the tops of his reading glasses. "Nothing to fret about. Just look at those chubby cheeks."

Troy studied himself in the bathroom mirror. He looked like a squirrel with a face full of nuts. It wasn't funny. He fought an overwhelming desire to spit and keep on spitting, as if he could get rid of the teeth, which were like coarse, salty pebbles against his tongue. Only belief in Lida could drive the fearful sickness away. And yet hadn't she grown colder toward him again? Had that been Lida walking off after school with someone else?

The tooth he found the next day was the worst so far: greenish with mold, carious, its roots eaten away. The smell lingered in the air and on Troy's fingers. But in spite of its foulness, Troy caressed it. He didn't hide it in the shed but kept it in his pocket, so that he could touch it and know its power. He sensed that the rewards would be greater this time around. Lida would be his.

A plan unfolded; he knew just what to do. Ask her to go for an evening walk along the river, when the sun was fire falling behind the new bridge, when a cool breeze was picking up. There in the nearly dark he would have the courage he could never muster in broad daylight. In the shadows he could find the right words to speak. He trembled at the thought of holding her, kissing her lips.

He phoned her with confidence, knowing she would not refuse. She agreed readily to meet him on River Street. He showered and dressed carefully. He rinsed his mouth with Listerine, for once oblivious of the claustrophobic feeling of his teeth. He ran through the streets. No need to search the ground now.

She was waiting for him on the promenade. She seemed impatient, but her smile was unsullied,[5] immaculate.[6] He took her hand, and they began walking into the west, toward the bridge. He felt so happy. He felt as if his heart would burst.

Lida's voice, tinged with the slightest irritation, broke the rapturous[7] silence. "Cat got your tongue or something?"

He nervously fingered the putrid tooth in his pocket. He wanted to speak, to tell her how much he cared. But he was nervous about how the words would sound coming from the rabble of his mouth.

He wanted so much to kiss her. Better to kiss her and forget the words.

She stopped and leaned against the railing, looking out into the river. Faint sounds of music came from the restaurants behind them.

5. **unsullied** [un sul′ ēd]: not soiled, clean.
6. **immaculate** [i mak′ yə lit]: absolutely clean, without spot or fault.
7. **rapturous** [rap′ chər əs]: full of joy.

The water was roiled by the paddle of the *River Belle*, getting ready to take the tourists over to the island.

"Sometimes you can see a dolphin here," she said.

He put his hand gently on her shoulder. Felt her tremble under his hesitant touch. She turned to him expectantly. The setting sun blazed in her hair. He had never seen her so beautiful.

He wished he could tell her: *Lida, I love you.*

She raised herself on tiptoe, so that her lips reached his.

Happiness burst in his heart. He put his own lips against hers and felt her responding, melting against him. He lost himself to her.

And then suddenly the heat of her body against his chest was gone. His lips felt the cold chill of night air. He opened his eyes.

She was backing away.

"My God," she said. "Oh, my God. Your mouth is full of teeth!"

Her rosebud lips were twisted in horror.

At that moment, before Lida's screams drew the attention of the passersby, before the people started staring and pointing at him, he wanted to shout that he was sorry. He wanted to go back in time. He wanted . . .

"Willie," he tried to say. But from his mouth came only the growling moan of suffocating decay.

PATRICIA WINDSOR

Patricia Windsor was born in 1938 in New York City, where she grew up in the Bronx. She started writing when she was ten. "My parents gave me a battered old typewriter to bang on," she has said. At sixteen, Windsor had planned out "hundreds of novels and long lists of titles." She also had thirty-five rejection slips from publishers she'd asked to publish her work!

Years later, Windsor published her first novel for young adults. Now she has written more than a dozen books. She has also raised a family, taught, and worked as an editor, a counselor, and a volunteer. One of her book titles expresses her point of view: *Home Is Where Your Feet Are Standing*.

Asking Big Questions About the Literature

How do people respond to strange and unusual stories?

LITERATURE STUDY

Hyperbole

Have you ever noticed how sounds seem louder than usual when you're alone or afraid? In order to create fear or suspense, a writer uses a technique called **hyperbole**, in which sights and sounds are exaggerated beyond the ordinary. Find examples of hyperbole in the literature selections you have read. Then, in your journal, express how they made you feel. Share your responses with a partner. Did your partner respond the same way? If not, why not? (*See "Hyperbole" on page 118.*)

MAKE
A RESPONSE CHART

How did your classmates respond to each literature selection in this unit? Did you hear the words "awesome" and "bizarre" or the expression "on the edge of my seat?" On a sheet of paper, make a chart for each selection like the ones below. Pass the sheet around the class so that everyone can record their response to each selection they've read. What do readers agree or disagree about and why?

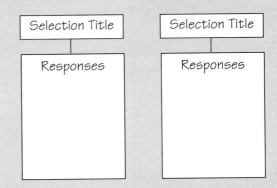

Making A TERROR–METER

With a partner, discuss your response to the literature selections you've read. Did you feel surprise, suspense, unease, fear, or terror as you read? Make a "terror-meter" like the one shown below for each selection you've read. Show the intensity of each emotion you felt by shading in your terror-meter. Then write a short paragraph explaining why the selection made you feel that way.

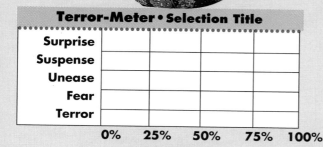

Terror-Meter • Selection Title				
Surprise				
Suspense				
Unease				
Fear				
Terror				

0%   25%   50%   75%   100%

Write an ADVICE COLUMN

Many of the characters in the literature selections in this unit find themselves in disturbing situations. Imagine you're a character from a literature selection that you've read. Write a letter to an advice column, asking for help. "Send" your letter to a classmate. When you've received a similar letter yourself, write a response, suggesting ways of avoiding misfortune.

Interview a Character

With a partner, choose a character from a literature selection that you've read. Then role-play the character and an interviewer. Let the interviewer ask about the character's situation and state of mind. Switch roles and interview other characters. Perform your interviews for the class.

Asking Big Questions About the Literature

How do writers make strange and unusual stories work?

A WRITER'S Glossary

Look back at page 11 for the list of techniques used to make weird stories work. Then study the literature selections you've read for examples of each of the four techniques. Group the selections in a web like the one on this page. Next to each selection title, make a short note of how the technique is used in that selection.

Writing A Word of Warning

Many of the characters in the literature selections of this unit find themselves overcome by the unexpected. Choose a character from a literature selection you've read. Write a letter warning him or her of the dangerous events that lie ahead. Help your character avoid disaster.

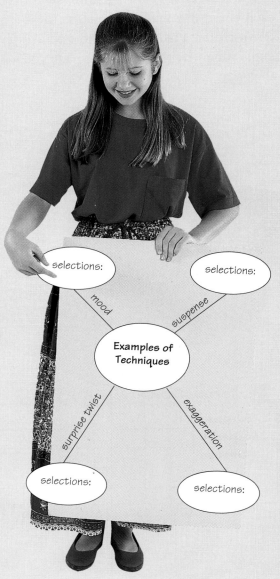

selections:

selections:

mood

suspense

Examples of Techniques

surprise twist

exaggeration

selections:

selections:

Design A BOOK JACKET

Design a book jacket for your favorite literature selection in this unit. Your book jacket could represent an object, a character, or an important event in the story. To create your jacket, draw, paint, or assemble a collage of pictures from newspapers or magazines. On the back of your book jacket, write a short "blurb" describing what happens in the story. Try to make your blurb as exciting as the story you describe. When you've finished, stage a book fair that showcases your classmates' book jackets and your own.

Act It Out

With a group of three or four other students, choose a scene from a literature selection you've read, and act it out. Discuss what techniques the writer used to make the scene work. Then use these techniques to make the scene into a script for a skit, radio drama, video, or TV episode. When you have written the script, add props, sound effects, music, and a set. Work out the details, choose tasks, and put the scene together. Get ready to perform it for classmates.

LITERATURE STUDY

Foreshadowing

Foreshadowing—giving hints or clues about the coming events in a story —is one technique writers use to keep a reader's attention. For example, in "August Heat," the artist's sketch looks forward to coming events. With a partner, choose a literature selection that held your interest. Look through the selection for foreshadowing clues. List these clues in your journal and write a short paragraph describing how each clue foreshadows the story's events. *(See "Foreshadowing" on page 119.)*

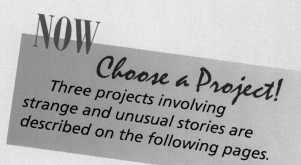

NOW *Choose a Project!*

Three projects involving strange and unusual stories are described on the following pages.

Writing Workshop

"This story is totally excellent!" "That movie's not worth the price of the popcorn!" Whenever you make comments like these, you're acting as a critic. Now, in this project, you'll have the chance to become a *real* critic and write a review of a strange story. Your **purpose** in a review is to *evaluate*—to judge how good something is and to express why you feel that way. Your **audience** will be the people who'll read your review when you submit it to a newspaper or magazine.

Prewriting

GETTING STARTED

As you decide on a story to review, it might help to try some freewriting in your journal. Make a list of weird stories by brainstorming, talking to others, and looking through library listings. The stories could come from this unit or from any other source.

Choose a story that's unfamiliar or one you'd like to reread. Then take notes as you read. Write a response to the story. What seems particularly interesting to you about the story? Was anything disappointing? Your review will be stronger if you use evidence to support your statement of judgment.

The Adventures of Sherlock Holmes

The Time Machine

Stories of Ray Bradbury

Stories of Roald Dahl

Prewriting
BEGINNING TO EVALUATE

Before you begin your first draft, find examples of reviews in newspapers and magazines. How are these reviews organized? Does the critic describe the plot briefly before explaining his or her opinion of the story? Or does the critic give her or his opinion in the opening paragraph? Decide how you would like to set up *your* review. Then ask yourself what audience the critic is writing for. How will *your* review be geared to *your* audience?

Now think about your reactions to the story you have chosen. How strongly did you react to the story? What emotions did you feel? Were the characters, settings, and dialogue all believable? How effectively did the author use elements like hyperbole and foreshadowing?

In your journal, make a value chart of literary elements like the one below. Provide a rating for each literary element in the story you have chosen. In another column, explain the reasons behind your rating.

Title	Those Three Wishes		
	Rating	**Reason**	
How exciting was the plot?	5	Good, unexpected plot twist at the end	
How interesting was the setting?			
Key: Poor 1		Fair 2-3	Excellent 4-5

Drafting YOUR REVIEW

Now that you've used your chart to evaluate the story, you're ready to draft your review. Remember your **purpose**—to write a review—and your **audience** when you write. Present your opinions and arguments clearly and precisely.

- Make sure that your beginning contains a statement of judgment. Adam Steinhoff, a student writer, introduces his review of the short story "August Heat" on pages 110-111 with a personal response that gives his statement of judgment of the work. " 'August Heat', by William Fryer Harvey, is a very imaginative and scary short story with a plot that is full of surprises."

- Tell why you did or didn't like the work. Support your opinions with reasons. Use your chart to help you explain what you thought about the different literary elements of the story. For example, Adam liked the way the author described the heat: "He describes this aspect of the setting so well that you begin to feel the heat yourself."

- End by summarizing your response to the work. Recommend the work to your audience, telling them why they should or shouldn't read it. Adam ends by giving the story he read his enthusiastic approval: " 'August Heat' by William Fryer Harvey is a 'must-read' weird story."

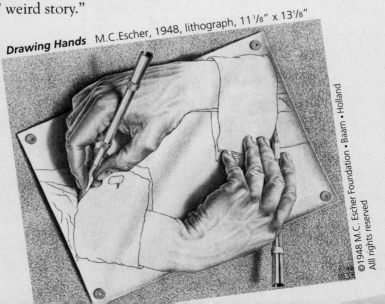

Drawing Hands M.C. Escher, 1948, lithograph, 11 1/8" x 13 1/8"

Revising *YOUR REVIEW*

Let a partner or writing group read your draft with a critical eye. Encourage your reader to give you advice on ways of improving your review. Do you give clear, logical reasons for your opinions? Does your judgment seem balanced and fair? Finally, do you answer all the questions that someone unfamiliar with the story might ask? Make changes to strengthen your review.

Editing *YOUR REVIEW*

After you've revised your draft, work with a partner or writing group to edit your review. Read one another's reviews and check for errors in spelling, grammar, and punctuation— you don't want your mechanics to be the strange and unusual part of your review! Correct your errors and make a publishable copy of your review.

Publishing *YOUR REVIEW*

Now let your audience enjoy your review. Brainstorm ways of getting your review published, and write your ideas in your journal. Here are some ideas to help you get started.

- Send your review to magazines read by people your age and to the school newspaper.
- Work with a group of classmates to publish a collection of reviews for the school library.
- Send your review to a local radio station.

"August Heat"
review by Adam Steinhoff
West Palm Beach, Florida

"August Heat," by William Fryer Harvey, is a very imaginative and scary short story with a plot that is full of surprises. The story begins with an artist, James Clarence Withencroft, writing about the events of a very strange day as he waits for the day to end. Throughout the story, Withencroft describes the heat he felt that day. He describes this aspect of the setting so well that you begin to feel the heat yourself. In the story, he says it was "oppressively hot" and that when he went for a walk, the heat rose from the street "as an almost palpable wave."

On the day this story takes place, Withencroft's mind is wandering when an idea for a sketch comes to him. The idea is so overwhelming that he loses track of time. He spends about four hours drawing a man with a terrible look on his face standing in front of a judge in a courtroom. Without knowing why, he rolls up the sketch, puts it in his pocket, and goes for a walk. He walks five or six miles without remembering anything.

When Withencroft stops, he is at the gate of a stone mason who carves tombstones. The man is smiling and whistling while he carves the stone...and he looks like the man in the artist's sketch. After Withencroft enters the mason's workshop, the two men talk about the heat. The mason agrees that it is tremendously hot and has to stop every minute and wipe the sweat off his head.

This is where the story starts getting interesting. The mason is working on a tombstone for an exhibition. The name and birthday he made up for the sample are Withencroft's, while the date of Withencroft's death happens to be the day the story takes place. The author keeps building the suspense as the two men learn that their imaginary ideas actually represent real people and events that have not yet happened. The artist drew the mason without ever having seen him, and the mason carved the artist's name, birthday, and date of death without knowing him. As the suspense increases, you feel the heat that Withencroft feels as he slowly realizes what is about to happen to him.

I liked this story a lot. The ending is so subtle that it sneaks up on you. "August Heat" by William Fryer Harvey is a "must-read" weird story.

PROJECT 2

Cooperative Learning

MAKING A BOARD GAME

Did you know that people have been playing chess for 1,500 years? Have you ever wondered who invented chess or other board games? Perhaps it was someone like you! This project will give you a chance to create a board game for all ages, based on a literature selection you have read in this unit.

The PROCESS

With your class, make a list of modern board games. Then divide into teams, with each team studying a different board game. Present your research to the class for a discussion. What do these games have in common? What makes them so popular?

In a group of three to five students, think about the literature selections in this unit. Discuss which selection your group would like to turn into a board game. When you have chosen a selection, make sure that everyone reads it. Then discuss which literary elements from the selection could be included in the game. Are there plot twists that could be represented in the layout of the board? Are there evil characters who could give penalty points if your marker falls on their space? Write all your ideas in your journal.

Divide the work that each person will have to do to create the game. You will probably need a designer to plan how the board will be set up, a rules maker to plan how to play the game and decide on the number of players, a materials person to collect the art supplies and the dice and markers, and a title inventor to come up with the name of the game. In your journal, make a chart like the one below to keep track of who will be responsible for each task.

Title	Task	Person Responsible
Designer	Plans setup of board	
Rules maker	Plans how to play the game	
Materials person	Gets art supplies	
Title inventor	Thinks of name for the game	

Members of the group should work closely with each other to create the board game. The designer and rules maker especially will have to stay in close contact during this development phase.

The PRODUCT

Now that you know what your board game will look like, you're ready to make the board itself. Let the materials person paint or draw the spaces on the board. Help the rules maker create a booklet that explains how the game is played. Then write an ad for the game. Finally organize a board game championship.

Helping Your Community

A STORYTELLING PERFORMANCE

Imagine you're sitting around a campfire with a group of friends. Each person tells a story with a weird and mysterious plot. As the campfire glows brighter, everyone focuses on the storyteller. This is the scene you and a group of classmates will perform to entertain the school community.

Planning
THE TIME AND PLACE

Choose a time and place for your performance. Could you create a campfire atmosphere in your classroom, school auditorium, or playground? Check with teachers and school officials to explore the possibilities.

Next you should consider your audience. Who will be listening as you take turns performing your campfire tales? Will your audience consist of younger children or of students your age?

Choosing
THE STORIES

With a group of five or six classmates, create a list of weird stories. Think of stories you know or stories you've read in this unit, and search the library for stories you haven't read.

Which would be the best stories to tell? With your group, make a list of questions to use in evaluating, or judging, the performance quality of each story. Use your notes and activities from this unit to help you create this list. Here are a few examples of questions you might ask.

- How will the audience respond to it?
- Does it build suspense? How?
- Can it be told in an exciting way? How?
- Can it be told in the time we have?

Planning THE EVENT

After the group has agreed on a story for each person to tell, work out the details of your performance. Brainstorm things to do and find out. How can you create the right mood without using a real campfire? What props and sound effects might you use? Will you design advertising posters or broadcast an announcement over the PA system? Don't forget to ask school officials for permission and advice.

Use a chart like the one shown to organize your tasks.

Job	Who'll do it	What's to be done

Telling YOUR STORIES

Rehearse your stories as a group. Estimate how long each story will take to tell. Then tell your stories in front of an audience. After your performance, consider presenting it in some other form, such as a video or a tape recording. You might also contact schools, community centers, or other places that might be interested. Who knows? You and your group might become famous as the Campfire Storytellers.

Putting It All Together

What Have You Learned About the Theme?

As you worked through this unit, you not only read strange and unusual stories but thought, wrote, listened to, and talked about them. What do you know now that you didn't know before? In particular, what have you learned about what goes into a strange and unusual story? Look over your writing and the other activities that you did for this unit. Then write your own strange and unusual story. Your story could be one that you've invented or it could be based on an event in your life.

STRANGE TALE

Prewriting and Drafting   Brainstorm a list of strange events in your life. Has anything mysterious ever happened to you that you've never been able to explain? Write about it in your journal. You could also invent weird happenings to add to your list.

Before you begin your draft, look through the literature selections in this unit. Notice that many of them are told from the first person point of view, as if the person telling the story actually experienced the events. If you tell your story with the "I" of your own voice, your readers will be more likely to believe that your strange and unusual story is true.

Now draft your strange and unusual story. Think about your setting. Make sure the events of your plot unfold logically. See if you can include a surprise twist in the plot. Use foreshadowing to create suspense. Finally remember to include a mix of dialogue and description.

Revising and Editing   Now work with a partner. Exchange stories and read with a critical eye. Ask your partner to suggest improvements to the content of your writing. Check the grammar, punctuation, and spelling too.

Publishing   Make your final revisions and publish your story. Post it up on a bulletin board so that your classmates can read it.

Evaluating Your Work

Discuss the Big Questions on pages 10-11 with a partner. Can you answer all the questions easily now? In your journal, write two or three sentences to tell how your responses to the Big Questions have changed after your work in this unit.

Think Back About Your Work

Think back on your work in this unit and evaluate what you did — your reading, writing, activities, and projects. Don't be too hard on yourself, but do be honest.

Finally write a note to your teacher. Explain what you did as you worked through the unit and what you learned from the experience. Use the following questions to help you write your note.

- Which literature selections in this unit did you enjoy most?

- Which selections did you enjoy least?

- Which activity in the unit did you enjoy most?

- Which did you enjoy least?

- If you were to repeat your project, what would you do the same way? What would you do differently?

- What did you learn from working on the project?

- What did you learn in this unit about strange and unusual stories?

- How would you rate your work in this unit? Use the following scale and give at least three reasons for your rating.

  1 = Outstanding   3 = Fair
  2 = Good   4 = Not as good as it could have been

HYPERBOLE

What Is Hyperbole?

Hyperbole is a form of exaggeration. Authors use hyperbole to make someone or something seem more impressive than it would normally appear. For example, in the beginning of "The Wish" by Roald Dahl, the child describes the hall carpet in these words: "A tremendous carpet. Bigger than the tennis lawn. Much bigger than that." In this example, hyperbole is used to express how the child sees the world around him. Hyperbole can also be used to create other effects for the reader, such as a sense of mystery and fear.

Writing a Description   Find an example of hyperbole in one of the literature selections that you've read. Study the way the author has used exaggeration to create effects of mystery or fear. For example, in "August Heat," the temperature is described as unbearable. The intense heat of the story is used to express the main character's growing terror and to create a mysterious effect.

After you've studied the way the author has used this technique in a literature selection you've read, use the same technique to describe a familiar object or person. Write your description in your journal.

Writing a Scene from a Play   Choose two characters from different literature selections you've read in this unit. Then, in your journal, write a short scene from a play in which these two characters meet under strange or mysterious circumstances. Use hyperbole in the dialogue. If you like, ask a classmate to help you perform the scene in front of the class.

What Is Foreshadowing?

Foreshadowing is a technique writers use to give hints or clues about the coming events in a story. For example, in "August Heat," James Withencroft draws a sketch of an imaginary criminal, a man whom he meets for the first time later the same day. Withencroft's sketch foreshadows, or looks forward to, future events. Because foreshadowing suggests knowledge of future happenings, it can be used to create strange, eerie effects.

Rewriting a Conclusion   Look through the literature selections that you've read for examples of foreshadowing. Study the authors' techniques. Then choose one or two literature selections that you have read in this unit. Change the ending of each selection by rewriting the story's conclusion. Make sure that your new conclusion is very different from the conclusion in the original version. Then write a short paragraph foreshadowing the story's new conclusion.

Writing About Your Life   Choose an important event in your life, such as moving to a new neighborhood or making a new friend. Then write a story in which this event becomes the story's conclusion. Use foreshadowing to prepare your readers for the ending. Make sure that your hints or clues are vague enough that you don't give away the ending.

GLOSSARY OF LITERARY TERMS

A

alliteration   Repetition of the first sound—usually a consonant sound—in several words of a sentence or a line of poetry.

allusion   An author's indirect reference to someone or something that is presumed to be familiar to the reader.

anecdote   A short narrative about an interesting or a humorous event, usually in the life of a person.

antagonist   The person or force opposing the protagonist, or main character in a literary work. [See also *protagonist*.]

autobiography   A person's written account of his or her own life.

B

ballad   A poem, often a song, that tells a story in simple verse.

biography   An account of a person's life, written by another person.

blank verse   Unrhymed poetry.

C

character   A person or an animal that participates in the action of a work of literature. A *dynamic character* is one whose thoughts, feelings, and actions are changeable and

lifelike; a *static character* always remains the same. [See also *protagonist, antagonist*.]

characterization   The creation of characters through the characters' use of language and through descriptions of their appearance, thoughts, emotions, and actions. [See also *character*.]

chronology   An arrangement of events in the order in which they happen.

cliché   An overused expression that is trite rather than meaningful.

climax   The highest point of tension in the plot of a work of literature. [See also *plot*.]

comedy   An amusing play that has a happy ending.

conclusion   The final part or ending of a piece of literature.

concrete poem   A poem arranged on the page so that its punctuation, letters, and lines make the shape of the subject of the poem.

conflict   A problem that confronts the characters in a piece of literature. The conflict may be *internal* (a character's struggle within himself or herself) or *external* (a character's struggle against nature, another person, or society). [See also *plot*.]

context   The general sense of words that helps readers to understand the meaning of unfamiliar words and phrases in a piece of writing.

D

description   An author's use of words to give the reader or listener a mental picture, an impression, or an understanding of a person, place, thing, event, or idea.

dialect   A form of speech spoken by people in a particular group or geographical region that differs in vocabulary, grammar, and pronunciation from the standard language.

dialogue   The spoken words and conversation of characters in a work of literature.

drama   A play that is performed before an audience according to stage directions and using dialogue. Classical drama has two genres: *tragedy* and *comedy*. Modern drama includes *melodrama, satire, theater of the absurd*, and *pantomime*. [See also *comedy, play*, and *tragedy*.]

dramatic poetry   A play written in the form of poetry.

E

epic   A long narrative poem—written in a formal style and meant to be read aloud—that relates the adventures and

experiences of one or more great heroes or heroines.

essay   Personal nonfiction writing about a particular subject that is important to the writer.

excerpt   A passage from a larger work that has been taken out of its context to be used for a special purpose.

exposition   Writing that explains, analyzes, or defines.

extended metaphor   An elaborately drawn out metaphor. [See also *metaphor*.]

F

fable   A short, simple story whose purpose is to teach a lesson, usually with animal characters who talk and act like people.

fantasy   Imaginative fiction about unrealistic characters, places, and events.

fiction   Literature, including the short story and the novel, that tells about imaginary people and events.

figurative language
Language used to express ideas through figures of speech: descriptions that aren't meant to be taken literally. Types of figurative language include *simile*, *metaphor*, *extended metaphor*, *hyperbole*, and *personification*.

figure of speech   A type of figurative language, not meant to be taken literally, that expresses something in such a way that it brings the thing to life in the reader's or listener's imagination. [See also *figurative language*.]

flashback   A break in a story's action that relates a past happening in order to give the reader background information about a present action in the story.

folktale   A story that has been passed along from storyteller to storyteller for generations. Kinds of folktales include *tall tales*, *fairy tales*, *fables*, *legends*, and *myths*.

foreshadowing   The use of clues to create suspense by giving the reader or audience hints of events to come.

free verse   Poetry that has no formal rhyme scheme or metrical pattern.

G

genre   A major category of art. The three major literary genres are poetry, prose, and drama.

H

haiku   A three-line Japanese verse form. In most haiku, the first and third lines have five syllables, while the second line has seven. The

traditional haiku describes a complicated feeling or thought in simple language through a single image.

hero/heroine   The main character in a work of literature. In heroic literature, the hero or heroine is a particularly brave, noble, or clever person whose achievements are unusual and important. [See also *character*.]

heroic age   The historical period in western civilization—from about 800 B.C. through A.D. 200—during which most works of heroic literature, such as myths and epics, were created in ancient Greece and Rome.

hubris   Arrogance or excessive pride leading to mistakes; the character flaw in a hero of classical tragedy.

hyperbole   An obvious exaggeration used for emphasis. [See also *figurative language*.]

I

idiom   An expression whose meaning cannot be understood from the ordinary meaning of the words. For example, *It's raining cats and dogs*.

imagery   The words and phrases in writing that appeal to the senses of sight, hearing, taste, touch, and smell.

irony   An effect created by a sharp contrast between what is expected and what is real. An *ironic twist* in a plot is an event that is the complete opposite of what the characters have been hoping or expecting will happen. An *ironic statement* declares the opposite of the speaker's literal meaning.

J

jargon   Words and phrases used by a group of people who share the same profession or special interests in order to refer to technical things or processes with which they are familiar. In general, jargon is any terminology that sounds unclear, overused, or pretentious.

L

legend   A famous folktale about heroic actions, passed along by word of mouth from generation to generation. The legend may have begun as a factual account of real people and events but has become mostly or completely fictitious.

limerick   A form of light verse, or humorous poetry, written in one five-line stanza with a regular scheme of rhyme and meter.

literature   The branch of art that is expressed in written language and includes all written genres.

lyric poem   A short poem that expresses personal feelings and thoughts in a musical way. Originally, lyrics were the words of songs that were sung to music played on the lyre, a stringed instrument invented by the ancient Greeks.

M

metamorphosis   The transformation of one thing, or being, into another completely different thing or being, such as a caterpillar's change into a butterfly.

metaphor   Figurative language in which one thing is said to be another thing. [See also *figurative language*.]

meter   The pattern of rhythm in lines of poetry. The most common meter, in poetry written in English, is iambic pentameter, that is, a verse having five metrical feet, each foot of verse having two syllables, an unaccented one followed by an accented one.

mood   The feeling or atmosphere that a reader senses while reading or listening to a work of literature.

motivation   A character's reasons for doing, thinking, feeling, or saying something. Sometimes an author will make a character's motivation obvious from the beginning. In realistic fiction and drama, however, a character's motivation may be so complicated that the reader discovers it gradually, by studying the character's thoughts, feelings, and behavior.

myth   A story, passed along by word of mouth for generations, about the actions of gods and goddesses or superhuman heroes and heroines. Most myths were first told to explain the origins of natural things or to justify the social rules and customs of a particular society.

N

narration   The process of telling a story. For both fiction and nonfiction, there are two main kinds of narration, based on whether the story is told from a first-person or third-person point of view. [See also *point of view*.]

narrative poem   A poem that tells a story containing the basic literary ingredients of fiction: character, setting, and plot.

narrator   The person, or voice, that tells a story. [See also *point of view, voice*.]

nonfiction   Prose that is factually true and is about real people, events, and places.

nonstandard English
Versions of English, such as slang and dialects, that use pronunciation, vocabulary, idiomatic expressions, grammar, and punctuation that differ from the accepted "correct" constructions of English.

novel A long work of narrative prose fiction. A novel contains narration, a setting or settings, characters, dialogue, and a more complicated plot than a short story.

onomatopoeia The technique of using words that imitate the sounds they describe, such as *hiss*, *buzz*, and *splash*.

oral tradition Stories, poems, and songs that have been kept alive by being told, recited, and sung by people over many generations. Since the works were not originally written, they often have many different versions.

P

parable A brief story—similar to a fable, but about people—that describes an ordinary situation and concludes with a short moral or lesson to be learned.

personification Figurative language in which an animal, an object, or an idea is given human characteristics. [See also *figurative language*.]

persuasion A type of speech or writing whose purpose is to convince people that something is true or important.

play A work of dramatic literature written for performance by actors before an audience. In classical or traditional drama, a play is divided into five acts, each containing a number of scenes. Each act represents a distinct phase in the development of the plot. Modern plays often have only one act and one scene.

playwright The author of a play.

plot The sequence of actions and events in fiction or drama. A traditional plot has at least three parts: the *rising action*, leading up to a turning point that affects the main character; the *climax*, the turning point or moment of greatest intensity or interest; and the *falling action*, leading away from the conflict, or resolving it.

poetry Language selected and arranged in order to say something in a compressed or nonliteral way. Modern poetry may or may not use many of the traditional poetic techniques that include *meter*, *rhyme*, *alliteration*, *figurative language*, *symbolism*, and *specific verse forms*.

point of view The perspective from which a writer tells a story. *First-person* narrators tell the story from their own point of view, using pronouns such as *I* or *me*. *Third-person* narrators, using pronouns such as *he*, *she*, or *them*, may be *omniscient* (knowing everything about all characters), or *limited* (taking the point of view of one character). [See also *narration*.]

propaganda Information or ideas that may or may not be true, but are spread as though they are true, in order to persuade people to do or believe something.

prose The ordinary form of written and spoken language used to create fiction, nonfiction, and most drama.

protagonist The main character of a literary work. [See also *character* and *characterization*.]

R

refrain A line or group of lines that is repeated, usually at the end of each verse, in a poem or a song.

repetition The use of the same formal element more than once in a literary work, for emphasis or in order to achieve another desired effect.

resolution The falling action in fiction or drama,

including all of the developments that follow the climax and show that the story's conflict is over. [See also *plot*.]

rhyme scheme A repeated pattern of similar sounds, usually found at the ends of lines of poetry or poetic drama.

rhythm In poetry, the measured recurrence of accented and unaccented syllables in a particular pattern. [See also *meter*.]

S

scene The time, place, and circumstances of a play or a story. In a play, a scene is a section of an act. [See also *play*.]

science fiction Fantasy literature set in an imaginary future, with details and situations that are designed to seem scientifically possible.

setting The time and place of a work of literature.

short story Narrative prose fiction that is shorter and has a less complicated plot than a novel. A short story contains narration, at least one setting, at least one character, and usually some dialogue.

simile Figurative language that compares two unlike things, introduced by the words "like" or "as." [See also *figurative language*.]

soliloquy In a play, a short speech spoken by a single character when he or she is alone on the stage. A soliloquy usually expresses the character's innermost thoughts and feelings, when he or she thinks no other characters can hear.

sonnet A poem written in one stanza, using fourteen lines of iambic pentameter. [See also *meter*.]

speaker In poetry, the individual whose voice seems to be speaking the lines. [See also *narration*, *voice*.]

stage directions The directions, written by the playwright, to tell the director, actors, and theater technicians how a play should be dramatized. Stage directions may specify such things as how the setting should appear in each scene, how the actors should deliver their lines, when the stage curtain should rise and fall, how stage lights should be used, where on the stage the actors should be during the action, and when sound effects should be used.

stanza A group of lines in poetry set apart by blank lines before and after the group; a poetic verse.

style The distinctive way in which an author composes a work of literature in written or spoken language.

suspense An effect created by authors of various types of fiction and drama, especially adventure and mystery, to heighten interest in the story.

symbol An image, person, place, or thing that is used to express the idea of something else.

T

tall tale A kind of folk tale, or legend, that exaggerates the characteristics of its hero or heroine.

theme The main idea or underlying subject of a work of literature.

tone The attitude that a work of literature expresses to the reader through its style.

tragedy In classical drama, a tragedy depicts a noble hero or heroine who makes a mistake of judgment that has disastrous consequences.

V

verse A stanza in a poem. Also, a synonym for poetry as a genre. [See also *stanza*.]

voice The narrator or the person who relates the action of a piece of literature. [See also *speaker*.]

ACKNOWLEDGMENTS

"The Wish" from *Someone Like You* by Roald Dahl, copyright 1953 by Roald Dahl. Reprinted by permission of Alfred A. Knopf, Inc.

"The Fear" by Robert Frost. From *The Poetry of Robert Frost* edited by Edward Connery Lathem. Copyright © 1958 by Robert Frost. Copyright © 1967 by Lesley Frost Ballantine. Copyright 1930, 1939, ©1969 by Henry Holt and Company, Inc. Reprinted by permission of Henry Holt and Company, Inc.

"I Used to Live Here Once" by Jean Rhys. Copyright © 1976 by Jean Rhys. Included in W.W. Norton & Company's *Jean Rhys: The Collected Short Stories*. Reprinted by permission of the Wallace Literary Agency, Inc.

"Those Three Wishes" by Judith Gorog is used by permission of the author.

The Hitch-Hiker by Lucille Fletcher, copyright 1947 by Lucille Fletcher. Reprinted by permission of the William Morris Agency, Inc.

"The Lost Colony" by Dan Lacy from *The Colony of North Carolina* by Dan Lacy. Copyright © 1975 by Dan Lacy. Used with permission of Franklin Watts, Inc., New York.

"Teeth" by Patricia Windsor, copyright © 1992 by Patricia Windsor, from *Short Circuits* by Donald Gallo, Editor. Used by permission of Dell Books, a division of Bantam Doubleday Dell Publishing Group, Inc.

ILLUSTRATION

13-16 Dragon by Dave Shepherd; 18-47 Christopher Bing; 86-91 Background type by Dave Shepherd; 92-101 Amy Wasserman.

PHOTOGRAPHY

4 *l, r* Sarah Putnam/©D.C. Heath; 5 Art Collection Foundation, Barbados; 6 Richard Haynes/©D.C. Heath; 8 From *The Mysteries of Harris Burdick* by Chris Van Allsburg. ©1984 by Chris Van Allsburg. Reprinted by permission of Houghton Mifflin Co. All rights reserved; 10 *t* Sandy Roessler/The Stock Market; *b* John Owens/©D.C. Heath; 11 *t* Skjold/The Image Works; *b* Jim Whitmer/Stock Boston; 12-13 The Metropolitan Museum of Art, Frederick C. Hewitt Fund, 1910. 10.61.3; 17 Courtesy of Farrar, Straus and Giroux, Inc.; 47 *inset* The Bettman Archive; 49 Private Collection/Bridgeman Art Library, London; 53 UPI/Bettman Newsphotos; 54-55 ©1946 M.C. Escher Foundation-Baarn-Holland. All rights reserved; 54-61 *background* PhotoDisc; 58 ©1948 M.C. Escher Foundation-Baarn-Holland. All rights reserved; 62-63, 64 Art Collection Foundation, Barbados; 65 Jerry Bauer; 66-67 J. Netherton/The Image Bank; 69 Alison Speckman/Courtesy of the Putnam & Grosset Group; 70-85 Computer photo illustration by Jim Carroll; 85 *inset* Photo by George George; 86, 89 *detail* British Museum, Bridgeman Art Library, London; 90-91 British Museum/Michael Holford, London; 91 *b* Courtesy of McGraw Hill, Inc.; 101 *inset* Photo by Chuck Windsor/Courtesy of Harper Collins Publishers; 103 Tony Freeman/ PhotoEdit; 104 Nancy Sheehan/©D.C. Heath; 106 *t* Elizabeth Hamlin/Stock Boston; *b* Nancy Sheehan/ ©D.C. Heath; 108 ©1948 M.C. Escher Foundation-Baarn-Holland. All rights reserved;111 Laurie Rubin/Tony Stone Images; 112 *t* Jean Claude LeJeune/Stock Boston; *b* Susan Lapides; 114 *t* J. Sulley/The Image Works; *b* Richard Hutchings/PhotoEdit; **Back cover** *t* Richard Haynes/©D.C. Heath; *c* Sarah Putnam/©D.C. Heath; *b* John Owens/©D.C. Heath.

Full Pronunciation Key for Footnoted Words

(Each pronunciation and definition is adapted from *Scott, Foresman Advanced Dictionary* by E.L. Thorndike and Clarence L. Barnhart.)

The pronunciation of each footnoted word is shown just after the word, in this way: **abbreviate** [ə brē′ vē āt]. The letters and signs used are pronounced as in the words below. The mark ′ is placed after a syllable with primary or heavy accent, as in the example above. The mark ′ after a syllable shows a secondary or lighter accent, as in **abbreviation** [ə brē′ vē ā′ shən].

Some words, taken from foreign languages, are spoken with sounds that do not otherwise occur in English. Symbols for these sounds are given in the key as "foreign sounds."

a	hat, cap	j	jam, enjoy	u	cup, butter	**foreign sounds**	
ā	age, face	k	kind, seek	u̇	full, put		
ä	father, far	l	land, coal	ü	rule, move	Y as in French *du*.	
		m	me, am	v	very, save	Pronounce (ē) with	
b	bad, rob	n	no, in	w	will, woman	the lips rounded as	
ch	child, much	ng	long, bring	y	young, yet	for (ü).	
d	did, red			z	zero, breeze		
		o	hot, rock	zh	measure, seizure	à as in French *ami*.	
e	let, best	ō	open, go			Pronounce (ä) with	
ē	equal, be	ô	order, all	ə represents:		the lips spread and	
ėr	term, learn	oi	oil, voice		a in about	held tense.	
		ou	house, out		e in taken		
f	fat, if				i in pencil	œ as in French *peu*.	
g	go, bag	p	paper, cup		o in lemon	Pronounce (ā) with the	
h	he, how	r	run, try		u in circus	lips rounded as for (ō).	
		s	say, yes				
i	it, pin	sh	she, rush			N as in French *bon*.	
ī	ice, five	t	tell, it			The N is not pro-	
		th	thin, both			nounced, but shows	
		ᴛʜ	then, smooth			that the vowel before	
						it is nasal.	
						H as in German *ach*.	
						Pronounce (k) without	
						closing the breath	
						passage.	

Adventures and Adventurers

EATH
DDLE LEVEL
TERATURE

HEATH
MIDDLELEVEL
LITERATURE

Adventures and Adventurers

THEME
CHALLENGES AND ACHIEVEMENTS

AUTHORS

Donna Alvermann
Linda Miller Cleary
Kenneth Donelson
Donald Gallo
Alice Haskins
J. Howard Johnston
John Lounsbury
Alleen Pace Nilsen
Robert Pavlik
Jewell Parker Rhodes
Alberto Alvaro Ríos
Sandra Schurr
Lyndon Searfoss
Julia Thomason
Max Thompson
Carl Zon

D.C. Heath and Company
Lexington, Massachusetts / Toronto, Ontario

STAFF CREDITS

EDITORIAL Barbara A. Brennan, Helen Byers, Christopher Johnson, Kathleen Kennedy Kelley, Owen Shows, Rita M. Sullivan
Proofreading: JoAnne B. Sgroi

CONTRIBUTING WRITERS Nance Davidson, Florence Harris

SERIES DESIGN Robin Herr

BOOK DESIGN Caroline Bowden, Daniel Derdula, Susan Geer, Diana Maloney, Angela Sciaraffa, Bonnie Chayes Yousefian
Art Editing: Carolyn Langley

PHOTOGRAPHY *Series Photography Coordinator*: Carmen Johnson
Photo Research Supervisor: Martha Friedman
Photo Researchers: Wendy Enright, Linda Finigan, Po-yee McKenna, PhotoSearch, Inc., Gillian Speeth, Denise Theodores
Assignment Photography Coordinators: Susan Doheny, Gayna Hoffman, Shawna Johnston

COMPUTER PREPRESS Ricki Pappo, Kathy Meisl
Richard Curran, Michele Locatelli

PERMISSIONS Dorothy B. McLeod

PRODUCTION Patrick Connolly

Cover Photograph: © Zefa/Josef Mallaun, The Stock Market. **Cover Design:** Steve Snider

Published simultaneously in Canada

Printed in the United States of America

International Standard Book Number: 0-669-32104-4 (soft cover)
4 5 6 7 8 9 10-RRD-99 98 97

International Standard Book Number: 0-669-38173-X (hard cover)
4 5 6 7 8 9 10-RRD-99 98 97

Middle Level Authors

Donna Alvermann, University of Georgia
Alice Haskins, Howard County Public Schools, Maryland
J. Howard Johnston, University of South Florida
John Lounsbury, Georgia College
Sandra Schurr, University of South Florida
Julia Thomason, Appalachian State University
Max Thompson, Appalachian State University
Carl Zon, California Assessment Collaborative

Literature and Language Arts Authors

Linda Miller Cleary, University of Minnesota
Kenneth Donelson, Arizona State University
Donald Gallo, Central Connecticut State University
Alleen Pace Nilsen, Arizona State University
Robert Pavlik, Cardinal Stritch College, Milwaukee
Jewell Parker Rhodes, Arizona State University
Alberto Alvaro Ríos, Arizona State University
Lyndon Searfoss, Arizona State University

Teacher Consultants

Suzanne Aubin, Patapsco Middle School, Ellicott City, Maryland
Judy Baxter, Newport News Public Schools, Newport News, Virginia
Saundra Bryn, Director of Research and Development, El Mirage, Arizona
Lorraine Gerhart, Elmbrook Middle School, Elm Grove, Wisconsin
Kathy Tuchman Glass, Burlingame Intermediate School, Burlingame, California
Lisa Mandelbaum, Crocker Middle School, Hillsborough, California
Lucretia Pannozzo, John Jay Middle School, Katonah, New York
Carol Schultz, Jerling Junior High, Orland Park, Illinois
Jeanne Siebenman, Grand Canyon University, Phoenix, Arizona
Gail Thompson, Garey High School, Pomona, California
Rufus Thompson, Grace Yokley School, Ontario, California
Tom Tufts, Conniston Middle School, West Palm Beach, Florida
Edna Turner, Harpers Choice Middle School, Columbia, Maryland
C. Anne Webb, Buerkle Junior High School, St. Louis, Missouri
Geri Yaccino, Thompson Junior High School, St. Charles, Illinois

CONTENTS

THE LITERATURE

Knight with maiden German, 14th century, illuminated manuscript

ASKING BIG QUESTIONS ABOUT THE LITERATURE

What makes an adventure? 102

How do people react to their adventures? 103

What are adventurers like? 104

How are you an adventurer? 105

ADVENTURE MAZE

*A*fter reading a thrilling adventure story, does your imagination sweep you into your own adventures? You can use some of those imaginings to plan a daring journey that challenges the traveler at every turn. Look at this maze. Can you find the way to the center? Create a similar Adventure Maze on paper and watch a classmate find a way through it.

Build an adventure. 1

Finding a path through a maze can be an adventure, but it's not enough of a challenge for your travelers. You'll need to provide some surprises along the way. Alone or with a group, brainstorm challenging obstacles that a daring traveler might face. What kind of surprises do travelers encounter in TV and movie adventures? Do they encounter volcanoes? Earthquakes? A tunnel of snakes? Make a list of obstacles and challenges that you could build into your maze.

Put it all together.

Now design your maze. Follow these steps.

1. Draw a large square or circle and divide it into equal parts.
2. Draw a path through the parts. Then add twists, turns, and dead ends.
3. Add obstacles at the twists and turns. Force the traveler to choose between dangers.

When you're satisfied, copy the maze neatly. Decorate it too.

Enjoy your adventure.

Ask a classmate to travel through the maze, explaining his or her decisions. Watch and listen. What challenges does the traveler avoid, face, dread, enjoy? Why?

In your journal, write about your own adventure in planning the maze. What was a challenge, and what was exciting? You may find that creating an adventure can be an adventure in itself.

Asking Big Questions About the Theme

? What makes an adventure?

What stories, movies, TV shows, and experiences come to mind when you think of the word *adventure*? What features do all adventures share? In a small group, discuss these questions. Then create an exciting adventure. Write the first paragraph of an adventure story on a sheet of paper. Take turns adding paragraphs to the story. Allow each person just one minute of writing time.

Share the adventure with other groups or the class. Discuss which are the best adventures and why.

? How do people react to their adventures?

Imagine that you and a friend have just been shipwrecked on a tropical island. How do you feel? Would you be frightened or would you see your adventure as an exciting challenge? Act out the scene with a partner. Then perform your scene for classmates and watch their performances. Compare your reactions to their reactions by making a diagram like the one below.

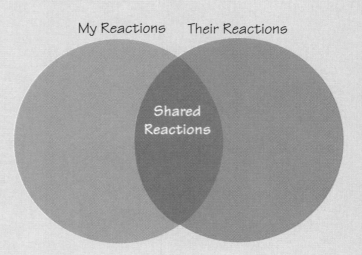

My Reactions   Their Reactions

Shared Reactions

What are adventurers like?

Someone's in danger on Menace Mountain, and a daring adventurer is needed to come to the rescue! Write a want ad for an adventurer. Work with a partner or group to decide what qualities to ask for in the ad. First, discuss the qualities of some real or fictional adventurers. Then, in your journal, make a Word Map like the one below. List words, phrases, actions that the word *adventurer* brings to mind. Finally write an ad for an adventurer.

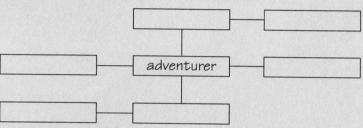

adventurer

How are you an adventurer?

In your journal, write a response to this final Big Question. Use some of the sentence starters below to get your ideas going.

- My biggest (strangest, funniest, most exciting) adventure was . . .
- I am an adventurer because . . .
- Things I find exciting are . . .
- When faced with a challenge, I feel . . .

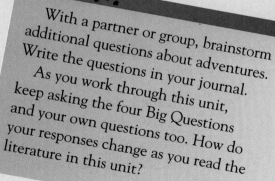

NOW Think!

With a partner or group, brainstorm additional questions about adventures. Write the questions in your journal. As you work through this unit, keep asking the four Big Questions and your own questions too. How do your responses change as you read the literature in this unit?

Portrait of Annie Peck

Friday, August 28-
Saturday, September 5, 1908
Yungay, Peru

Annie Smith Peck pushed open the shutters and leaned out the window. She looked past the square in Yungay's[1] center, down a narrow dirt road lined by red-roofed houses, past the fields of wheat and corn, up to the snow-capped twin peaks of Huascarán,[2] the highest mountain in Peru. It was a maze of snow and

1. **Yungay** [yün′ gī]
2. **Huascarán** [wäs kä rän′]

EFUSED TO BE CLIMBED

DOREEN RAPPAPORT

ice at over 22,000 feet (6,700 meters) above sea level. No one had ever climbed it to the top.

Huascarán is shaped like a horse's saddle. Thousands of feet of rocky slopes lead to an immense glacier that spans the twin peaks. The glacier is a moving mass of ice. Anyone climbing it may encounter dangerous crevasses—deep fissures[3] that drop suddenly into abysses[4]—and snow avalanches that unexpectedly thunder down.

Climate is another danger. Ice-cold winds batter the mountain.

3. **fissures** [fish′ ərz]: long, narrow splits.
4. **abysses** [ə bis′ əz]: deep openings in the earth.

At such high altitudes there is less oxygen to breathe. The body's metabolism[5] slows down. Every step tests a person's physical endurance to its limits. No wonder no one had ever reached the top.

In the last four years Annie had tried five times to scale these snowy peaks and icy crags, and five times she had failed. Her last attempt had been only ten days ago.

People constantly asked her why she pursued this dangerous, impossible dream. Annie didn't try to make them understand. She didn't think that people who viewed mountains from valleys or from railroad trains could ever understand the beauty and power of those white-domed peaks floating toward the deep blue of the sky, belonging more to heaven than to earth.

But it wasn't only the beauty of mountains that attracted Annie. Ever since childhood Annie had taken on challenges. As the youngest child and only girl among three brothers, she had learned not to be intimidated by men's supposedly superior physical strength and endurance. When her brothers refused to let her join them in their games, she practiced until she was as good as they were, if not better. When her brothers went off to college, Annie vowed she would go too, even though there were only a few women's colleges and fewer coed colleges at that time. In 1874 she gained admission to the University of Michigan. She majored in Greek and excelled in every subject she studied. But earning a college degree wasn't enough for Annie. She went on to get a master's in Greek and became one of the first women college professors in the United States.

In 1885, on a trip through Switzerland, Annie saw the 14,690 foot (4,478 meter) Matterhorn, and her passion for the classics started to give way to a passion for mountain climbing. She became determined to scale its "frowning walls." She prepared by climbing smaller mountains in Greece and Switzerland. In 1888 she and her oldest brother scaled California's 14,162 foot (4,316 meter) Mount Shasta. In 1895 she became the third woman to conquer the Matterhorn.

5. **metabolism** [mə tab′ ə liz′ əm]: bodily processes that maintain life in a living being.

She became instantaneously famous. People marveled at the endurance and courage of this woman, forty-five years old and barely five feet tall. Her climbing outfit—a hip-length tunic,[6] short pants, high boots and a canvas hat tied with a veil under her chin—created as much of a sensation as her daring achievement. How unladylike, men said, and many women agreed. But Annie refused to wear floor-length skirts like other women climbers. It was ridiculous and dangerous to dress "like a lady."

Annie's triumph over the Matterhorn propelled her on. She gave up teaching and became a full-time climber, supporting herself by lecturing about her adventures. By 1900, having achieved over twenty successful climbs, she was recognized as one of the world's foremost climbers in a field still considered a man's sport.

But that wasn't enough for Annie either. She became determined to conquer a mountain no man had ever conquered. That mountain was Huascarán.

Annie closed the shutters, picked up her clothing sack and a heavy wool poncho and went downstairs. The four porters were carrying the expedition equipment outside. One sack held the ice axes, climbing irons, poles and ropes. Annie's lightweight silk tent and the sleeping bags were rolled up in the corner. The kerosene stove and kettles filled a third sack. Food was in a fourth bag. In a fifth bag were Annie's camera and a hypsometer, which she would use to measure the altitude at the top of Huascarán to establish its exact height.

Annie gave her clothing and poncho to one of the men. As temperatures dropped on the climb, she would eventually wear everything in the sack: two woolen face masks, fur mittens, black woolen sleeves, three suits of lightweight wool underwear, two pairs of tights, two pairs of woolen stockings, knickers,[7] two flannel shirts, a jacket and two sweaters. Her hiking boots were big and clumsy. They had to be four sizes larger than her regular shoes to accommodate the heavy stockings.

6. **tunic** [tü′nik]: a long shirt.
7. **knickers** [nik′ərz]: short, loose trousers gathered at the knee.

Unfortunately none of her clothing was water- or windproof. Admiral Peary,[8] the famous Arctic explorer, had lent her a waterproof Eskimo suit, but on her last climb it had fallen irretrievably out of a porter's hands into a crevasse.

She went outside. Her guides, Gabriel Zumtaugwald and Rudolf Taugwalder, were supervising the packing of supplies on the horses. Like other expert climbers, Annie favored Swiss guides. They knew so much about snow and rock that they always chose the most practical and safe paths even when in unfamiliar territory.

Gabriel and Rudolf were skilled but stubborn, and impatient whenever Annie made suggestions—even though she was their employer and knew the mountain better than they did. They wouldn't listen when she suggested they wear at least two pairs of wool stockings. Her guides of two years ago, wearing two pairs of stockings, had barely escaped losing their toes to frostbite. They didn't like taking advice from a woman.

The party set off on horseback for the three-hour ride to the copper mines, where they would rest overnight before hiking to the snow line. The horses trotted down the narrow walled road out of the village and soon ascended to where the houses became more scattered. The air was fragrant with blossoms of yellow broom and blue larkspur. Fields of wheat and corn blanketed the landscape with deep yellows. On the mountain snow was falling. An occasional villager, bent from years of working in the fields, passed them on the road.

When they arrived at the mines, Annie felt faint and a bit sick. She didn't know why. The ride had been easy enough. She ate a small bowl of soup and two boiled eggs and lay down to take a nap. But sleep did not come easily.

When Annie saw clouds over the mountain the next morning, she postponed the ascent. The fresh snow needed at least another day of melting by the sun and freezing at night to make the mountain suitable for climbing.

8. **Admiral Peary** [pir′ē]: United States naval officer who discovered the North Pole in 1909.

Saddle and north peak of Huascarán

At eight A.M. the next day they set out for the snow line. The walking was easy. Within six hours, they reached the first campsite, set up their tents, had soup and tea, and went to bed at sunset.

By seven the following morning they were at the glacier. The porters put climbing irons over their shoes to bite into the surface of snow and ice. Annie and the guides wore boots studded with nails. Annie's studs weren't as pointed as her guides', but she didn't want to wear climbing irons. On the last ascent the strap on one of Annie's irons had been too tight. It had hindered her circulation. Two of her toes and the top of her right foot had gotten slightly frostbitten.

The climbing continued to be easy. Annie's instinct to wait the extra day had been right. The snow was easy to walk on. In seven hours they were well up in the saddle of the mountain. They pitched their tent under a snow wall. But despite the wall's shelter, a chilling wind swept through the tent all night.

There was no wind the next morning, but the air was thin and bitter cold. Annie thought it was the coldest day she had ever experienced on the mountain in all her climbs.

The ascent became radically steeper. Gabriel went first, probing for crevasses with his pickaxe and cutting small zigzag steps up the almost perpendicular[9] wall. Annie, tied to a rope with Rudolf and a porter named Lucas, followed, pushing her pole into the glassy surface. The pole's pointed iron provided leverage,[10] but the climbing was difficult and exhausting.

An hour later they reached a bridge of ice over a crevasse. Annie hesitated to cross it because there was no way to tell how strong it was. Rudolf crawled quickly over it on his hands and knees, then sat on the other side and wound the rope, still tied to Annie and the porter, around his ice axe to anchor it. Annie hurried across next, then knotted her length of rope around her ice axe. Lucas was carrying too much on his back to hurry across. He stepped cautiously onto the ice bridge and suddenly slipped off the bridge and disappeared into the crevasse. Annie heard his cry as she gripped the rope more firmly to keep from being pulled over with him.

"Quick, quick." Gabriel, tied to the other three porters on a second rope, motioned for the porters to untie themselves. He threw their rope down to Lucas, who—though hanging head down—managed to tie it to his own rope and miraculously turn himself upright. He tugged on the rope. Annie and the men pulled him up. Annie was relieved to see him, but was dismayed to see that his

9. **perpendicular** [pėr′ pən dik′ yə lər]: very steep, vertical.
10. **leverage** [lev′ ər ij]: increased ability to climb.

pack, with the new stove in it, was not with him. They couldn't go on without the stove.

"I'll go down for it," Gabriel said, and within seconds he was lowered down on a rope. Annie was worried. They were at least 19,000 feet above sea level. Exerting oneself at this height was dangerous. And maybe it was a fool's errand. There was no telling how deep the crevasse was or if Gabriel could even find the pack.

She waited impatiently. Ten minutes later Gabriel pulled on the rope. They hauled him up. The pack, with the stove in it, was in his hands.

They moved on. By dark they were at the top of the saddle. Tomorrow, with any luck, she would reach the top. *Finally, after all these years.*

Winds battered the tent all night and were so fierce the next morning that Annie suggested postponing the final climb until the wind died down.

"It's too dangerous," she said, "and we need rest." She was exhausted from the last two days and knew that the men had to be too, even though they wouldn't admit it.

"It'll be less windy higher up," countered Rudolf.

"I know this mountain," Annie argued. "Unless the wind dies down altogether, it'll be worse higher up."

"I think Rudolf's right," said Gabriel. "We should go on."

Annie yielded reluctantly. They agreed to leave the porters behind.

She was wearing every stitch of clothing she had packed but the poncho. She didn't want to put it on yet. It was too clumsy. She slipped a mask over her face and neck and put on her fur mittens. Rudolf put on his face mask. Gabriel didn't have a mask. Annie offered him her extra one and was surprised when he graciously accepted it.

"Could one of you carry my poncho?" This was asking a big favor, for at this altitude every extra bit of weight was a strain.

Rudolf acted as if he didn't hear her. "I'll do it," said Gabriel, even though he was already burdened with the food sack and the bag with hypsometer and camera.

Within an hour of climbing the sun was higher in the sky and Annie's hands were sweating inside the fur mittens. She took off her fur mittens and exchanged them for two pairs of woolen mittens in Rudolf's sack. One pair did not cover the fingers.

Up, up, the climbing was slow and strenuous. The cold winds had blown away the lighter snow on the surface, and the glacier was like glass.

"I've never seen such large patches of ice on any mountain in Switzerland," Rudolf said.

"I told you Huascarán is the fiercest mountain in the world," Annie said proudly.

They turned a ridge, and the wind knifed through Annie. She took her poncho from Gabriel. She needed her fur mittens. They stopped, and Rudolf opened his sack.

"Which ones first?" he asked, tucking Annie's wool sleeves and fur mittens under his right arm.

Hold on to them tight, Annie thought, but she didn't say it.

"The sleeves."

Rudolf reached under his arm, but the wind got there first. Annie watched a fur mitten blow over the precipice.[11] She was furious. There was no way to retrieve it. The woolen gloves would never be warm enough, and now her hands would probably get frostbitten.

Rudolf apologized. Annie ignored the apology. She hastily put the one fur mitten on over the other gloves on her right hand, which carried her pickaxe. It was more exposed to the cold than the left hand.

Up, up. The air was so thin, Annie had trouble breathing. It became harder and harder to move her legs. It was even hard pushing the pickaxe into the icy surface.

They stopped to eat. The meat and bread had frozen in the sack, but it didn't matter. They were too tired to eat much anyway. They nibbled on chocolate and raisins and drank the partially frozen tea in Rudolf's canteen.

"I'm too tired to go any farther," Rudolf announced.

Annie didn't want to stop. They were probably only an hour

---

11. **precipice** [pres′ ə pis]: very steep, almost vertical mountainside.

Highest camp, east side of Huascarán

away from the top. *So close now!* "You can rest and we'll go ahead," she said to Rudolf.

"No, let's all rest for an hour and then go on," said Gabriel. Annie agreed reluctantly.

The hour's rest did little to revive them. When they started climbing again, the cold, thin air was so debilitating[12] that they had to stop frequently.

At three P.M. they rounded the final rise leading to the top of the mountain. The wind was stronger than ever. Annie's left hand felt numb. She pulled off her mitten and saw that the hand was nearly black. She rubbed her fingers vigorously with snow to revive the circulation. The rubbing made her fingers ache, a good sign that

12. **debilitating** [di bil′ ə tāt ing]: causing to become weak.

they weren't frostbitten. She tucked her hands inside the poncho, grateful for its length.

"We'd better measure the altitude now," said Gabriel. "It may be too windy at the top."

They untied themselves from each other. Rudolf wandered off, but Annie paid no attention. She was too busy shielding the hypsometer from the wind as Gabriel struck one match after another, hoping to light the candles so they could boil the water. A hypsometer is an instrument that is able to determine altitude in relation to the boiling point of water, which decreases as altitude increases. Annie wanted to know exactly how high she was and whether she had set a world's record.

She looked around for Rudolf. *Where is he? Maybe if he helped, we could get the candles lit.* After twenty tries, they gave up. Annie was disappointed. Now she could only estimate how high the mountain really was.

"We'd better move on to the top. It's half past three," said Gabriel.

Annie looked around for Rudolf again.

Suddenly he appeared. "I've been to the top," he said.

How dare he steal the honor? He wouldn't have dared do this if I were a man. Just an hour ago he wanted to quit. And he hasn't done half as much work as Gabriel. The guides knew she expected, as was the tradition, that as organizer of the expedition she would be the first to place her foot on the top of the mountain.

I won't tell him now how mad I am, but if we get down alive, I'll tell him. If we get down alive . . . The thought frightened her.

She set out for the top without a word. The winds battered her, and several times she had to stop and lean on her pickaxe to catch her breath.

"Don't go too near the edge," warned Gabriel, stepping aside to let her arrive first on the top of the mountain.

I'm here after all these years. She wanted to shout for joy, but there was no time to waste. Soon it would be dark. It had taken seven hours to climb to the top. How long would it take to go down? Steep rocks and icy slopes were far more dangerous to descend than to climb. She hurriedly photographed the views on all sides.

They tied themselves together again. Rudolf led, cutting the steps. Annie was in the middle, Gabriel at the rear. Their lives depended on Gabriel. If they slipped and he couldn't hold the rope to stop their fall, all three could plunge to death.

They turned a ridge and confronted a sixty-degree slope. "Be careful," said Gabriel.

Something black flew by.

"What is it?" Annie cried.

"One of my mittens," said Rudolf. "I took it off to fasten my shoe."

Rudolf worked fast, cutting the steps the size of toeholds. Small steps were fine going up, but dangerous going down. Annie zigzagged her way down the steep slope. There was nothing to hold on to. She wished she had her climbing irons now. She needed that kind of grip on this glassy surface.

She missed a step and slid three feet. Gabriel's strong hands held the rope tightly, and she regained her footing. A few seconds later she missed another step and slipped again. She was about to yell, "It's not serious," when she slid again. Five, ten, fifteen feet down the incline. Again Gabriel's strong hands checked her fall.

Studio photograph of Annie Peck on the summit of Huascarán

"Get up," he yelled, but the rope was twisted so tightly around her waist that she couldn't move. The men came to her and hauled her up.

They moved on. Her poncho, swaying wide in the wind, constantly hid her view of her next step. Down, down she stepped. Again she slipped. Her fall pulled Rudolf down, too. Gabriel's strong hands checked both their falls.

I don't think we'll make it down alive. It's too dark and too slippery. And I'm so tired.

She slid again and again. She tried to convince herself that they would make it down alive.

She lost track of how much time was passing as she concentrated on each step. She wasn't even aware, three hours later, that they were on the gentler slope just over the campsite until Gabriel shouted, "We're safe. Now you can slide if you like."

Annie laughed. They untied themselves from each other and dragged their tired bodies toward the tent. It was half past ten. They were too tired to eat and almost too tired to lie down. But safety felt good.

In the tent Annie noticed both of Rudolf's hands were black. "Rub them hard," she said. But Rudolf was so weak, he couldn't do it. *I'll do it,* thought Annie, but she was too tired to do it. *I'll get a porter to do it.* But in her tiredness, she forgot.

The three climbers huddled together on one side of the tent across from the porters. Annie wrapped the blankets around herself and the two men. When she realized the middle was the warmest spot, she moved to the outside and let Rudolf be in the center.

When they awakened the next morning, the wind was fierce. They were too exhausted to complete the rest of the trip down the mountain. By Thursday the wind had abated,[13] and feeling more rested, they started down the mountain. They arrived at the mine two days later, on Saturday morning, September 5, about 10 A.M. After breakfast, they returned to Yungay.

Becoming the first person to climb to the top of Huascarán brought Annie world fame. The Peruvian government gave her a gold medal. In

---

13. **abated** [ə bāt′ əd]: lessened in force.

1928 the Lima Geographical Society named the north peak of Huascarán *Ana Peck*. But Annie's triumph over Huascarán was marred for her by the subsequent[14] amputation of Rudolf's left hand, a finger of his right hand and half of one foot.

Because the hypsometer had not worked, Annie could only estimate Huascarán's height. At the saddle she and her guides had measured the altitude at 20,000 feet (6,100 meters). Based on this figure, they estimated that the north and south peaks were at least 23,000 feet (7,000 meters), making Huascarán the highest mountain in Peru and the highest mountain ever scaled by a man or woman.

Fanny Bullock Workman, up to this time the world's highest woman climber, challenged Annie's estimate of Huascarán. Bullock Workman sent a team of scientists to Yungay to measure Huascarán by triangulation: This method uses trigonometry to measure height. Bullock Workman's team concluded that the north and south peaks were no more than 21,812 feet (6,648 meters) and 22,187 feet (6,763 meters) respectively.

Annie eventually conceded that Huascarán was "not so lofty" as she had hoped. Bullock Workman still held the world's altitude record for a woman climber, but Annie had succeeded in climbing a mountain that no man or woman had ever climbed. Annie continued climbing until she was eighty-two years old.

14. **subsequent** [sub′ sə kwənt]: following or happening next.

DOREEN RAPPAPORT

Doreen Rappaport lives in New York City and is the author of several books for young people. Rappaport has also worked on educational programs in American history, literature, and music. The selection you've just read is from *Living Dangerously: American Women Who Risked Their Lives for Adventure*. She has also edited a collection of short autobiographies called *American Women: Their Lives in Their Words*. Rappaport's other books are *The Boston Coffee Party, Escape from Slavery*, and *Trouble at the Mines*.

The Mountain That Refused to Be Climbed 25

FROM

BURNING

GARY SNYDER

JOHN MUIR ON MT. RITTER:

After scanning its face again and again,
I began to scale it, picking my holds
With intense caution. About half-way
To the top, I was suddenly brought to
A dead stop, with arms outspread   5
Clinging close to the face of the rock
Unable to move hand or foot
Either up or down. My doom
Appeared fixed. I MUST fall.
There would be a moment of   10
Bewilderment, and then,
A lifeless rumble down the cliff
To the glacier below.
My mind seemed to fill with a
Stifling smoke. This terrible eclipse   15
Lasted only a moment, when life blazed
Forth again with preternatural[1] clearness.
I seemed suddenly to become possessed
Of a new sense. My trembling muscles
Became firm again, every rift and flaw in   20
The rock was seen as through a microscope,
My limbs moved with a positiveness and precision
With which I seemed to have
Nothing at all to do.

1. **preternatural** [prē′ tər nach′ ər əl]: something above or beyond
   nature.

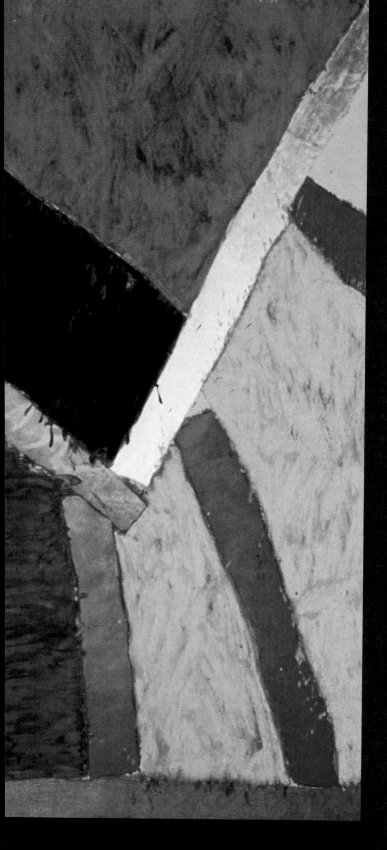

GARY SNYDER

Gary Snyder was born in 1930 in San Francisco. As a young boy growing up in California, Oregon, and Washington, Snyder loved the wilderness and was upset by the destruction of the Pacific Northwest forests. He began to study how Native American cultures live in harmony with nature. As he grew older, Snyder became an expert mountain climber. He worked as a seaman, logger, trail crew member, and forest lookout.

Asian art and Buddhism interested Snyder as well. Many of his poems draw on ancient chants and songs from both Asian and Native American cultures. The poem you've just read is the eighth segment of a long poem sequence called "Burning."

Le Grotte Vecchie (or Untitled)
Michael Goldberg, 1981, powders, pastels, and chalk on canvas, 108¼" x 87"

The Stars, My Goal: Guion Stewart Bluford, Jr.

JIM HASKINS

As the twentieth century progressed, humankind turned its eyes to the unexplored expanse of outer space. While small discoveries were continually being made about our home planet, the earth, the frontier to be explored now stretched beyond the planet and spread to the stars. The 1960s saw years of effort to break the bonds of gravity, effort that had begun with the launching of *Sputnik I* [1] by the Soviet Union in 1957. Inspired by that launching and the concomitant interest in a space program in the United States, a young black high school student, Guion Stewart (Guy) Bluford, Jr., also turned his eyes to the stars.

Guy Bluford was born on November 22, 1942, in Philadelphia, Pennsylvania. His mother was a teacher of special education and his father a mechanical engineer.

---

1. *Sputnik I* [sput′ nik]: first satellite put into space by the former Soviet Union in 1957.

Even as a baby Guy took after his father, showing an interest in mechanical things. He wanted to know how they worked. Guy had lots of mechanical toys to take apart, . . . but what he liked best were things that flew.

That interest was to fill his childhood. His room was filled with airplane models and pictures of airplanes. His interest wasn't so much in flying them, but in designing them. He was fascinated with the way they were put together, why they flew. His father encouraged this curiosity and made his many engineering books available to Guy. Guy knew very early that he wanted to be an aerospace engineer. Guy knew he wanted to design, build, and fly spacecraft, and when he was fifteen and *Sputnik I* was launched, his dreams became even more real.

In the late 1950s, just as the days of the civil rights movement[2] were beginning, the idea of a black man becoming an aerospace engineer was barely conceivable[3] to many people. Although encouraged at home, Guy didn't receive that same encouragement at school. His high school guidance counselor didn't urge him to pursue his goal and go to college; in fact, he was told that he wasn't college material. He was told that he should aim for a technical school or learn a mechanical trade. However, he says,

I really wasn't too concerned about what that counselor said. I just ignored it. I'm pretty sure that all of us have had times when somebody told us we couldn't do this or shouldn't do that. I had such a strong interest in aerospace engineering by then that nothing a counselor said was going to stop me.

2. **civil rights movement:** movement that aimed to assure that every United States citizen, regardless of race or sex, has the rights guaranteed by the Constitution.
3. **conceivable** [kən sēʹ və bəl]: possible to imagine.

In the fall of 1960, Guy started college at Pennsylvania State University, in the aerospace engineering program. In addition to his regular studies, Guy also joined the air force Reserve Officers Training Corps (ROTC), hoping to become a pilot. In his junior year, however, he failed a physical and couldn't qualify as a pilot. During ROTC summer camp that year, he at least passed the flight physical—and got his first ride in an air force T-33 plane. "I changed directions right then and there," he said. "I decided to go into the Air Force as a pilot. I thought that if I were a pilot, I would be a better engineer." During his senior year at Penn State, Guy flew as a pilot in the air force ROTC and, upon graduation, received the ROTC's Distinguished Graduate Award.

While at Penn State, Guy had met and married Linda Tull, a fellow student; after graduation he joined the air force, moving to Arizona with his wife and new son, Guion III, who had been born in June of 1964. His second son, James Trevor, was born in 1965, just at the time the Vietnam War was becoming an important factor in the lives of many Americans.

For the next several years, Guy saw little of his family. As pilot of an F-4C fighter plane, he was assigned to the 557th Tactical Fighter Squadron, based in Cam Ranh Bay,[4] South Vietnam. During his tour of duty he flew 144 combat missions and received ten air force medals. But he had not forgotten his goal of becoming an aerospace engineer and flying in outer space.

When Guy returned to the United States, he applied to the Air Force Institute of Technology, receiving a master's degree in 1974 and, in 1978, a Ph.D. in aerospace engineering. His doctoral thesis was entitled "A Numerical Solution of Supersonic and Hypersonic Viscous Flow Fields Around Thin Planar Delta Wings." As he explains:

Delta wings are triangular wings. I calculated how the air goes around the wings at speeds greater than the speed of sound—three to four times the

4. **Cam Ranh Bay** (käm rän bā]

speed of sound and faster. If you had picked a place anywhere along a wing, I could have told you what the pressure, the density, and the velocity of the air was above and below that place. I developed a computer program that could do that.

The same year Guy received his Ph.D., he applied to enter the astronaut training program at NASA (the National Aeronautics and Space Administration). NASA seemed, to Guy, to be the ideal place to put both his engineering and piloting skills to use, although he wasn't sure if he would be accepted. In 1978 alone, 8,878 other people had applied for the program. A few weeks later, however, he learned that he had been accepted. It was the fulfillment of a dream. Bluford and his family quickly moved to Houston, where he began his training.

The astronaut training program lasted a year and involved studying subjects such as shuttle systems, geology, medicine, aerodynamics,[5] communications, and astronomy. It also involved a great deal of travel.

Sputnik, 1957

We went to a lot of the NASA space centers, including Kennedy Space Center at Cape Canaveral, Florida; Marshall Space Center in Huntsville, Alabama, where they develop the engines; and Rockwell Aircraft Company on the West Coast, where they build the shuttles. We traveled around the country, meeting all of the people associated with the shuttle program.

5. **aerodynamics** [er′ ō dī nam′ iks]: branch of science that deals with pressure or resistance on flying bodies by air or other gases in motion.

By 1979, Guy Bluford was a full-fledged astronaut, qualified to go into space. He spent the next several years in further training, flying the "shuttle simulators" in both Houston and California, hoping and waiting, as were all the astronauts, to be chosen for that special ride beyond the skies of earth.

The shuttle program had begun in 1972, three years after Neil Armstrong and Edwin Aldrin had taken their historic walk on the moon. After the moon landing, interest in the space program had waned[6] somewhat. The 1970s were full of problems here on earth that diverted public interest: the Watergate scandals[7] of the Nixon administration, the Vietnam War,[8] and rising inflation[9] in the economy. One reason NASA began the shuttle program was to save money. The shuttle, unlike earlier rockets, was reusable. More versatile than the earlier rockets, it served not only as transportation, but also as a laboratory and living quarters. It could carry many things into space and was, compared to the rockets, much larger.

The first space shuttle, *Columbia*, was launched in April of 1981. The second shuttle, *Challenger*, went into service in 1983. On its second flight—two months before the flight Guy Bluford would be on—one of three mission specialists was Dr. Sally Ride, the first American woman in space.

Guy Bluford did not want to be known as merely a "black astronaut": he wanted to be known as a man who did a good job. All of the astronauts shared this view. As Sally Ride said about all the publicity her flight had generated, "I didn't go into the space program to make money or be famous." In 1983, when Guy was told that he was scheduled for the next *Challenger* flight, he was exhilarated—

---

6. **waned** [wānd]: lessened, grown smaller.
7. **Watergate scandals:** burglary of the Democratic Party Headquarters in 1972 at the Watergate buildings in Washington, D.C., and other illegal actions, resulting in the resignation of President Richard M. Nixon.
8. **Vietnam War** [vē et′ näm′]: war fought by South Vietnam, the United States, and their allies against the Vietcong (communist guerrillas), North Vietnam, and their allies from about 1957 to 1973.
9. **inflation** [in flā′ shən]: sharp increase in prices caused by the circulation of too much paper money or bank credit.

not to be the first black American in space, but because, finally, he would be doing what he had dreamed of all his life: putting *all* his skills to use.

On August 30, 1983, thunderstorms had swept across the sandy expanse of Cape Canaveral, Florida, but the air was now clear. In the hot, damp night, the *Challenger* stood over five stories high on launch pad 39-A. It was lighted both from above, by lights on the gantry,[10] and from below, as this would be the first nighttime launch since *Apollo 17* in 1972.

The five men inside the *Challenger* were busy checking equipment, listening to the hollow voice of mission control as the final countdown proceeded. Aboard were thirty-four-year-old Dale Gardner, a navy fighter pilot and engineer; Dr. William Thornton, at fifty-four the oldest person to fly in space; Richard Truly, a Vietnam War veteran and test pilot, who would serve as commander of the shuttle; thirty-nine-year-old Daniel Brandenstein, a navy commander; and Guion Bluford, Jr., who would serve as mission specialist. Guy was in charge of the experiments the crew were to conduct during the flight.

Portrait of Guy Bluford

Just before lift-off, the crew received a message from President Ronald Reagan. "With this effort," he said, "we acknowledge proudly the first ascent of a black American into space." But Guy wasn't thinking of that; he was thinking of the flight. He was eager, curious, and excited, but not afraid: "We'd spent so much time training for the mission and riding in shuttle simulators[11] that we were pretty well prepared. It's like preparing for an exam. You study as much as you can, and the better prepared you are, the less frightened you are about taking the exam."

10. **gantry** [gan′ trē]: bridge-like framework for supporting the space shuttle while on the ground.
11. **simulators** [sim′ yə lāt ərz]: mock space shuttles that imitate a real journey into space to prepare the astronauts for the real thing.

At 2:32 A.M., August 30, 1983, fire blazed from the rockets and lit up the Florida landscape. As Richard Truly described it, "It got brighter and brighter. When the boosters separated it was 500 times brighter than I remember [from past launches]." Dale Gardner tried to twist around for a better view; "I damn near blinded myself," he said later. The brightness of the rockets' flare surprised all of the men.

"But otherwise, there weren't any surprises," Guy said. "What amazed me was that the shuttle flew just like the simulator said it was going to fly. The only differences were the motion, the vibration, and the noise. You don't get those in simulators. When I felt the movement and heard the noise, I thought, Hey, this thing really does take off and roar!"

Once in orbit, Bluford began to operate one of the main experiments, an electrophoresis[12] system designed to separate living cells, aimed at one day producing new medical advances. It was difficult, initially, to work in weightlessness, but also exhilarating. Although all the men had trained for weightlessness in a water-immersion tank,[13] it was still a new sensation. But everything was new and exciting. Circling the earth every ninety minutes, the crew slept, ate, and did their work in that new frontier—space.

On September 5, the shuttle glided to a perfect landing back on earth, at Edwards Air Force Base in California. Only later did NASA reveal that the crew had been in

12. **electrophoresis** [i lek′ trō fə rē′ sis]: movement of extremely small particles of matter influenced by an electric field.
13. **water-immersion tank** [i mėr′ zhən]: tank in which astronauts prepare for the weightlessness of space.

danger: The lining of a solid fuel booster's[14] nozzle had almost burned through during launching. Such an accident would have thrown the shuttle wildly off course, causing it to crash. Fourteen seconds—the time it would have taken for the lining to burn all the way through—was all that had separated the crew and shuttle from disaster.

All who venture to explore the unknown recognize the threat of disaster. This possibility doesn't stop them, however; risk is part of the job. So is determination. Throughout his life, Guion Bluford had one goal in mind—to work and fly in space, and he was determined to let nothing get in the way of achieving that goal. As he has said, it was "difficult at times—I had to struggle through those courses at Penn State—but if you really want to do something and are willing to put in the hard work it takes, then someday—bingo, you've done it!" With this kind of stick-to-itiveness, it isn't surprising that Guy Bluford became the first black American explorer of space.

14. **solid fuel booster:** rocket engine used as the principal force that allows a rocket or a missile to take off.

JIM HASKINS

Jim Haskins was born in 1941 in Montgomery, Alabama. After attending college in Arizona, Haskins went to New York City for graduate study and stayed.

Haskins's first book, *Diary of a Harlem Schoolteacher*, developed from his experience teaching Special Education at a New York City public school. After that, he wanted to write for young people: "I knew exactly the kinds of books I wanted to do—books about current events and books about important black people." He has written the biographies of many public figures, including Barbara Jordan. Haskins says, "I want children today, black and white, to be able to find books about black people and black history in case they want to read them."

WHAT I WANT TO BE WHEN I GROW UP

MARTHA BROOKS

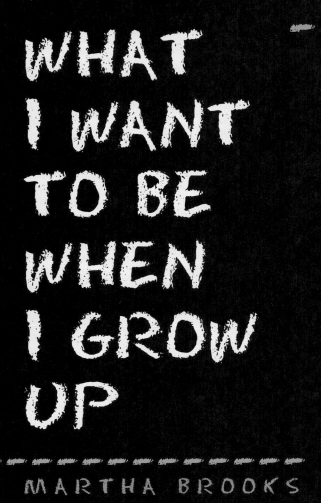

On the third Thursday afternoon of every month, I take my mother's hastily written note to the office where the school secretary, Mrs. Audrey Plumas, a nervous lady with red blotchy skin, looks at it and tells me I can go. Then I leave George J. Sherwood Junior High, walk down to the corner, and wait for the 2:47 bus which will get me downtown just in time for my four o'clock orthodontic[1] appointment.

I hate taking the bus. It's always too hot even in thirty-below-zero weather. The fumes and the lurching make me sick. The people are weird.

Mom says with the amount of money she's forking out to give me a perfect smile I shouldn't complain. "Andrew," she says cheerfully, "taking the bus is an education. It's a rare opportunity for people of all types and from all walks of life to be in an enforced environment that allows them to really get a close look at one another." She then adds, meaningfully, "Think of it as research for your life's work." She goes on like that even though she can't possibly know what she's talking about because she's a business executive who drives a brand-new air-conditioned Volvo to work every day.

I made the mistake, a while ago, of telling her I want to be a journalist when I grow up. Out of all the things I've ever wanted to be—an undersea photographer, a vet for the London Zoo, a missionary in Guatemala—she feels this latest choice is the most practical and has latched on to it like it's the last boat leaving the harbor.

1. **orthodontic** [ôr′ thə don′ tik]: having to do with straightening teeth.

She feels that, at fourteen, I have to start making "important career choices." This, in spite of the fact that my teeth stick out from having stopped sucking my thumb only six years ago.

On the bus last month, I happened to sit across the aisle from a girl with pasty white skin and pale eyes lined in some kind of indigo[2] gunk. We were right at the front, near the driver. The bus was so full there was no escape. She kept smiling like she had an imaginary friend. Every so often she'd lean forward and go, "Phe-ew," breathing right on me. The woman beside me wanted the whole bench to herself and edged me over with her enormous thighs until I was flattened against the metal railing. (I can't stand older women who wear stockings rolled, like floppy little doughnuts, down to their ankles.) She then took the shopping bag from her lap and mashed it between her ankles and mine as a further precaution[3] that I wouldn't take up any more room than I had coming to me. Hot, numb with misery, and totally grossed out, I closed my eyes and lost track of time. I went six extra stops and was fifteen minutes late for my appointment.

The old lady who runs the orthodontist's office also seems to run Dr. Fineman, who only appears, mole-like, to run his fingers along your gums and then scurries off to other patients in other rooms. This old lady doesn't like kids unless they are with a parent. The first few months I went with my mother. Mrs. G. Blahuta, Receptionist (that's the sign on this dinosaur's desk), smiled and told me what a brave boy I was. She even exchanged recipes with my mother. That was four years ago. This past time, when I arrived late and gasping because I'm slightly asthmatic,[4] Mrs. Blahuta (the orthodontist calls her Gladys; she has purple hair) scowled and asked me to come to the desk, where I stood, wishing I could die, while she shrilled at me about inconsiderate teenagers who think of no one but themselves and show so little responsibility and motivation it's a wonder they can dress themselves in the morning.

Shaking with humiliation, I sat down to wait my turn beside a blond girl with gold hairs on her beautiful tanned legs. She had been pretending to read a glamour magazine. Her eyebrows shot up as I sat down. She primly[5] inched away and gave me her

2. **indigo** [in′ də gō]: deep violet-blue.
3. **precaution** [pri kô′ shən]: something done beforehand in the hope of getting good results.
4. **asthmatic** [az mat′ ik]: having asthma, a disease that causes breathing difficulties.

back like she was a cat and I was some kind of bug she couldn't even be bothered to tease.

On the trip home another gorgeous pristine-type girl swayed onto the bus two stops after mine. She sat down in the empty seat in front of me and opened the window I'd been too weak from my previous ordeals to tackle. This lifesaving breeze hit my face, along with the sweet, stirring scent of her musky perfume. Gratefully I watched the back of her neck. (She wore her hair up. The backs of girls' necks make me crazy.)

After about five more stops a sandy-haired man, whose stomach rolled like a pumpkin over the belt of his green work pants, got on the bus and sat down beside this breath-stopping girl. She didn't even seem to know he was there, and with great interest stretched her long neck to get a close look at a passing trailer truck loaded with pigs. Their moist snouts poked at whatever air they could get at and you could tell they were on their way to the slaughterhouse. (Why else would pigs be spending a day in the city?)

The sandy-haired man readjusted his cap that was almost too small for his very large head. "Look at all them sausages!" he exclaimed, laughing really loudly at his dumb joke. The girl kept right on looking at the pigs. I could have died for her, but except for her nostrils that flared delicately and her slightly stiffened neck and shoulders, she didn't appear to be bothered at all.

The man playfully nudged her. "Hey!" he chortled, in a voice that could be heard all over the bus. "You like pork chops?"

She turned from the pigs (I noticed her incredibly long eyelashes that were light at the tips) and stared straight at him. His face went into a silly fixed smile. "Excuse me," she said cooly, and got up to leave.

"Oh, your stop comin' up, little lady?" he bellowed as he got up quickly. Pulling at his cap brim, he let her past.

She walked about four steps down the aisle and moved in beside an expensively dressed Chinese lady with bifocals[6] who looked suspiciously back at us, then frowned. I frowned at the fat man so she'd know it had been him, and not me, causing all the commotion.

I couldn't believe it when the man, calling more attention to himself,

5. **primly** [prim′lē]: extremely neatly.
6. **bifocals** [bī fō′ kəlz]: lenses on glasses that have two sections, one for distant vision and the other for near vision.

The Bus Driver George Segal, 1962, plaster, wood, and metal, 7'5" x 51⁵/₈" x 6'4³/4", The Museum of Modern Art, New York

leaned forward and poked a business-type suit person! He said, in what possibly for him was a whisper, "Guess she don't like pigs." The suit person gave him a pained over-the-shoulder smile.

The man finally settled back. "I used to live on a farm. Yup. I did. I really did," he continued to nobody in particular because everybody near was pretending to look out of windows, or read, or be very concerned with what time their watches gave.

"Whew! It's hot!" He all of a sudden got up and reached over the suit person, ruffling his hair. "Oh sorry," he said. "Mind if I open this?" He tugged open the suit's window. The suit shot him a look that suggested he wasn't dealing with a full deck. Which he probably wasn't.

I prayed he would leave, but ten minutes later the girl of my dreams got off the bus. I was left staring at the pork chop man's thick, freckled neck.

His stop wasn't until one before mine. As we pulled away I watched him walk over and strike up a conversation with another complete stranger who was too polite to ignore him.

Like I said, you have to put up with some very weird people when you take the bus.

Today, I pleaded with my mother to drive me downtown. She lay on the couch popping painkillers because yesterday she fell and twisted an ankle and suffered a very small fracture as well. She isn't in a cast or anything and it's her left foot so she doesn't need it to drive with. When I asked her nicely for the second time, explaining that she wouldn't even have to get out of the car, she glared at me a moment and burst into tears. I don't understand why she's so selfish. I hope she gets a migraine[7] from watching soap operas all day.

Can you believe it? I was late

7. **migraine** [mī′ grān]: a severe headache.

again for my appointment. I tried to explain to the purple-haired dinosaur that I'd missed my bus on account of being kept late in science class. (I had to rewrite a test I'd messed up the first time because I was away sick the day the teacher told us to study for it and my friend Gordon, the jerk, was supposed to tell me and forgot to.)

Mrs. Blahuta said snidely that she was surprised I was only twenty minutes late and did I intend to put in an appearance at my next monthly appointment or would they all be kept in suspense until the final moment of the working day, which was five o'clock. Sharp!

She kept me until every last person, except myself, had been checked over. At five to five she ushered me in to the orthodontist as his last appointment for the day. He processed me as if I were some dog in a laboratory and then Gladys dismissed me by holding out my next month's appointment slip like it was a bone I'd probably bury.

I got out onto the street, saw my bus departing, and made a silent vow that for at least a month I wasn't going to speak to any person over the age of eighteen.

At five twenty-two I boarded my bus and all the seats were taken. As we got under way, I suddenly felt sick. I clung to the nearest pole while the bus lurched, braked, accelerated, and picked up three or four passengers at every stop. Heated bodies armed with parcels, babies, books, and briefcases pressed past me. Into his microphone, the driver ordered everyone to the back. I didn't budge. When his voice began to sound as if it were coming from inside a vacuum cleaner, another wave of nausea overcame me and my hands, hot and wet, slipped down the pole.

I hate getting motion sickness. I'm sometimes so sensitive that just looking at, say, a movie of people going fast in a roller coaster can almost make me lose my last meal. Whenever I'm sick in the car, Mom says, "Fix your eyes on objects that are the furthest away. Don't look at anything that'll pass you by."

Remembering that, I turned to face the front of the bus. The furthest thing in my view was the pork chop man. As he was coming straight toward me, I shifted my gaze past his shoulder to a spot of blue that was, I guess, the sky. The bus took another shift and the sudden lurch swung me quickly around to where I'd been. I very nearly lost my battle with nausea to the skirts of a person wearing purple paisley.

Somebody gripped my arm, and said, "One of youse has to get up. This boy's going to be sick."

Immediately two people vacated their seats. Next thing I knew I was sitting beside a window with the pork chop man. He reached around behind me and tugged until wind hit my face.

"Hang your head out, now," he roared. "If you have to puke your guts out just go ahead and don't be shy." He patted my back in a fatherly way with one enormous hand while the other hung like a grizzly paw along the back end of my seat.

I did as I was told, breathed deeply for several seconds, and brought my head back in to have a look at him. I don't think I've ever seen such an enormous man. Up close, I realized he wasn't really so much fat as there was just an awful lot of him. "Name's Earl," he said, solemnly.

"Thanks, Earl," I said. "I'm Andrew."

"Don't have to thank me, Andrew. I joined A.A. two years ago. Haven't touched a drop since. I remember how it felt to be real sick."

I wanted to explain that I wasn't a drinker, but was overcome by another terrible feeling that I might lose control. Earl said, "Hold on, kid," and shoved my head out the window again.

We didn't talk much after that. It wasn't until my stop was coming up that I realized he'd just missed his.

I pulled the buzzer cord and said, "You missed your stop."

"How'd you know that?"

"I noticed you when you were on the bus one other time," I mumbled, embarrassed.

Earl sat back and looked straight ahead. He looked like a man who'd been struck by a thought that was almost too big to handle.

The bus arrived at my stop and Earl hurriedly got to his feet to let me past. I stepped off the bus with him right behind. On the street he said, still amazed, "You noticed me?"

The bus fumed noisily on past us.

"Yeah. Well—there was this girl, first. You came and sat beside her . . ." I trailed off.

"You know," said Earl, "just between you and me, city people aren't friendly. They don't notice nothing. See that old lady, there?"

At the light, an old girl tottered off the curb and started to cross the street. She carried two plastic Safeway bags full of groceries.

Out of the corner of his mouth, in a lisping whisper, Earl informed me, "If she was to fall and hurt herself just enough so she could still walk, not one person would stop and offer to help her home with those bags."

"That's true," I said, thinking that

if they did, they'd probably turn around and help themselves to her purse.

We started across the street. I felt better, now that we were off the bus. I actually started to feel a little hungry. I wondered how I was going to say good-bye to Earl. I was afraid he might want to talk to me for a long time. He walked slowly and I felt obliged to keep pace with him.

We reached the other side and stopped on the sidewalk. All the while he kept going on about the time he'd taken some guy to emergency at the General Hospital. The guy had almost bled to death before they could get anybody's attention.

Without hardly pausing to breathe, Earl cornered me with his desperately lonely eyes and launched into another story. I made out like I was really interested but to tell the truth I was thinking about my favorite TV program, which would be on that very moment, and about how Mom sits with me on the sofa, sometimes, while we eat our dinner and watch it together.

"Well," said Earl, too heartily, "I can see that you're going to be okay and I shouldn't keep you. Probably missed your supper, eh?"

He stuck out his hand, that massive freckled paw. Surprised, I took it and it surrounded mine in an amazingly gentle way. "Thanks," I said again.

"Told you not to mention it," said Earl. "We've all got to help each other out, don't we, buddy? But I can see I don't have to tell you that. You're different. You notice things."

MARTHA BROOKS

Martha Brooks was born in Manitoba, Canada. She grew up on the grounds of a tuberculosis sanatorium where her parents worked. When her sister left for college, Brooks says that her departure "drastically reduced the teenage population of the place where we lived." The remaining small society of very ill and very interesting people inspired some of the characters Brooks later created.

Brooks's teenage daughter was another source of inspiration. Brooks's books for young adults include *Paradise Café and Other Stories* and *Only a Paper Moon*.

WHEN IN REALITY

MAURICE KENNY

I wrote in my journal
I had eaten only an orange
and some cheese this morning,
and drunk a pot of coffee dry.
When in truth, at dawn, I had eaten   5
lizards, coyotes, silver and cactus,
and a lone laborer in the desert.
I drank sky, sun and clouds;
my eyes consumed plains, mountains,
countries, continents;   10
worlds rumbled in my belly.
Tonight I slice and fork the western moon,
crunch on stars,
and drink the whine of wolves.

MAURICE KENNY

Maurice Kenny lives in Saranac Lake, New York, in the Iroquois country where he grew up. He has also spent a lot of time in Brooklyn, New York. "I hibernate in the city," he has said. But what Kenny has called his "home itch" always draws him back to the land where he feels he belongs.

Kenny's works include *Tokonwatonti* and *Greyhounding This America*.

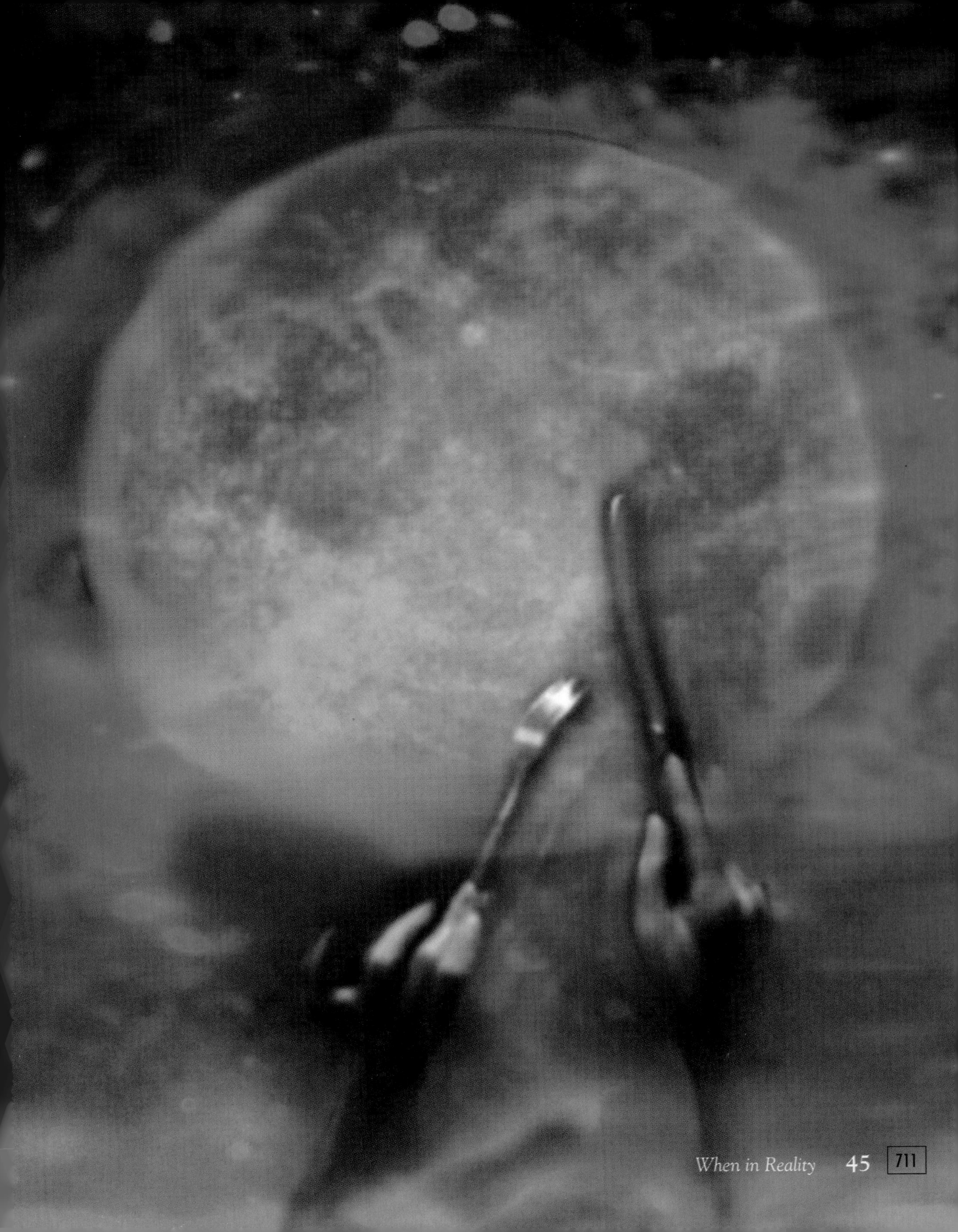

from *The*

True Confessions of Charlotte Doyle

AVI

F or a second time I stood in the forecastle. The room was as dark and mean as when I'd first seen it. Now, however, I stood as a petitioner[1] in sailor's garb. A glum Fisk was at my side. It hadn't been easy to convince him I was in earnest about becoming one of the crew. Even when he begrudged[2] a willingness to believe in my sincerity he warned that agreement from the rest of the men would be improbable. He insisted I lay the matter before them immediately.

So it was that three men from Mr. Hollybrass's watch, Grimes, Dillingham, and Foley, were the next to hear my plea. As Fisk had foretold, they were contemplating[3] me and my proposal with very little evidence of favor.

---

1. **petitioner** [pə tish′ ən ər]: someone who asks a person in authority for a benefit.
2. **begrudged** [bi grudjd′]: was reluctant to admit.
3. **contemplating** [kon′ təm plāt ing]: looking at for a long time.

"I do mean it," I said, finding boldness with repetition, "I want to be the replacement for Mr. Johnson."

"You're a girl," Dillingham spat out contemptuously.[4]

"A *pretty* girl," Foley put in. It was not meant as a compliment. "Takes more than canvas britches to hide that."

"And a gentlewoman," was Grimes's addition, as though that was the final evidence of my essential uselessness.

"I want to show that I stand with you," I pleaded. "That I made a mistake."

"A mistake?" Foley snapped. "Two able-bodied men have died!"

"Besides," Dillingham agreed, "you'll bring more trouble than good."

"You can teach me," I offered.

"God's fist," Grimes cried. "She thinks this a school!"

"And the captain," Foley asked. "What'll he say?"

"He wants nothing to do with me," I replied.

"That's what he *says*. But you were his darling girl, Miss Doyle. We takes you in and he'll want you back again. Where will that put us?"

So it went, round and round. While the men made objections, while I struggled to answer them, Fisk said nothing.

Though I tried to keep my head up, my eyes steady, it was not easy. They looked at me as if I were some loathsome *thing*. At the same time, the more objections they made, the more determined I was to prove myself.

"See here, Miss Doyle," Dillingham concluded, "it's no simple matter. Understand, you sign on to the articles, so to speak, and you *are* on. No bolting to safe harbors at the first blow or when an ill word is flung your way. You're a hand or you're not a hand, and it won't go easy, that's all that can ever be promised."

"I know," I said.

"Hold out *your* hands," he demanded.

Fisk nudged me. I held them out, palms up.

---

4. **contemptuously** [kən temp′ chü əs lē]: scornfully, with disrespect.

Foley peered over them. "Like bloody cream," he said with disgust. "Touch mine!" he insisted and extended his. Gingerly, I touched one of them. His skin was like rough leather.

"That's the hands you'd get, miss. Like an animal. Is that what you want?"

"I don't care," I said stoutly.[5]

Finally it was Dillingham who said, "And are you willing to take your place in the rigging[6] too? Fair weather or foul?"

That made me pause.

Fisk caught the hesitation. "Answer," he prompted.

"Yes," I said boldly.

They exchanged glances. Then Foley asked, "What do the others think?"

Fisk shook his head and sighed. "No doubt they'll speak the same."

Suddenly Grimes said, "Here's what I say: let her climb to the royal yard.[7] If she does it and comes down whole, and *still* is willing to serve, then I say let her sign and be bloody damned like the rest of us."

"And do whatever she's called on to do!"

"No less!"

With no more than grunts the men seemed to agree among themselves. They turned toward me.

"*Now* what does Miss Doyle say?" Grimes demanded.

I swallowed hard, but all the same I gave yet another "Yes."

Foley came to his feet. "All right then. I'll go caucus[8] the others." Out he went.

Fisk and I retreated to the galley[9] while I waited for word. During that time he questioned me regarding my determination.

"Miss Doyle," he pressed, "you have agreed to climb to the top

5. **stoutly:** bravely.
6. **rigging:** the masts, sails, and ropes on a ship.
7. **royal yard:** the highest beam fastened across the mast, used to support the sail.
8. **caucus** [kô′ kəs]: consult, ask.
9. **galley** [gal′ ē]: kitchen of a ship.

of the royal yard. Do you know that's the highest sail on the main mast? One hundred and thirty feet up. You can reach it only two ways. You can shimmy up the mast itself. Or you can climb the shrouds,[10] using the ratlines[11] for your ladder."

I nodded as if I fully grasped what he was saying. The truth was I didn't even wish to listen. I just wanted to get past the test.

"And Miss Doyle," he went on, "if you slip and fall you'll be lucky to drop into the sea and drown quickly. No mortal could pluck you out fast enough to save you. Do you understand that?"

I swallowed hard but nodded. "Yes."

"Because if you're *not* lucky you'll crash to the deck. Fall that way and you'll either maim or kill yourself by breaking your neck. Still certain?"

"Yes," I repeated, though somewhat more softly.

"I'll give you this," he said with a look that seemed a mix of admiration and contempt, "Zachariah[12] was right. You're as steady a girl as ever I've met."

Foley soon returned. "We're agreed," he announced. "Not a one stands in favor of your signing on, Miss Doyle. Not with what you are. We're all agreed to that. But if you climb as high as the royal yard and make it down whole, and if you still want to sign on, you can come as equal. You'll get no more from us, Miss Doyle, but no less either."

Fisk looked at me for my answer.

"I understand," I said.

"All right then," Foley said. "The captain's still in his cabin and not likely to come out till five bells.[13] You can do it now."

"*Now?*" I quailed.[14]

"Now before never."

10. **shrouds:** pairs of ropes that reach from a mast to the side of a ship.
11. **ratlines:** small ropes that cross the shrouds of a ship, used as steps for climbing.
12. **Zachariah** [zak ə rī′ ə]
13. **five bells:** 2:30, 6:30, or 10:30; on ships, a certain number of bells are sounded each half hour to give the time.
14. **quailed** [kwāld]: shrank back in fear.

So it was that the four men escorted me onto the deck. There I found that the rest of the crew had already gathered.

Having fully committed myself, I was overwhelmed by my audacity.[15] The masts had always seemed tall, of course, but never so tall as they did at that moment. When I reached the deck and looked up my courage all but crumbled. My stomach turned. My legs grew weak.

Not that it mattered. Fisk escorted me to the mast as though I were being led to die at the stake. He seemed as grim as I.

15. **audacity** [ô das′ ə tē]: reckless daring, boldness.

from *The True Confessions of Charlotte Doyle*   51

To grasp fully what I'd undertaken to do, know again that the height of the mainmast towered one hundred and thirty feet from the deck. This mast was, in fact, three great rounded lengths of wood, trees, in truth, affixed one to the end of the other. Further, it supported four levels of sails, each of which bore a different name. In order, bottom to top, these were called the main yard, topsail, topgallant, and finally royal yard.

My task was to climb to the top of the royal yard. And come down. In one piece. If I succeeded I'd gain the opportunity of making the climb fifty times a day.

As if reading my terrified thoughts Fisk inquired gravely, "How will you go, Miss Doyle? Up the mast or on the ratlines?"

Once again I looked up. I could not possibly climb the mast directly. The stays and shrouds with their ratlines would serve me better.

"Ratlines," I replied softly.

"Then up you go."

I will confess it, at that moment my nerves failed. I found myself unable to move. With thudding heart I looked frantically around. The members of the crew, arranged in a crescent, were standing like death's own jury.

It was Barlow who called out, "A blessing goes with you, Miss Doyle."

To which Ewing added, "And this advice, Miss Doyle. Keep your eyes steady on the ropes. Don't you look down. Or up."

For the first time I sensed that some of them at least wanted me to succeed. The realization gave me courage.

With halting steps and shallow breath, I approached the rail only to pause when I reached it. I could hear a small inner voice crying, "Don't! Don't!"

But it was also then that I heard Dillingham snicker, "She'll not have the stomach."

I reached up, grasped the lowest deadeye,[16] and hauled myself atop the rail. That much I had done before. Now, I maneuvered to

16. **deadeye** [ded′ī]: round, flat, wooden block that fastens the shrouds of a ship.

the outside so that I would be leaning *into* the rigging and could even rest on it.

Once again I looked at the crew, *down* at them, I should say. They were staring up with blank expressions.

Recollecting Ewing's advice, I shifted my eyes and focused them on the ropes before me. Then, reaching as high as I could into one of the middle shrouds, and grabbing a ratline, I began to climb.

The ratlines were set about sixteen inches one above the other, so that the steps I had to take were wide for me. I needed to pull as much with arms as climb with legs. But line by line I did go up, as if ascending an enormous ladder.

After I had risen some seventeen feet I realized I'd made a great mistake. The rigging stood in sets, each going to a different level of the mast. I could have taken one that stretched directly to the top. Instead, I had chosen a line which went only to the first trestletree, to the top of the lower mast.

For a moment I considered backing down and starting afresh. I stole a quick glance below. The crew's faces were turned up toward me. I understood that they would take the smallest movement down as retreat. I had to continue.

And so I did.

Now I was climbing inside the lank gray-white sails, ascending, as it were, into a bank of dead clouds.

Beyond the sails lay the sea, slate-gray and ever rolling. Though the water looked calm, I could feel the slow pitch and roll it caused in the ship. I realized suddenly how much harder this climb would be if the wind were blowing and we were well underway. The mere thought made the palms of my hands grow damp.

Up I continued till I reached the main yard. Here I snatched another glance at the sea, and was startled to see how much bigger it had grown. Indeed, the more I saw of it the *more* there was. In contrast, the *Seahawk* struck me as having suddenly grown smaller. The more I saw of *her,* the *less* she was!

I glanced aloft. To climb higher I now had to edge myself out upon the trestletree and then once again move up the next set of ratlines as I'd done before. But at twice the height!

Wrapping one arm around the mast—even up here it was too big to reach around completely—I grasped one of the stays and edged out. At the same moment the ship dipped, the world seemed to twist and tilt down. My stomach lurched. My heart pounded. My head swam. In spite of myself I closed my eyes. I all but slipped, saving myself only by a sudden grasp of a line before the ship yawed the opposite way. I felt sicker yet. With everwaning strength I clung on for dearest life. Now the full folly of what I was attempting burst upon me with grotesque reality. It had been not only stupid, but suicidal. I would never come down alive!

And yet I had to climb. This was my restitution.[17]

When the ship was steady again, I grasped the furthest rigging, first with one hand, then the other, and dragged myself higher. I was heading for the topsail, fifteen feet further up.

Pressing myself as close as possible into the rigging, I continued to strain upward, squeezing the ropes so tightly my hands cramped. I even tried curling my toes about the ratlines.

At last I reached the topsail spar,[18] but discovered it was impossible to rest there. The only place to pause was three *times* higher than the distance I'd just come, at the trestletree just below the topgallant spar.

By now every muscle in my body ached. My head felt light, my heart an anvil. My hands were on fire, the soles of my feet raw. Time and again I was forced to halt, pressing my face against the rigging with eyes closed. Then, in spite of what I'd been warned not to do, I opened them and peered down. The *Seahawk* was like a wooden toy. The sea looked greater still.

I made myself glance up. Oh, so far to go! How I forced myself to move I am not sure. But the thought of backing down now was just as frightening. Knowing only that I could not stay still, I crept upward, ratline by ratline, taking what seemed to be forever with

17. **restitution** [res′ tə tü′ shən]: act of making up for damage or injury done.
18. **topsail spar** [top′ sāl′ spär]: strong pole used to support the sail that is above the lowest sail on a mast.

each rise until I finally reached the level just below the topgallant spar.

A seasoned sailor would have needed two minutes to reach this point. I had needed thirty!

Though I felt the constant roll of the ship, I had to rest there. What seemed like little movement on deck became, up high, wild swings and turns through treacherous air.

I gagged, forced my stomach down, drew breath, and looked out. Though I didn't think it possible, the ocean appeared to have grown greater yet. And when I looked down, the upturned faces of the crew appeared like so many tiny bugs.

There were twenty-five or so more feet to climb. Once again I grasped the rigging and hauled myself up.

This final climb was torture. With every upward pull the swaying of the ship seemed to increase. Even when not moving myself, I was flying through the air in wild, wide gyrations. The horizon kept shifting, tilting, dropping. I was increasingly dizzy, nauseous, terrified, certain that with every next moment I would slip and fall to death. I paused again and again, my eyes on the rigging inches from my face, gasping and praying as I had never prayed before. My one hope was that, nearer to heaven now, I could make my desperation heard!

Inch by inch I continued up. Half an inch! Quarter inches! But then at last with trembling fingers, I touched the spar of the royal yard. I had reached the top.

from *The True Confessions of Charlotte Doyle* 55

Once there I endeavored to rest again. But there the metronome[19] motion of the mast was at its most extreme, the *Seahawk* turning, tossing, swaying as if trying to shake me off—like a dog throwing droplets of water from its back. And when I looked beyond I saw a sea that was infinity itself, ready, eager to swallow me whole.

I had to get back down.

As hard as it was to climb up, it was, to my horror, harder returning. On the ascent I could see where I was going. Edging down I had to grope blindly with my feet. Sometimes I tried to look. But when I did the sight of the void below was so sickening, I was forced to close my eyes.

Each groping step downward was a nightmare. Most times my foot found only air. Then, as if to mock my terror, a small breeze at last sprang up. Sails began to fill and snap, puffing in and out, at times smothering me. The tossing of the ship grew—if that were possible—more extreme.

Down I crept, past the topgallant where I paused briefly on the trestletree, then down along the longest stretch, toward the mainyard. It was there I fell.

I was searching with my left foot for the next ratline. When I found a hold and started to put my weight upon it, my foot, slipping on the slick tar surface, shot forward. The suddenness of it made me lose my grip. I tumbled backward, but in such a way that my legs became entangled in the lines. There I hung, *head downward*.

I screamed, tried to grab something. But I couldn't. I clutched madly at nothing, till my hand brushed against a dangling rope. I grabbed for it, missed, and grabbed again. Using all my strength, I levered myself up and, wrapping my arms into the lines, made a veritable[20] knot of myself, mast, and rigging. Oh, how I wept! my entire body shaking and trembling as though it would break apart.

19. **metronome** [met′ rə nōm]: device that moves back and forth in musical time for practicing on musical instruments; here, the back and forth motion of the mast.
20. **veritable** [ver′ ə tə bəl]: real, actual.

When my breathing became somewhat normal, I managed to untangle first one arm, then my legs. I was free.

I continued down. By the time I reached the mainyard I was numb and whimpering again, tears coursing from my eyes.

I moved to the shrouds I'd climbed, and edged myself past the lowest of the sails.

As I emerged from under it, the crew gave out a great "Huzzah!"

Oh, how my heart swelled with exaltation!

Finally, when I'd reached close to the very end, Barlow stepped forward, beaming, his arms uplifted. "Jump!" he called. "Jump!"

But now, determined to do it all myself, I shook my head. Indeed, in the end I dropped down on my own two India-rubber legs—and tumbled to the deck.

No sooner did I land than the crew gave me another "Huzzah!" With joyous heart I staggered to my feet. Only then did I see Captain Jaggery push through the knot of men and come to stand before me.

A V I

Avi Wortis was born in 1937 in New York City. He grew up in a family of readers, writers, and story-tellers. "I do believe that if you want to be a writer you have to read a lot," he says.

Avi first wrote plays and novels for adults. When he became a father, he began inventing stories just for children and young people—such as the adventure story called "Night Journeys"—that you might not be able to put down.

The Kitchen Knight

MARGARET HODGES

In the springtime, when the Round Table was in its glory, King Arthur always held a high feast. But before he sat down at the table, he liked to hear something new, or some adventure. Once, when he was waiting to keep the feast at a seaside castle, he looked from a window and saw in the courtyard a tall young man riding a poor horse and followed by a dwarf. The young man dismounted and the dwarf led the horse away.

Then the stranger came into the hall. He was a goodly young fellow. His manner was friendly, modest, and mild. He was big, broad in the shoulders, and handsome, the very sort to bring news of an adventure. So Arthur made him welcome to the feast and sat down at the table with all his knights around him.

"God bless you, King Arthur," said the young stranger, "and God bless the fellowship of the Table Round. I have come to ask you for three favors. Today I ask for the first. Give me meat and drink for one year. At the end of the year I will ask my other two favors."

"Granted," said Arthur, "for my heart tells me that you will prove to be a man of great worth. What is your name?"

"I cannot tell you," said the youth.

"A goodly young man like you does not know his own name?" said the king in jest. Then he told Sir Kay, his steward,[1] to give the youth the best of meat and drink and all other things that a lord's son should have.

"There is no need for that expense," Kay said to himself. "A gentleman would have asked for a good horse and armor. This fellow is a peasant, as overgrown as a weed, and wanting nothing but meat and drink. He can work and eat in the kitchen. At the end of a year he will be fat as a hog."

Now Arthur's best knight, Sir Lancelot, was kind to the young man because of his own great gentleness and courtesy, while Sir Kay was always rude to the stranger. But the boy took his place in the kitchen and shared the work without complaint. When the kitchen lads competed in sports, the unknown youth was a winner. When the knights jousted,[2] he was always watching.

1. **steward** [stü′ərd]: man who has charge of food and table service.
2. **jousted** [joust′əd]: fought on horseback, armed with spears called lances.

Single Knight on Horseback
Illuminated manuscript page, from Codex Manesse, 14th Century, University Library, Heidelberg, Germany

So a year passed, and once again the king wished to hear of some adventure before he sat down at the springtime feast. Then there came a squire[3] who said to the king, "Sir, you may sit down to eat, for here comes a lady with a strange adventure to tell."

At once, a proud lady came into the hall and said, "Sir, I have come to you because your knights are the noblest in the world. I ask one of them to help my sister, who is held prisoner in her castle."

"What is her name?" asked the king. "And where does she dwell?"

"I will not tell you," said the lady. "But the tyrant[4] who holds her prisoner in her castle is Sir Ironside, the Red Knight of the Red Plain. He is evil, and as strong as seven men."

Then the tall kitchen boy stepped forward and knelt before the king. "Sir," he said, "I have been for twelve months in your kitchen and have had my meat and drink as you promised. Now I will ask my last favors. Let me have this adventure, and let Sir Lancelot ride after me. If I win my spurs,[5] let him make me a knight."

The king was well pleased. "All this shall be done," he said.

But the lady cried, "For shame! Must I have a kitchen boy for my champion?" And she took her horse and rode off.

Then there came into the courtyard the same dwarf who had arrived with the stranger a year before. He was leading a fine horse which carried on its back a breastplate and sword. The kitchen boy took the sword and armor, and mounted the horse. Then he asked Sir Lancelot to follow, and without shield or lance rode after the lady. The dwarf rode behind.

Sir Kay rode after them and ordered them to stop, for he thought the kitchen boy unworthy to be the champion of so proud a lady. The boy rode on.

Sir Kay called angrily, "Fellow, do you not know my voice?"

The boy turned his horse and answered, "I know you for the most ill-mannered knight of King Arthur's court."

3. **squire** [skwīr]: young nobleman who served a knight until he himself became a knight.
4. **tyrant** [tī′rənt]: cruel or unjust ruler.
5. **win my spurs** [spėrz]: idiom meaning "succeed."

Kay put his spear in the saddle rest and rode straight upon him, and the kitchen boy came fast upon Kay with his sword in hand. He thrust Kay's spear aside and struck such a blow that Kay fell from his horse and lay stunned on the ground. Then the kitchen boy took Sir Kay's spear and shield. He put the dwarf on Kay's horse, mounted his own, and rode after the lady.

Sir Lancelot had seen the whole adventure. When he and his squires caught up with the youth, he said, "You fought well, more like a giant than a man."

"Sir, do you think I shall some day be worthy of knighthood?" asked the kitchen boy.

"You are worthy this day," said Lancelot. "I will knight you here and now. But first, tell me your name and family."

"I am Gareth of Orkney, from the islands far to the north, and I am nephew to the king," said the young man, "but the king must not know until I have truly won my spurs."

Then Lancelot dubbed Gareth a knight and returned to Arthur's court, while his squires had to carry Sir Kay on a shield.

Sir Gareth rode on and overtook the proud lady. "Is it you again?" she said. "You smell of the kitchen and your clothes are foul with kitchen grease under your armor. Do you think I like you better for wounding that knight? You did not fight fairly. Go away, you lubber,[6] you turner of spits[7] and washer of ladles."

"Madam," said Gareth, "say what you will, I shall fight against any knight who bars your way. I will follow this adventure to the end, or die in the attempt."

"You would not face the Red Knight of the Red Plain for all the soup in the kitchen," said she.

"I will try," he said.

At the day's end they came to a castle where a knight offered them good cheer and set a table for them. But the lady said, "This kitchen boy is more fit for pig-sticking than for sitting with a lady of high degree."

6. **lubber** [lub′ ər]: big, clumsy, stupid fellow.
7. **spits:** sharp-pointed, slender bars on which meat is roasted.

The knight of the castle was ashamed of her words. He took Gareth to another table and ate there with him, leaving the proud lady to sit by herself.

The next day Gareth rode on with her, and she never gave him a civil word. Then they came to a black field and saw a black hawthorn[8] tree with a black banner and a black shield hanging on it. Beside the tree stood a great black horse covered with trappings of black silk. And on the horse sat a knight in black armor, barring the way.

"Lady," said he, "have you brought this knight to be your champion against me?"

"No," she said, "he is only a kitchen boy, and I would gladly be rid of him."

"Then I will take his horse and armor from him," said the knight in black armor. "It would be a shame to do more harm than that to a kitchen boy."

"I am about to cross your field," said Gareth. "Let us see if you can take my horse and armor." Then they rode against each other and came together with a sound like thunder. The knight in black armor smote Gareth with many strokes and hurt him full sore, but Gareth fought back and brought him to the ground. He won the black horse and the black armor, and rode after the lady.

"Away, kitchen boy," she said. "Out of the wind. The smell of your clothes offends me. Alas, that such a knave[9] as you should fell so good a knight, and all by luck. But the Red Knight will kill you. Away, flee while you can."

"Lady," said Gareth, "you are not courteous to speak to me as you do. Always you say that I should be beaten by knights that we meet, but for all that, they lie in the dust."

Then they came to a meadow, new mown and full of blue pavilions.[10] The lady said, "A noble knight comes in fair weather with five hundred

---

8. **hawthorn** [hô′ thôrn]: small tree of the rose family with fragrant white, red, or pink flowers.
9. **knave** [nāv]: tricky, dishonest man.
10. **pavilions** [pə vil′ yənz]: tent-like open buildings used for shelter.

knights to joust in this meadow. You had better flee before he sets upon you with all his knights."

"If he is noble, he will not set upon me with five hundred knights," said Gareth. "And if they come one at a time, I will face them as long as I live."

Then the lady was ashamed and said, "I pray you, save yourself while you can. You and your horse have fought hard and long, and you will have the hardest fight of all when we come to my sister's castle."

Gareth answered, "Be that as it may, I shall deal with this knight now, and we shall come to your sister's castle while it is still daylight."

"What manner of man are you!" said the lady. "Never did a woman treat a knight so shamefully as I have you, and you have always answered me courteously. Only a man of noble blood would do so."

Two Knights on Horseback Fighting Illuminated manuscript page, from Codex Manesse, 14th Century, University Library, Heidelberg, Germany

He answered, "I am Gareth, the king's nephew. I ate my meat in his kitchen so that I might know who are my true friends, and I never minded your words, for the more you angered me, the better I fought."

"Alas," she said, "forgive me."

"With all my heart," said Gareth. "And now that we are friends, I think there is no knight living but I am strong enough to face him."

Then the knight of the blue pavilions clad all in blue armor came against Gareth, and Gareth rode against him with such force that their spears broke in pieces and their horses fell to the earth. But the two knights sprang to their feet and drew their swords and gave many great strokes until their shields and their armor were hewn to bits. At last, Sir Gareth gave such a blow that the blue knight begged for mercy, saying, "I and my five hundred knights shall always be at your command."

Then he made Gareth and the lady welcome in his own pavilion and Sir Gareth told how he was going to fight against the Red Knight of the Red Plain to relieve the fair lady's sister.

The blue knight answered, "The Knight of the Red Plain is the most fearsome and perilous[11] knight now living." And he asked the lady, "Is it not your sister Linesse who is besieged[12] by the Red Knight? Is not your name Linette?"

"All this is true," she said.

Then Gareth and Linette rode on together until they came close to the Castle Perilous, and they saw that from the branch of a sycamore tree[13] nearby there hung a great ivory horn.

"Fair sir," said Linette, "if any knight blows this horn, the Red Knight will come to do battle. His strength increases until midday, so do not blow the horn before high noon."

"I will fight him at his strongest," said Sir Gareth, and he blew the horn so eagerly that the Castle Perilous rang with the sound, and those within looked over the walls and out the windows. Then the Red Knight armed himself, and all was blood-red—his armor, spear, and shield—and he rode to a little valley close by the castle so that all within and without might see the battle.

Linette pointed to a far window in a tower of the castle, and said, "Yonder is my sister Linesse."

Sir Gareth said, "Even from afar, she seems a fair lady. I will gladly do battle for her." Then he raised his hand to her and in her far window the lady raised her hand to him.

But the Red Knight called to Sir Gareth, "Look not at her but at me. She is my lady and I have fought many battles for her."

---

11. **perilous** [per′ ə ləs]: dangerous.
12. **besieged** [bi sējd′]: surrounded by armed forces in order to force surrender.
13. **sycamore tree** [sik′ ə môr]: tall shade tree with broad leaves.

"I think it was a waste of labor," said Gareth. "To love one who does not love you is great folly.[14] I will rescue her or die in the attempt."

"Talk no more with me," said the Red Knight. "Make yourself ready."

Then they put their spears in their rests and came together with all the might they had. They smote each other with such force that both knights fell to the ground, and all within the castle thought their necks had been broken. But they rose and put their shields before them and ran together like two fierce lions. They battled till it was past noon. Again and again they came face to face, locked in struggle, and now and again they unlaced their helmets and sat down to rest. And when Gareth's helmet was off, he looked at the distant window, and the faraway face of the lady Linesse made his heart light and joyful.

At last the Red Knight smote Gareth such a blow that Gareth lost his sword and fell to the ground.

Then Linette cried out, "Sir Gareth, what has become of your courage? My sister is watching you."

When Gareth heard that, he leaped to his feet and picked up his sword. He struck the sword from the Red Knight's hand and smote him on the helmet so that he fell, and Gareth pinned him to the earth. Then the Red Knight asked for mercy, and many of his noble knights came to Sir Gareth and begged him to spare the life of the Red Knight. "For," said they, "his death will not help you, and his misdeeds cannot be undone. Therefore let him right the wrongs he has done, and we will all be your men."

"Fair lords," said Gareth, "I will release him. But let him yield himself to the lady of the castle."

"This I will do," said the Red Knight, and he went to the castle to ask forgiveness of the lady Linesse. She received him kindly. But when Gareth went to the castle, she sent a message to the gateway, saying, "Go your way, Sir Knight, until I know more of you."

Then secretly she sent a knight to follow Gareth and to capture the dwarf so that she could question him.

14. **folly** [fol′ ē]: foolishness.

Knight with Maiden Illuminated page, from Codex Manesse, 14th Century, University Library, Heidelberg , Germany

Sir Gareth rode away with his dwarf sorrowfully. They rode here and there, and knew not where they rode, until it was dark night. Then, weary and sick at heart for love of the faraway lady, he gave his horse into the care of the dwarf and lay down to rest with his head on his shield.

And while Gareth slept, the knight sent by the lady came softly behind the dwarf. He picked him up and rode away with him as fast as ever he might. But the dwarf cried out to Sir Gareth for help. And Sir Gareth awoke and followed them through marsh[15] and moor[16] until he lost sight of them. Many times his horse and he plunged over their heads in deep mire, for he did not know his way. And while Sir Gareth was in such danger, the dwarf was telling the lady Linesse that her unknown champion was Sir Gareth of Orkney, nephew of King Arthur.

When at last Gareth found the castle again, he was angry, and he drew his sword, shouting to the guards that they must give back his dwarf.

The lady Linesse said, "I would speak with Sir Gareth, but he must not know who I am." Then the drawbridge was let down and the gate was opened. And when Sir Gareth rode in, his dwarf came to take the horse.

15. **marsh:** soft, wet land.
16. **moor:** open, rolling land, usually covered with short grasses and other vegetation.

"Oh, little fellow," said Sir Gareth, "I have been in much danger for your sake."

He washed, and the dwarf brought him clothing fit for a knight to wear. And when Gareth went into the great hall, he saw the lady Linesse disguised as a strange princess. They exchanged many fair words and kind looks. And Gareth thought, "Would to God that the faraway lady of the tower might prove to be as fair as this lady!"

They danced together, and the lady Linesse said to herself, "Now I know that I would rather Sir Gareth were mine than any king or prince in this world, and if I may not have him as my husband, I will have none. He is my first love, and he shall be the last."

And she told him that she was the same lady he had done battle for, and the one who had caused his dwarf to be stolen away "to know certainly who you were."

Then into the dance came Linette, who had ridden with him along so many perilous paths, and Sir Gareth took the lady Linesse by one hand and Linette by the other, and he was more glad than ever before.

Thus ends the tale of Sir Gareth of Orkney.

MARGARET HODGES

Margaret Hodges was born in 1911 in Indianapolis, Indiana. She went east for college. Much later, when her children were grown, Hodges went back to school for a Master's degree in library science. She then began a long career as a children's librarian in Pittsburgh, Pennsylvania, and as a storyteller on radio. All along, she was writing.

Hodges has written numerous kinds of books. One kind she calls "stories based on the adventures and misadventures of my three sons." She has also written biographies of "little-known or disregarded characters who have contributed in an important way to history." One is *Hopkins of the Mayflower: Portrait of a Dissenter.*

For young people, Hodges has written travel books and has retold folktales, myths, and legends such as "The Kitchen Knight."

John Savage

The Getaway

Whenever I get sleepy at the wheel, I always stop for coffee. This time, I was going along in western Texas and I got sleepy. I saw a sign that said GAS EAT, so I pulled off. It was long after midnight: What I expected was a place like a bunch of others, where the coffee tastes like copper and the flies never sleep.

What I found was something else. The tables were painted wood, and they looked as if nobody ever spilled the ketchup. The counter was spick-and-span. Even the smell was OK, I swear it.

Nobody was there, as far as customers. There was just this one old boy—really only about forty, getting gray above the ears—behind the counter. I sat down at the counter and ordered coffee and apple pie. Right away he got me started feeling sad.

I have a habit: I divide people up. Winners and losers. This old boy behind the counter was the kind that they *mean* well; they can't do enough for you, but their eyes have this gentle, faraway look, and they can't win. You know? With their clean shirt and their little bow tie? It makes you feel sad just to look at them. Only take my tip: Don't feel too sad.

He brought the coffee steaming hot, and it tasted like coffee. "Care for cream and sugar?" he asked. I said, "Please," and the cream was fresh and cold and thick. The pie was good, too.

A car pulled up outside. The old boy glanced out to see if they wanted gas, but they didn't. They came right in. The tall one said, "Two coffees. Do you have a road map we could look at?"

"I think so," the old boy said. He got their coffee first, and then started rooting through a pile of papers by the telephone, looking for a map. It was easy to see he was the type nothing's too much trouble for. Tickled to be of service.

I'm the same type myself, if you want to know. I watched the old boy hunting for his map, and I felt like I was looking in a mirror.

After a minute or two, he came up with the map. "This one's a little out of date, but . . . " He put it on the counter, beside their coffee.

The two men spread out the map and leaned over it. They were well dressed, like a couple of feed merchants.[1] The tall one ran his finger along the Rio Grande[2] and shook his head. "I guess there's no place to get across, this side of El Paso."[3]

He said it to his pal, but the old boy behind the counter heard him and lit up like a light bulb. "You trying to find the best way south? I might be able to help you with that."

"How?"

"Just a minute." He spent a lot of time going through the papers by the telephone again. "Thought I might have a

---

1. **feed merchants:** those who sell food for farm animals.
2. **Rio Grande** [rē′ ō grand]: river that forms part of the boundary between the United States and Mexico.
3. **El Paso** [el pas′ ō]: city in western Texas, on the Rio Grande.

newer map," he said. "Anything recent would show the Hackett Bridge. Anyway, I can tell you how to find it."

"Here's a town called Hackett," the tall one said, still looking at the map. "It's on the river, just at the end of a road. Looks like a pretty small place."

"Not any more. It's just about doubled since they built the bridge."

"What happens on the other side?" The short one asked the question, but both of the feed-merchant types were paying close attention.

"Pretty fair road, clear to Chihuahua.[4] It joins up there with the highway out of El Paso and Juarez."[5]

The tall man finished his coffee, folded the map, put it in his pocket, and stood up. "We'll take your map with us," he said.

The old boy seemed startled, like a new kid at school when somebody pokes him in the nose to show him who's boss. However, he just shrugged and said, "Glad to let you have it."

The feed merchants had a little conference on the way out; talking in whispers. Then they stopped in the middle of the floor, turned around, reached inside their jackets, and pulled guns on us. Automatic pistols, I think they were. "You sit where you are and don't move," the tall one said to me. "And *you*, get against the wall."

Both of us did exactly what they wanted. I told you we were a lot alike.

The short man walked over and pushed one of the keys of the cash register. "Every little bit helps," he said, and he scooped the money out of the drawer. The tall man set the telephone on the floor, put his foot on it, and jerked the wires out. Then they ran to their car and got in. The short man leaned out the window and shot out one of my tires. Then they took off fast.

I looked at the old boy behind the counter. He seemed a little pale, but he didn't waste any time. He took a screwdriver out of a drawer and squatted down beside the telephone. I said, "It doesn't always pay to be nice to people."

---

4. **Chihuahua** [chē wä′ wä]: state in northern Mexico; its capital has the same name.
5. **Juarez** [hwär′ es]: city in northern Mexico, across the Rio Grande from El Paso, Texas.

He laughed and said, "Well, it doesn't usually cost anything," and went on taking the base plate off the telephone. He was a fast worker, actually. His tongue was sticking out of the corner of his mouth. In about five minutes he had a dial tone coming out of the receiver. He dialed a number and told the Rangers about the men and their car. "They did?" he said. "Well, well, well. . . . No, not El Paso. They took the Hackett turnoff." After he hung up, he said, "It turns out those guys robbed a supermarket in Wichita Falls."[6]

I shook my head. "They sure had me fooled. I thought they looked perfectly all right."

The old boy got me another cup of coffee, and opened himself a bottle of pop. "They fooled me, too, at first." He wiped his mouth. "Then I got a load of their shoulder holsters when they leaned on the counter to look at the map. Anyway, they had mean eyes, I thought. Didn't you?"

"Well, I didn't at the time."

We drank without talking for a while, getting our nerves back in shape. A pair of patrol cars went roaring by outside and squealed their tires around the Hackett turnoff.

I got to thinking, and I thought of the saddest thing yet. "You *knew* there was something wrong with those guys, but you still couldn't keep from helping them on their way."

He laughed. "Well, the world's a tough sort of place at best, is how I look at it."

"I can understand showing them the map," I said, "but I would never have told about the bridge. Now there's not even an outside chance of catching them. If you'd kept your mouth shut, there'd at least be some hope."

"There isn't any—"

"Not a shred," I went on. "Not with a car as fast as they've got."

The way the old boy smiled made me feel better about him and me. "I don't mean there isn't any hope," he said. "I mean there isn't any bridge."

6. **Wichita Falls** [wich′ i tô′]: city in northern Texas.

NOTHING TO BE AFRAID OF

J A N   M A R K

"Robin won't give you any trouble," said Auntie Lynn. "He's very quiet."

Anthea knew how quiet Robin was. At present he was sitting under the table, and until Auntie Lynn had mentioned his name, she had forgotten that he was there.

Auntie Lynn put an overnight bag on the armchair.

"There's plenty of clothes, so you won't need to do any washing, and there's a spare pair of pajamas in case—well, you know. In case . . ."

"Yes," said Mum firmly. "He'll be all right. I'll ring you tonight and let you know how he's getting along." She looked at the clock. "Now, hadn't *you* better be getting along?"

She saw Auntie Lynn to the front door and Anthea heard them saying good-bye to each other. Mum almost told Auntie Lynn to stop worrying and have a good time, which would have been a mistake because Auntie Lynn was going up north to a funeral.

Deep in the Forest Rex Lau, 1985, oil on carved hydro-stone, 26" x 24", Private collection

Auntie Lynn was not really an aunt, but she had once been at school with Anthea's mum, and she was the kind of person who couldn't manage without a handle to her name; so Robin was not Anthea's cousin. Robin was not anything much, except four years old, and he looked a lot younger; probably because nothing ever happened to him. Auntie Lynn kept no pets that might give Robin germs, and never bought him toys that had sharp corners to dent him or wheels that could be swallowed. He wore knitted balaclava[1] helmets and pompom hats in winter to protect his tender ears, and a knitted undershirt in summer in case he overheated himself and caught a chill from his own sweat.

"Perspiration," said Auntie Lynn.

His face was as pale and flat as a saucer of milk, and his eyes floated in it like drops of cod-liver oil.[2] This was not so surprising, as he was full to the back teeth with cod-liver oil; also with extract of malt, concentrated orange juice, and calves'-foot jelly. When you picked him up you expected him to squelch, like a hot-water bottle full of half-set custard.

Anthea lifted the tablecloth and looked at him.

"Hello, Robin."

Robin stared at her with his flat eyes and went back to sucking his wooly doggy that had flat eyes also, of sewn-on felt, because glass ones might find their way into Robin's appendix and cause damage. Anthea wondered how long it would be before he noticed that his mother had gone. Probably he wouldn't, any more than he would notice when she came back.

Mum closed the front door and joined Anthea in looking under the table at Robin. Robin's mouth turned down at the corners, and Anthea hoped he would cry so that they could cuddle him. It seemed impolite to cuddle him before he needed it. Anthea was afraid to go any closer.

1. **balaclava** [bä lə klä′ və]: close-fitting, knitted woolen cap that covers the head, neck, and tops of the shoulders.
2. **cod-liver oil** [kod′ liv′ ər]: oil from the liver of codfish, used in medicine as a source of vitamins A and D.

"What a little troll," said Mum sadly, lowering the tablecloth. "I suppose he'll come out when he's hungry."

Anthea doubted it.

Robin didn't want any lunch or any tea.

"Do you think he's pining?" said Mum. Anthea did not. Anthea had a nasty suspicion that he was like this all the time. He went to bed without making a fuss and fell asleep before the light was out, as if he were too bored to stay awake. Anthea left her bedroom door open, hoping that he would have a nightmare so that she could go in and comfort him, but Robin slept all night without a squeak, and woke in the morning as flat faced as before. Wall-eyed Doggy looked more excitable than Robin did.

"If only we had a proper garden," said Mum, as Robin went under the table again, leaving his breakfast eggs scattered round the plate. "He might run about."

Anthea thought that this was unlikely, and in any case they didn't have a proper garden, only a yard at the back and a stony strip in front, without a fence.

"Can I take him to the park?" said Anthea.

Mum looked doubtful. "Do you think he wants to go?"

"No," said Anthea, peering under the tablecloth. "I don't think he wants to do anything, but he can't sit there all day."

"I bet he can," said Mum. "Still, I don't think he should. All right, take him to the park, but keep quiet about it. I don't suppose Lynn thinks you're safe in traffic."

"He might tell her."

"Can he talk?"

Robin, still clutching wall-eyed Doggy, plodded beside her all the way to the park, without once trying to jam his head between the library railings or get run over by a bus.

"Hold my hand, Robin," Anthea said as they left the house, and he clung to her like a lamprey.[3]

3. **lamprey** [lam′ prē]: ocean and freshwater animal with a body like an eel's body and a large, round mouth for attaching itself to other fish.

The park was not really a park at all; it was a garden. It did not even pretend to be a park, and the notice by the gate said KING STREET GARDENS, in case anyone tried to use it as a park. The grass was as green and as flat as the front-room carpet, but the front-room carpet had a path worn across it from the door to the fireplace, and here there were more notices that said KEEP OFF THE GRASS, so that the gritty white paths went obediently round the edge, under the orderly trees that stood in a row like the queue[4] outside a fish shop. There were bushes in each corner and one shelter with a bench in it. Here and there brown holes in the grass, full of raked earth, waited for next year's flowers, but there were no flowers now, and the bench had been taken out of the shelter because the shelter was supposed to be a summerhouse, and you couldn't have people using a summerhouse in winter.

Robin stood by the gates and gaped, with Doggy depending limply from his mouth where he held it by one ear, between his teeth. Anthea decided that if they met anyone she knew, she would explain that Robin was only two, but very big for his age.

"Do you want to run, Robin?"

Robin shook his head.

"There's nothing to be afraid of. You can go all the way round, if you like, but you mustn't walk on the grass or pick things."

Robin nodded. It was the kind of place that he understood.

Anthea sighed. "Well, let's walk around, then."

They set off. At each corner, where the bushes were, the path diverged. One part went in front of the bushes, one part round the back of them. On the first circuit[5] Robin stumped glumly beside Anthea in front of the bushes. The second time round she felt a very faint tug at her hand. Robin wanted to go his own way.

This called for a celebration. Robin could think. Anthea crouched down on the path until they were at the same level.

"You want to walk round the back of the bushes, Robin?"

---

4. **queue** [kyü]: line of people waiting their turn.
5. **circuit** [sėr′ kit]: route or way around.

"Yiss," said Robin.

Robin could *talk*.

"All right, but listen." She lowered her voice to a whisper. "You must be very careful. That path is called Leopard Walk. Do you know what a leopard is?"

"Yiss."

"There are two leopards down there. They live in the bushes. One is a good leopard and the other's a bad leopard. The good leopard has black spots. The bad leopard has red spots. If you see the bad leopard, you must say, 'Die leopard die or I'll kick you in the eye,' and run like anything. Do you understand?"

Robin tugged again.

"Oh no," said Anthea. "I'm going *this* way. If you want to go down Leopard Walk, you'll have to go on your own. I'll meet you at the other end. Remember, if it's got red spots, run like mad."

Robin trotted away. The bushes were just high enough to hide him, but Anthea could see the pompom on his hat doddering along. Suddenly the pompom gathered speed, and Anthea had to run to reach the end of the bushes first.

"Did you see the bad leopard?"

"No," said Robin, but he didn't look too sure.

"Why were you running, then?"

"I just wanted to."

"You've dropped Doggy," said Anthea. Doggy lay on the path with his legs in the air, halfway down Leopard Walk.

"You get him," said Robin.

"No, *you* get him," said Anthea. "I'll wait here." Robin moved off reluctantly. She waited until he had recovered Doggy and then shouted, "I can see the bad leopard in the bushes!" Robin raced back to safety. "Did you say, 'Die leopard die or I'll kick you in the eye'?" Anthea demanded.

"No," Robin said guiltily.

"Then he'll *kill* us," said Anthea. "Come on, run. We've got to get to that tree. He can't hurt us once we're under that tree."

They stopped running under the twisted boughs of a weeping

ash. "This is a python tree," said Anthea. "Look, you can see the python wound round the trunk."

"What's a python?" said Robin, backing off.

"Oh, it's just a great big snake that squeezes people to death," said Anthea. "A python could easily eat a leopard. That's why leopards won't walk under this tree, you see, Robin."

Robin looked up. "Could it eat us?"

"Yes, but it won't if we walk on our heels." They walked on their heels to the next corner.

"Are there leopards down there?"

"No, but we must never go down there anyway. That's Poison Alley. All the trees are poisonous. They drip poison. If one bit of poison fell on your head, you'd die."

"I've got my hat on," said Robin, touching the pompom to make sure.

"It would burn right through your hat," Anthea assured him. "Right into your brains. *Fzzzzzzz.*"

They bypassed Poison Alley and walked on over the manhole cover that clanked.

"What's that?"

"That's the Fever Pit. If anyone lifts that manhole cover, they get a terrible disease. There's this terrible disease down there, Robin, and if the lid comes off, the disease will get out and people will die. I should think there's enough disease down there to kill everybody in this town. It's ever so loose, look."

"Don't lift it! Don't lift it!" Robin screamed, and ran to the shelter for safety.

"Don't go in there," yelled Anthea. "That's where the Greasy Witch lives." Robin bounced out of the shelter as though he were on elastic.

"Where's the Greasy Witch?"

"Oh, you can't see her," said Anthea, "but you can tell where she is because she smells so horrible. I think she must be somewhere about. Can't you smell her now?"

Robin sniffed the air and clasped Doggy more tightly.

Bob as Blackie Holly Roberts, 1984, oil on silver print, 20" x 24", Private collection

"And she leaves oily marks wherever she goes. Look, you can see them on the wall."

Robin looked at the wall. Someone had been very busy, if not the Greasy Witch. Anthea was glad on the whole that Robin could not read.

"The smell's getting worse, isn't it, Robin? I think we'd better go down here and then she won't find us."

"She'll see us."

"No, she won't. She can't see with her eyes because they're full of grease. She sees with her ears, but I expect they're all waxy. She's a filthy old witch, really."

They slipped down a secret-looking path that went round the back of the shelter.

"Is the Greasy Witch down here?" said Robin fearfully.

"I don't know," said Anthea. "Let's investigate." They tiptoed round the side of the shelter. The path was damp and slippery. "Filthy old witch. She's certainly *been* here," said Anthea. "I think she's gone now. I'll just have a look."

She craned her neck round the corner of the shelter. There was a sort of glade in the bushes, and in the middle was a standpipe, with a tap on top. The pipe was wrapped in canvas, like a scaly skin.

"Frightful Corner," said Anthea. Robin put his cautious head round the edge of the shelter.

"What's that?"

Anthea wondered if it could be a dragon, up on the tip of its tail and ready to strike, but on the other side of the bushes was the brick back wall of the King Street Public Conveniences, and at that moment she heard the unmistakable sound of flushing.

"It's a Lavatory Demon," she said. "Quick! We've got to get away before the water stops, or he'll have us."

They ran all the way to the gates, where they could see the church clock, and it was almost time for lunch.

Auntie Lynn fetched Robin home next morning, and three days later she was back again, striding up the path like a warrior queen going into battle, with Robin dangling from her hand and Doggy dangling from Robin's hand.

Mum took her into the front room, closing the door. Anthea sat on the stairs and listened. Auntie Lynn was in full throat and furious, so it was easy enough to hear what she had to say.

"I want a word with that young lady," said Auntie Lynn. "And I want to know what she's been telling him." Her voice dropped, and Anthea could hear only certain fateful words: "Leopards . . . poison trees . . . snakes . . . diseases!"

Mum said something very quietly that Anthea did not hear, and then Auntie Lynn turned up the volume once more.

"Won't go to bed unless I leave the door open . . . wants the light on . . . up and down to him all night . . . won't go to the bathroom on his own. He says the—the—" she hesitated. "The *toilet* demons will get him. He nearly broke his neck running downstairs this morning."

Mum spoke again, but Auntie Lynn cut in like a bandsaw.[6]

"Frightened out of his wits! He follows me everywhere."

The door opened slightly, and Anthea got ready to bolt, but it was Robin who came out, with his thumb in his mouth and circles round his eyes. Under his arm was soggy Doggy, ears chewed to nervous rags.

Robin looked up at Anthea through the banisters.

"Let's go to the park," he said.

6. **bandsaw:** saw consisting of a steel belt running over two pulleys.

JAN MARK

Jan Mark was born in 1943 in Welwyn, England. He became a teacher of art and English and did not become a "serious writer" until he was in his thirties. He says it took him that long "to develop a voice of my own." Mark has been a full-time writer since 1975. He won a fiction award for his first book, *Thunder and Lightnings.*

Mark has said that he tries to "present readers with a situation they may recognize and supplement with their own experience." He likes to drop a character into a strange environment; the story comes from the character's reactions. Two of his books are *Handles* and *At the Sign of the Dog and Rocket.* Mark has also written television plays and radio dramas.

Leslie Marmon Silko

Seeing good places
for my hands
I grab the warm parts of the cliff
and I feel the mountain as I climb.

Somewhere around here   5
yellow spotted snake is sleeping on his rock
in the sun.

So
please, I tell them
watch out,   10
don't step on the spotted yellow snake
he lives here.
The mountain is his.

Red and Yellow Cliffs Georgia O' Keeffe, 1940, oil on canvas, 24" x 36", The Metropolitan Museum of Art, New York

LESLIE MARMON SILKO

Leslie Marmon Silko was born in 1948 in Albuquerque, New Mexico, and grew up on the Laguna reservation. As an adult, Silko began writing novels, short stories, and poems about Native American life. One of her books is called *Ceremony*. Another book, *Storyteller*, is a collection of both poems and short stories. Silko has also written a screenplay for television.

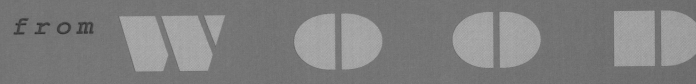

The adventure really begins in differences—the great differences between people and animals, between the way we live now and the way we once lived, between the Mall and the Woods.

Primarily the difference between people and animals is that people use fire. People create fire, and animals don't. Oh, there are minor things— like cars and planes and all the other inventions we seem to have come up with. But in a wild state, the real difference is that we use controlled fire.

And it was in the business of fire that I came to the first of many amazements inside the woods.

It started with a campfire.

I was on a hundred-mile run in deep winter with new dogs— pups, really, just over a year old. I had gone beyond the trapping

SONG

Gary Paulsen

stage and was training new dogs for a possible attempt on the Iditarod.[1] The pups had lived in kennels, mostly. They had only been on short training runs so that almost everything they saw on this run was new to them. They had to learn to understand as they ran.

A cow in a field was a marvel and had to be investigated; it took me half an hour to get untangled from the fence. A ruffed grouse[2] that flew down the trail ahead of us had to be chased. A red squirrel took the whole team off the trail into the woods, piling into deep drifts and leaving us all upside down and packed with snow.

1. **Iditarod** [ī dit′ ə rod]: competitive dog-sled race that takes place in Alaska, usually in March.
2. **ruffed grouse** [rufd grous]: brown bird with a tuft of gleaming black feathers on each side of the neck.

It was, in short, a day full of wonders for them and when night came and it was time to stop—you can really only do about twenty miles a day with young dogs—we found a soft little clearing in the spruce trees. I made beds for them and when they were fed and settled, or as settled as young dogs can get, I made a fire hole in the snow in the center of the clearing, next to the sled, and started a small fire with some dead popple.³ It was not a cold night so the fire was very small, just enough to melt some snow and make tea. The flames didn't get over a foot high—but the effect was immediate and dramatic.

The dogs went crazy with fear. They lunged against their chains, slamming and screaming. I went to them and petted them and soothed them and at length they accepted the fire. I put their frozen blocks of meat around the edges of the flames to soften, and fed them warm meat. Then they sat and stared at the flames, the whole ring of them.

Of course they had never seen fire, or flame, in the kennel—it was all completely new to them. But the mystery was why they would automatically fear it. They had seen many new things that day, and they didn't fear anything but the fire.

And when they were over the fear of it, they were fascinated with it. I stretched my foam pad and sleeping bag out in the sled to settle in for the night. This is a complicated process. The felt liners for my shoepacs⁴ had to be taken off and put down inside the bag so my body heat could dry them for the next day. My parka had to be turned inside out so all the sweat from the day could freeze and be scraped off in the morning. Any wet clothing had to be flattened and worked down into the bag to dry as well. While I was doing all this in the light from my head lamp, I let the fire die down.

Just as I started to slide into the bag one of the dogs started to sing. It was the sad song.

They have many songs and I don't know them all. There is a happy song they sing when the moon is full on the snow and they are fed and there is a rain song, which is melancholy—they don't like rain very much—and there is a song they sing when you have been

3. **popple** [pop′ əl]: poplar tree.
4. **shoepacs:** insulated boots for cold weather.

with them in the kennel and start to walk away, a come-back-and-don't-go-away sad song.

That was the song one dog had started to sing. When I turned to look at him he was staring where the fire had died down into a cup in the snow, and in a moment the rest of them had picked up the song and were wailing and moaning for the lost fire, all staring where the flames had been.

In an hour they had gone from some coded, genetic[5] fear of fire, to understanding fire, to missing it when it went away.

Cave people must have gone through this same process. I wondered how long it had taken us to understand and know fire. The pups had done it in an hour and I thought as I pulled the mummy bag up over my head and went to sleep how smart they were or perhaps how smart we weren't and thought we were.

Sometimes when they run it is not believable. And even when the run is done and obviously happened it is still not believable.

On a run once when it was the perfect temperature for running, twenty below—cold enough for the dogs to run cool, but not so bitterly cold as to freeze anything exposed—I thought I would just let them go and see what they wanted to do. I wouldn't say a word, wouldn't do anything but stand on the back of the sled—unless a bootie[6] or a quick snack was needed. I'd let them run at an easy lope. I thought I would let them go until they wanted to stop and then only run that way from then on, and they ran to some primitive instinct, coursed and ran for seventeen hours without letup.

One hundred and seventy-five miles.

And they didn't pant, weren't tired, could have done it again. I nearly froze—just a piece of meat on the back of the sled—but they ran and ran in a kind of glory and even now I can't quite believe it.

The second incident with fire was much the same—something from another world, another time. It happened, but is not quite believable.

We had run long in a day—a hundred and fifty miles—with an

5. **genetic** [je net′ ik]: inherited, inborn.
6. **bootie** [bü′ tē]: covering for the dogs' paws.

adult team in good shape. The terrain had been rough, with many moguls (mounds of snow) that made the sled bounce in the trail. I had taken a beating all day and I was whipped. I made beds and fed the dogs and built up a large fire. It had been a classic run but I was ready for sleep. It was nearly thirty below when I crawled into the sleeping bag.

I was just going to sleep, with my eyes heavy and the warmth from the fire in my face, when the dogs started an incredible uproar.

I opened my eyes and there was a deer standing right across the fire from me.

A doe. Fairly large—more than a year old—standing rigid, staring at me straight on in the face across the fire. She was absolutely petrified with terror.

At first I thought she had somehow stupidly blundered into the camp and run past the dogs to the fire.

But she hung there, staring at me, her ears rotating with the noise of the dogs around her. She did not run and still did not run and I thought she must be a medicine doe sent to me; a spirit doe come in a dream to tell me something.

Then I saw the others.

Out, perhaps thirty yards or more beyond the camp area, but close enough for the fire to shine in their eyes—the others. The wolves. There was a pack of brush wolves and they had been chasing her. I couldn't tell the number, maybe five or six; they kept moving in agitation and it was hard to pin them down, but they were clearly reluctant to let her go, although they were also clearly afraid of me and being close to me. Unlike timber wolves, brush wolves are not endangered, not protected, and are trapped heavily. We are most definitely the enemy, and they worried at seeing me.

And when I saw them I looked back at the doe and could see that she was blown. Her mouth hung open and spit smeared down both sides with some blood in it. They must have been close to getting her when she ran to the camp.

And the fire.

She must have smelled her death to make the decision she made. To run through the circle of dogs, toward the fire and the man was a mad gamble—a gamble that I wasn't a deer hunter, that the dogs weren't loose or they would have been on her like the wolves, that somehow it would be better here.

All those choices to make at a dead, frantic run with wolves pulling at her.

This time it had worked.

I sat up, half raised, afraid to move fast lest she panic and run back into the wolves. I had more wood next to the sled and I slowly put a couple of pieces on the fire and leaned back again. The wolves were very nervous now and they moved away when I put the wood on the fire, but the doe stayed nearby for a long time, so long that some of the dogs actually went back to lying down and sleeping.

She didn't relax. Her body was locked in fear and ready to fly at the slightest wrong move, but she stayed and watched me, watched the fire until the wolves were well gone and her sides were no longer heaving with hard breathing. She kept her eye on me, her ears on the dogs. Her nostrils flared as she smelled me and the fire and when she was ready— perhaps in half an hour but it seemed like much more—she wheeled, flashed her white tail at me, and disappeared.

The dogs exploded into noise again when she ran away, then we settled back to watching the fire until sleep took us. I would have thought it all a dream except that her tracks and the tracks of the wolves were there in the morning.

Fear comes in many forms but perhaps the worst scare is the one that isn't anticipated; the one that isn't really known about until it's there. A sudden fear. The unexpected.

And again, fire played a role in it.

We have bear trouble. Because we feed processed meat to the dogs there is always the smell of meat over the kennel. In the summer it can be a bit high because the dogs like to "save" their food sometimes for a day or two or four—burying it to dig up later. We live on the edge of wilderness and consequently the meat smell brings any number of visitors from the woods.

Skunks abound, and foxes and coyotes and wolves and weasels—all predators. We once had an eagle live over the kennel for more than a week, scavenging from the dogs, and a crazy group of ravens has pretty much taken over the puppy pen. Ravens are protected by the state and they seem to know it. When I walk toward the puppy pen with the buckets of meat it's a toss-up to see who gets it—the pups or the birds. They have actually pecked the puppies away from the food pans until they have gone through and taken what they want.

Spring, when the bears come, is the worst. They have been in hibernation[7] through the winter, and they are hungry beyond caution. The meat smell draws them like flies, and we frequently have two or three around the kennel at the same time. Typically they do not bother us much—although my wife had a bear chase her from the garden to the house one morning—but they do bother the dogs.

They are so big and strong that the dogs fear them, and the bears trade on this fear to get their food. It's common to see them scare a dog into his house and take his food. Twice we have had dogs killed by rough bear swats that broke their necks—and the bears took their food.

7. **hibernation** [hī bėr nā′ shən]: inactive state, like sleep, into which bears enter during the winter.

We have evolved an uneasy peace with them but there is the problem of familiarity. The first time you see a bear in the kennel it is a novelty, but when the same ones are there day after day, you wind up naming some of them (old Notch-Ear, Billy-Jo, etc.). There gets to be a too relaxed attitude. We started to treat them like pets.

A major mistake.

There was a large male around the kennel for a week or so. He had a white streak across his head which I guessed was a wound scar from some hunter—bear hunting is allowed here. He wasn't all that bad so we didn't mind him. He would frighten the dogs and take their hidden stashes now and then, but he didn't harm them and we became accustomed to him hanging around. We called him Scarhead and now and again we would joke about him as if he were one of the yard animals.

At this time we had three cats, forty-two dogs, fifteen or twenty chickens, eight ducks, nineteen large white geese, a few banty hens—one called Hawk will come up again later in the book[8]—ten fryers we'd raised from chicks and couldn't (as my wife put it) "snuff and eat," and six woods-wise goats.

The bears, strangely, didn't bother any of the yard animals. There must have been a rule, or some order to the way they lived because they would hit the kennel and steal from the dogs but leave the chickens and goats and other yard stock completely alone—although you would have had a hard time convincing the goats of this fact. The goats spent a great deal of time with their back hair up, whuffing and blowing snot at the bears—and at the dogs who would *gladly* have eaten them. The goats never really believed in the truce.

There is not a dump or landfill to take our trash to and so we separate it—organic,[9] inorganic—and deal with it ourselves. We burn the paper in a screened enclosure and it is fairly efficient, but it's impossible to get all the food particles off wrapping paper, so when it's burned the food particles burn with it.

And give off a burnt food smell.

8. **later in the book**: reference to Chapter 5 in Gary Paulsen's book *Woodsong*.
9. **organic** [ôr gan′ ik]: from plants or animals.

And nothing draws bears like burning food. It must be that they have learned to understand human dumps—where they spend a great deal of time foraging.[10] And they learn amazingly fast. In Alaska, for instance, the bears already know that the sound of a moose hunter's gun means there will be a fresh gut pile when the hunter cleans the moose. They come at a run when they hear the shot. It's often a close race to see if the hunter will get to the moose before the bears take it away. . . .

Because we're on the south edge of the wilderness area we try to wait until there is a northerly breeze before we burn so the food smell will carry south, but it doesn't always help. Sometimes bears, wolves, and other predators are already south, working the sheep farms down where it is more settled—they take a terrible toll of sheep—and we catch them on the way back through.

That's what happened one July morning.

Scarhead had been gone for two or three days and the breeze was right, so I went to burn the trash. I fired it off and went back into the house for a moment—not more than two minutes. When I came back out Scarhead was in the burn area. His tracks (directly through the tomatoes in the garden) showed he'd come from the south.

He was having a grand time. The fire didn't bother him. He was trying to reach a paw in around the edges of flame to get at whatever smelled so good. He had torn things apart quite a bit—ripped one side off the burn enclosure—and I was having a bad day and it made me mad.

I was standing across the burning fire from him and without thinking—because I was so used to him—I picked up a stick, threw it at him, and yelled, "Get out of here."

10. **foraging** [fôr´ ij ing]: searching for food.

I have made many mistakes in my life, and will probably make many more, but I hope never to throw a stick at a bear again.

In one rolling motion—the muscles seemed to move within the skin so fast that I couldn't take half a breath—he turned and came for me. Close. I could smell his breath and see the red around the sides of his eyes. Close on me he stopped and raised on his back legs and hung over me, his forelegs and paws hanging down, weaving back and forth gently as he took his time and decided whether or not to tear my head off.

I could not move, would not have time to react. I knew I had nothing to say about it. One blow would break my neck. Whether I lived or died depended on him, on his thinking, on his ideas about me—whether I was worth the bother or not.

I did not think then.

Looking back on it I don't remember having one coherent[11] thought when it was happening. All I knew was terrible menace. His eyes looked very small as he studied me. He looked down on me for what seemed hours. I did not move, did not breathe, did not think or do anything.

And he lowered.

Perhaps I was not worth the trouble. He lowered slowly and turned back to the trash and I walked backward halfway to the house and then ran—anger growing now—and took the rifle from the gun rack by the door and came back out.

He was still there, rummaging through the trash. I worked the bolt and fed a cartridge in and aimed at the place where you kill bears and began to squeeze. In raw anger, I began to take up the four pounds of pull necessary to send death into him.

And stopped.

Kill him for what?

That thought crept in.

Kill him for what?

For not killing me? For letting me know it is wrong to throw

11. **coherent** [kō hir′ ənt]: logical, sensible.

sticks at four-hundred-pound bears? For not hurting me, for not killing me, I should kill him? I lowered the rifle and ejected the shell and put the gun away. I hope Scarhead is still alive. For what he taught me, I hope he lives long and is very happy because I learned then—looking up at him while he made up his mind whether or not to end me—that when it is all boiled down I am nothing more and nothing less than any other animal in the woods.

GARY PAULSEN

Gary Paulsen was born in 1939 in Minneapolis, Minnesota. As a child, he lived in many different places, such as an army base in the Philippines where his father was stationed. When Paulsen grew up he tried a number of careers, including some time in the U.S. Army. He tried working as a teacher, electronics engineer, actor, farmer, rancher, truck driver, migrant farm worker, singer, sailor, and professional archer. Finally he became a full-time writer.

Paulsen has written nearly sixty books and more than two hundred short stories and articles. Most of his novels and how-to books are written for young people. Many of them, like *Woodsong, Dogsong, Tracker,* and *Hatchet,* are about experiences in the wild.

Paul Revere's

Henry Wadsworth Longfellow

Listen, my children, and you shall hear
Of the midnight ride of Paul Revere.
On the eighteenth of April, in seventy-five;
Hardly a man is now alive
Who remembers that famous day and year.   5

He said to his friend, "If the British march
By land or sea from the town tonight,
Hang a lantern aloft in the belfry[1] arch
Of the North Church tower as a signal light,—
One, if by land, and two, if by sea;   10
And I on the opposite shore will be,
Ready to ride and spread the alarm
Through every Middlesex[2] village and farm,
For the country folk to be up and to arm."

Then he said "Good night!" and with muffled oar   15
Silently rowed to the Charlestown[3] shore,
Just as the moon rose over the bay,
Where swinging wide at her moorings lay
The *Somerset*, British man-of-war;
A phantom[4] ship, with each mast and spar   20

1. **belfry** [bel′ fre]: church tower.
2. **Middlesex:** a county in Massachusetts.
3. **Charlestown:** in 1775, a town across the harbor from Boston, Massachusetts.
4. **phantom** [fan′ təm]: ghostly, shadowy in appearance.

Across the moon like a prison bar,
And a huge black hulk, that was magnified
By its own reflection in the tide.

Meanwhile, his friend, through alley and street,
Wanders and watches with eager ears,   25
Till in the silence around him he hears
The muster[5] of men at the barrack[6] door,
The sound of arms, and the tramp of feet,
And the measured tread of the grenadiers[7]
Marching down to their boats on the shore.   30

5. **muster:** group, gathering.
6. **barrack** [bar′ ək]: building where soldiers live.
7. **grenadiers** [gren′ ə dirz′]: soldiers in a special regiment of the
   British Army.

Horse and Rider
weather vane, c. 1900,
polychromed sheet metal,
35″ x 38″ x ½″,
Shelburne Museum,
Vermont

Then he climbed the tower of the Old North Church
By the wooden stairs, with stealthy[8] tread,
To the belfry chamber overhead,
And startled the pigeons from their perch
On the somber rafters, that round him made   35
Masses and moving shapes of shade,—
By the trembling ladder, steep and tall,
To the highest window in the wall,
Where he paused to listen and look down
A moment on the roofs of the town,   40
And the moonlight flowing over all.

Beneath, in the churchyard, lay the dead,
In their night encampment on the hill,
Wrapped in silence so deep and still
That he could hear, like a sentinel's[9] tread,   45
The watchful night wind, as it went
Creeping along from tent to tent,
And seeming to whisper, "All is well!"
A moment only he feels the spell
Of the place and the hour, and the secret dread   50
Of the lonely belfry and the dead;
For suddenly all his thoughts are bent
On a shadowy something far away,
Where the river widens to meet the bay,—
A line of black that bends and floats   55
On the rising tide, like a bridge of boats.

Meanwhile, impatient to mount and ride,
Booted and spurred, with a heavy stride
On the opposite shore walked Paul Revere.
Now he patted his horse's side,   60

8. **stealthy** [stel′ thē]: quiet and secretive.
9. **sentinel** [sen′ tə nəl]: guard.

Lantern from Old North Church
The Concord Museum, Concord, MA

Now gazed at the landscape far and near,
Then, impetuous,[10] stamped the earth,
And turned and tightened his saddle girth;[11]
But mostly he watched with eager search
The belfry tower of the Old North Church,   65
As it rose above the graves on the hill,
Lonely and spectral[12] and somber and still.
And lo! as he looks, on the belfry's height
A glimmer, and then a gleam of light!
He springs to the saddle, the bridle he turns,   70
But lingers and gazes, till full on his sight
A second lamp in the belfry burns!

A hurry of hoofs in a village street,
A shape in the moonlight, a bulk in the dark,
And beneath, from the pebbles, in passing, a spark   75
Struck out by a steed flying fearless and fleet;
That was all! And yet, through the gloom and the light,
The fate of a nation was riding that night;
And the spark struck out by that steed, in his flight,
Kindled the land into flame with its heat.   80

He has left the village and mounted the steep,
And beneath him, tranquil[13] and broad and deep,
Is the Mystic,[14] meeting the ocean tides;
And under the alders[15] that skirt its edge,
Now soft on the sand, now loud on the ledge,   85
Is heard the tramp of his steed as he rides.

10. **impetuous** [im pech′ ü əs]: acting suddenly.
11. **girth:** strap.
12. **spectral** [spek′ trəl]: ghostly.
13. **tranquil** [trang′ kwəl]: calm, peaceful.
14. **Mystic** [mis′ tik]: river in Massachusetts.
15. **alders** [ôl′ dərz]: type of birch trees that grow in moist areas.

It was twelve by the village clock,
When he crossed the bridge into Medford town.
He heard the crowing of the cock,   90
And the barking of the farmer's dog,
And felt the damp of the river fog,
That rises after the sun goes down.

It was one by the village clock,
When he galloped into Lexington.[16]
He saw the gilded weathercock[17]   95
Swim in the moonlight as he passed,
And the meeting-house windows, blank and bare,
Gaze at him with a spectral glare,
As if they already stood aghast[18]
At the bloody work they would look upon.   100

It was two by the village clock,
When he came to the bridge in Concord town.
He heard the bleating of the flock,
And the twitter of birds among the trees,
And felt the breath of the morning breeze   105
Blowing over the meadows brown.
And one was safe and asleep in his bed
Who at the bridge would be first to fall,
Who that day would be lying dead,
Pierced by a British musket ball.   110

16. **Lexington:** town in Massachusetts where the first
    battle of the American Revolution was fought on
    April 19, 1775.
17. **weathercock:** weather vane in the shape of a rooster.
18. **aghast** [ə gast′]: surprised, amazed.

Bootmaker's trade sign c. 1900,
wood painted, 34 1/2" x 9" x 21",
Shelburne Museum, Vermont

You know the rest. In the books you have read,
How the British Regulars[19] fired and fled,—
How the farmers gave them ball for ball,
From behind each fence and farmyard wall,
Chasing the redcoats[20] down the lane,   115
Then crossing the fields to emerge again
Under the trees at the turn of the road,
And only pausing to fire and load.

So through the night rode Paul Revere;
And so through the night went his cry of alarm   120
To every Middlesex village and farm,—
A cry of defiance and not of fear,
A voice in the darkness, a knock at the door,
And a word that shall echo forevermore!
For, borne on the night wind of the past,   125
Through all our history, to the last,
In the hour of darkness and peril and need,
The people will waken and listen to hear
The hurrying hoof-beats of that steed,
And the midnight message of Paul Revere.   130

19. **British Regulars:** members of the permanent army of Great Britain.
20. **redcoats:** British soldiers.

HENRY WADSWORTH LONGFELLOW

Henry Wadsworth Longfellow [1807-1882] was born in Portland, Maine. He attended Harvard University and then studied and traveled in Europe. Longfellow published his first poems while in college. He lived for many years in Boston, Massachusetts.

Longfellow became known as a poet of adventure and patriotism. His poem "The Song of Hiawatha" became a classic. Longfellow was also concerned with social injustice. In 1842, well before the Civil War, Longfellow spoke out about slavery in his book *Poems on Slavery*.

Asking Big Questions About the Literature

What makes an adventure?

LITERATURE STUDY

Setting

The time and place in which the action of a story occurs is called the **setting.** A good adventure often takes place in a dangerous or unfamiliar setting, such as a mountain top or a space shuttle. In your journal, write a paragraph for each literature selection you have read, explaining why the setting is important for the adventure. (*See "Setting" on page 118.*)

Write a
GREETING CARD

Imagine that you're on one of the adventures that you've read about in the literature selections. Write a greeting card to the folks back home, explaining what makes your adventure different from an ordinary, quiet vacation.

MAKE AN ADVENTURE CHART

Make a chart like the one below, showing what makes an adventure in each selection that you've read. When you've finished, use your chart to write a short essay describing the features of a typical adventure story.

Literature Selection	Features of Adventure
"The Mountain That Refused to Be Climbed"	a challenging goal dangerous terrain adventurer pursuing a dream

How do people react to their adventures?

COMPARING Adventures

Make a chart like the one below, showing how different characters in the selections you have read react to their adventures. Then use your chart to help you write a short essay comparing the characters' reactions.

Write a
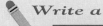
DIARY ENTRY

Imagine that you are a character in one of the literature selections you've read. How do you feel about the adventure you're on? Write a diary entry from that character's point of view. Describe your reactions to the story's events.

Selection	Type of Adventure	Character	Reaction

LITERATURE STUDY

Character

A **character** is a person or an animal that participates in the action of a work of literature. Choose a character from a literature selection you've read in this unit. Then write an adventure story of your own that features the same character. Show how he or she would react to a very different situation. (*See "Character" on page 119.*)

Asking Big Questions About the Literature

What are adventurers like?

LITERATURE STUDY

Character

A good writer will reveal the personality of a **character** through his or her thoughts, words, and deeds. If you were making one of the selections you've read into a movie, which actor or actress would you cast as the adventurer? Write this person a letter explaining why you think he or she would be good for the role. (*See "Character" on page 119.*)

Write a Magazine

ARTICLE

Write a magazine cover story called "Adventurer of the Year." Choose a character from a literature selection you've read. Write an article about this character in which you describe the character's achievements and personality.

A Map of Qualities

In a group, discuss adventurers you've read about. Write a list of their qualities in the center of a journal page. Then make a Quality Map like the one below by surrounding the list with the circled names of adventurers you read about in this unit. Draw a line from each quality to the appropriate character or characters. Then write a character profile of your favorite adventurer.

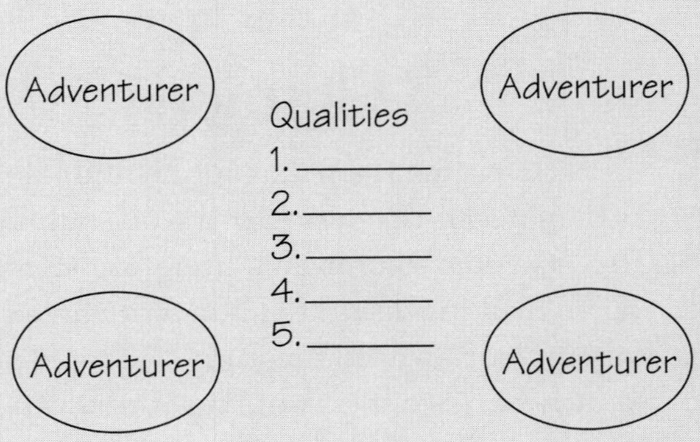

Adventurer

Adventurer

Qualities
1. _____
2. _____
3. _____
4. _____
5. _____

Adventurer

Adventurer

How are you an adventurer?

Self-Evaluation Chart

Think of the adventurers in the selections you've read. What qualities made them good adventurers? Do you share any of these qualities? Make a self-evaluation chart like the one below. List your good qualities. Beside each quality, describe the time when this quality helped you in a challenging situation.

Good Quality	When It Helped
_____	_____
_____	_____
_____	_____

LITERATURE STUDY

Setting

The **setting**—the time and place in which a story's action occurs—often determines the plot of an adventure. Look through the fiction selections in this unit for stories in which the setting affected the plot. Then think of a time when your surroundings presented you with a challenge. Show how you faced this challenge by writing a short adventure story, with yourself as the main character. Include a good description of the setting. (*See "Setting" on page 118.*)

News Story About You

Many adventurers are trailblazers. Look through the selections in this unit for examples of people who were the first in the world to achieve some goal. Now imagine yourself achieving something unique. Then write a news article or broadcast reporting your achievement. Share your article or broadcast with classmates.

NOW *Choose a Project!*

Three projects involving adventure are described on the following pages. Which one is for you?

PROJECT 1

Writing Workshop

WRITING A TRAVEL BROCHURE

If you could lead an expedition, where would you go? What would you do? In this project, you'll plan the adventure of a lifetime. After you've researched your destination, you'll publish a travel brochure to present to your **audience** of classmates. The **purpose** of your brochure will be to present a travel plan so exciting that your classmates will want to join you in your adventure.

Prewriting
GETTING STARTED

First collect some travel brochures from local travel agencies or the library. Study them to see how they are set up. To help you choose a destination, start with some freewriting in your journal. Is there some place that you've always wanted to visit? Brainstorm a list of places. Use a globe or atlas in the library to help you with your list. Write down the names of interesting places you find in world atlases, encyclopedias, travel books, and magazines. Ask yourself these questions to limit your topic:

- Is it a place where there will be lots of things to do?
- Will we be able to get around easily?
- Will the climate be right?

Then choose a destination.

Researching YOUR DESTINATION

Now research your destination. Again, use the library to gather information. Take notes as you find the answers to these questions:

- What will the weather be like?
- What will the local food be like?
- What are the main geographic features?
- What are the main points of interest?
- What plants and animals will we find?

To take notes, write your question at the top of an index card or sheet of paper. Below the question, write the information and its source. You'll use these cards when you organize your information into the different paragraphs of your travel brochure.

When you have gathered information about your destination, ask yourself these questions and write the answers in your journal.

- Will we be staying in one place or traveling around?
- How will we travel and where will we stay?
- What risks and challenges will we face?
- What will we need to take with us?

Show your list of questions to one or more classmates. Is there anything else they'd like to know? Consider their suggestions. Think about your *itinerary*, or the schedule you will follow during your trip.

Drafting
....
**YOUR TRAVEL
BROCHURE**

Before you draft your travel brochure, remember both your **purpose**—to make your destination sound appealing to other travelers—and your **audience**.

- Write an introduction that will catch your audience's attention. For example, Luke Hohreiter, a student writer, asks a question to introduce his travel guide on pages 110-111. "Are you ready for a vacation?" Who wouldn't answer "Yes!"

- Use each index card that you filled out during your research phase to write a paragraph on a different subject. Write separate paragraphs on the geography, the weather, and the main points of interest of your destination. Notice that Luke has written separate paragraphs on Costa Rica's climate, geography, food, and tourist attractions.

- Draft a conclusion that will make readers start packing! Luke writes that "Costa Rica has all the characteristics of the perfect getaway at half the price of any other vacation of the same quality." Who could ask for more?

- Include an itinerary, if you have one. Under the headings Day 1, Day 2, and so on, outline the schedule of your expedition. Don't forget to work in traveling time to and from the country you've chosen.

Revising
YOUR TRAVEL BROCHURE

You've finished your first draft. Is it complete? Is it clear? Is it exciting? Does it have all the information that a potential traveler might need? Show it to a classmate or your writing group. Would it persuade others to join you on this adventure? Look it over carefully yourself, too. Get more information, make changes, and reorganize your paragraphs if necessary. Do whatever you need to do to make your expedition sound absolutely terrific.

Editing
YOUR TRAVEL BROCHURE

After you've revised your draft, work with a partner or writing group to edit your travel brochure. Read one another's guides and check for errors in grammar, punctuation, and spelling. Correct your errors and make a publishable copy of your brochure. Remember that a good editing job now will mean happy travelers later.

Publishing
YOUR TRAVEL BROCHURE

Look through magazines and books for pictures of your destination. If you can't cut them out, xerox them and arrange them next to the text of your travel brochure. Then present your guide to the class or combine your brochures into a travel book.

TRAVEL BROCHURE
by Luke Hohreiter
West Palm Beach, Florida

Are you ready for a vacation? Do you want to enjoy a week of blissful leisure in a tropical paradise, relaxing on the beach, hiking along a steep mountain trail, or even white water rafting down a swift, pristine river? If this is the kind of adventure you are looking for, Costa Rica is the place for you. Its pleasant climate and peaceful atmosphere, as well as its exotic beauty, provide the perfect escape from your hectic daily schedule.

Costa Rica's climate is wet most of the year and the temperature depends on the altitude. In some parts it rains about 300 days out of the year, but it also has a dry season, so plan accordingly. Because altitude determines the temperature, you could take a hike in the mountains and be greeted by a gentle snow flurry or relax on the beach while sipping a cold drink and basking in the sun. Although over the course of your vacation you will experience all of these diverse climates, the beginning of your adventure will take place in an area with weather so beautiful it is called the place of "Eternal Spring." This region is known as the Central Valley and consists of San José, Heredia, Alajuela, and Cartago.

Costa Rica has some of the most diverse geography in the world. Central Costa Rica consists mostly of dense jungles except for the Central Valley which rests on a large plateau. As you travel to the east and west, you will find great mountain ranges that stretch across

the country. The mountains eventually slope into foothills and then into miles and miles of tropical savannahs. From there, savannahs melt away into white, sandy beaches which are excellent fishing grounds.

If food is high on your agenda, you won't be disappointed with the local entrees. In the countryside you may find more traditional cuisine, which is often vegetarian. In San José, however, you will find "International Cuisine," a combination of North American and European dishes. The main course of each meal is usually some type of meat, either beef, chicken, or fish, with rice and cabbage on the side. A traditional and very common dish is casado, which is a serving of meat, usually beef, and rice, beans, and cabbage. After your meal, you might have cajeta, which is a dessert dish that consists of heavy milk fudge.

After spending a night in one of Costa Rica's lovely hotels, a visit to one of its major tourist attractions— a world-renowned national park— would be most appealing. One of the most well-known and popular parks among tourists is Santa Rosa. This park is known for its scenic hiking trails and its many species of exotic birds.

As you can see, Costa Rica has all the characteristics of the perfect getaway at half the price of any other vacation of the same quality. For these reasons and many more, it would be the best choice for a fun and interesting place to visit.

Itinerary

Day One

Depart from Miami
Arrive in San José
Check into hotel
Have dinner at a local restaurant

Day Two

Tour of San José
Lunch at hotel
Tour of nearby towns

Day Three

Travel to the coast by bus
Check into hotel and head to local river
for white-water rafting

2 Cooperative Learning

Have you ever dreamed of searching for lost treasure? In this project, you and a group of classmates will plan a treasure hunt for charity or just for fun. It will be an "obstacle course" with a trail of clues leading to a hidden treasure.

The PROCESS

First, decide on your main purpose. Will it be for entertainment or charity? Then select the "hunters"—the people who'll search for the hidden treasure. Finally decide what the treasure itself will be.

Organize your project into steps. First, you need to agree on the main steps: researching your theme, finding a place and time for the hunt, mapping out the hunt, creating clues, and so on. It may help to create a Job Sequence Chain like the one shown.

Then come up with a theme for your adventure. It could be based on a famous historical adventure or a scientific discovery. For example, if you choose an Egyptian theme, you could bury copies of objects belonging to the Pharaoh. Divide into teams studying history, science, and other subjects. Discuss the team's findings and choose a theme for your hunt.

Now form task teams. Each team will work to complete one major step, while keeping in close contact with the other teams. Remember that one team's decision may affect another team's plan. The map team and the clue team especially will have to work closely together.

- Job Sequence Chain
- Step One: Researching the theme
- Step Two
- Step Three
- Step Four
- Step Five
- Step Six: The Hunt

Within each team, make a work plan like the one below that shows each person's responsibility.

Team Member	Responsibility
Bill	
Sue	
Chris	

When the teams have completed their tasks, meet together as a group and finalize your plan.

The HUNT

Write your clues and plant them. Put the treasure in its hiding place. Explain the theme to the hunters before they begin their search. Then let the game begin!

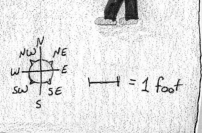

CLUES to find King Tut's Treasure

1. One half of the way between the boy's right index finger and the tip of the dark palm tree leaf, go due North for two feet.

2. Three quarters of the way between this point and the bottom right corner of the pyramid go West for four feet.

3. When you get to this point, go south for three feet and start digging.

by Michael Maloney, Grade 7, Bath, Maine

PROJECT 3

Helping Your Community

CELEBRATING LOCAL ADVENTURERS

If you think adventurers are found only in movies and books, look around you! Your community is full of adventurers. In this project, you'll work with a partner or group to put together a tribute to the adventurers in your community.

The SEARCH

First, decide on the form your tribute will take. Could you make a book or assemble a "Wall of Adventurers" in your school or community? Could you present a slide show or make a video?

Then decide whether to create a profile of adventurers from your school, neighborhood, or town. Start your search for adventurers by asking yourself the Big Question "What are adventurers like?"

To gather information on adventurers in your school, scan back issues of school publications. For information on adventurers in your town, look at newspapers and books on local history. Make a list of community adventurers.

Choose people from the list. Research historical figures in the library. Contact any living adventurers and interview them directly. Use the following questions to help you get the information you need.

- What did the adventurer do?
- What is the adventurer's background?
- What does the adventurer feel about his or her achievement?

Marc Freedman, round-the-world cyclist, in front of signs at Red Center, Australia

Now write a short piece of biographical information about each adventurer. Collect photographs of the adventurers as well. Form a design group that will arrange the information for presentation.

The PRESENTATION

Decide when and where to present your project. Are there other organizations that might be interested in your project? You may find many others who would be interested in your tribute to the adventurers in your community.

These photographs were taken during Marc Freedman's round-the-world bicycling trip. During his eight-year journey, Marc spent five years on the road and three years working in various countries along the way.

Marc Freedman with Guatemalan children

Marc Freedman resting on a rock in Zimbabwe, Africa

Melissa Johnson at South Island, New Zealand

Putting It All Together

What Have You Learned About Adventures?

Now that your adventures in this unit are over, consider how your ideas on this theme have changed. You've read and thought about a world of exciting challenges. Show what you learned about adventures by writing an adventure story in which you are the main character.

YOUR EXCELLENT ADVENTURE

Prewriting and Drafting Look back at all the writing you did for this unit—in your journal, in response to your reading, and in the Writing Workshop. Does any of the material help you with ideas for a fantastic adventure of your own? For example, if you worked on the Writing Workshop, you could live out your travel plan in your imagination. Brainstorm ideas for a fabulous adventure that takes place anywhere in the universe. It could take place under the sea, on another planet, or even during another period of history. Whatever you

choose as the setting of your story, just remember that this story will be about *you*.

Now draft your story. You could begin by describing the setting, with a quotation from yourself as the main character. Fill your plot with challenges that must be overcome. Let the story's events build to an exciting conclusion. Remember to include dialogue.

Revising and Editing Work with a partner or writing group. Exchange stories and ask for comments on and advice about the content of your writing. Have your partner or group check your errors in grammar, spelling, and punctuation.

Publishing Rewrite your story neatly and give it a title. Post it on a class bulletin board so that your classmates can read it. If you like, you could gather all your classmates' stories into a book entitled *Our Excellent Adventures*.

Evaluating Your Work

Think Back About the Big Questions

Think about the Big Questions on pages 10-11. Discuss your thoughts with a partner, especially your thoughts about questions that still seem hard to answer. Compare your ideas now with your ideas when you started this unit. Record your current thoughts in your journal.

Think Back About Your Work

Now think about the whole unit. What did you do? How did you do? To evaluate your work, including your reading, your writing, your activities, and your project, write a note to your teacher. Explain what you've done during this unit and what you've learned. Use the following questions to help you write your note.

- Which literature selections in this unit did you like the most? Why?
- What was your favorite activity in this unit? Why?
- What was your least favorite activity? Why?
- If you were to do your project again, what parts would you do the same way? What parts would you do differently?
- What did you learn as you worked on your project or projects?
- What have you learned in this unit about adventure and adventurers?
- How would you rate your work in this unit? Use the following scale and give at least three reasons for your rating.

  1 = Outstanding   3 = Fair
  2 = Good   4 = Not as good as it could have been

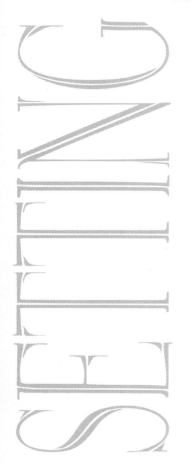

SETTING

What Is Setting?   **Setting** is the time and place in which the action of a story or a poem occurs. The setting may be described at the beginning of the story, or it may be presented through details that appear as the story unfolds. In an adventure story, the setting often has an important role in the plot. In "The Mountain That Refused to Be Climbed," for example, the setting is one reason why the adventure takes place. Because of this, the setting is described in great detail. We learn that the mountain "is a moving mass of ice. Anyone climbing it may encounter dangerous crevasses—deep fissures that drop suddenly into abysses—and snow avalanches that unexpectedly thunder down."

Rewriting a Setting   Choose a character from a literature selection that you've read. Write an adventure story in which the character wakes up in an entirely different setting. How would the setting affect the outcome of the plot? How would the character react to this new setting, given what you know about the character from the selection you've read?

Comparing Settings   Choose two selections that you've read in this unit that have very different settings. Then write a short essay comparing how the adventurers in the selections react to the settings. What does each character's reaction tell you about that character's personality?

What Is Character?

A **character** is a person or an animal that participates in the action of a work of literature. To make characters believable, authors give them personality traits and describe their physical appearance. A good writer will try to visualize a character in great detail and allow the character's personality to express itself through his or her thoughts, words, and actions. For example, in "The True Confessions of Charlotte Doyle" we learn a great deal about Charlotte's courage and determination through her thoughts and movements as she struggles up the ship's mast, proving that she is as brave as any sailor.

A Talk Show Choose an adventurous character from a literature selection you've read. With a partner, conduct an interview between this character and a televison talk show host. The talk show host should ask the character about the events in the literature selection as if they actually happened. The person who plays the character should assume his or her personality as if the events actually happened. Perform your interview in front of the class.

Creating a Character Create a female or male super adventurer who has the good qualities of all the adventurers you've read about. Then write the opening paragraphs of a story about this character. Provide the super adventurer with some challenge that she or he must overcome. Show what the character is like through his or her thoughts, words, and actions.

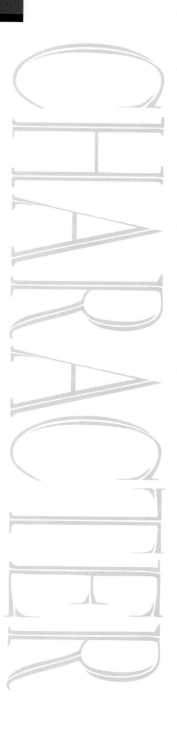

GLOSSARY OF LITERARY TERMS

A

alliteration   Repetition of the first sound—usually a consonant sound—in several words of a sentence or a line of poetry.

allusion   An author's indirect reference to someone or something that is presumed to be familiar to the reader.

anecdote   A short narrative about an interesting or a humorous event, usually in the life of a person.

antagonist   The person or force opposing the protagonist, or main character in a literary work. [See also *protagonist*.]

autobiography   A person's written account of his or her own life.

B

ballad   A poem, often a song, that tells a story in simple verse.

biography   An account of a person's life, written by another person.

blank verse   Unrhymed poetry.

C

character   A person or an animal that participates in the action of a work of literature. A *dynamic character* is one whose thoughts, feelings, and actions are changeable and lifelike; a *static character* always remains the same. [See also *protagonist, antagonist*.]

characterization   The creation of characters through the characters' use of language and through descriptions of their appearance, thoughts, emotions, and actions. [See also *character*.]

chronology   An arrangement of events in the order in which they happen.

cliché   An overused expression that is trite rather than meaningful.

climax   The highest point of tension in the plot of a work of literature. [See also *plot*.]

comedy   An amusing play that has a happy ending.

conclusion   The final part or ending of a piece of literature.

concrete poem   A poem arranged on the page so that its punctuation, letters, and lines make the shape of the subject of the poem.

conflict   A problem that confronts the characters in a piece of literature. The conflict may be *internal* (a character's struggle within himself or herself) or *external* (a character's struggle against nature, another person, or society). [See also *plot*.]

context   The general sense of words that helps readers to understand the meaning of unfamiliar words and phrases in a piece of writing.

D

description   An author's use of words to give the reader or listener a mental picture, an impression, or an understanding of a person, place, thing, event, or idea.

dialect   A form of speech spoken by people in a particular group or geographical region that differs in vocabulary, grammar, and pronunciation from the standard language.

dialogue   The spoken words and conversation of characters in a work of literature.

drama   A play that is performed before an audience according to stage directions and using dialogue. Classical drama has two genres: *tragedy* and *comedy*. Modern drama includes *melodrama, satire, theater of the absurd*, and *pantomime*. [See also *comedy, play*, and *tragedy*.]

dramatic poetry   A play written in the form of poetry.

E

epic   A long narrative poem—written in a formal style and meant to be read aloud—that relates the adventures and

experiences of one or more great heroes or heroines.

essay   Personal nonfiction writing about a particular subject that is important to the writer.

excerpt   A passage from a larger work that has been taken out of its context to be used for a special purpose.

exposition   Writing that explains, analyzes, or defines.

extended metaphor   An elaborately drawn out metaphor. [See also *metaphor*.]

F

fable   A short, simple story whose purpose is to teach a lesson, usually with animal characters who talk and act like people.

fantasy   Imaginative fiction about unrealistic characters, places, and events.

fiction   Literature, including the short story and the novel, that tells about imaginary people and events.

figurative language Language used to express ideas through figures of speech: descriptions that aren't meant to be taken literally. Types of figurative language include *simile*, *metaphor*, *extended metaphor*, *hyperbole*, and *personification*.

figure of speech   A type of figurative language, not meant to be taken literally, that expresses something in such a way that it brings the thing to life in the reader's or listener's imagination. [See also *figurative language*.]

flashback   A break in a story's action that relates a past happening in order to give the reader background information about a present action in the story.

folktale   A story that has been passed along from storyteller to storyteller for generations. Kinds of folktales include *tall tales*, *fairy tales*, *fables*, *legends*, and *myths*.

foreshadowing   The use of clues to create suspense by giving the reader or audience hints of events to come.

free verse   Poetry that has no formal rhyme scheme or metrical pattern.

G

genre   A major category of art. The three major literary genres are poetry, prose, and drama.

H

haiku   A three-line Japanese verse form. In most haiku, the first and third lines have five syllables, while the second line has seven. The traditional haiku describes a complicated feeling or thought in simple language through a single image.

hero/heroine   The main character in a work of literature. In heroic literature, the hero or heroine is a particularly brave, noble, or clever person whose achievements are unusual and important. [See also *character*.]

heroic age   The historical period in western civilization—from about 800 B.C. through A.D. 200—during which most works of heroic literature, such as myths and epics, were created in ancient Greece and Rome.

hubris   Arrogance or excessive pride leading to mistakes; the character flaw in a hero of classical tragedy.

hyperbole   An obvious exaggeration used for emphasis. [See also *figurative language*.]

I

idiom   An expression whose meaning cannot be understood from the ordinary meaning of the words. For example, *It's raining cats and dogs*.

imagery   The words and phrases in writing that appeal to the senses of sight, hearing, taste, touch, and smell.

irony   An effect created by a sharp contrast between what is expected and what is real. An *ironic twist* in a plot is an event that is the complete opposite of what the characters have been hoping or expecting will happen. An *ironic statement* declares the opposite of the speaker's literal meaning.

J

jargon   Words and phrases used by a group of people who share the same profession or special interests in order to refer to technical things or processes with which they are familiar. In general, jargon is any terminology that sounds unclear, overused, or pretentious.

L

legend   A famous folktale about heroic actions, passed along by word of mouth from generation to generation. The legend may have begun as a factual account of real people and events but has become mostly or completely fictitious.

limerick   A form of light verse, or humorous poetry, written in one five-line stanza with a regular scheme of rhyme and meter.

literature   The branch of art that is expressed in written language and includes all written genres.

lyric poem   A short poem that expresses personal feelings and thoughts in a musical way. Originally, lyrics were the words of songs that were sung to music played on the lyre, a stringed instrument invented by the ancient Greeks.

M

metamorphosis   The transformation of one thing, or being, into another completely different thing or being, such as a caterpillar's change into a butterfly.

metaphor   Figurative language in which one thing is said to be another thing. [See also *figurative language*.]

meter   The pattern of rhythm in lines of poetry. The most common meter, in poetry written in English, is iambic pentameter, that is, a verse having five metrical feet, each foot of verse having two syllables, an unaccented one followed by an accented one.

mood   The feeling or atmosphere that a reader senses while reading or listening to a work of literature.

motivation   A character's reasons for doing, thinking, feeling, or saying something. Sometimes an author will make a character's motivation obvious from the beginning. In realistic fiction and drama, however, a character's motivation may be so complicated that the reader discovers it gradually, by studying the character's thoughts, feelings, and behavior.

myth   A story, passed along by word of mouth for generations, about the actions of gods and goddesses or superhuman heroes and heroines. Most myths were first told to explain the origins of natural things or to justify the social rules and customs of a particular society.

N

narration   The process of telling a story. For both fiction and nonfiction, there are two main kinds of narration, based on whether the story is told from a first-person or third-person point of view. [See also *point of view*.]

narrative poem   A poem that tells a story containing the basic literary ingredients of fiction: character, setting, and plot.

narrator   The person, or voice, that tells a story. [See also *point of view, voice*.]

nonfiction   Prose that is factually true and is about real people, events, and places.

nonstandard English
Versions of English, such as slang and dialects, that use pronunciation, vocabulary, idiomatic expressions, grammar, and punctuation that differ from the accepted "correct" constructions of English.

novel   A long work of narrative prose fiction. A novel contains narration, a setting or settings, characters, dialogue, and a more complicated plot than a short story.

O

onomatopoeia   The technique of using words that imitate the sounds they describe, such as *hiss*, *buzz*, and *splash*.

oral tradition   Stories, poems, and songs that have been kept alive by being told, recited, and sung by people over many generations. Since the works were not originally written, they often have many different versions.

P

parable   A brief story—similar to a fable, but about people—that describes an ordinary situation and concludes with a short moral or lesson to be learned.

personification   Figurative language in which an animal, an object, or an idea is given human characteristics. [See also *figurative language*.]

persuasion   A type of speech or writing whose purpose is to convince people that something is true or important.

play   A work of dramatic literature written for performance by actors before an audience. In classical or traditional drama, a play is divided into five acts, each containing a number of scenes. Each act represents a distinct phase in the development of the plot. Modern plays often have only one act and one scene.

playwright   The author of a play.

plot   The sequence of actions and events in fiction or drama. A traditional plot has at least three parts: the *rising action*, leading up to a turning point that affects the main character; the *climax*, the turning point or moment of greatest intensity or interest; and the *falling action*, leading away from the conflict, or resolving it.

poetry   Language selected and arranged in order to say something in a compressed or nonliteral way. Modern poetry may or may not use many of the traditional poetic techniques that include *meter*, *rhyme*, *alliteration*, *figurative language*, *symbolism*, and *specific verse forms*.

point of view   The perspective from which a writer tells a story. *First-person* narrators tell the story from their own point of view, using pronouns such as *I* or *me*. *Third-person* narrators, using pronouns such as *he*, *she*, or *them*, may be *omniscient* (knowing everything about all characters), or *limited* (taking the point of view of one character). [See also *narration*.]

propaganda   Information or ideas that may or may not be true, but are spread as though they are true, in order to persuade people to do or believe something.

prose   The ordinary form of written and spoken language used to create fiction, nonfiction, and most drama.

protagonist   The main character of a literary work. [See also *character* and *characterization*.]

R

refrain   A line or group of lines that is repeated, usually at the end of each verse, in a poem or a song.

repetition   The use of the same formal element more than once in a literary work, for emphasis or in order to achieve another desired effect.

resolution   The falling action in fiction or drama,

including all of the developments that follow the climax and show that the story's conflict is over. [See also *plot*.]

rhyme scheme   A repeated pattern of similar sounds, usually found at the ends of lines of poetry or poetic drama.

rhythm   In poetry, the measured recurrence of accented and unaccented syllables in a particular pattern. [See also *meter*.]

S

scene   The time, place, and circumstances of a play or a story. In a play, a scene is a section of an act. [See also *play*.]

science fiction   Fantasy literature set in an imaginary future, with details and situations that are designed to seem scientifically possible.

setting   The time and place of a work of literature.

short story   Narrative prose fiction that is shorter and has a less complicated plot than a novel. A short story contains narration, at least one setting, at least one character, and usually some dialogue.

simile   Figurative language that compares two unlike things, introduced by the words "like" or "as." [See also *figurative language*.]

soliloquy   In a play, a short speech spoken by a single character when he or she is alone on the stage. A soliloquy usually expresses the character's innermost thoughts and feelings, when he or she thinks no other characters can hear.

sonnet   A poem written in one stanza, using fourteen lines of iambic pentameter. [See also *meter*.]

speaker   In poetry, the individual whose voice seems to be speaking the lines. [See also *narration*, *voice*.]

stage directions   The directions, written by the playwright, to tell the director, actors, and theater technicians how a play should be dramatized. Stage directions may specify such things as how the setting should appear in each scene, how the actors should deliver their lines, when the stage curtain should rise and fall, how stage lights should be used, where on the stage the actors should be during the action, and when sound effects should be used.

stanza   A group of lines in poetry set apart by blank lines before and after the group; a poetic verse.

style   The distinctive way in which an author composes a

work of literature in written or spoken language.

suspense   An effect created by authors of various types of fiction and drama, especially adventure and mystery, to heighten interest in the story.

symbol   An image, person, place, or thing that is used to express the idea of something else.

T

tall tale   A kind of folk tale, or legend, that exaggerates the characteristics of its hero or heroine.

theme   The main idea or underlying subject of a work of literature.

tone   The attitude that a work of literature expresses to the reader through its style.

tragedy   In classical drama, a tragedy depicts a noble hero or heroine who makes a mistake of judgment that has disastrous consequences.

V

verse   A stanza in a poem. Also, a synonym for poetry as a genre. [See also *stanza*.]

voice   The narrator or the person who relates the action of a piece of literature. [See also *speaker*.]

ACKNOWLEDGMENTS

Grateful acknowledgment is made for permission to reprint the following copyrighted material.

"The Mountain That Refused to Be Climbed" from *Living Dangerously: American Women Who Risked Their Lives for Adventure.* Copyright © 1991 by Doreen Rappaport. By permission of HarperCollins Publishers.

From "Burning" by Gary Snyder from *Myths and Texts.* Copyright © 1978 by Gary Snyder. Reprinted by permission of New Directions Publishing Corp.

"The Stars, My Goal: Guion Stewart Bluford, Jr." by Jim Haskins from *Against All Opposition: Black Explorers in America.* Copyright © 1992 by Jim Haskins. Used with permission of Walker Publishing Company, 720 Fifth Avenue, New York, NY 10019, 1-800-289-2553.

"What I Want to Be When I Grow Up" by Martha Brooks from *Paradise Cafe and Other Stories.* Copyright © 1988 by Martha Brooks. By permission of Little, Brown and Company.

"When in Reality" by Maurice Kenny from *Words in the Blood: Contemporary Indian Writers of North and South America,* edited by Jamake Highwater. Copyright ©1984 by Jamake Highwater.

From *The True Confessions of Charlotte Doyle* by Avi. Copyright © 1990 by Avi. Used with permission of Orchard Books, New York.

"The Kitchen Knight" by Margaret Hodges. Text copyright © 1990 by Margaret Hodges. All rights reserved. Reprinted by permission of Holiday House.

"The Getaway" by John Savage is reprinted from the *Saturday Evening Post,* May 7, 1966, Issue No. 10.

"Nothing to Be Afraid Of" by Jan Mark. Copyright © 1991 by Jan Mark. By permission of HarperCollins Publishers.

"The Time We Climbed Snake Mountain" by Leslie Marmon Silko from *StoryTeller.* Copyright © 1981 by Leslie Marmon Silko. By permission of the author.

From *Woodsong* by Gary Paulsen, copyright © 1990 by Gary Paulsen. By permission of Bradbury Press, an Affiliate of Macmillan, Inc.

ILLUSTRATION

8 Maze by Dave Shepherd.

PHOTOGRAPHY

4 *l* Richard Haynes/©D.C. Heath; *r* Sarah Putnam/©D.C. Heath; 5 Universitätsbibliothek Heidelberg, Germany; 6 Julie Bidwell/©D.C. Heath; 8-9 Brian Seed/Tony Stone Images; 10 *t* Sarah Putnam/©D.C. Heath; *b* Richard Haynes/©D.C. Heath; 11 *t* John Owens/©D.C. Heath; *c* Jim Whitmer/Stock Boston; *b* Sarah Putnam/©D.C. Heath; 12 *inset A Search for the Apex of America* by Annie S. Peck, New York, Dodd, Mead and Company, 1911. General Research Division, New York Public Library Astor, Lenox and Tilden Foundations; 12-13 Rob Crandall/The Image Works; 16-17, *background,* 20-21 *background,* 21, 23 *A Search for the Apex of America* by Annie S. Peck, New York, Dodd, Mead and Company, 1911. General Research Division, New York Public Library Astor, Lenox and Tilden Foundations; 25 Courtesy of HarperCollins Publishers; 26-27 Albright-Knox Art Gallery, Buffalo, NY. George B. and Jenny R. Mathews Fund, 1981; 27 *l* Virginia Schedhler. Courtesy of New Directions Corp.; 28 *inset* Courtesy of Abbeville Press; 28-35 Navaswan/FPG International; 29 *insets* Courtesy of Abbeville Press; 31 *inset* Sovfoto; 33, 34-35 *c* NASA; 37 Private Collection, courtesy of Marlborough Gallery. ©Richard Estes/VAGA, New York, 1995. Photo courtesy of the Allan Stone Gallery, New York; 40 The Museum of Modern Art, New York, Philip Johnson Fund. ©George Segal/VAGA, NY, 1995; 43 Courtesy of Little Brown and Company; 44 *inset* Courtesy of White Pine Press; 44-45 Computer photo illustration by Jim Carroll; 46 *inset* G. Brimacombe/The Image Bank; 46-51 Superstock; 51 *inset* Tibor Bognar/The Stock Market; 52-55 Superstock; 55 *inset* DRS Productions/Steve Mason/The Stock Market; 56-57 Superstock; 58, 63, 66 Universitätsbibliothek Heidelberg, Germany; 67 Courtesy of Holiday House; 68-71 Jan Halaska/Photo Researchers; 72 Courtesy of Rex Lau; 79 ©Holly Roberts, Collection of Pamela Portwood and Mark Taylor. Courtesy Etherton Stern Gallery, Tuscon, AZ; 81 Courtesy of HarperCollins Publishers; 83 *t* The Metropolitan Museum of Art, Alfred Stieglitz Collection. Bequest of Georgia O'Keeffe, 1986. (1987.377.4); *b* Gus Nitsche; 84-85 Ken Graham/AllStock; 88 Stephen Krasemann/AllStock; 93 Darrell Gulin/AllStock; 95 Courtesy of Penguin USA; 96-97 Shelburne Museum, Shelburne, VT. Photo by Ken Burris; 98-99 Photograph courtesy of the Concord Museum, Concord, MA; 100 Shelburne Museum, Shelburne, VT. Photo by Ken Burris; 101 *inset* Historical Pictures/Stock Montage, Inc.; 103 Nancy Sheehan/©D.C. Heath; 106 *t* Elizabeth Hamlin/Stock Boston; *b* David J. Sams/Stock Boston; 107 Michael Fogden/DRK; 109 Alon Reininger/Leo de Wys, Inc.; 110 Bill Bachman/Leo de Wys, Inc.; 111 Bob Krist/Leo de Wys, Inc.; 112 Jean-Claude Lejeune/Stock Boston; 113 Ken O'Donoghue/©D.C. Heath; 114 *t* J. Sulley/The Image Works; *b,* 115 *l, tr* Marc Freedman; *br* Melissa Johnson. **Back cover** *t* Skjold/The Image Works; *c* John Owens/©D.C. Heath; *b* Sarah Putnam/©D.C. Heath.

Full Pronunciation Key for Footnoted Words

(Each pronunciation and definition is adapted from *Scott, Foresman Advanced Dictionary* by E.L. Thorndike and Clarence L. Barnhart.)

The pronunciation of each footnoted word is shown just after the word, in this way: **abbreviate** [ə brē′ vē āt]. The letters and signs used are pronounced as in the words below. The mark ′ is placed after a syllable with primary or heavy accent, as in the example above. The mark ′ after a syllable shows a secondary or lighter accent, as in **abbreviation** [ə brē′ vē ā′ shən].

Some words, taken from foreign languages, are spoken with sounds that do not otherwise occur in English. Symbols for these sounds are given in the key as "foreign sounds."

a	hat, cap	j	jam, enjoy	u	cup, butter	**foreign sounds**
ā	age, face	k	kind, seek	u̇	full, put	
ä	father, far	l	land, coal	ü	rule, move	Y as in French *du*.
		m	me, am	v	very, save	Pronounce (ē) with
b	bad, rob	n	no, in	w	will, woman	the lips rounded as
ch	child, much	ng	long, bring	y	young, yet	for (ü).
d	did, red			z	zero, breeze	
		o	hot, rock	zh	measure, seizure	à as in French *ami*.
e	let, best	ō	open, go			Pronounce (ä) with
ē	equal, be	ô	order, all	ə represents:		the lips spread and
ėr	term, learn	oi	oil, voice		a in about	held tense.
		ou	house, out		e in taken	
f	fat, if				i in pencil	œ as in French *peu*.
g	go, bag	p	paper, cup		o in lemon	Pronounce (ā) with the
h	he, how	r	run, try		u in circus	lips rounded as for (ō).
		s	say, yes			
i	it, pin	sh	she, rush			N as in French *bon*.
ī	ice, five	t	tell, it			The N is not pro-
		th	thin, both			nounced, but shows
		ᴛʜ	then, smooth			that the vowel before
						it is nasal.

H as in German *ach*. Pronounce (k) without closing the breath passage.

LEVEL S

H E A T H
MIDDLELEVEL
LITERATURE

Survival!

▼
T H E M E
SURVIVAL

A U T H O R S

Donna Alvermann
Linda Miller Cleary
Kenneth Donelson
Donald Gallo
Alice Haskins
J. Howard Johnston
John Lounsbury
Alleen Pace Nilsen
Robert Pavlik
Jewell Parker Rhodes
Alberto Alvaro Ríos
Sandra Schurr
Lyndon Searfoss
Julia Thomason
Max Thompson
Carl Zon

D.C. Heath and Company
Lexington, Massachusetts / Toronto, Ontario

797

STAFF CREDITS

EDITORIAL	Barbara A. Brennan, Helen Byers, Christopher Johnson, Kathleen Kennedy Kelley, Owen Shows, Rita M. Sullivan
	Proofreading: JoAnne B. Sgroi
CONTRIBUTING WRITERS	Nance Davidson, Florence Harris
SERIES DESIGN	Robin Herr
BOOK DESIGN	Caroline Bowden, Daniel Derdula, Susan Geer, Diana Maloney, Angela Sciaraffa, Bonnie Chayes Yousefian
	Art Editing: Carolyn Langley
PHOTOGRAPHY	*Series Photography Coordinator:* Carmen Johnson
	Photo Research Supervisor: Martha Friedman
	Photo Researchers: Wendy Enright, Linda Finigan, Po-yee McKenna, PhotoSearch, Inc., Gillian Speeth, Denise Theodores
	Assignment Photography Coordinators: Susan Doheny, Gayna Hoffman, Shawna Johnston
COMPUTER PREPRESS	Ricki Pappo, Kathy Meisl
	Richard Curran, Michele Locatelli
PERMISSIONS	Dorothy B. McLeod
PRODUCTION	Patrick Connolly

Cover Photographs: left, Jeff Albertson, Stock Boston; right, Charles Gatewood, The Image Works.
Cover Design: Robin Herr

Published simultaneously in Canada

Printed in the United States of America

International Standard Book Number: 0-669-32106-0 (soft cover)
   4 5 6 7 8 9 10-RRD-99 98 97

International Standard Book Number: 0-669-38175-6 (hard cover)
   4 5 6 7 8 9 10-RRD-99 98 97

Middle Level Authors

Donna Alvermann, University of Georgia
Alice Haskins, Howard County Public Schools, Maryland
J. Howard Johnston, University of South Florida
John Lounsbury, Georgia College
Sandra Schurr, University of South Florida
Julia Thomason, Appalachian State University
Max Thompson, Appalachian State University
Carl Zon, California Assessment Collaborative

Literature and Language Arts Authors

Linda Miller Cleary, University of Minnesota
Kenneth Donelson, Arizona State University
Donald Gallo, Central Connecticut State University
Alleen Pace Nilsen, Arizona State University
Robert Pavlik, Cardinal Stritch College, Milwaukee
Jewell Parker Rhodes, Arizona State University
Alberto Alvaro Ríos, Arizona State University
Lyndon Searfoss, Arizona State University

Teacher Consultants

Suzanne Aubin, Patapsco Middle School, Ellicott City, Maryland
Judy Baxter, Newport News Public Schools, Newport News, Virginia
Saundra Bryn, Director of Research and Development, El Mirage, Arizona
Lorraine Gerhart, Elmbrook Middle School, Elm Grove, Wisconsin
Kathy Tuchman Glass, Burlingame Intermediate School, Burlingame, California
Lisa Mandelbaum, Crocker Middle School, Hillsborough, California
Lucretia Pannozzo, John Jay Middle School, Katonah, New York
Carol Schultz, Jerling Junior High, Orland Park, Illinois
Jeanne Siebenman, Grand Canyon University, Phoenix, Arizona
Gail Thompson, Garey High School, Pomona, California
Rufus Thompson, Grace Yokley School, Ontario, California
Tom Tufts, Conniston Middle School, West Palm Beach, Florida
Edna Turner, Harpers Choice Middle School, Columbia, Maryland
C. Anne Webb, Buerkle Junior High School, St. Louis, Missouri
Geri Yaccino, Thompson Junior High School, St. Charles, Illinois

CONTENTS

THE LITERATURE

Rippled Surface M.C. Escher
©1950 M.C. Escher Foundation, Baarn, Holland.
All rights reserved

Contents 5

Still Life With Indian Toys Elizabeth Blackadder

ASKING BIG QUESTIONS ABOUT THE LITERATURE

PROJECTS

1 WRITING WORKSHOP

WRITING A SURVIVAL NARRATIVE
106-111

What qualities help people survive? Interview a survivor. Then write a nonfiction narrative based on your interview.

2 COOPERATIVE LEARNING

PRODUCING A SURVIVAL KIT 112-113

What would you need to survive during a blizzard or a heat wave? Build a kit to help someone through a survival challenge.

3 HELPING YOUR COMMUNITY

PREPARING A SURVIVAL MANUAL
114-115

How would you prepare for a hurricane or a tornado? How did you survive your first day in seventh grade—or the morning's ride on the subway? Prepare a booklet giving survival tips.

You've survived a plane crash into a lake in the winter woods. You and other passengers have struggled out of the sinking plane. What items do you need most to ensure your survival?

Test your survival skills by taking this survival challenge with your classmates—all together or in smaller groups.

SURVIVAL CHALLENGE!

1 What's your situation?

- Your light plane crashed into a lake during a storm.
- The pilot and copilot were killed in the crash. After the crash, the plane sank completely into the lake.
- You and all the other passengers escaped the crash uninjured. You are all dressed in winter clothing appropriate for your hometown—jeans, sweaters, sneakers, and coats.
- Shortly before the crash, the pilot announced that you were twenty miles northwest of a small town. The plane was off course, however, and the pilot had no time to radio for help.

2 What are your survival conditions?

The picture on the right describes your survival setting. Look closely at the picture and write down everything you can tell about your setting.

What decisions do you need to make?

You've managed to save the items below from the sinking plane. Given your survival situation and your setting, which of these items will be most important for your survival? Assume that the number of surviving passengers is the same as the number of persons in your group, and that you and the other passengers have decided to stay together. Choose the five items that would be most useful to your survival.

Make your decisions about the importance of each item by reaching a *consensus.* That means that each of you must agree on the importance of each item before it becomes one of the items on your list. Consensus can be difficult to reach. Not everyone will agree at first. Together, try to make each item chosen at least partially agreeable to everyone in the group. Write down each item that you choose and explain in detail how it would help you survive.

bandage kit (with 28 feet of 2-in. gauze)

two ski poles

ball of steel wool

knife

map

thirty feet of rope

cigarette lighter (without fluid)

family-size chocolate bar (one per person)

newspapers (one per person)

flashlight with batteries

compass

extra shirt and pants for each sur-

Now think of one additional item (something not on the list) that you think would also help you survive in this situation. Add that item to your list and explain why you think that it is important.

Asking Big Questions About the Theme

What survival challenges do people face?

In your journal, list three survival challenges that you've faced—at school, at home, or in your neighborhood. Maybe a hurricane threatened your home, or your best friend moved to another state. With a partner or in a small group, compare the challenges you've listed with the ones listed by your classmates.

What decisions do people make to survive?

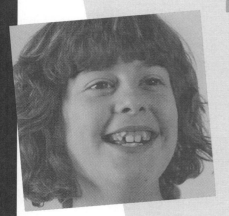

What decisions have *you* had to make to survive? Match one decision with each challenge that you listed in your journal. Perhaps you decided to tape the windows in your house before the hurricane, or you agreed to keep in touch with your friend by letter. Would you make the same decisions again? Why or why not? Write about your decisions in your journal and then discuss them with a partner or a group.

What qualities does a survivor have?

In your journal, write the word *survivor* at the center of a cluster or a web. Then work with a partner or a group to fill in the web with words that describe the qualities of a survivor. Share your web or cluster with your classmates.

survivor

How do people help one another survive?

With a partner or in a small group, tell a story about a time someone helped you survive or a time you helped someone survive. Use a story map like the one below to organize your story.

Characters (Who?)
Setting (Where and when?)
Problem (What?)
Events (What happened?)
Outcome (How did things turn out?)

NOW Think!

With a partner or in a small group, brainstorm a list of your own questions about survival. Write your list in your journal.

As you read the literature and do a project for this unit, think about the four Big Questions as well as your own questions. Ask yourself how each selection of literature, each activity, and each project helps you answer each question better.

FROM

HATCHET

GARY PAULSEN

His eyes snapped open, hammered open, and there were these things about himself that he knew instantly.

He was unbelievably, viciously[1] thirsty. His mouth was dry and tasted foul and sticky. His lips were cracked and felt as if they were bleeding and if he did not drink some water soon he felt that he would wither[2] up and die. Lots of water. All the water he could find.

He knew the thirst and felt the burn on his face. It was midafternoon and the sun had come over him and cooked him while he slept and his face was on fire, would blister, would peel. Which did not help the thirst, made it much worse. He stood, using the tree to pull himself up because there was still some pain and much stiffness, and looked down at the lake.

It was water. But he did not know if he could drink it. Nobody had ever told him if you could or could not drink lakes. There was also the thought of the pilot.

Down in the blue with the plane, strapped in, the body . . .

Awful, he thought. But the lake was blue, and wet-looking, and his mouth and throat raged with the thirst and he did not know where there might be another form of water he could drink. Besides, he had probably swallowed a ton of it while he was swimming out of the plane and getting to shore. In the movies they always showed the hero finding a clear spring with pure sweet water to drink but in the movies they didn't have plane wrecks and swollen foreheads and aching bodies and thirst that tore at the hero until he couldn't think.

Brian took small steps down the bank to the lake. Along the edge there were thick grasses and the water looked a little murky[3] and there were small things swimming in the water, small bugs. But there was a log extending about twenty feet out into the water of the lake—a beaver drop from some time before—with old limbs sticking up, almost like handles. He balanced on the log, holding himself up with the limbs, and teetered[4] out past the weeds and murky water.

---

1. **viciously** [vish′ əs lē]: in a severely unpleasant way.
2. **wither** [with′ ər]: to become dry and lifeless.
3. **murky** [mėr′ kē]: dark and thick.
4. **teetered** [tē′ tərd]: swayed or rocked unsteadily.

When he was out where the water was clear and he could see no bugs swimming he kneeled on the log to drink. A sip, he thought, still worrying about the lake water—I'll just take a sip.

But when he brought a cupped hand to his mouth and felt the cold lake water trickle past his cracked lips and over his tongue he could not stop. He had never, not even on long bike trips in the hot summer, been this thirsty. It was as if the water were more than water, as if the water had become all of life, and he could not stop. He stooped and put his mouth to the lake and drank and drank, pulling it deep and swallowing great gulps of it. He drank until his stomach was swollen, until he nearly fell off the log with it, then he rose and stagger-tripped his way back to the bank.

Where he was immediately sick and threw up most of the water. But his thirst was gone and the water seemed to reduce the pain in his head as well—although the sunburn still cooked his face.

"So." He almost jumped with the word, spoken aloud. It seemed so out of place, the sound. He tried it again. "So. So. So here I am."

And there it is, he thought. For the first time since the crash his mind started to work, his brain triggered and he began thinking.

Here I am—and where is that?

Where am I?

He pulled himself once more up the bank to the tall tree without branches and sat again with his back against the rough bark. It was hot now, but the sun was high and to his rear and he sat in the shade of the tree in relative comfort. There were things to sort out.

Here I am and that is nowhere. With his mind opened and thoughts happening it all tried to come in with a rush, all of what had occurred and he could not take it. The whole thing turned into a confused jumble that made no sense. So he fought it down and tried to take one thing at a time.

He had been flying north to visit his father for a couple of months, in the summer, and the pilot had had a heart attack and had died, and the plane had crashed somewhere in the Canadian north woods but he did not know how far they had flown or in what direction or where he was . . .

Slow down, he thought. Slow down more.

My name is Brian Robeson and I am thirteen years old and I am alone in the north woods of Canada.

All right, he thought, that's simple enough.

I was flying to visit my father and the plane crashed and sank in a lake.

There, keep it that way. Short thoughts.

I do not know where I am.

Which doesn't mean much. More to the point, *they* do not know where I am—*they* meaning anybody who might be wanting to look for me. The searchers.

They would look for him, look for the plane. His father and mother would be frantic.[5] They would tear the world apart to find him. Brian had seen searches on the news, seen movies about lost planes. When a plane went down they mounted extensive searches and almost always they found the plane within a day or two. Pilots all filed flight plans—a detailed plan for where and when they were going to fly, with all the courses explained. They would come, they would look for him. The searchers would get government planes and cover both sides of the flight plan filed by the pilot and search until they found him.

Maybe even today. They might come today. This was the second day after the crash. No. Brian frowned. Was it the first day or the second day? They had gone down in the afternoon and he had spent the whole night out cold. So this was the first real day. But they could still come today. They would have started the search immediately when Brian's plane did not arrive.

Yeah, they would probably come today.

Probably come in here with amphibious[6] planes, small bushplanes[7] with floats that could land right here on the lake and pick him up and take him home.

---

5. **frantic** [fran′ tik]: wild with grief, fear, or pain.
6. **amphibious** [am fib′ ē əs]: able to travel on land or water.
7. **bushplanes** [bush′ plānz′]: airplanes used to fly over unsettled areas.

Which home? The father home or the mother home. He stopped the thinking. It didn't matter. Either on to his dad or back to his mother. Either way he would probably be home by late night or early morning, home where he could sit down and eat a large, cheesy, juicy burger with tomatoes and double fries with ketchup and a thick chocolate shake.

And there came hunger.

Brian rubbed his stomach. The hunger had been there but something else—fear, pain—had held it down. Now, with the thought of the burger, the emptiness roared at him. He could not believe the hunger, had never felt it this way. The lake water had filled his stomach but left it hungry, and now it demanded food, screamed for food.

And there was, he thought, absolutely nothing to eat.

Nothing.

What did they do in the movies when they got stranded like this? Oh, yes, the hero usually found some kind of plant that he knew was good to eat and that took care of it. Just ate the plant until he was full or used some kind of cute trap to catch an animal and cook it over a slick little fire and pretty soon he had a full eight-course meal.

The trouble, Brian thought, looking around, was that all he could see was grass and brush. There was nothing obvious to eat and aside from about a million birds and the beaver he hadn't seen animals to trap and cook, and even if he got one somehow he didn't have any matches so he couldn't have a fire . . .

Nothing.

It kept coming back to that. He had nothing.

Well, almost nothing. As a matter of fact, he thought, I don't know what I've got or haven't got. Maybe I should try and figure out just how I stand. It will give me something to do—keep me from thinking of food. Until they come to find me.

Brian had once had an English teacher, a guy named Perpich, who was always talking about being positive, thinking positive, staying on top of things. That's how Perpich had put it—stay positive and stay on top of things. Brian thought of him now—wondered how to stay positive and stay on top of this. All Perpich would say is that I have to get motivated.[8] He was always telling kids to get motivated.

Brian changed position so he was sitting on his knees. He reached into his pockets and took out everything he had and laid it on the grass in front of him.

It was pitiful enough. A quarter, three dimes, a nickel, and two pennies. A fingernail clipper. A billfold with a twenty dollar bill— "In case you get stranded at the airport in some small town and have to buy food," his mother had said—and some odd pieces of paper.

And on his belt, somehow still there, the hatchet his mother had given him. He had forgotten it and now reached around and took it out and put it in the grass. There was a touch of rust already forming on the cutting edge of the blade and he rubbed it off with his thumb.

That was it.

He frowned. No, wait—if he was going to play the game, might as well play it right. Perpich would tell him to quit messing around. Get motivated. Look at *all* of it, Robeson.

He had on a pair of good tennis shoes, now almost dry. And socks. And jeans and underwear and a thin leather belt and a T-shirt with a windbreaker so torn it hung on him in tatters.

And a watch. He had a digital watch still on his wrist but it was broken from the crash—the little screen blank—and he took it off and almost threw it away but stopped the hand motion and lay the watch on the grass with the rest of it.

There. That was it.

No, wait. One other thing. Those were all the things he had, but he also had himself. Perpich used to drum that into them—"You are your most valuable asset.[9] Don't forget that. *You* are the best thing you have."

Brian looked around again. I wish you were here, Perpich. I'm hungry and I'd trade everything I have for a hamburger.

"I'm hungry." He said it aloud. In normal tones at first, then louder and louder until he was yelling it. "I'm hungry, I'm hungry, I'm hungry!"

8. **motivated** [mō′ tə vā′ tid]: wanting to act.
9. **asset** [as′ et]: something of value.

When he stopped there was sudden silence, not just from him but the clicks and blurps and bird sounds of the forest as well. The noise of his voice had startled everything and it was quiet. He looked around, listened with his mouth open, and realized that in all his life he had never heard silence before. Complete silence. There had always been some sound, some kind of sound.

It lasted only a few seconds, but it was so intense that it seemed to become part of him. Nothing. There was no sound. Then the bird started again, and some kind of buzzing insect, and then a chattering and a cawing, and soon there was the same background of sound.

Which left him still hungry.

Of course, he thought, putting the coins and the rest back in his pocket and the hatchet in his belt—of course if they come tonight or even if they take as long as tomorrow the hunger is no big thing. People have gone for many days without food as long as they've got water. Even if they don't come until late tomorrow I'll be all right. Lose a little weight, maybe, but the first hamburger and a malt and fries will bring it right back.

A mental picture of a hamburger, the way they showed it in the television commercials, thundered into his thoughts. Rich colors, the meat juicy and hot . . .

He pushed the picture away. So even if they didn't find him until tomorrow, he thought, he would be all right. He had plenty of water, although he wasn't sure if it was good and clean or not.

He sat again by the tree, his back against it. There was a thing bothering him. He wasn't quite sure what it was but it kept chewing at the edge of his thoughts. Something about the plane and the pilot that would change things . . .

Ahh, there it was—the moment when the pilot had his heart attack his right foot had jerked down on the rudder[10] pedal and the plane had slewed[11] sideways. What did that mean? Why did that keep coming into his thinking that way, nudging and pushing?

10. **rudder** [rud′ ər]: a structure used to steer the aircraft.
11. **slewed** [slüd]: turned or twisted.

from *Hatchet* **19**

It means, a voice in his thoughts said, that they might not be coming for you tonight or even tomorrow. When the pilot pushed the rudder pedal the plane had jerked to the side and assumed a new course. Brian could not remember how much it had pulled around, but it wouldn't have had to be much because after that, with the pilot dead, Brian had flown for hour after hour on the new course.

Well away from the flight plan the pilot had filed. Many hours, at maybe 160 miles an hour. Even if it was only a little off course, with that speed and time Brian might now be sitting several hundred miles off to the side of the recorded fight plan.

And they would probably search most heavily at first along the flight plan course. They might go out to the side a little, but he could easily be three, four hundred miles to the side. He could not know, could not think of how far he might have flown wrong because he didn't know the original course and didn't know how much they had pulled sideways.

Quite a bit—that's how he remembered it. Quite a jerk to the side. It pulled his head over sharply when the plane had swung around.

They might not find him for two or three days. He felt his heartbeat increase as the fear started. The thought was there but he fought it down for a time, pushed it away, then it exploded out.

They might not find him for a long time.

And the next thought was there as well, that they might never find him, but that was panic and he fought it down and tried to stay positive. They searched hard when a plane went down, they used many men and planes and they would go to the side, they would know he was off from the flight path, he had talked to the man on the radio, they would somehow know . . .

It would be all right.

They would find him. Maybe not tomorrow, but soon. Soon. Soon.

They would find him soon.

Gradually, like sloshing[12] oil his thoughts settled back and the panic was gone. Say they didn't come for two days—no, say they

12. **sloshing** [slosh′ ing]: splashing.

didn't come for three days, even push that to four days—he could live with that. He would have to live with that. He didn't want to think of them taking longer. But say four days. He had to do something. He couldn't just sit at the bottom of this tree and stare down at the lake for four days.

And nights. He was in deep woods and didn't have any matches, couldn't make a fire. There were large things in the woods. There were wolves, he thought, and bears—other things. In the dark he would be in the open here, just sitting at the bottom of a tree.

He looked around suddenly, felt the hair on the back of his neck go up. Things might be looking at him right now, waiting for him—waiting for dark so they could move in and take him.

He fingered the hatchet at his belt. It was the only weapon he had, but it was something.

He had to have some kind of shelter. No, make that more: He had to have some kind of shelter and he had to have something to eat.

He pulled himself to his feet and jerked the back of his shirt down before the mosquitos could get at it. He had to do something to help himself.

I have to get motivated, he thought, remembering Perpich. Right now I'm all I've got. I have to do something.

GARY PAULSEN

Gary Paulsen was born in 1939 in Minneapolis. Because his father was in the military, the family moved constantly. Paulsen recalls when he first entered a public library and received a library card from the librarian. "When she handed me the card, she handed me the world." He continues, "I roared through everything she gave me and in the summer I read a book a day." At one time, Paulsen bred and trained huskies for dogsled teams and based his novel *Dogsled* on the experience.

The excerpt that you've just read is a chapter from Paulsen's well-known novel *Hatchet*. The novel tells the story of Brian Robeson's challenges, setbacks, and triumphs in his effort to survive.

Rippled Surface M.C. Escher, 1950, linoleum cut, 10 1/2" x 12 5/8"

STAYING ALIVE

David Wagoner

Staying alive in the woods is a matter of calming down
At first and deciding whether to wait for rescue,
Trusting to others,
Or simply to start walking and walking in one direction
Till you come out—or something happens to stop you.   5
By far the safer choice
Is to settle down where you are, and try to make a living
Off the land, camping near water, away from shadows.
Eat no white berries;
Spit out all bitterness. Shooting at anything   10
Means hiking further and further every day
To hunt survivors;
It may be best to learn what you have to learn without a gun,
Not killing but watching birds and animals go
In and out of shelter   15
At will. Following their example, build for a whole season:
Facing across the wind to your lean-to,[1]
You may feel wilder,
And nothing, not even you, will have to stay in hiding.

1. **lean-to** [lēn′ tü′]: rough shelter built against a post or tree and open on one side.

If you have no matches, a stick and a fire-bow   20
Will keep you warmer,
Or the crystal² of your watch, filled with water, held up to the sun
Will do the same, in time. In case of snow,
Drifting toward winter,
Don't try to stay awake through the night, afraid of freezing—   25
The bottom of your mind knows all about zero;
It will turn you over
And shake you till you waken. If you have trouble sleeping
Even in the best of weather, jumping to follow
The unidentifiable noises of the night and feeling   30
Bears and packs of wolves nuzzling your elbow,
Remember the trappers
Who treated them indifferently³ and were left alone.
If you hurt yourself, no one will comfort you
Or take your temperature,   35
So stumbling, wading, and climbing are as dangerous as flying.
But if you decide, at last, you must break through
In spite of all danger,
Think of yourself by time and not by distance,
     counting
Wherever you're going by how long it takes you;   40
No other measure
Will bring you safe to nightfall. Follow no streams:
     they run
Under the ground or fall into wilder country.
Remember the stars
And moss when your mind runs into circles. If it should rain,   45
Or the fog should roll the horizon⁴ in around you,
Hold still for hours
Or days, if you must, or weeks, for seeing is believing
In the wilderness. And if you find a pathway,

---

2. **crystal** [kris′ tl]: a clear plastic or glass cover on the face of a watch.
3. **indifferently** [in dif′ ər ənt lē′]: without interest or attention.
4. **horizon** [hə rī′ zn]: line where the earth and sky seem to meet.

Retrace⁵ it left or right—someone knew where he was going
Once upon a time, and you can follow
Hopefully, somewhere,
Just in case. There may even come, on some uncanny⁶ evening,
A time when you're warm and dry, well fed, not thirsty,   55
Uninjured, without fear,
When nothing, either good or bad, is happening.
This is called staying alive. It's temporary.

5. **retrace** [rē trās′]: go or trace back over.
6. **uncanny** [un kan′ ē]: strange and mysterious; weird.

Puddle M.C. Escher, 1952, woodcut, 9 ¹/₂" x 12

What occurs after
Is doubtful. You must always be ready for something
    to come bursting   60
Through the far edge of a clearing, running toward you,
Grinning from ear to ear
And hoarse with welcome. Or something crossing and hovering[7]
Overhead, as light as air, like a break in the sky,
Wondering what you are.   65
Here you are face to face with the problem of recognition.
Having no time to make smoke, too much to say,
You should have a mirror
With a tiny hole in the back for better aiming, for reflecting
Whatever disaster you can think of, to show   70
The way you suffer.

7. **hovering** [huv′ ər ing]: suspended in air.

Dewdrop M.C. Escher, 1948, mezzotint, 7 " x 9⁵/₈ "

These body signals have universal[8] meaning: If you are lying
Flat on your back with arms outstretched behind you,
You say you require
Emergency treatment; if you are standing erect and holding   75
Arms horizontal,[9] you mean you are not ready;
If you hold them over
Your head, you want to be picked up. Three of anything
Is a sign of distress. Afterward, if you see
No ropes, no ladders,   80
No maps or messages falling, no searchlights or trails blazing,
Then chances are, you should be prepared to burrow
Deep for a deep winter.

8. **universal** [yü nə ver′ səl]: belonging to all.
9. **horizontal** [hôr′ ə zon′ tl]: at right angles to a vertical line.

DAVID WAGONER

The poet and novelist David Wagoner was born
in 1926 and raised in an industrial area of Indiana
between Gary and Chicago, Illinois. For years he has
written volumes of poetry and novels about the coastal areas of the
Pacific Northwest where he lives. In addition to having received many
awards for his writing, Wagoner is also Chancellor of the Academy of
American Poets and editor of *Poetry Northwest* and the Princeton Poetry
Series. He combines his writing with his career as a college professor at
the University of Washington.

from
Mississippi Solo

Eddy Harris

*T*oo many marvelous days in a row and you begin to get used to it, to think that's the way it's supposed to be. Too many good days, too many bad days—you need some break in the monotony[1] of one to appreciate the other. If you only get sunshine, someone said, you end up in a desert.

I guess I'd had enough hard days to last me for a while, enough scary times to be able to appreciate the peaceful, easy, glorous days. On the way to Natchez,[2] I had another one, and I took full advantage of it to do absolutely nothing. No singing, no thinking, no talking to myself. Just feeling. Watching the river, noticing the changes in color, seeing the way it rises and falls depending on the wind and on what lies on the river bed. Each change had something to say, and I listened to the river. The river was talking to me, changing colors from puce[3] to brown to thick, murky[4] green. Saying nothing. The idle chatter you get when you walk with your favorite niece or nephew going no place in particular with nothing special on your minds and the little kid just jabbers away because it's comfortable and he feels like it. The river was like that to me. A comfortable buddy sharing a lazy day.

1. **monotony** [mə not´ nē]: sameness.
2. **Natchez** [nach´ əz]: city in southwest Mississippi on the Mississippi River.
3. **puce** [pyüs]: purplish brown.
4. **murky** [mėr´ kē]: dark and thick.

Nothing else mattered then. Going someplace or not. Arriving in New Orleans or shooting past and landing in Brazil. I didn't care about anything. The river kept me company and kept me satisfied. Nothing else mattered.

Then the river whispered, "Get ready. Get ready."

The day turned gray and strange. Clouds rolled overhead in wild swirls like batter in a bowl. I could see the rainstorm forming off in the distance but swirling rapidly toward me like a dark gray avalanche.[5] I felt the river dip down and up—a shallow dale[6] in the water. I passed from the cool moisture surrounding me and into a pocket of thin air hot and dry. It was as though a gap had opened in the clouds and the sun streamed through to boil the water and heat up this isolated[7] patch of river a scant[8] thirty yards long. My first thought was to shed a shirt and stay cool, but when I passed through the far curtain of the insulated air, I knew I had better do just the opposite. I drifted and donned[9] my yellow rain suit and hood. The sky above grew serious and advanced in my direction with the speed of a hurricane. Looking for a place to land, I scanned the shore. There was no shore. Only trees. Because of the heavy rains and high water, the shore had disappeared, and the new shoreline of solid earth had been pushed back through the trees and beyond the woods. How far beyond, I couldn't tell. I looked across to the other side of the river half a mile away. No way could I have made it over there. Halfway across and the wind would have kicked up and trapped me in the middle.

The leading edge of the storm came, and the first sprinkles passed over like army scouts. The wooded area lasted only another hundred yards or so, and I thought I could easily get there before the rains arrived. I could then turn left and find ground to pull out and wait

5. **avalanche** [av′ ə lanch]: large mass of snow, ice, dirt, or rocks falling quickly down the side of a mountain.
6. **dale** [dāl]: valley.
7. **isolated** [ī′ sə lāt əd]: set apart.
8. **scant** [skant]: barely enough.
9. **donned** [dond]: put on clothing.

out the storm. But the voice of the river came out and spoke to me teasingly but with a chill of seriousness down my spine. I could have ignored it, but as if reading my thoughts and not wanting me to fight it, the river grabbed the end of the canoe and turned me toward the trees. I thought I was looking for land. I wasn't. I was looking for shelter.

The urge to get into the trees came on me quite suddenly and really without thought or effort on my part. Almost an instinct.

No sooner had I ducked into the trees than the sky split open with a loud crash and a splintery crackle of lightning. I was not going to make it through the trees. The wind came in at hurricane strength. The tips of the trees bent way over and aimed toward the ground, like fishing rods hooked on a big one. Water flooded like the tide rushing upstream. The trees swooshed loudly as the leaves and branches brushed hard together. Branches fell. Rains came and poured down bucketfuls.

The trees were tall and no more than three feet around. I maneuvered[10] the canoe as best I could in the wind and rushing water, turned it to face upstream, and kept my back to the rain, which slanted in at a sharp angle. I reached out for the sturdiest tree I could get my arms around and I held on.

Water everywhere. The river sloshed over the side and into the canoe. I tried to keep the stern pointed right into the flow so the canoe could ride the waves, but it didn't work. The canoe was twisted about, and water poured over the side. The rain was heavier than any I had ever been in or seen before. It really was more like a tropical storm. The heavy winds, the amount of water, the warmth of the air, and the cold rain. Only my neck was exposed to the rain. When the rain hit my neck, it ran under the rain suit and very cold down my back.

The wind shifted as the storm came directly overhead. Water streamed straight down. I was drenched, and the canoe was filling up quickly. Anything in the canoe that could float was floating. If the rain continued for long or if the wind kept up strong and the rain kept spilling into the canoe, I would sink. But I was not worried, hardly more than concerned. In fact I enjoyed the feeling of the water all around me and on me, enveloping me like a cocoon,[11]

10. **maneuvered** [mə nü′ vərd]: moved skillfully.
11. **cocoon** [kə kün′]: protective silk covering spun by larvae of various insects.

and despite the drama I felt no real threat. I was more amazed than anything, trying to analyze the voice I had heard or whatever instinct or intuition[12] it was that urged me to park in these trees. It had been something so very definite that I could feel it and yet so ethereal[13] that I could not put my finger on it. So I stopped trying and just sat there patiently waiting and hugging my tree. I was one with this river, and nothing could happen to me.

The storm slid forward, and the rain slanted in on my face. Then it moved on farther up the river to drench someone else. It was gone as suddenly as it had arisen. Only the trailing edge was left, a light rain that lasted almost until I reached Natchez.

12. **intuition** [in′ tü ish′ ən]: immediate understanding of truths or facts without reasoning.
13. **ethereal** [i thir′ ē əl]: light, airy.

E D D Y   H A R R I S

Eddy Harris is an African American journalist who grew up in St. Louis, Missouri. He remembers sitting on the levee and watching the Mississippi River. "As a child," he says in his book *Mississippi Solo*, "I feared this river more than I feared God. As an adult now, I fear it even more."

Despite this fear, Harris says, he wanted to find some way to be a part of the river. When he was thirty years old, Harris planned his canoe trip—his imagination fired by an elderly friend who encouraged the expedition and who told him that there are worse things than failure.

Eddy Harris graduated from Stanford University in California and has traveled through Europe and Central America as a journalist. He lives near the banks of the Mississippi, in Kirkwood, Missouri.

I, Hungry Hannah,

Cassandra Glen . . .

NORMA FOX MAZER

When Mr. Augustus Francher's heart burst, I told Crow we were going to the service at Bascind's Funeral Home because, afterward, at Mrs. Francher's house, there would be food.

"How are we supposed to get in? Nobody asked us," he said.

"They will. First we go to the service—to show respect, you know. Mrs. Francher sees us there and she says, 'You two fine young people must come over to my house after the funeral and have some delicious food.' "

"Safety Pin Francher says that? Wake up, Hannah dreamer."

"Maybe she won't say it exactly that way," I admitted.

"Maybe she won't." Crow mocked. "Forget it. I don't want to go." He scraped his Adidas on the curb.

"You never want to go anywhere." Just because of his face. He had to go to school, he couldn't get out of that, but he didn't like to go anyplace else where there were a lot of people.

"You go," he said.

"Not without you." We went everywhere together. We had been friends since we were four years old. "Just think of all that food," I urged Crow. "I bet there'll be those little tiny fancy hot dogs with toothpicks stuck in them. You know how good they smell? And a baked ham stuck all over with cloves and slices of pineapple on top. There's got to be a cake—maybe a three-layer chocolate cake with chocolate icing—and ice cream and tons of cookies. She's got the whole store to choose from."

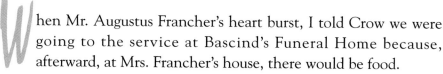

Salads, Sandwiches and Desserts Wayne Thiebaud, 1962, oil on canvas, 55" x 72", Sheldon Memorial Art Gallery, University of Nebraska, Lincoln

I talked about food until Crow couldn't stand it. "I'll go, I'll go, since you want to do it so much."

"Just for me. Big-hearted you."

Crow was always hungry. His elbows stuck out like sticks. His stepfather, Willie, was on half time at the Buffalo Chemical Works, but even when he was on full time and they had more money, Crow was hungry.

Willie said workingmen had to get fed first. (That was Willie.) Then, said Willie, came the littlest kids, Jay, Mike, Chris, and Kelly. After that came the women—Crow's mother and Willie's two daughters, Lisa and Janet. After that, said Willie, came older boys. That was Crow. His mom always saved him something, but he never got enough to eat.

In the funeral parlor, we signed our names in the guest book. David James Alpern. Hannah C. Glen. We followed two men into the chapel and Crow sat down in the last row. If there'd been a darkest corner, he would have chosen that. I sat down next to him.

In the front row, Mrs. Francher sniffled loudly. She was tall and shaped like a summer squash, skinny on top and swelling out on the bottom. In the store she always wore a dark green smock held together with safety pins. Today she had on a black dress and black hat, no safety pins anywhere in sight.

Crow's stomach rumbled and then mine did, like a two-piece band. "What'd you have for breakfast?" I whispered. He shrugged. I had had two grape jelly sandwiches and a glass of instant milk. After she got laid off at the paper-bag factory, my mother began buying powdered milk instead of whole milk. She said it was cheaper and just as good for us. Every day she went out looking for work. As soon as she found a job, we'd have real milk again and plenty of eggs. At night, instead of macaroni and cheese, we'd have hamburgers that sizzled delicious-smelling fat all over the stove and vegetables cooked with hunks of margarine. And for dessert we'd have cookies and freestone peaches in thick syrup.

A man wearing a peppermint-striped tie passed us and then came back. I thought he was going to say something about Crow. Once, on a bus, a man said in a loud voice to the woman with him that Crow's parents should do something about his face. Mostly, people just stared.

"You, young lady," Peppermint Tie said, "shouldn't be chewing gum in here."

I spit the gum out into my hand. As soon as Peppermint Tie went by I put it up under my upper lip to save for later. Crow said it made him hungrier to chew gum. It was just the opposite for me.

Sometimes I thought that if Crow didn't have that stuff on his face he would be prettier than a girl. He had high cheekbones and his eyes were dark and shining, but it was hard to notice because his face looked as if it had been splashed with gobs of rusty paint. A splash like a map of Tennessee covered half his forehead, wandered down over his left eye, and dribbled out onto his cheek. Another splash around his mouth and chin looked like a mushy baked apple, and a splash on his neck looked like a four-legged spider.

A minister came into the chapel from a side door and stood near the open coffin. He cleared his throat. "Good afternoon, friends." He began talking about Mr. Francher. "Augustus Francher has left us. He was a fine, upstanding[1] man."

No, I thought, that's wrong. He was a fine man, but he didn't stand up any more than he had to. Mr. Francher was fat, his face was round and yellow as a lemon pie, and he wheezed when he talked. If he and Mrs. Francher were both in the store, she waited on the customers and Mr. Francher sat on a high stool in front of the cash register. He always wore big soft shoes, a white shirt with a little bow tie, and baggy black pants.

"He lived a good life," the minister said. "He had charity in his heart and we are saddened that he has been struck down in his prime." Mrs. Francher sniffled loudly and called out, "Oh, Augustus, Augustus."

Mr. and Mrs. Francher's grocery store was in the front of their house. Dried salamis hung in the window over dusty stacks of Campbell's baked beans and Diet Pepsi. Lots of mornings when Crow

Detail from
Salads, Sandwiches and Desserts
Wayne Thiebaud

1. **upstanding** [up stan′ ding]: honorable.

and I walked past on the way to school, Mr. Francher's round yellow face would be in the window, between the salamis, and he would wink at me.

At the end of the month when my mom was short of money, she'd send me to Francher's Groceteria for half a pound of bologna and a can of spaghetti for supper. "Tell Francher to put it on the bill, Hanny," she'd say.

And I'd go off, hoping and hoping that it would be Mr. Francher in the store. If it was Mrs. Francher, she'd finger a safety pin on her smock, click her tongue, and look up what we owed in her account book. "Twenty-five dollars and seventy-six cents. You'd better pay something on that." And she'd hold out her hand as if I had money in my pocket. I would try not to look at the tub of creamy-looking potato salad in the case or the round of cheese on the counter with the sharp cheese knife lying next to it. "Go home and see what your mother wants to pay on account," she'd order.

But if it was Mr. Francher, he'd put his hand on my shoulder, look right at me with his brown eyes that were bright as a chipmunk's, and say, "Now, daughter, just tell your mother not to forget she should pay up soon." And he'd pull the can of spaghetti down from the shelf. Once he'd told me that long ago he'd had a little sister who died, and her name, too, was Hannah. "A nice old-fashioned name," he said. He was shorter than his wife and, sitting on his stool, he would munch on cream-filled doughnuts, then wash them down with long sips from a bottle of soda. My mother said he was his own best customer.

The minister was through talking about Mr. Francher and everybody stood up to walk around the coffin where he lay, wearing a dark suit and tie, his hands folded together over his big round stomach. I stopped in surprise. He looked like a baby in a crib, a huge baby who would, at any moment, open his eyes and chuckle. His cheeks were puffed out and shining.

Mrs. Francher stood off to one side with another woman, also in black. They were holding hands. I walked slowly past the coffin, looking back at Mr. Francher over my shoulder. Was he really gone?

Was it true that when I went to Francher's the next time, there would be no Mr. Francher to say, "Now, daughter . . ."? No Mr. Francher anymore to wink at me through the salamis? My eyes filled. Just then I understood that he was dead and what it meant.

Behind me, Crow jabbed his finger into my back, reminding me why we were there. "Mrs. Francher," I said. Her eyes were dark and puffy. She looked at me, through me. I didn't think she recognized me.

It was the other woman who answered. "Yes?" She was not as tall as Mrs. Francher, but she was shaped the same: summer squash. "What is it, dear?" she said. "What do you want?"

"I—can we—I'm sorry about Mr. Francher," I said. "I wish—I'm sorry."

Mrs. Francher's eyes focused. "You're the Glen girl." She reached up to the neck of her dress and a glimmer of surprise (that there was no safety pin there?) seemed to cross her face. I thought she was going to ask when my mother would pay up.

And fast, not so brave now that I was face-to-face with her, I said, "Can we, can Crow and—can David and I come after the funeral to your house?"

She grabbed my arm and bent close to me. "You came to the service. I didn't know you loved him so much."

I nodded dumbly. She smelled of chocolate mints and mothballs.

"And him?" Flapping her hand in Crow's direction, she looked away from him, but the other woman stared.

A man reached past me and pressed Mrs. Francher's shoulder. "My sympathies, Berenice."

"Thank you, Jack. Do you know my sister? This is my sister, Celia. Come to the house," she said. "You're coming to the house after, aren't you?"

"We'll be there," he said. "Jane made a meat pie."

"Move on, dear, move on," Mrs. Francher's sister said. She was all in black, too. "People are waiting. Move, children."

My mouth watered. A meat pie! "Thank you, we'll come to your house," I said, sort of low and fast, as we walked by Mrs. Francher and her sister.

Vertumnus (Emperor Rudolf II) Guiseppe Archimboldo, 1590, oil on wood, 70.5 x 57.5 cm, Skoklosters Slott, Sweden

Outside, cars with headlights on were lined up for the drive to the cemetery. Mrs. Francher and her sister got into Bascind's long black limousine. A chauffeur with a black peaked cap drove.

"I'm not going to die the way old Francher did," Crow said as we walked down the street. "I'm not going to wait around for it to come get me. When I'm ready, I'm going to do it myself."

"You mean kill yourself?"

He nodded. "I've thought about it a lot. I might do it soon."

"Soon? Now that is truly dumb. I never heard anything so magnifico dumb."

"Give me one good reason."

"I'll give you ten good reasons. You're too young. You don't know what you're saying. You get these ideas in your head and you think they mean something. Sometimes you make me so mad!"

"Now there's a good reason."

"Besides," I said coldly, "it's against the law."

"Oh, dear, dear, dear. I forgot that. After I stick my head in the oven some night, they're going to arrest my corpse and send it to jail for life."

"Would you please knock it off! I don't want you dead. So just forget it."

"Even if I leave you my track shoes?" He held up a foot temptingly.

"Oh, your brothers would get them."

"I'll make a will," he said. "I'll leave them to you in my will."

We sat on the stoop in front of my house where we could watch down the block to see when Mrs. Francher arrived back from the cemetery.

"Go get us some paper and pencils," Crow said.

"You want to play tic-tac-toe? Again?" It was his favorite game and no wonder, he always won.

"I'm going to write my will. You can do yours, too. Everybody should have a will."

"Not kids."

"Who says? Putting my track shoes in my will makes it official. You get them, nobody else."

"I don't want your track shoes, and I don't want to make a will. I'm not going to die."

"Well, not right away," he agreed. "But you never know. I bet Mr. Francher didn't think he was going to drop dead. Give me your key, I'll go in and get the stuff if you're too lazy."

"You are one magnifico pest." I went into the apartment, tore paper out of my notebook, and grabbed two pencil stubs from the coffee tin in the kitchen. I didn't want to use up my ball-point pen.

"Make sure you leave me something good," Crow said when I sat down next to him again. He smoothed out his piece of paper on his knee.

"This is dumb," I said. Crow was already scribbling away. "I don't even know how to start."

"Don't be difficult, Hanny." He held up his paper and read out, " 'I, David James Alpern, being of exceptionally sound mind and not so good body, do hereby make my last will and testament.' That's the way you begin. That's all there is to it. Then 'I leave to etcetera, etcetera.' "

After a while, I wrote. "I, the hungry Hannah Cassandra Glen, being of possibly sound mind and passably[2] sound body, do hereby make my last will. I leave—"

But I couldn't think of anything I had that anyone would want. No, that was a lie. I didn't want to give my things away. I fingered the string of blue coral around my neck and thought of the green and white afghan[3] on my bed, which my grandmother had made years before for my mother. It always somehow made me think of a spring day. I had never told anyone that, not even Crow. Then there were the six little glass chicks that my father had sent me when I was five, the last thing he ever sent me. The chicks sometimes marched across the top of my bureau, bumping into the jam jar in which I kept barrettes, shoelaces, and rubber bands, and sometimes made a magic circle on the floor at the side of my bed where I could see them as soon as I woke.

2. **passably** [pas′ ə blē]: fairly.
3. **afghan** [af′ gən]: blanket made of knitted yarn.

I peered over Crow's shoulder. He had just left an extra toilet plunger to his stepfather. I thought about putting down that I left a terri-fico job making magnifico money (maybe as a private secretary to a very important person) to my mother. "Aren't you done yet?" I asked.

"In a minute." He kept writing and crossing out and writing.

My stomach rumbled. What if Mrs. Francher and her sister wouldn't let us in? No way, you kids, all you want is food, you don't care about poor Mr. Francher being dead.

I cleaned my fingernails and cuffed up the bottom of my Levis. They were my best pair. My mother had found them in a church rummage sale. "Not even worn at the knees, Hanny!"

Crow turned over his paper to write on the other side. "Anyone would think you're serious about this," I said.

"I am." He covered his paper with his arm. "No peeking. I'll read it to you when I'm done."

I wrote down that I left Crow my afghan, but I crossed it out. How could I give that up? I was ashamed of my greediness and willed him my glass chicks. He probably wouldn't even like them.

Finally he stopped writing. "Okay. *Fini.*"

"What now?" I said. "You get out there in traffic and let a car run over you so I can get your track shoes?"

"I wouldn't do it that way. It's not sure enough. Let me tell you, when I do it, I'm not botching[4] it up."

"Read me your will or shut up."

"I, David James Alpern (aka[5] Crow)," he read, "being of exception-ally sound mind and not so good body, leave to my best friend, Hannah Glen, my mighty brain, including all the words she doesn't know—"

"Thanks a lot."

"—a lifetime supply of Tootie Frooty gum—"

"Gimme a break!"

He stopped reading. "Are you going to listen?"

"I'll listen, I'll listen."

---

4. **botching** [boch′ ing]: ruining or spoiling.
5. **aka** [ā kā ā]: also known as.

"—a lifetime supply of Tootie Frooty gum and my track shoes. To my mother, M*A*S*H[6] reruns forever and a quiet day. An extra toilet plunger to my stepfather, Willie. To my brothers, Jay and Mike, snot-free noses—shut up please so people can sleep!—birthdays at Burger King, and a snow shovel so you can make some money in the winter. To my sisters, Kelly and Chris, all the tangerines y'all want, a box full of chocolate chip cookies that never goes empty, and Wonder Woman tee shirts, red for Kelly, green for Chris. To Lisa and Janet, getting out of the house safe, thanks for the sandwich under the door, and winning all their volleyball games. And finally to all those others, teachers, acquaintances, enemies, and strangers, good good goodby, y'all, I'm not sorry to leave."

He glanced at me, the way he does, quick and sideways, so you don't get a good look at his face. "Like it? Think it was funny?"

I had to admit leaving a toilet plunger to his stepfather was fairly hilarious. "That's humor."

"Also there was some serious stuff in there," he said. "Like thanking Lisa and Janet. I thought that was important because when I die they might not know that I really like them. Read me yours."

"Nothing to read." I was hungry and that always made me feel mean.

"Didn't you leave me anything?"

"No." I tore up the paper and stuffed the scraps in my pocket. "Why aren't they back yet?" I said and I had a terrible thought. What if Mrs. Francher and her sister were going to have the food part of the funeral someplace else, not in their apartment behind the store? I thought about eating bread and jelly again for lunch and crackers and pasty milk for supper.

Just then the long black funeral car passed us. It stopped in front of Francher's Groceteria and Mrs. Francher and her sister got out. Other cars pulled up, one after the other. People spilled out, a whole crowd, all of them going into Mrs. Francher's house.

6. **M*A*S*H** [mash]: popular television show about a mobile army surgical hospital (M.A.S.H.) during the Korean War.

I spit on my fingers and scrubbed at my cheeks. "Do I look okay? Is my face clean? You better pull up your pants so you don't step on them."

"Maybe we shouldn't go, Hanny," Crow said all of a sudden.

"What? Now you say it? After all this? I know you, you're getting cold feet just because there's going to be a bunch of people there. Who cares, Crow? There's going to be *food*. Don't be gutless."

"If you're so brave, go yourself."

"I will," I shouted, "but you can just forget about eating any of that food, because I'm not bringing any back for you, Mr. Crow David Gutless."

"Shut up, Hanny, you have a big fat mouth!"

We went down the street, not speaking. The cars were gone. The store was locked and dark. In the window a sign said CLOSED ON ACCOUNT OF A DEATH IN THE FAMILY. Were they eating up all the food, the meat pies and the baked ham and the cookies and cakes? I led the way around the side and knocked on the door.

Nobody came. I knocked again. There was a white lace curtain on the window of the door. "You and your ideas. They're not going to let us in," Crow said, and the door swung open.

"We're here," I said to Mrs. Francher. She was in her stocking feet. She looked at me, then at Crow, as if she expected people, all right, but not us two. "We came to—" I almost said *eat*. I put my hand over my mouth and said, "We came to pay our respects."

"What?"

"Pay our respects." Behind me I sensed Crow moving away, disappearing down the path.

Mrs. Francher's sister appeared and they stood in the doorway, side by side. They seemed to me like two swollen black balloons. From the room behind them, wonderful smells of meat and cooked fruit drifted toward me. I wanted to cry. "We're here," I said again.

Mrs. Francher looked at her sister. "Oh . . . You take care of it, Celia." She walked away, a funny duck-footed walk in her stocking feet.

"Well . . . well . . ." Mrs. Francher's sister said. "Just you?"

"No, me and my friend. Cr—David," I yelled to him. My mouth was full of saliva and I smiled hard and said, "We were both friends of Mr. Francher's. We were always friends."

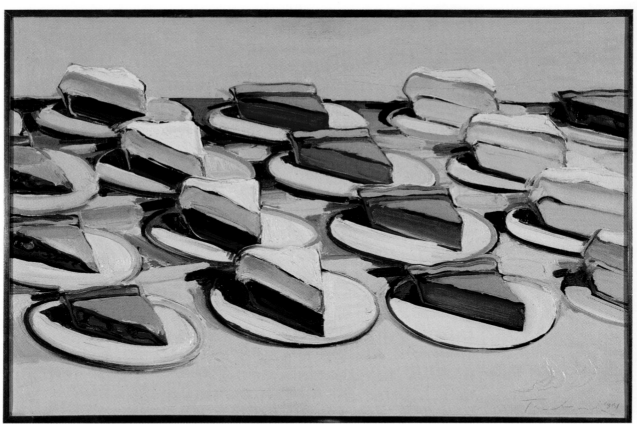

Mrs. Francher's sister sighed and looked over her shoulder and finally said, "I suppose you can come in, then."

The living room was warm and crowded. People stood around in little clumps with glasses in their hands, talking. The curtains were drawn and there were pictures and little statues everywhere, on tables, on top of the TV, and on little hanging shelves above the couch.

A long table, loaded with food, took up almost the whole dining room. I squeezed Crow's hand. Our quarrel was forgotten. In the center of the table were two crystal bowls, one filled with apples, pears, grapes, and bananas, the other brimming with a fizzing red punch. There were platters of roast beef, ham, turkey, and salami, little fluted cups filled with butter, a wooden board with a cutting knife, and different kinds of cheeses. There was applesauce and fruit salad, baked potatoes wrapped in silver paper, tomatoes and cucumbers, bread and rolls and cakes and all kinds of hot casseroles.

Pies, Pies, Pies Wayne Thiebaud, 1961, oil on canvas, 20" x 30",
Crocker Art Museum, Sacramento, CA

"What should we do?" Crow whispered.

"Eat," I said, but first I slipped an apple and a pear and slices of ham and roast beef into my pockets. How surprised my mother would be tonight when she came home and found the refrigerator full. "Oh, Hanny," she'd say "you shouldn't have done that, that's not nice." But she'd eat a slice of roast beef (her favorite) and then polish an apple on her shirt and cut it in half to share with me.

Crow and I filled plates with food. We found a place near a window away from people and began eating as fast as possible. We ate everything on our plates and went back to the table for more. People talked and laughed and no one bothered with us.

Crow's cheeks and lips were shiny with grease. We ate without stopping until neither of us could eat any more.

When we left, I was wonderfully full. Crow rubbed his bulging stomach and whispered, "Well, guess I'll go on living a little longer." And hearing that, I thought without shame how glad I was that Mr. Francher had died and left us this feast. I imagined him looking like a great baby in his coffin, winking at me and saying in his wheezy voice, which had always sounded to me like dark rough honey, "Now, daughter, now, daughter . . ."

NORMA FOX MAZER

Norma Fox Mazer was born in New York City and lived there until she was four. Mazer's father drove a delivery truck, and her mother worked in clothing stores. Because of her background, her stories are about working-class towns and families. Her fiction also reflects her experiences as one of three sisters and the mother of three daughters.

Mazer herself feels that her appeal lies in her ordinariness. She has commented, "I should like my writing to give meaning to ordinary moments. In my books and stories, I want people to eat chocolate pudding, break a dish, yawn, look in a store window, wear socks with holes in them." Norma Fox Mazer lives in central New York with her husband.

JACK LONDON

To Build a Fire

Day had broken cold and gray, exceedingly cold and gray, when the man turned aside from the main Yukon[1] trail and climbed the high earth-bank, where a dim and little-traveled trail led eastward through the fat spruce timberland. It was a steep bank, and he paused for breath at the top, excusing the act to himself by looking at his watch. It was nine o'clock. There was no sun nor hint of sun, though there was not a cloud in the sky. It was a clear day, and yet there seemed an intangible[2] pall[3] over the face of things, a subtle gloom that made the day dark, and that was due to the absence of sun. This fact did not worry the man. He was used to the lack of sun. It had been days since he had seen the sun, and he knew that a few more days must pass before that cheerful orb,[4] due south, would just peep above the skyline and dip immediately from view.

1. **Yukon** [yū′ kän]: a river that flows northwest across Alaska from the Yukon Territory in Canada to the Bering Sea.
2. **intangible** [in tan′ jə bəl]: not able to be felt or touched.
3. **pall** [pôl]: a dark, gloomy covering.
4. **orb** [ôrb]: a form in the shape of a circle, usually in the sky.

The man flung a look back along the way he had come. The Yukon lay a mile wide and hidden under three feet of ice. On top of this ice were as many feet of snow. It was all pure white, rolling in gentle undulations[5] where the ice-jams of the freeze-up had formed. North and south, as far as his eye could see, it was unbroken white, save for a dark hair-line that curved and twisted from around the spruce-covered island to the south, and that curved and twisted away into the north, where it disappeared behind another spruce-covered island. This dark hair-line was the trail—the main trail—that led south five hundred miles to the Chilcoot Pass,[6] Dyea,[7] and salt water; and that led north seventy miles to Dawson, and still on to the north a thousand miles to Nulato, and finally to St. Michael on Bering Sea,[8] a thousand miles and half a thousand more.

But all this—the mysterious, far-reaching hair-line trail, the absence of sun from the sky, the tremendous cold, and the strangeness and weirdness of it all—made no impression on the man. It was not because he was long used to it. He was a newcomer in the land, a *chechaquo*, and this was his first winter. The trouble with him was that he was without imagination. He was quick and alert in the things of life, but only in the things, and not in the significances. Fifty degrees below zero meant eighty-odd degrees of frost. Such fact impressed him as being cold and uncomfortable, and that was all. It did not lead him to meditate upon his frailty[9] as a creature of temperature, and upon man's frailty in general, able only to live within certain narrow limits of heat and cold; and from there on it did not lead him to the conjectural[10] field of immortality and man's place in the universe. Fifty degrees below zero stood for a bite of frost that hurt and that must be guarded against by the use of

---

5. **undulations** [un′ jə lā′ shəns]: a series of wavelike curves.
6. **Chilcoot Pass** [chil′ küt]: a pass in the coast range of the northern Rocky Mountains.
7. **Dyea** [dī′ ā]: a village in southeast Alaska that became the starting point for the trail over Chilcoot Pass.
8. **Bering Sea** [bir′ ing]: part of the North Pacific Ocean, which receives the Yukon River and connects by the Bering Strait with the Arctic Ocean.
9. **frailty** [frāl′ tē]: weakness.
10. **conjectural** [kən jek′ chər əl]: based on a guess.

mittens, ear-flaps, warm moccasins, and thick socks. Fifty degrees below zero was to him just precisely fifty degrees below zero. That there should be anything more to it than that was a thought that never entered his head.

As he turned to go on, he spat speculatively. There was a sharp, explosive crackle that startled him. He spat again. And again, in the air, before it could fall to the snow, the spittle crackled. He knew that at fifty below spittle crackled on the snow, but this spittle had crackled in the air. Undoubtedly it was colder than fifty below—how much colder he did not know. But the temperature did not matter. He was bound for the old claim on the left fork of Henderson Creek, where the boys were already. They had come over across the divide from the Indian Creek country, while he had come the roundabout way to take a look at the possibilities of getting out logs in the spring from the islands in the Yukon. He would be in to camp by six o'clock; a bit after dark, it was true, but the boys would be there, a fire would be going, and a hot supper would be ready. As for lunch, he pressed his hand against the protruding bundle under his jacket. It was also under his shirt, wrapped up in a handkerchief and lying against the naked skin. It was the only way to keep the biscuits from freezing. He smiled agreeably to himself as he thought of those biscuits, each cut open and sopped in bacon grease, and each enclosing a generous slice of fried bacon.

He plunged in among the big spruce trees. The trail was faint. A foot of snow had fallen since the last sled had passed over, and he was glad he was without a sled, traveling light. In fact, he carried nothing but the lunch wrapped in the handkerchief. He was surprised, however, at the cold. It certainly was cold, he concluded, as he rubbed his numb nose and cheek-bones with his mittened hand. He was a warm-whiskered man, but the hair on his face did not protect the high cheek-bones and the eager nose that thrust itself aggressively into the frosty air.

At the man's heels trotted a dog, a big native husky, the proper wolf-dog, gray-coated and without any visible or temperamental difference from its brother, the wild wolf. The animal was depressed by the tremendous cold. It knew that it was no time for traveling. Its instinct told it a truer tale than was told to the man by the man's judgment. In reality, it was not merely colder than fifty below zero; it was colder than sixty below, than seventy below. It was seventy-five below zero. Since the freezing point is thirty-two above zero, it meant that one hundred and seven degrees of frost obtained. The dog did not know anything about thermometers. Possibly in its brain there was no sharp consciousness of a condition of very cold such as was in the man's brain. But the brute had its instinct. It experienced a vague but menacing[11] apprehension[12] that subdued it and made it slink along at the man's heels, and that made it question eagerly every unwonted[13] movement of the man as if expecting him to go into camp or to seek shelter somewhere and build a fire. The dog had learned fire, and it wanted fire, or else to burrow under the snow and cuddle its warmth away from the air.

The frozen moisture of its breathing had settled on its fur in a fine powder of frost, and especially were its jowls,[14] muzzle,[15] and eyelashes whitened by its crystalled[16] breath. The man's red beard and mustache were likewise frosted, but more solidly, the deposit taking the form of ice and increasing with every warm, moist breath he exhaled. Also, the man was chewing tobacco, and the muzzle of ice held his lips so rigidly that he was unable to clear his chin when he expelled the juice. The result was that a crystal beard of the color and solidity of amber was increasing its length on his chin. If he fell down it would shatter itself, like glass, into brittle fragments. But he did not mind the appendage.[17] It was the penalty all tobacco-chewers paid in that country, and he had been out before in two cold snaps. They had not been so cold as this, he knew, but by the spirit thermometer at Sixty Mile[18] he knew they had been registered at fifty below and fifty-five.

He held on through the level stretch of woods for several miles,

---

11. **menacing** [men′ is ing]: threatening.
12. **apprehension** [ap′ ri hen′ shən]: dread of danger, fear.
13. **unwonted** [un wun′ tid]: not usual.
14. **jowls** [jouls]: folds of flesh under the jaw.
15. **muzzle** [muz′ əl]: nose, mouth, and jaws of an animal.
16. **crystalled** [kris′ tld]: warm breath turned to ice in the frigid air; looks like bits of glass.
17. **appendage** [ə pen′ dij]: a thing attached to something larger.
18. **Sixty Mile** [sik′ stē]: a village in the western part of the Yukon near the Alaskan border.

crossed a wide flat, and dropped down a bank to the frozen bed of a small stream. This was Henderson Creek, and he knew he was ten miles from the forks. He looked at his watch. It was ten o'clock. He was making four miles an hour, and he calculated that he would arrive at the forks at half-past twelve. He decided to celebrate that event by eating his lunch there.

The dog dropped in again at his heels, with a tail drooping discouragement, as the man swung along the creek-bed. The furrow of the old sled-trail was plainly visible, but a dozen inches of snow covered the marks of the last runners. In a month no man had come up or down that silent creek. The man held steadily on. He was not much given to thinking, and just then particularly he had nothing to think about save that he would eat lunch at the forks and that at six o'clock he would be in camp with the boys. There was nobody to talk to; and, had there been, speech would have been impossible because of the ice-muzzle on his mouth. So he continued monotonously[19] to chew tobacco and to increase the length of his amber beard.

Once in a while the thought reiterated[20] itself that it was very cold and that he had never experienced such cold. As he walked along he rubbed his cheek-bones and nose with the back of his mittened hand. He did this automatically, now and again changing hands. But rub as he would, the instant he stopped his cheek-bones went numb, and the following instant the end of his nose went numb. He was sure to frost his cheeks; he knew that, and experienced a pang of regret that he had not devised a nose-strap of the sort Bud wore in cold snaps. Such a strap passed across the cheeks, as well, and saved them. But it didn't matter much, after all. What were frosted cheeks? A bit painful, that was all; they were never serious.

Empty as the man's mind was of thoughts, he was keenly observant, and he noticed the changes in the creek, the curves and bends and timber-jams,[21] and always he sharply noted where he placed his feet. Once, coming around a bend, he shied[22] abruptly, like a startled horse, curved away from the place where he had been walking, and retreated

---

19. **monotonously** [mə notʹ n əs lē']: continuously without change.
20. **reiterated** [rē itʹ ə rāt' əd]: frequently repeated.
21. **timber-jams** [timʹ bər jams]: logs pressed together in a creek stopping the flow of water.
22. **shied** [shīd]: started back or aside suddenly.

several paces back along the trail. The creek he knew was frozen clear to the bottom,—no creek could contain water in that arctic winter,—but he knew also that there were springs that bubbled out from the hillsides and ran along under the snow and on top the ice of the creek. He knew that the coldest snaps never froze these springs, and he knew likewise their danger. They were traps. They hid pools of water under the snow that might be three inches deep, or three feet. Sometimes a skin of ice half an inch thick covered them, and in turn was covered by the snow. Sometimes there were alternate layers of water and ice-skin, so that when one broke through he kept on breaking through for a while, sometimes wetting himself to the waist.

That was why he had shied in such panic. He had felt the give under his feet and heard the crackle of a snow-hidden ice-skin. And to get his feet wet in such a temperature meant trouble and danger. At the very least it meant delay, for he would be forced to stop and build a fire, and under its protection to bare his feet while he dried his socks and moccasins. He stood and studied the

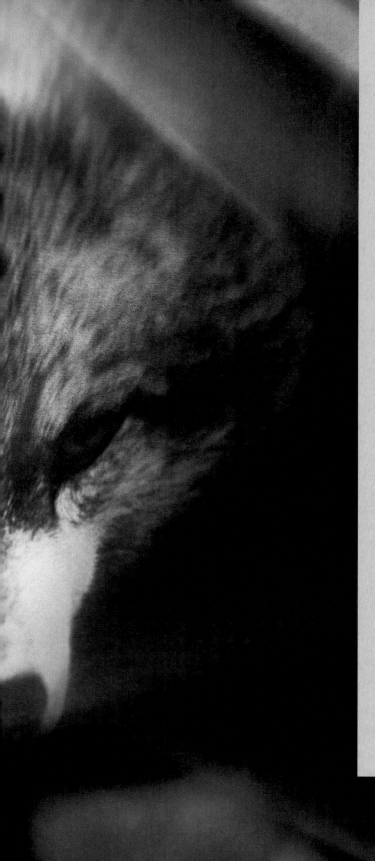

creek-bed and its banks, and de-cided that the flow of water came from the right. He reflected a while, rubbing his nose and cheeks, then skirted to the left, stepping gingerly and testing the footing for each step. Once clear of the danger, he took a fresh chew of tobacco and swung along at his four-mile gait.

In the course of the next two hours he came upon several similar traps. Usually the snow above the hidden pools had a sunken, candied appearance that advertised the danger. Once again, however, he had a close call; and once, suspect-ing danger, he compelled the dog to go on in front. The dog did not want to go. It hung back until the man shoved it forward, and then it went quickly across the white, un-broken surface. Suddenly it broke through, floundered to one side, and got away to firmer footing. It had wet its forefeet and legs, and al-most immediately the water that clung to it turned to ice. It made quick efforts to lick the ice off its legs, then dropped down in the snow and began to bite out the ice that had formed between the toes. This was a matter of instinct. To permit the ice to remain would mean sore feet. It did not know this, it merely obeyed the mysterious prompting that arose from the deep crypts[23] of its being. But the man knew, having achieved a judgment on the subject, and he removed the mitten from his right hand and helped tear out the ice-particles. He did not expose his fingers more than a minute, and was astonished at the swift numbness that smote[24] them. It certainly was cold. He pulled on the mitten hastily, and beat the hand savagely across his chest.

At twelve o'clock the day was at its brightest. Yet the sun was too far south on its winter journey to clear the horizon. The bulge of the earth intervened between it and Henderson Creek, where the man walked under a clear sky at noon and cast no shadow. At half-past twelve, to the minute, he arrived at the forks of the creek. He was pleased at the speed he had made. If he kept it up, he would certainly be with the boys by six. He unbuttoned his jacket and shirt and drew forth his lunch. The action consumed no more than a quarter of a minute, yet in that brief moment the numbness laid hold of the exposed fingers. He did not put the mitten on, but, instead struck the fingers a dozen sharp smashes against his leg. Then he sat down on a snow-covered log to eat. The sting that followed upon the striking of his fingers against his leg ceased so quickly that he was startled. He had had no chance to take a bite of biscuit. He struck the fingers repeatedly and returned them to the mitten, baring the other hand for the purpose of eating. He tried to take a mouthful, but the ice-muzzle prevented. He had forgotten to build a fire and thaw out. He chuckled at his foolishness, and as he chuckled he noted the numbness creeping into the exposed fingers. Also, he noted that the stinging which had first come to his toes when he sat down was already passing away. He wondered whether the toes were warm or numb. He moved them inside the moccasins and decided that they were numb.

He pulled the mitten on hurriedly and stood up. He was a bit frightened. He stamped up and down until the stinging returned into the feet. It certainly was cold, was his thought. That man from Sulphur Creek had spoken the truth when

---

23. **crypts** [kripts]: hidden depths like an underground room.
24. **smote** [smōt]: struck or came with great force.

telling how cold it sometimes got in the country. And he had laughed at him at the time! That showed one must not be too sure of things. There was no mistake about it, it *was* cold. He strode up and down, stamping his feet and threshing his arms, until reassured by the returning warmth. Then he got out matches and proceeded to make a fire. From the undergrowth, where high water of the previous spring had lodged a supply of seasoned twigs, he got his firewood. Working carefully from a small beginning, he soon had a roaring fire, over which he thawed the ice from his face and in the protection of which he ate his biscuits. For the moment the cold of space was outwitted. The dog took satisfaction in the fire, stretching out close enough for warmth and far enough away to escape being singed.

When the man had finished, he filled his pipe and took his comfortable time over a smoke. Then he pulled on his mittens, settled the earflaps of his cap firmly about his ears, and took the creek trail up the left fork. The dog was disappointed and yearned back toward the fire. This man did not know cold. Possibly all the generations of his ancestry had been ignorant of cold, of real cold, of cold one hundred and seven degrees below freezing point. But the dog knew; all its ancestry knew, and it had inherited the knowledge. And it knew that it was not good to walk abroad in such fearful cold. It was the time to lie snug in a hole in the snow and wait for a curtain of cloud to be drawn across the face of outer space whence this cold came. On the other hand, there was no keen intimacy between the dog and the man. The one was the toil-slave of the other, and the only caresses it had ever received were the caresses of the whiplash and of harsh and menacing throat-sounds that threatened the whiplash. So the dog made no effort to communicate its apprehension to the man. It was not concerned in the welfare of the man; it was for its own sake that it yearned back toward the fire. But the man whistled, and spoke to it with the sound of whiplashes, and the dog swung in at the man's heel and followed after.

The man took a chew of tobacco and proceeded to start a new amber beard. Also, his moist breath quickly powdered with white his mustache, eyebrows, and lashes. There did not seem to be so many springs on the left fork of the Henderson, and for half an hour the man saw no signs of any. And then it happened. At a place where there were no signs, where the soft, unbroken snow seemed to advertise solidity beneath, the man broke through. It was not deep. He wet himself halfway to the knees before he floundered out to the firm crust.

He was angry, and cursed his luck aloud. He had hoped to get into camp with the boys at six o'clock, and this would delay him an hour, for he would have to build a fire and dry out his foot-gear. This was imperative at that low temperature—he knew that much; and he turned aside to the bank, which he climbed. On top, tangled in the underbrush about the trunks of several small spruce trees, was a high-water deposit of dry firewood—sticks and twigs, principally, but also larger portions of seasoned branches and fine, dry, last-year's grasses. He threw down several large pieces on top of the snow. This served for a foundation and prevented the young flame from drowning itself in the snow it otherwise would melt. The flame he got by touching a match to a small shred of birch bark that he took from his pocket. This burned even more readily than paper. Placing it on the foundation, he fed the young flame with wisps of dry grass and with the tiniest dry twigs.

He worked slowly and carefully, keenly aware of his danger. Gradually, as the flame grew stronger, he increased the size of the twigs with which he fed it. He squatted in the snow, pulling the twigs out from their entanglement in the brush and feeding directly to the flame. He knew there must be no failure. When it is seventy-five below zero, a man must not fail in his first attempt to build a fire—that is, if his feet are wet. If his feet are dry, and he fails, he can run along the trail for half a mile and restore his circulation. But the circulation of wet and freezing feet cannot be restored by running when it is seventy-five below. No matter how fast he runs, the wet feet will freeze the harder.

All this the man knew. The old-timer on Sulphur Creek had told him about it the previous fall, and now he was appreciating the advice. Already all sensation had gone out of his feet. To build the fire he had been forced to remove his mittens, and the fingers had quickly gone numb. His pace of four miles an hour had kept his heart pumping blood to the surface of his body and to all the extremities. But the instant he stopped, the action of the pump eased down. The cold of space smote the unprotected tip of the planet, and he, being on that unprotected tip, received the full force of the blow. The blood of his body recoiled[25] before it. The blood was alive, like the dog, and like the dog it wanted to hide away and cover it-self up from the fearful cold. So long as he walked four miles an hour, he pumped that blood, will-nilly, to the surface; but now it ebbed away and sank down into the recesses of his body. The extremities were the first to feel its absence. His wet feet froze the faster, and his exposed fingers numbed the faster, though they had not yet begun to freeze. Nose and cheeks were already freezing, while the skin of all his body chilled as it lost its blood.

But he was safe. Toes and nose and cheeks would be only touched by the frost, for the fire was beginning to burn with strength. He was feeding it with twigs the size of his finger. In another minute he would be able to feed it with branches the size of his wrist, and then he could remove his wet foot-gear, and, while it dried, he could keep his naked feet warm by the fire, rubbing them at first, of course, with snow. The fire was a success. He was safe. He remembered the advice of the old-timer on Sulphur Creek, and smiled. The old-timer had been very serious in laying down the law that no man must travel alone in the Klondike after fifty below. Well, here he was; he had had the acci-dent; he was alone; and he had saved himself. Those old-timers were rather womanish, some of them, he thought. All a man had to do was to keep his head; and he was all right. Any man who was a man could travel alone. But it was sur-prising, the rapidity with which his cheeks and nose were freezing. And he had not thought his fingers could go lifeless in so short a time. Lifeless they were, for he could scarcely make them move together to grip a twig, and they seemed remote from his body and from him. When he touched a twig, he had to look and see whether or not he had hold of it. The wires were pretty well down between him and his finger-ends.

All of which counted for little. There was the fire, snapping and crackling and promising life with every dancing flame. He started to untie his moccasins. They were coated with ice; the thick German socks were like sheaths of iron halfway to the knees; and the

25. **recoiled** [ri koild′]: drew back, reacted.

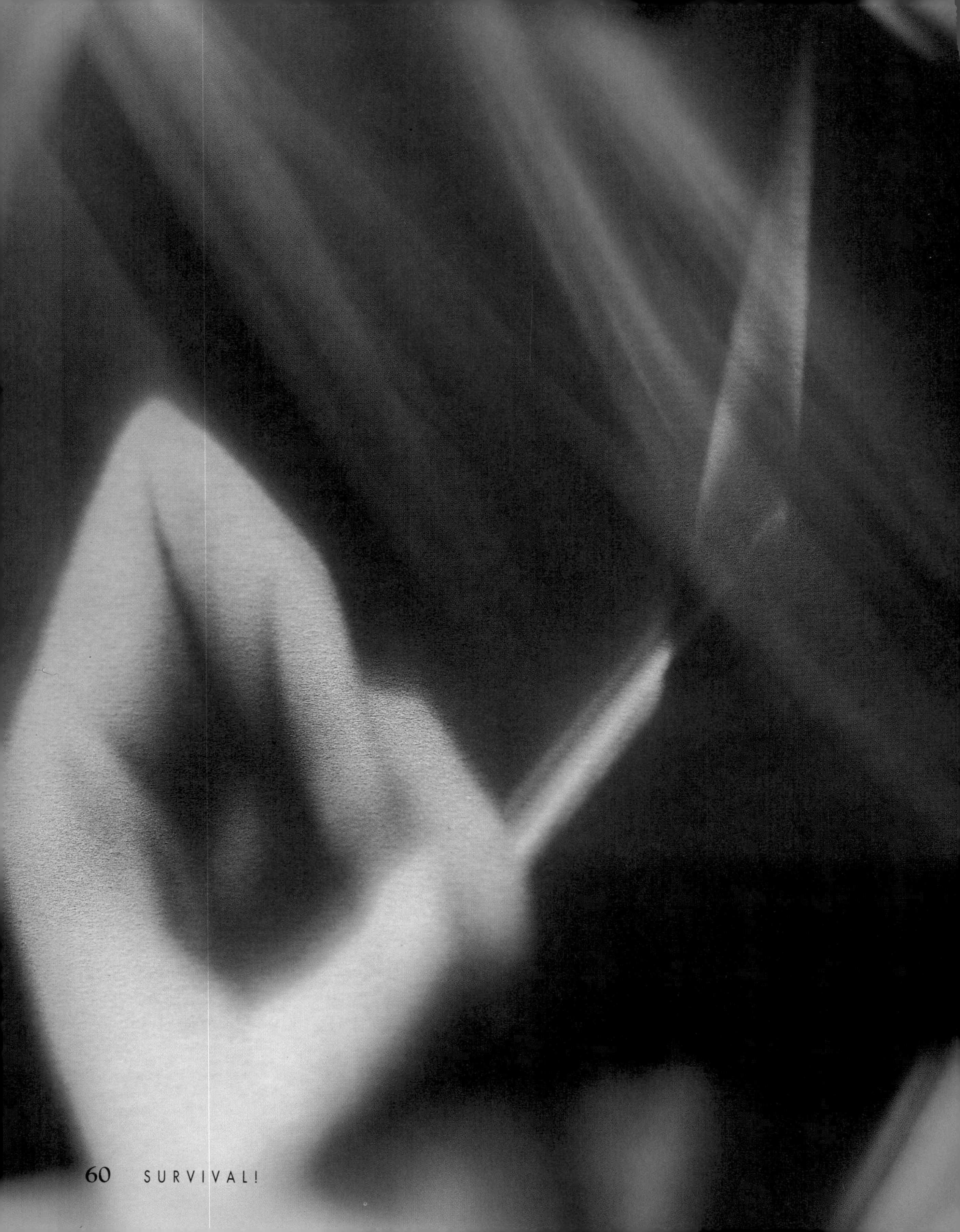

moccasin strings were like rods of steel all twisted and knotted as by some conflagration. For a moment he tugged with his numb fingers, then, realizing the folly of it, he drew his sheath-knife.

But before he could cut the strings, it happened. It was his own fault or, rather, his mistake. He should not have built the fire under the spruce tree. He should have built it in the open. But it had been easier to pull the twigs from the brush and drop them directly on the fire. Now the tree under which he had done this carried a weight of snow on its boughs. No wind had blown for weeks, and each bough was fully freighted. Each time he had pulled a twig he had communicated a slight agitation[26] to the tree—an imperceptible[27] agitation, so far as he was concerned, but an agitation sufficient to bring about the disaster. High up in the tree one bough capsized its load of snow. This fell on the boughs beneath, capsizing them. This process continued, spreading out and involving the whole tree. It grew like an avalanche,[28] and it descended without warning upon the man and the fire, and the fire was blotted out! Where it had burned was a mantle of fresh and disordered snow.

The man was shocked. It was as though he had just heard his own sentence of death. For a moment he sat and stared at the spot where the fire had been. Then he grew very calm. Perhaps the old-timer on Sulphur Creek was right. If he had only had a trail-mate he would have been in no danger now. The trail-mate could have built the fire. Well, it was up to him to build the fire over again, and this second time there must be no failure. Even if he succeeded, he would most likely lose some toes. His feet must be badly frozen by now, and there would be some time before the second fire was ready.

Such were his thoughts, but he did not sit and think them. He was busy all the time they were passing through his mind. He made a new foundation for a fire, this time in the open, where no treacherous tree could blot it out. Next, he gathered dry grasses and tiny twigs from the high-water flotsam. He could not bring his fingers together to pull them out, but he was able to gather

26. **agitation** [aj′ ə tā′ shən]: vigorous shaking.
27. **imperceptible** [im′ pər sep′ tə bəl]: very slight.
28. **avalanche** [av′ ə lanch]: a large mass of snow tumbling down.

them by the handful. In this way he got many rotten twigs and bits of green moss that were undesirable, but it was the best he could do. He worked methodically, even collecting an armful of the larger branches to be used later when the fire gathered strength. And all the while the dog sat and watched him, a certain yearning wistfulness in its eyes, for it looked upon him as the fire-provider, and the fire was slow in coming.

When all was ready, the man reached in his pocket for a second piece of birch bark. He knew the bark was there, and, though he could not feel it with his fingers, he could hear its crisp rustling as he fumbled for it. Try as he would, he could not clutch hold of it. And all the time, in his consciousness, was the knowledge that each instant his feet were freezing. This thought tended to put him in a panic, but he fought against it and kept calm. He pulled on his mittens with his teeth, and threshed his arms back and forth, beating his hands with all his might against his sides. He did this sitting down, and he stood up to do it; and all the while the dog sat in the snow, its wolf-brush of a tail curled around warmly over its forefeet, its sharp wolf-ears pricked forward intently as it watched the man. And the man, as he beat and threshed with his arms and hands, felt a great surge of envy as he regarded the creature that was warm and secure in its natural covering.

After a time he was aware of the first far-away signals of sensation in his beaten fingers. The faint tingling grew stronger till it evolved into a stinging ache that was excruciating,[29] but which the man hailed with satisfaction. He stripped the mitten from his right hand and fetched forth the birch bark. The exposed fingers were quickly going numb again. Next he brought out his bunch of sulphur matches. But the tremendous cold had already driven the life out of his fingers. In his effort to separate one match from the others, the whole bunch fell in the snow. He tried to pick it out of the snow, but failed. The dead fingers could neither touch nor clutch. He was very careful. He drove the thought of his freezing feet, and nose, and cheeks, out of his mind, devoting his whole soul to the matches. He watched, using the sense of vision in place of touch, and when he saw his fingers on each side the bunch, he closed them—that is, he willed to close them, for the wires were down, and the fingers did not

29. **excruciating** [ek skrü′ shē ā ting]: very painful.

obey. He pulled the mitten on the right hand, and beat it fiercely against his knee. Then, with both mittened hands, he scooped the bunch of matches, along with much snow, into his lap. Yet he was no better off.

After some manipulation he managed to get the bunch between the heels of his mittened hands. In this fashion he carried it to his mouth. The ice crackled and snapped when by a violent effort he opened his mouth. He drew the lower jaw in, curled the upper lip out of the way, and scraped the bunch with his upper teeth in order to separate a match. He succeeded in getting one, which he dropped on his lap. He was no better off. He could not pick it up. Then he devised a way. He picked it up in his teeth and scratched it on his leg. Twenty times he scratched before he succeeded in lighting it. As it flamed he held it with his teeth to the birch bark. But the burning brimstone went up his nostrils and into his lungs, causing him to cough spasmodically.[30] The match fell into the snow and went out.

The old-timer on Sulphur Creek was right, he thought in the moment of controlled despair that ensued: after fifty below, a man should travel with a partner. He beat his hands, but failed in exciting any sensation. Suddenly he bared both hands, removing the mittens with his teeth. He caught the whole bunch between the heels of his hands. His arm-muscles not being frozen enabled him to press the hand-heels tightly against the matches. Then he scratched the bunch along his leg. It flared into flame, seventy sulphur matches at once! There was not wind to blow them out. He kept his head to one side to escape the strangling fumes, and held the blazing bunch to the birch bark. As he so held it, he became aware of sensation in his hand. His flesh was burning. He could smell it. Deep down below the surface he could feel it. The sensation developed into pain that grew acute. And still he endured it, holding the flame of the matches clumsily to the bark that would not light readily because his own burning hands were in the way, absorbing most of the flame.

At last, when he could endure no more, he jerked his hands apart. The blazing matches fell sizzling into the snow, but the birch bark was alight. He began laying dry grasses and the tiniest twigs on the flame. He could not pick and choose, for he had to

---

30. **spasmodically** [spaz mod′ ik lē]: suddenly, very irregularly.

lift the fuel between the heels of his hands. Small pieces of rotten wood and green moss clung to the twigs, and he bit them off as well as he could with his teeth. He cherished the flame carefully and awkwardly. It meant life, and it must not perish. The withdrawal of blood from the surface of his body now made him begin to shiver, and he grew more awkward. A large piece of green moss fell squarely on the little fire. He tried to poke it out with his fingers, but his shivering frame made him poke too far, and he disrupted the nucleus of the little fire, the burning grasses and tiny twigs separating and scattering. He tried to poke them together again, but in spite of the tenseness of the effort, his shivering got away with him, and the twigs were hopelessly scattered. Each twig gushed a puff of smoke and went out. The fire-provider had failed. As he looked apathetically about him, his eyes chanced on the dog, sitting across the ruins of the fire from him, in the snow, making restless, hunching movements, slightly lifting one forefoot and then the other, shifting its weight back and forth on them with wistful eagerness.

The sight of the dog put a wild idea into his head. He remembered the tale of the man, caught in a blizzard, who killed a steer and crawled inside the carcass, and so was saved. He would kill the dog and bury his hands in the warm body until the numbness went out of them. Then he could build another fire. He spoke to the dog, calling it to him; but in his voice was a strange note of fear that frightened the animal, who had never known the man to speak in such way before. Something was the matter, and its suspicious nature sensed danger—it knew not what danger, but somewhere, somehow, in its brain arose an apprehension of the man. It flattened its ears down at the sound of the man's voice, and its restless, hunching movements and the liftings and shiftings of its forefeet became more pronounced; but it would not come to the man. He got on his hands and knees and crawled toward the dog. This unusual posture again excited suspicion, and the animal sidled[31] mincingly[32] away.

The man sat up in the snow for a moment and struggled for calmness. Then he pulled on his mittens, by means of his teeth, and got upon his

31. **sidled** [sī′ dld]: slowly moved sideways.
32. **mincingly** [min′ sing lē]: with very exact short steps.

feet. He glanced down at first in order to assure himself that he was really standing up, for the absence of sensation in his feet left him unrelated to the earth. His erect position in itself started to drive the webs of suspicion from the dog's mind; and when he spoke peremptorily,[33] with the sound of whiplashes in his voice, the dog rendered its customary allegiance and came to him. As it came within reaching distance, the man lost his control. His arms flashed out to the dog, and he experienced genuine surprise when he discovered that his hands could not clutch, that there was neither bend nor feeling in the fingers. He had forgotten for the moment that they were frozen and that they were freezing more and more. All this happened quickly, and before the animal could get away, he encircled its body with his arms. He sat down in the snow, and in this fashion held the dog, while it snarled and whined and struggled.

But it was all he could do, hold its body encircled in his arms and sit there. He realized that he could not kill the dog. There was no way to do it. With his helpless hands he could neither draw nor hold his sheath-knife nor throttle the animal. He released it, and it plunged wildly away, with tail between its legs, and still snarling. It halted forty feet away and surveyed him curiously, with ears sharply pricked forward. The man looked down at his hands in order to locate them, and found them hanging on the ends of his arms. It struck him as curious that one should have to use his eyes in order to find out where his hands were. He began threshing his arms back and forth, beating the mittened hands against his sides. He did this for five minutes, violently, and his heart pumped enough blood up to the surface to put a stop to his shivering. But no sensation was aroused in the hands. He had an impression that they hung like weights on the ends of his arms, but when he tried to run the impression down, he could not find it.

A certain fear of death, dull and oppressive, came to him. This fear quickly became poignant as he realized that it was no longer a mere matter of freezing his fingers and toes, or of losing his hands and feet, but that it was a matter of life and death with the chances against him. This threw him into a panic, and he turned and ran up the creek-bed

---

33. **peremptorily** [pə remp′ tə ri lē]: with authority.

along the old, dim trail. The dog joined in behind and kept up with him. He ran blindly, without intention, in fear such as he had never known in his life. Slowly, as he plowed and floundered through the snow, he began to see things again,—the banks of the creeks, the old timber-jams, the leafless aspens, and the sky. The running made him feel better. He did not shiver. Maybe, if he ran on, his feet would thaw out; and, anyway, if he ran far enough, he would reach camp and the boys. Without doubt he would lose some fingers and toes and some of his face; but the boys would take care of him, and save the rest of him when he got there. And at the same time there was another thought in his mind that said he would never get to the camp and the boys; that it was too many miles away, that the freezing had too great a start on him, and that he would soon be stiff and dead. This thought he kept in the background and refused to consider. Sometimes it pushed itself forward and demanded to be heard, but he thrust it back and strove to think of other things.

It struck him as curious that he could run at all on feet so frozen that he could not feel them when they struck the earth and took the weight of his body. He seemed to himself to skim along above the surface, and to have no connection with the earth. Somewhere he had once seen a winged Mercury,[34] and he wondered if Mercury felt as he felt when skimming over the earth.

His theory of running until he reached camp and the boys had one flaw in it: he lacked the endurance. Several times he stumbled, and finally he tottered, crumpled up, and fell. When he tried to rise, he failed. He must sit and rest, he decided, and next time he would merely walk and keep on going. As he sat and regained his breath, he noted that he was feeling quite warm and comfortable. He was not shivering, and it even seemed that a warm glow had come to his chest and trunk. And yet, when he touched his nose or cheeks, there was no sensation. Running would not thaw them out. Nor would it thaw out his hands and feet. Then the thought came to him that the frozen portions of his body must be extending. He tried to keep this thought down, to forget it, to think of something else; he was aware of the panicky feeling that it

---

34. **Mercury** [mer′ kyə rē]: a Roman god who serves as a messenger for the other gods.

caused, and he was afraid of the panic. But the thought asserted itself, and persisted, until it produced a vision of his body totally frozen. This was too much, and he made another wild run along the trail. Once he slowed down to a walk, but the thought of the freezing extending itself made him run again.

And all the time the dog ran with him, at his heels. When he fell down a second time, it curled its tail over its forefeet and sat in front of him, facing him, curiously eager and intent. The warmth and security of the animal angered him, and he cursed it till it flattened down its ears appeasingly.[35] This time the shivering came more quickly upon the man. He was losing in his battle with the frost. It was creeping into his body from all sides. The thought of it drove him on, but he ran no more than a hundred feet, when he staggered and pitched headlong. It was his last panic. When he had recovered his breath and control, he sat up and entertained in his mind the conception of meeting death with dignity. However, the conception did not come to him in such terms. His idea of it was that he had been making a fool of himself, running around like a chicken with its head cut off—such was the simile[36] that occurred to him. Well, he was bound to freeze anyway, and he might as well take it decently. With this new-found peace of mind came the first glimmerings of drowsiness. A good idea, he thought, to sleep off to death. It was like taking an anaesthetic.[37] Freezing was not so bad as people thought. There were lots worse ways to die.

He pictured the boys finding his body next day. Suddenly he found himself with them, coming along the trail and looking for himself. And, still with them, he came around a turn in the trail and found himself lying in the snow. He did not belong with himself any more, for even then he was out of himself, standing with the boys and looking at himself in the snow. It certainly was cold, was his thought. When he got back to the States he could tell the folks what real cold was. He drifted on from this to a vision of the old-timer

35. **appeasingly** [ə pēz′ ing lē]: calmly, quietly.
36. **simile** [sim′ ə lē]: a comparison of two different things that shows a likeness between them.
37. **anaesthetic** [an′ əs thet′ ik]: a substance, like ether, that causes loss of feeling or pain.

on Sulphur Creek. He could see him quite clearly, warm and comfortable, and smoking a pipe.

"You were right, old hoss; you were right," the man mumbled to the old-timer of Sulphur Creek.

Then the man drowsed off into what seemed to him the most comfortable and satisfying sleep he had ever known. The dog sat facing him and waiting. The brief day drew to a close in a long, slow twilight. There were no signs of a fire to be made, and, besides, never in the dog's experience had it known a man to sit like that in the snow and make no fire. As the twilight drew on, its eager yearning for the fire mastered it, and with a great lifting and shifting of forefeet, it whined softly, then flattened its ears down in anticipation of being chidden[38] by the man. But the man remained silent. Later, the dog whined loudly. And still later it crept close to the man and caught the scent of death. This made the animal bristle and back away. A little longer it delayed, howling under the stars that leaped and danced and shone brightly in the cold sky. Then it turned and trotted up the trail in the direction of the camp it knew, where were the other food-providers and fire-providers.

38. **chidden** [chid′ ən]: scolded, blamed.

JACK LONDON

Jack London [1876-1916] was born in San Francisco into a poor family and suffered many hardships in his life. He left school after completing the eighth grade so that he could go to work along the Oakland waterfront. As a young man, he traveled across the United States and in Canada, working as a sailor, an oyster pirate, an Alaskan gold prospector, and a seal hunter. At age twenty-eight, he became a writer. London was an adventurer attracted to high-risk situations. He wrote many stories describing a person or an animal struggling to survive.

In Response to Executive Order 9066: All Americans of Japanese Descent Must Report to Relocation Centers

DWIGHT OKITA

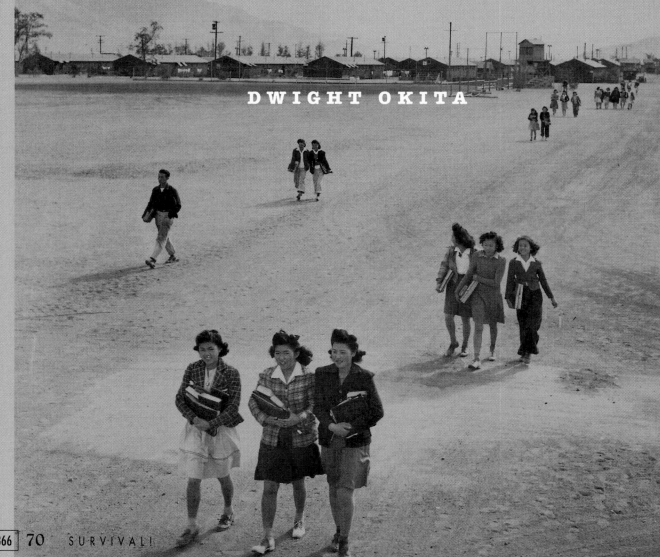

Dear Sirs:
Of course I'll come. I've packed my galoshes[1]
and three packets of tomato seeds. Janet calls them
"love apples." My father says where we're going
they won't grow.   5

I am a fourteen-year-old girl with bad spelling
and a messy room. If it helps any, I will tell you
I have always felt funny using chopsticks
and my favorite food is pizza.

My best friend is a white girl named Denise—   10
we look at boys together. She sat in front of me
all through grade school because of our names:
O'Connor, Ozawa. I know the back of Denise's head very well.
I tell her she's going bald. She tells me I copy on tests.
We are best friends.   15

I saw Denise today in Geography class.
She was sitting on the other side of the room.
"You're trying to start a war," she said, "giving secrets away
to the Enemy, Why can't you keep your big mouth shut?"
I didn't know what to say.   20
I gave her a packet of tomato seeds
and asked her to plant them for me, told her
when the first tomato ripened
she'd miss me.

1. **galoshes** [gə losh′ iz]: high plastic or rubber overshoes worn in wet weather.

D W I G H T   O K I T A

Dwight Okita was born in 1958. His parents were both interned during World War II in the relocation centers set up by the United States government for the 120,000 Americans of Japanese descent. His father was released for military service and fought in Europe with the most decorated 442nd Division, made up entirely of Japanese Americans.

Okita lives in Chicago where he works as a poet and video-maker. His latest book, *Crossing with the Light*, was published in 1993.

Internment camp for Americans of Japanese descent during World War II

LA BAMBA

GARY SOTO

Manuel was the fourth of seven children and looked like a lot of kids in his neighborhood: black hair, brown face, and skinny legs scuffed from summer play. But summer was giving way to fall: the trees were turning red, the lawns brown, and the pomegranate[1] trees were heavy with fruit. Manuel walked to school in the frosty morning, kicking leaves and thinking of tomorrow's talent show. He was still amazed that he had volunteered. He was going to pretend to sing Ritchie Valens's[2] "La Bamba" before the entire school.

Why did I raise my hand? he asked himself, but in his heart he knew the answer. He yearned[3] for the limelight.[4] He wanted applause as loud as a thunderstorm, and to hear his friends say, "Man, that was bad!" And he wanted to impress the girls, especially Petra Lopez, the second-prettiest girl in his class. The prettiest was already taken by his friend Ernie. Manuel knew he should be reasonable, since he himself was not great-looking, just average.

Manuel kicked through the fresh-fallen leaves. When he got to school he realized he had forgotten his math workbook. If the teacher found out, he would have to stay after school and miss practice for the talent show. But fortunately for him, they did drills that morning.

---

1. **pomegranate** [pom′ gran′ it]: a tree that bears a reddish fruit with many seeds.
2. **Ritchie Valens** [Richard Valenzuela, 1940-1959]: one of the legends of the golden age of rock and the composer of the Latin rock song "La Bamba."
3. **yearned** [yérnd]: felt a longing or desire for something.
4. **limelight** [līm līt]: the center of public attention.

During lunch Manuel hung around with Benny, who was also in the talent show. Benny was going to play the trumpet in spite of the fat lip he had gotten playing football.

"How do I look?" Manuel asked. He cleared his throat and started moving his lips in pantomime.[5] No words came out, just a hiss that sounded like a snake. Manuel tried to look emotional, flailing[6] his arms on the high notes and opening his eyes and mouth as wide as he could when he came to *"Para bailar la baaaaammmba."*[7]

After Manuel finished, Benny said it looked all right, but suggested Manuel dance while he sang. Manuel thought for a moment and decided it was a good idea.

"Yeah, just think you're like Michael Jackson or someone like that," Benny suggested. "But don't get carried away."

During rehearsal, Mr. Roybal, nervous about his debut[8] as the school's talent coordinator, cursed under his breath when the lever that controlled the speed on the record player jammed.

"Darn," he growled, trying to force the lever. "What's wrong with you?"

"Is it broken?" Manuel asked, bending over for a closer look. It looked all right to him.

Mr. Roybal assured Manuel that he would have a good record player at the talent show, even if it meant bringing his own stereo from home.

Manuel sat in a folding chair, twirling his record on his thumb. He watched a skit about personal hygiene, a mother-and-daughter violin duo,[9] five first-grade girls jumping rope, a karate kid breaking boards, three girls singing "Like a Virgin," and a skit about the pilgrims. If the record player hadn't been broken, he would have gone after the karate kid, an easy act to follow, he told himself.

5. **pantomime** [pan′ tə mīm]: **a** gesture without words.
6. **flailing** [flā′ ling]: moving or swinging about forcefully.
7. ***Para bailar la baaaaammmba*** [pah′-rah by-lahr′lah bam′-ba]: to dance the bamba.
8. **debut** [dā′ byü]: a first public appearance.
9. **duo** [du′ ō]: two people performing together.

As he twirled his forty-five record, Manuel thought they had a great talent show. The entire school would be amazed. His mother and father would be proud, and his brothers and sisters would be jealous and pout.[10] It would be a night to remember.

Benny walked onto the stage, raised his trumpet to his mouth, and waited for his cue.[11] Mr. Roybal raised his hand like a symphony conductor and let it fall dramatically. Benny inhaled and blew so loud that Manuel dropped his record, which rolled across the cafeteria floor until it hit a wall. Manuel raced after it, picked it up, and wiped it clean.

"Boy, I'm glad it didn't break," he said with a sigh.

That night Manuel had to do the dishes and a lot of homework, so he could only practice in the shower. In bed he prayed that he wouldn't mess up. He prayed that it wouldn't be like when he was a first-grader. For Science Week he had wired together a C battery and a bulb, and told everyone he had discovered how a flashlight worked.

10. **pout** [pout]: push out the lips as a sulky child does.
11. **cue** [kyü]: an action, a speech, or a word that gives a signal to an actor, singer, or musician.

He was so pleased with himself that he practiced for hours pressing the wire to the battery, making the bulb wink a dim, orangish light. He showed it to so many kids in his neighborhood that when it was time to show his class how a flashlight worked, the battery was dead. He pressed the wire to the battery, but the bulb didn't respond. He pressed until his thumb hurt and some kids in the back started snickering.[12]

But Manuel fell asleep confident that nothing would go wrong this time.

The next morning his father and mother beamed at him. They were proud that he was going to be in the talent show.

"I wish you would tell us what you're doing," his mother said. His father, a pharmacist who wore a blue smock with his name on a plastic rectangle, looked up from the newspaper and sided with his wife. "Yes, what are you doing in the talent show?"

"You'll see," Manuel said with his mouth full of Cheerios.

The day whizzed by, and so did his afternoon chores and dinner. Suddenly he was dressed in his best clothes and standing next to Benny backstage, listening to the commotion[13] as the cafeteria filled with school kids and parents. The lights dimmed, and Mr. Roybal, sweaty in a tight suit and a necktie with a large knot, wet his lips and parted the stage curtains.

"Good evening, everyone," the kids behind the curtain heard him say. "Good evening to you," some of the smart-alecky kids said back to him.

"Tonight we bring you the best John Burroughs Elementary has to offer, and I'm sure that you'll be both pleased and amazed that our little school houses so much talent. And now, without further ado,[14] let's get on with the show." He turned and, with a swish of his hand, commanded, "Part the curtain." The curtains parted in jerks. A girl dressed as a toothbrush and a boy dressed as a dirty gray tooth walked onto the stage and sang:

12. **snickering** [snik′ ər ing′]: laughing in a disrespectful way.
13. **commotion** [kə mō′ shən]: bustle or stir; confusion.
14. **ado** [ə dü′]: fuss, trouble, or excitement.

Brush, brush, brush
Floss, floss, floss
Gargle the germs away—hey! hey! hey!

After they finished singing, they turned to Mr. Roybal, who dropped his hand. The toothbrush dashed around the stage after the dirty tooth, which was laughing and having a great time until it slipped and nearly rolled off the stage.

Mr. Roybal jumped out and caught it just in time. "Are you OK?"

The dirty tooth answered, "Ask my dentist," which drew laughter and applause from the audience.

The violin duo played next, and except for one time when the girl got lost, they sounded fine. People applauded, and some even stood up. Then the first-grade girls maneuvered[15] onto the stage while jumping rope. They were all smiles and bouncing ponytails as a hundred cameras flashed at once. Mothers "awhed" and fathers sat up proudly.

The karate kid was next. He did a few kicks, yells, and chops, and finally, when his father held up a board, punched it in two. The audience clapped and looked at each other, wide-eyed with respect. The boy bowed to the audience, and father and son ran off the stage.

Manuel remained behind the stage shivering with fear. He mouthed the words to "La Bamba" and swayed from left to right. Why did he raise his hand and volunteer? Why couldn't he have just sat there like the rest of the kids and not said anything? While the karate kid was on stage, Mr. Roybal, more sweaty than before, took Manuel's forty-five record and placed it on a new record player.

"You ready?" Mr. Roybal asked.

"Yeah . . ."

Mr. Roybal walked back on stage and announced that Manuel Gomez, a fifth-grader in Mrs. Knight's class, was going to pantomime Ritchie Valens's classic hit "La Bamba."

15. **maneuvered** [mə nü′ vərd]: moved into place.

The cafeteria roared with applause. Manuel was nervous but loved the noisy crowd. He pictured his mother and father applauding loudly and his brothers and sisters also clapping, though not as energetically.

Manuel walked on stage and the song started immediately. Glassy-eyed from the shock of being in front of so many people, Manuel moved his lips and swayed in a made-up dance step. He couldn't see his parents, but he could see his brother Mario, who was a year younger, thumb-wrestling with a friend. Mario was wearing Manuel's favorite shirt; he would deal with Mario later. He saw some other kids get up and head for the drinking fountain, and a baby sitting in the middle of an aisle sucking her thumb and watching him intently.

What am I doing here? thought Manuel. This is no fun at all. Everyone was just sitting there. Some people were moving to the beat, but most were just watching him, like they would a monkey at the zoo.

But when Manuel did a fancy dance step, there was a burst of applause and some girls screamed. Manuel tried another dance step. He heard more applause and screams and started getting into the groove as he shivered and snaked like Michael Jackson around the stage. But the record got stuck, and he had to sing

Para bailar la bamba
Para bailar la bamba
Para bailar la bamba
Para bailar la bamba

again and again.

Manuel couldn't believe his bad luck. The audience began to laugh and stand up in their chairs. Manuel remembered how the forty-five record had dropped from his hand and rolled across the cafeteria floor. It probably got scratched, he thought, and now it was stuck, and he was stuck dancing and moving his lips to the same words over and over. He had never been so embarrassed. He would have to ask his parents to move the family out of town.

After Mr. Roybal ripped the needle across the record, Manuel slowed his dance steps to a halt. He didn't know what to do except bow to the audience, which applauded wildly, and scoot off the stage, on the verge of tears. This was worse than the homemade flashlight. At least no one laughed then, they just snickered.

Manuel stood alone, trying hard to hold back the tears as Benny, center stage, played his trumpet. Manuel was jealous because he sounded great, then mad as he recalled that it was Benny's loud trumpet playing that made the forty-five record fly out of his hands. But when the entire cast lined up for a curtain call, Manuel received a burst of applause that was so loud it shook the walls of the cafeteria. Later, as he mingled with the kids and parents, everyone patted him on the shoulder and told him, "Way to go. You were really funny."

Funny? Manuel thought. Did he do something funny?

Funny. Crazy. Hilarious. These were the words people said to him. He was confused, but beyond caring. All he knew was that people were paying attention to him, and his brothers and sisters looked at him with a mixture of jealousy and awe.[16] He was going to pull Mario aside and punch him in the arm for wearing his shirt, but he cooled it. He was enjoying the limelight. A teacher brought him cookies and punch, and the popular kids who had never before given him the time of day now clustered around him. Ricardo, the editor of the school bulletin, asked him how he made the needle stick.

"It just happened," Manual said, crunching on a star-shaped cookie.

At home that night his father, eager to undo the buttons on his shirt and ease into his La-Z-Boy recliner, asked Manuel the same thing, how he managed to make the song stick on the words *"Para bailar la bamba."*

Manuel thought quickly and reached for scientific jargon[17] he had read in magazines. "Easy, Dad. I used laser tracking with high optics and low functional decibels per channel." His proud but confused father told him to be quiet and go to bed.

16. **awe** [ô]: a feeling of wonder.
17. **jargon** [jär′ gən]: the language of a special profession.

"Ah, *qué niños tan truchas*,"[18] he said as he walked to the kitchen for a glass of milk. "I don't know how you kids nowadays get so smart."

Manuel, feeling happy, went to his bedroom, undressed, and slipped into his pajamas. He looked in the mirror and began to pantomime "La Bamba," but stopped because he was tired of the song. He crawled into bed. The sheets were cold as the moon that stood over the peach tree in the backyard.

He was relieved that the day was over. Next year, when they asked for volunteers for the talent show, he wouldn't raise his hand. Probably.

18. *qué niños tan truchas* [kay nee′nyos tahn troo′chahs]: Spanish for "what very clever children."

GARY SOTO

Gary Soto was born in 1952 in Fresno, California, and worked on farms in the San Joaquin Valley. He entered college hoping to study geography, but his interest soon shifted to literature. Today, Gary Soto teaches English and Chicano studies at the University of California, Berkeley. Soto has published many collections of poetry and short stories as well as autobiographical sketches and essays. Many of Soto's works focus on his own childhood and adolescent experiences and his life growing up in a Mexican American family.

Still Life With Indian Toys Elizabeth Blackadder, 1982, watercolor, 37 ¹/₂" x 49 ¹/₂", National Museum of Women in the Arts, Washington, D.C.

Life Doesn't Frighten Me

MAYA ANGELOU

Shadows on the wall
Noises down the hall
Life doesn't frighten me at all
Bad dogs barking loud
Big ghosts in a cloud   5
Life doesn't frighten me at all.

Mean old Mother Goose
Lions on the loose
They don't frighten me at all
Dragons breathing flame   10
On my counterpane[1]
That doesn't frighten me at all.

1. **counterpane** [koun′ tər pān′]: bedspread.

Detail from **Still Life With Indian Toys** Elizabeth Blackadder

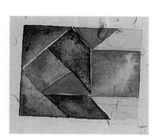

I go boo
Make them shoo
I make fun   15
Way they run
I won't cry
So they fly
I just smile
They go wild   20
Life doesn't frighten me at all.

Tough guys in a fight
All alone at night
Life doesn't frighten me at all.
Panthers in the park   25
Strangers in the dark
No, they don't frighten me at all.

That new classroom where
Boys all pull my hair
(Kissy little girls   30
With their hair in curls)
They don't frighten me at all.

Don't show me frogs or snakes
And listen for my scream,
If I'm afraid at all   35

It's only in my dreams.

I've got a magic charm
That I keep up my sleeve,
I can walk the ocean floor
And never have to breathe.   40

Life doesn't frighten me at all
Not at all
Not at all.
Life doesn't frighten me at all.

Details from **Still Life With Indian Toys** Elizabeth Blackadder

MAYA ANGELOU

Maya Angelou was born Marguerite Johnson in 1928 and was raised by her grandmother in Arkansas. In her autobiography, *I Know Why the Caged Bird Sings*, Angelou describes some of the experiences of her early years. Angelou studied dance in New York City and toured twenty-two countries in a production of the folk opera *Porgy and Bess*. She worked with Dr. Martin Luther King, Jr., before his death in 1968.

Angelou has also written poetry, magazine articles, and a television series. She has acted in and directed movies and plays. Angelou has been a lecturer and visiting professor at colleges and universities throughout the country. When she was invited to write and deliver her poem "On the Pulse of Morning" at the inauguration of President Bill Clinton, Maya Angelou's poetry was heard by millions of people around the world.

PANDORA'S BOX
CATHERINE GOURLEY

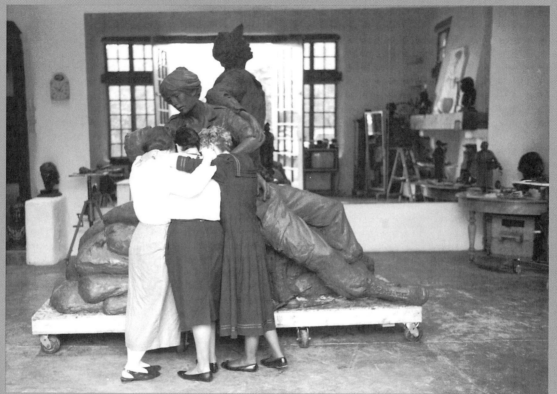

The models for the *Vietnam Women's Memorial* visit the studio of the sculptor.

INTRODUCTION

On a cool November morning in 1982, a sea of people gather on the green in Washington, D.C. They have come for the dedication of the Vietnam Veterans Memorial, soon to be known as "the Wall."

Alone in the crowd is a woman about 35 years old. She is wearing a boonie hat[1] with the word Pleiku[2] written on it. She is staring at the Wall, trying to understand why she can't remember the names. She remembers their faces. Why can't she remember their names?

1. **boonie hat:** a hat worn in the jungle for camouflage purposes.
2. **Pleiku:** a city in the central highlands of South Vietnam where a U.S. compound was located during the Vietnam War.

A man in a wheelchair approaches her. "When were you in 'Rocket City'?"

She looks blankly at him. "What?"

He smiles. "Your hat. When were you in Pleiku?"

"Oh." She touches the faded camouflage fabric. " '68 to '69."

"You were a nurse?"

She nods.

"You know, I never had the chance to say it over there. But all these years, I wanted to thank someone. If it weren't for you—I mean not you personally but people like you—I wouldn't be here today."

The woman closes her eyes. There is a wall inside her too. The whole time she was in Vietnam, she did not cry. She was afraid that if she started, she wouldn't be able to stop.

"Thanks, Nurse," the veteran says.

She has been back in the States 13 years, and still she hasn't cried. But she can't hold it back any longer. As the stranger disappears into the crowd, the wall that is inside the nurse begins to melt. She covers her face with her hands and cries.

CHARACTERS
(main parts in boldface)

Narrators 1, 2, 3

Dorie Carson, a young nurse

Mrs. Carson

Airline Captain

Max, a soldier

MP

Eva Johns, chief nurse

Millie, a nurse in Vietnam

Bobby, a chopper pilot

Corpsman

Turk

SCENE 1

Narrator 1: A few days later, Dorie Carson is back home in Minnesota visiting her mother.

Dorie: (*to her mother*) All he said was "Thanks Nurse." But those two words hit me like an 18-wheeler.

Mrs. Carson: You know, when you first came back from Vietnam, you didn't want to talk about it at all. I thought maybe you just needed a little time. But 13 years is too long, Dorie. Why don't you tell me what it was like over there?

Narrator 2: Dorie thinks of all the faces without names. She shakes her head.

Dorie: Why dredge up the past? I can't help them now.

Mrs. Carson: I kept all your letters.

Dorie: (*surprised*) You did?

Mrs. Carson: And your footlocker.

Dorie: My footlocker? But I told you to throw it out!

Mrs. Carson: It's in the attic. I never opened it. I figured one day you might want to go through your old things.

Dorie: Why should I?

Mrs. Carson: Because, Dorie, if you don't face your past, it will always haunt you.

SCENE 2

Narrator 3: The attic is in shadow. Dorie kneels by the footlocker.

Dorie: (*to herself*) Don't be afraid. It's only your old clothes.

Narr 1: She takes a deep breath and slowly lifts the lid.

Narr 2: The first thing that hits her is the smell of Vietnam, trapped inside the box for 13 years.

Narr 3: It smells like mud and diesel and blood and sweat mixed together.

Narr 1: She reaches inside and pulls out the fatigues she wore on her last day. Stiff spots of dried blood cover the front of the shirt.

Dorie: (*remembering*) I'd been on duty for 14 hours.

Narr 2: She picks up a combat boot. The thick red mud of Pleiku is still caked on the leather. There is a hole the size of a quarter in the sole.

Narr 3: Next, she removes her Army-issue blanket. It feels damp.

Narr 1: Suddenly, she remembers the monsoons in the central highlands of Vietnam and wind blowing so hard the rain slashed sideways.

Narr 2: She hears again the *whop-whop* of a chopper, then the thunder of artillery and the voice of the charge nurse shouting . . .

Eva: Red alert, Dorie! Red alert!

Narr 3: Dorie is kneeling on the floor of the attic in her mother's farmhouse in Minnesota, but she isn't really there at all.

Narr 1: It is 1968 again. She is 22 and on a plane bound for Vietnam.

SCENE 3

Narr 2: More than 200 men in uniform are on the flight. Dorie Carson is the only woman.

Narr 3: Most are 19 and 20. They have been talking nervously since leaving Travis Air Force Base in California.

Narr 1: Suddenly, the captain's voice is heard over the intercom.

Captain: We have just entered South Vietnam airspace.

Narr 2: Abruptly, the talking stops. Only the drone of the plane's engines can be heard.

Narr 3: Dorie looks at the faces around her. Each seems to be thinking what she is thinking . . .

Dorie: I'm going in, but will I get out . . . alive?

Narr 1: Minutes later, the plane begins its descent. Max, a soldier sitting across the aisle, smiles at Dorie.

Narr 2: Just as the plane is about to touch down, it suddenly veers up again, climbing into the sky.

Dorie: (*to Max*) What happened?

Max: (*tensely*) I don't know.

Narr 3: Again the plane circles and approaches the runway, but again the landing is aborted.

Captain: (*over the intercom*) We're having a little trouble this afternoon. It seems some Cong[3]

3. **Cong** [kông]: (short for "Vietcong") the Communist rebel force of South Vietnam.

American troops,
South Vietnam

snipers in the jungle below don't want us to land.

Max: Fine by me. Let's turn this bird around and go home.

Captain: We'll just hang up here awhile until our boys on the ground can clean the area out.

Max: *(to Dorie)* You scared?

Dorie: A little.

Max: What's a nice girl like you doing in a place like this anyway?

Dorie: *(proudly)* I volunteered.

Max: *(surprised)* Why?

Dorie: I'm a nurse. I want to help my country. How about you?

Max: Drafted.

Dorie: No, I mean are you scared?

Max: Not of dying. What scares me is losing a leg or an arm and ending up ten years from now a cripple on some street corner. No way could I deal with that! I'd rather die!

Narr 1: Again, the plane approaches the runway. Dorie grips the arms of her seat and holds her breath.

Narr 2: This time, the plane lands safely. Moments later, the door opens and two MPs[4] come aboard; one begins to bark orders.

4. **MPs:** short for "Military Police."

Soldier waiting at U.S. base at Da Nang,
South Vietnam, 1967

MP: OK. OK. Listen up. This ain't no tropical vacation you're on!

Max: (*quietly, to Dorie*) Oh, darn! And I brought my beach blanket.

Narr 3: The MPs are carrying M16s and wearing belts of bullets criss-crossed over their shoulders.

MP: (*firmly*) You will leave the plane and go directly to the buses waiting for you on the air-field. No stopping. No talking. No sweet good-byes to your bud-dies. Just move your butts and get on those buses!

Max: (*grimly*) Welcome to Vietnam.

SCENE 4

Narr 1: The charge nurse of the 71st Evacuation Hospital in Pleiku is Eva Johns. She is in her mid-40s and has served in two previous wars, World War II and the Korean.

Narr 2: This is Eva's second tour of duty in Vietnam.

Eva: (*cheerfully*) Welcome to Rocket City, Dorie. I'm happy to have you here. We're short-handed, but then we always are. Come on. I'll show you to your hootch.

Narr 3: Eva strides across the caked red ground toward a building made of metal and wood and screening.

Dorie: Why do you call it Rocket City?

Eva: Charlie[5] likes to keep us on our toes. We come under attack regularly. Especially at night.

Dorie: (*shocked*) But they told us at Fort Sam Houston that we wouldn't be sent to a combat area.

Eva: Yeah, well, what they didn't tell you at Fort Sam is that the whole *country* is a combat area. Be sure to keep your helmet close.

Narr 1: Inside the hootch, a half-dozen beds are arranged along the walls facing one another. Each bed has a nightstand and a metal lamp. Old filing cabinets act as makeshift walls separating each sleeping area.

Eva: Six nurses share this building. That means if you want privacy, you'll have to close your eyes. Now, try to get some rest. You're on duty first thing tomorrow, unless we get a red alert tonight.

Dorie: Red alert?

Eva: Mass casualties. They trained you in triage[6] of course?

Dorie: (*nods*) I also worked in an emergency room. I saw some bad stuff. Gunshot wounds. Car crashes.

Eva: It'll be a lot rougher here. Pleiku is smack in the middle of the fighting. Chopper pilots get our boys to us fast, sometimes within 15 or 20 minutes. That's good, but it's not pretty to look at. Just so you know. (*She turns to leave.*)

Dorie: Wait! How will I know if it's a red alert?

Eva: Honey, trust me. You'll know.

SCENE 5

Narr 2: Alone, Dorie unpacks a few things from her footlocker. Then she hears laughter coming from the screened porch.

Narr 3: Outside, a nurse and a soldier are holding each other, kissing.

Dorie: (*to herself*) What did she say? If I want privacy, close my eyes?

---

5. **Charlie:** a nickname for Vietcong guerrillas.
6. **triage:** three categories of casualties: immediate care, delayed treatment, and comfort care only.

Narr 1: Dorie lies down on her cot and covers her eyes with her arm. Almost immediately, she falls asleep.

Millie: Hi. You must be the new girl.

Narr 2: Dorie stirs, waking up. For a confusing moment, she has no idea where she is.

Narr 3: From somewhere beyond the hills outside comes the thunder of artillery. She sits up, alarmed.

Millie: Don't worry. It's outgoing. That means it's ours.

Narr 1: Then Dorie remembers. She is in a war zone. She is in Vietnam.

Millie: I'm Millie. Where're you from?

Dorie: Minnesota.

Millie: I'm from Indiana. I've been here four months, six days, and—

Narr 2: She looks at her watch.

Millie: —six hours.

Narr 2: The heat is suffocating. Dorie's shirt is wet with sweat, and her head aches from her hard sleep.

Dorie: Was that your boyfriend?

Millie: (*sarcastically*) No, he's a patient. I treat all my patients that way. It's amazing how it speeds up their recovery!

Narr 1: In spite of her fear and discomfort, Dorie smiles.

Millie: Bobby's a chopper pilot, and yes, he's my boyfriend. He's from South Bend! Can you believe that? I travel thousands of miles to fall in love with a guy who lives practically next door to my hometown.

Narr 2: The sound of heavy guns rumbles outside again. Dorie jumps.

Millie: You'll get used to it. When it's incoming, then you take cover.

Dorie: What's it really like?

Millie: A rocket attack? Bad news!

Dorie: No, I mean the wounded.

Millie: Nothing they could have told me at Fort Sam would have prepared me for this place. Nothing! I don't know what I'd do without Bobby and the babies.

Dorie: Babies? What babies?

Millie: From the villages. They come here for treatment. They make us laugh. They remind us that it's not all death and dying.

Narr 3: Millie returns to her cot. Dorie lies down again, wondering *What have I gotten myself into?*

SCENE 6

Narr 1: The rain is falling in sheets, as it has been for days. The thick red mud of Pleiku sticks to Dorie's boots.

Narr 2: In the hootch, her mattress and blanket are damp and mildewy. Dorie lies down anyway.

Narr 3: She has just ended a 14-hour shift. She is almost asleep when she hears the whop-whop of a chopper.

Dorie: (*moaning*) Oh, Bobby, no more. Don't bring us anymore wounded tonight.

Narr 1: It is not one chopper but many. Sirens begin to wail.

Narr 2: Outside, Eva shouts to Dorie as she slips in the mud.

Eva: Red alert, Dorie! Red alert!

Narr 3: Dorie grabs her helmet and goes out again into the rain.

SCENE 7

Narr 1: The choppers have already landed. Corpsmen carry litters of groaning soldiers to the hospital.

Narr 2: Over the beating roar of the rotors, Millie calls to Bobby, who is piloting a chopper.

Millie: How many?

Bobby: You don't want to know.

Narr 3: Bobby gives a thumbs up as he lifts off, heading again for the fighting beyond the mountain ridge.

Narr 1: Dorie has been in Pleiku just four weeks, but she knows exactly what to do.

Narr 2: She joins Millie, moving from litter to litter, examining the wounded and determining which soldiers have the best chance to survive and which are likely to die.

Dorie: (*to corpsman*) This one's a "can wait." Give him another unit of blood, and we can take him later.

Narr 3: She moves to another litter. The soldier has a single bullet hole in his stomach. Blood is bubbling in the corner of his mouth.

Corpsman: Vital signs are weak.

Narr 1: Gently, Dorie lifts the soldier's shoulders. The exit wound on his back is as large as a plate. Muscles and spine are exposed.

Turk: *(groaning)* Don't let me die. Not here. Alone. Not in the jungle.

Dorie: I'm here. You're not alone.

Narr 2: Dorie looks at the corpsman and shakes her head, silently signaling that this one's an "expectant." He'll likely die on the operating table. There are others who have a better chance of surviving if given immediate care.

Dorie: *(to soldier)* We're going to give you something for pain.

Turk: Am I going to make it?

Dorie: *(hesitates, then swallows)* Sure you are. What's your name?

Turk: Turk.

Dorie: Where are you from, Turk?

Turk: Texas. Did my buddies get out? Take care of my buddies!

Narr 3: Dorie looks up at the sky. More choppers are coming over the mountain ridge. They look ghostly in the rain and fog. She turns to Turk.

Dorie: Don't worry. We'll get them out.

Narr 1: He stares up at her—blankly. The corpsman has handed Dorie a syringe of morphine, but now he puts his hand on hers, stopping her from giving Turk the injection.

Corpsman: It's too late.

Dorie: *(determined)* No, it's not.

Corpsman: Dorie, he's gone. Save it for the next one.

Narr 2: Dorie stares at Turk. Chaos surrounds her—screaming soldiers, doctors shouting for assistance, the steady beating of choppers landing and lifting off again.

Dorie: I was just talking to him. He can't be gone.

Corpsman: You can't save them all.

Dorie: But I'm a nurse!

Narr 3: He takes the syringe from her. Numbly, Dorie moves to the next litter.

SCENE 8

Narr 1: An hour passes, then another. The "push" of wounded coming into the hospital continues.

Narr 2: The face is bloody, but the head wound is not serious. Dorie inserts a needle into the soldier's arm, starting a blood transfusion.

Narr 3: She thinks that something about this one is familiar.

7. **Bouncing Betty:** an explosive land mine.

Narr 1: Millie is cutting off the man's pant legs.

Millie: (*with disgust*) Not another Bouncing Betty.[7]

Narr 2: One leg is hanging from the torso by a thin strip of skin and blood. The bone of the other leg is protruding through the skin like a tree branch.

Millie: What kind of life is this kid going to have with no legs?

Narr 3: The soldier grabs Dorie's arm. Her heart stops. She *does* know him.

Dorie: Max!

Battle scenes, Vietnam

Max: You're the one. The girl from the plane.

Narr 1: She remembers what he had told her. He wasn't afraid of dying. He was afraid of being a cripple.

Max: How bad is it?

Narr 2: Dorie looks at Millie. Millie shakes her head. One leg certainly will be amputated.

Dorie: (*to Max*) It's pretty bad.

Corpsman: How do we tag this one?

Narr 3: Again, Dorie looks at Millie, but she has moved to the next litter. The decision is left to Dorie.

Narr 1: She looks again at Max's twisted legs. "I'd rather die," he had told her that day. But did he mean it? Did he *really* mean that?

Narr 2: Her heart is pounding, beating loudly like the whirring rotors of the choppers outside.

Narr 3: *It isn't fair!* she wanted to scream. She came to Vietnam to heal, not to decide who should live and who should die. She can't save them all, but which ones? *Which ones?*

Dorie: He's only 19.

Corpsman: They're all 19.

Narr 1: She cannot delay any longer. There are others who need her.

Dorie: He's "immediate." Move him into the operating room.

SCENE 9

Narr 2: By nine in the morning the push is over. A Vietnamese woman from the village is mopping up the mud and blood on the floor.

Narr 3: A few nurses are sitting at a table drinking coffee. Outside, rain is still falling.

Eva: In World War I, the feared weapon was mustard gas. Here, it's Bouncing Betties.

Bobby: (*teasing*) World War I? I knew you were old but not that old.

Eva: (*laughing*) Hey, I read about mustard gas. Okay, wise guy?

Dorie: I've been on my feet for 30 hours, picking bits of metal and filth from the bellies of kids, and the two of you sit here joking. How can you?

Millie: (*quietly*) If we didn't, we'd go crazy.

Bobby: She's right, Dorie. What happened last night will happen again and again, a hundred times more before we go home.

Narr 1: Dorie shivers. The numbness that crept inside her last night has not gone away.

Eva: Every war has had mass casualties, Dorie. What makes this one different is the choppers. Bobby gets the wounded to us so fast that men who would have died in other wars have a better chance of living.

Dorie: (*painfully*) Without arms and legs? Maybe they'd be better off if we didn't save them!

Millie: Dorie! How can you say that?

Narr 2: Dorie realizes what she has said. She looks apologetically at Eva.

Dorie: Oh Eva! I didn't mean it! I don't want them to die. But how can I help them when there are so many? How can I keep telling them they're going to be all right when I know they aren't?

Eva: Did you ever hear of the story of Pandora's box?

Dorie: I think so. In school.

Eva: The Greek gods warned Pandora not to open the box, but she did, and out flew all the evils and sorrows of mankind. That's kind of what being a nurse in wartime is like.

Dorie: So what you're saying is I should keep all this misery I'm feeling inside me?

Eva: No! The gods put one more thing inside the box—hope. Despite all the sorrows in the world Dorie, hope is still our sole comfort.

Dorie: *(bitterly)* Hope for what?

Eva: That we've made a difference in someone's life by being here.

SCENE 10

Narr 3: For the next few days, a lull hangs over Pleiku. No rocket tracers light up the night sky. Even the rain has slowed.

Narr 1: In the hospital, Dorie is changing the dressing on Max's right leg, which has been amputated close to the hip.

Dorie: You're lucky. They're moving you out tomorrow to a hospital ship.

Max: No, you got it all wrong. I'm not lucky. Guys like Turk are lucky.

Narr 2: The numbness inside Dorie grows thicker, like ice on a pond. She tries not to let it chill her voice.

Dorie: But you're alive! Turk's dead!

Max: *(bitterly)* Part of me is alive.

Narr 3: Dorie turns away. A Vietnamese baby is standing in her hospital crib, reaching for Dorie.

Dorie: *(softly to the baby)* Millie was right. You do remind us that it's not all death and dying but healing too.

Narr 1: Suddenly, the sirens begin to wail. The next instant, an explosion rocks the area outside the hospital.

Dorie: *(alarmed)* Incoming! *(to the patients in the ward)* Quick! Get under the beds!

Narr 2: Outside, tracers[8] score the black sky. Personnel run for the bunkers. But inside the hospital—

8. **tracers:** bullets with a burning substance that leaves a trail.

Narr 3: Dorie is frantically helping the wounded take cover on the floor under their beds, checking that their intravenous cords aren't tangled.

Narr 1: Max cannot be moved. He stares at her, eyes full of new terror.

Max: I don't want to die!

Dorie: You're not going to die. I won't let you! I'm a nurse, remember?

Narr 2: She pulls a mattress from an empty bed. He helps her maneuver it over his body.

Narr 3: A second explosion rocks the hospital, knocking out all the lights. In the darkness behind her, she hears the baby screaming for its mother.

Narr 1: Dorie returns for the child.

SCENE 11

Narr 2: In less than ten minutes, the siren stops its dreadful wailing.

Narr 3: Eva bursts through the hospital door.

Eva: Dorie?

Narr 1: A voice answers from the dark corner.

Dorie: We're okay. We're okay.

Narr 2: Eva points her flashlight at Dorie, who is huddling under a bed. She is hugging the child to her.

SCENE 12

Narr 3: The next morning, Dorie finds Max's bed empty.

Dorie: Where is he?

Millie: Somewhere on the South China Sea by now, I guess. The chopper came early for him.

Narr 1: Millie hands her a folded piece of paper.

Millie: He left this for you. Who is he anyway? An old friend of yours?

Narr 2: Dorie unfolds the paper. It reads simply "I will never forget you. Max." She folds the paper again.

Dorie: No. He isn't a friend. He's just a soldier I met on the plane.

SCENE 13

Narr 3: Weeks, and then months pass. The monsoons give way to drier weather, and still rocket tracers light up the night.

Narr 1: First Bobby and then Millie complete their tours of duty and return to "the world"—the States.

Narr 2: For Dorie, one day slips into another, becoming a blur of pushes, red alerts, and rocket attacks. It seems as if she has been in Pleiku forever.

Narr 3: For Dorie, "the world" is a fairy tale land she can go to only in her dreams and in the letters she writes to her mother.

Narr 1: Then, at last, a day arrives that is unlike all the others. It is her last day. Dorie is going home.

Narr 2: She leaves the hospital after working a 14-hour shift. Carelessly she tosses her bloody uniform and her combat boots into her footlocker on top of her army blanket.

Narr 3: Suddenly, her legs are wooden. She sinks onto her cot.

Eva: You're thinking you can't leave. I know. I felt that way too.

Narr 1: Eva is standing in the door.

Dorie: How can I leave when it isn't over? (*turns*) You didn't.

Eva: It's time to get on with your life again, Dorie.

Dorie: How? How do I put this behind me? I'm not the same person I was before I came here.

Eva: When you get back, you probably won't want to talk about what happened over here, but you should.

Dorie: No one would understand.

Eva: Remember Pandora's box?

Dorie: I don't have any hope left, Eva. Not after what I've seen here. All I have is guilt.

Eva: No, the hope is still there too, deep inside you. But you've got to open up the box and let the guilt and sorrows out before you can find it.

Narr 2: Outside, the chopper that will take her back to "the world" is stirring a tornado of red dust.

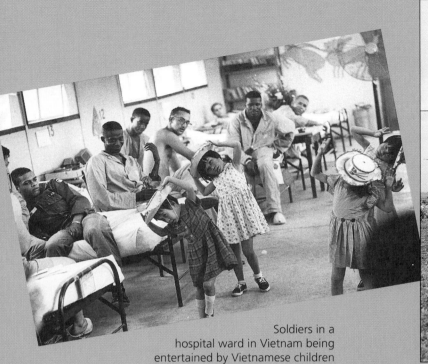

Soldiers in a hospital ward in Vietnam being entertained by Vietnamese children

Narr 3: The two women face each other and hug.

Narr 1: As the chopper lifts off Dorie watches Eva grow smaller and smaller until she can't see her at all anymore.

SCENE 14

Narr 2: In the attic in her mother's farmhouse in Minnesota, Dorie sits in the dark, alone.

Narr 3: It has taken 13 years for her finally to open Pandora's box. In her lap is a folded piece of paper, yellowed now, found deep inside the footlocker.

Dorie: *(reading)* "I will never forget you."

Narr 1: She has never forgotten him either, even though his name has been tucked away inside the footlocker until now. She has never forgotten his face.

Dorie: Max.

Narr 2: She has no idea what has become of him or if he's happy to be alive. All she has is this note.

Dorie: I was his hope. Now he is mine.

Mrs. Carson: Dorie?

Narr 3: The attic light goes on. Dorie blinks as if waking from a dream. Mrs. Carson comes up the stairs.

Mrs. Carson: You've been up here for hours. Are you all right?

Dorie: No. But I will be. (*smiling*) I'm going to be fine.

Narr 1: She slips the note into her pocket, then follows her mother down the stairs. She is ready now to talk.

Dorie: (*to mother*) I met this guy on the plane. His name was Max . . .

Narr 2: Left behind in the dark attic is the open footlocker. On the floor around it are Dorie's sorrows—the soiled uniform and boots and Army blanket.

CATHERINE GOURLEY

Catherine Gourley was born and grew up in Wilkes-Barre, Pennsylvania. She taught middle school for ten years and now works for *Weekly Reader,* creating *Read* magazine. She says she most enjoys writing historical fiction "and doing research in unusual places—like going down into mines." Her young adult novel, *The Courtship of Joanna*, is about a sixteen-year-old who comes to the Pennsylvania mining country that Gourley has been familiar with since childhood. Gourley also writes drama, such as *Pandora's Box,* for radio.

Gourley was in high school during the Vietnam War. She decided to write *Pandora's Box,* later, after learning that the names of service women had not been included on the Vietnam Veterans Memorial. The play developed out of her interviews with nurses. "No one turned me down," she says. Today, Gourley is pleased by the creation of the Vietnam Women's Memorial.

Asking Big Questions About the Literature

What survival challenges do people face?

Write about an EXPLORER

In history, some of the most courageous survivors have been explorers. Cabeza de Vaca, for example, was a Spanish explorer who survived years of near-starvation as he wandered, lost, through what is now the American Southwest. Choose an explorer who survived his or her explorations. Do some research and then, in an essay of several paragraphs, describe the survival challenges that this explorer overcame.

LITERATURE STUDY

Setting

In this unit, a character's challenge is often to survive the **setting**—the time and place of the story. Choose one short story you read in this unit and explain in your journal how the setting is the survival problem. Share your explanation with a partner or in a small group. Compare explanations with classmates who read the same short story. (See "Setting" on page 118.)

Write AND Discuss

What was the survival problem in each selection you read in this unit? Make a chart like the one shown of all the survival problems. Then, in your journal, write about how these problems are alike and how they are different.

Which character in this unit do you think faces the worst survival problem? Explain your choice in your journal. Then discuss your ideas with a partner or in a small group.

Literature	Survival Problem
"To Build a Fire"	temperature is below -50° F.

What decisions do people make to survive?

MAKING A DECISION CHAIN

With a partner, select a character from one of the selections. Write and circle the character's name on a piece of paper and brainstorm for several decisions that the character makes to survive. Take turns creating a decision chain like the one shown for the selection from *Mississippi Solo*. Draw a line from the character to another circle, write *decision* on the line, and write the decision in the circle. Draw a line from the decision and write *result* on the line. Enter the result and circle it. Evaluate the decisions with your partner by discussing the results.

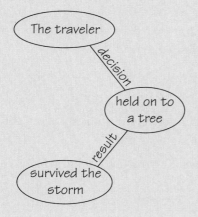

LITERATURE STUDY

Character

A **character** performs actions in a story or a play. To help you understand character, form a group of four students. Begin by agreeing on which character in this unit makes the most responsible survival decisions. Then let one member of the group write a topic sentence about that character.

EXAMPLE: (Character) makes the most responsible survival decisions.

Pass the paper around the group, taking turns adding a reason or a detail about the character that supports the topic sentence. Finally let the student who wrote the topic sentence add a concluding sentence. (*See "Character" on page 119.*)

Radio Broadcast

With a partner, plan and write a news interview based on one of the selections you've read or on a survival situation you've come across in the newspaper, on TV, or in the movies. The person who plays the newscaster should focus the interview questions on decisions the survivor had to make. The one who plays the survivor should explain the *hows* and *whys* of the decisions in a strong, dramatic manner. After rehearsing, perform your interview for your classmates.

Asking Big Questions About the Literature

What qualities does a survivor have?

RANK Survival Qualities

Working in a small group, choose from this unit one of the selections you've enjoyed reading. Brainstorm a list of at least six qualities that the characters in that selection have that are important to their survival. Then rank the qualities from *most important* to *least important*. Here are two qualities to help you start.

courage
imagination

Evaluate a Character

Work with a partner to fill out a report card of survival skills for one of your favorite characters in this unit. Agree on the survival qualities you'll use to evaluate the character. Partner A should fill in the survival quality and Partner B should fill in the grade and the first comment. Then reverse roles and continue until the report is complete. The model here gives the first two lines of a report card for Manuel of "La Bamba."

Character

As a reader, you learn about **characters** by noticing the same kinds of things you notice about new friends— how they act, what they look like, what they say. Choose your favorite character from the selections that you've read. In your journal, write about that character as though he or she is a new friend. Then share your thoughts with a partner or a group. Ask yourself questions like these.

What does the character say about himself or herself?

What do other charcters say about him or her?

How does the character act?

What does the character look like?

What survival qualities does the character have?

(See "Character" on page 119.)

Quality	Grade	Comment
Responsibility	Fair	forgot his math workbook
Coordination	Excellent	shivered and snaked onstage

How do people help one another survive?

RANK *Characters*

Rank the characters in the selections that you've read who helped other characters survive. Use a range of 1 through 5, with 1 = *most helpful* and 5 = *least helpful*. Explain each ranking and then compare your rankings with those of a partner.

Character	Rank	Explanation
Hannah	4	was a good friend to Crow

Respond

AND *Discuss*

If you were faced with a survival challenge, which character from the selections you read in this unit would you call on for help? Why? How could this character help you? Write your ideas in your journal and discuss them with a partner or in a small group. Then write a paragraph describing the character you've chosen and share it with a partner or group.

EXAMINE Current Events

Throughout history, people have helped one another survive—from individuals helping one another to nations assisting each other in times of crisis. Look through newspapers and magazines to find some current examples of individual and global assistance. Then create a booklet showing examples of how individuals and nations help each other survive.

NOW *Choose a Project!*

Three survival project choices are described on the following pages. Which one is for you?

Writing Workshop

WRITING A SURVIVAL NARRATIVE

One of the Big Questions in this unit asks, "What qualities does a survivor have?" This project will give you a chance to examine some of these qualities when you interview a real-life survivor. Then you'll use the interview to write a nonfiction, or true, story called a survival narrative. Your **purpose** in writing your survival narrative will be to tell a survivor's story. You and your classmates who choose this project will write survival stories and collect them into a booklet. By reading some of these stories, your **audience** may learn survival strategies of their own.

Prewriting
CHOOSING A STORY

To gather ideas for your survival narrative, you'll interview a survivor in your family or your community. Has anyone you know survived a life-threatening experience or illness?

Prewriting
....
CONDUCTING INTERVIEWS

To prepare for a successful interview, study the interview strategies in the box.

STRATEGIES FOR INTERVIEWING

- Write a letter to the survivor or use the telephone to arrange a convenient time for your interview. Don't forget to agree on how long the interview will be.
- Beforehand, prepare a list of questions like the ones below to ask the survivor.

    Describe the setting as if you could see, hear, taste, touch, and smell what was around you.

    Tell me what happened from the first moment you realized that your survival was threatened.

    What did you feel during the most frightening moments?

    What qualities do you have that helped you survive?

    What did you learn from your experience?

- Be on time for the interview and leave promptly at the agreed upon time.
- Let the survivor do most of the talking but encourage the survivor to recall the events in *chronological order*—the order in which they happened.
- Take careful notes or, if the survivor agrees, use a tape recorder during the interview. The notes should include a list of events the survivor experienced. Your interview notes might look like the ones below.
- Thank the survivor when the interview is over. Arrange for a follow-up interview so that you can share your writing with the survivor.

First: We were watching the weather report when the power went out.
Second: Everyone froze in shock.
Third: Mrs. Randolph reacted calmly.

Drafting
YOUR NARRATIVE

Once you've finished your interview, you're ready to draft your narrative. Follow these steps.

- Tell the story the way the survivor told it to you, but use the third-person point of view to report the events. Use the pronouns *he*, *she*, *they*, *him*, *her*, and *them*.

- In the first paragraph, introduce and describe your survivor. Be sure to mention the qualities your survivor has. For example, Kristen Foster, a student writer, describes the "reassuring confidence of Mrs. Randolph" in her survival narrative "More Than Just a Snowfall," on pages 110-111.

- Remember to put the events in chronological order. Use transition words such as *first*, *next*, *then*, and *finally* to help you move smoothly from one event to the next.

- Write an effective conclusion, referring to your introduction or summarizing your ideas. Kristen, for example, ends her narrative by pointing out that a threatening situation can actually unite a family. "The threat of having to survive had brought the Randolphs closer together."

Revising YOUR NARRATIVE

Read your story aloud to a partner or a group and ask for help as you revise. If you can, read your draft to the survivor you interviewed. Does your narrative convey the survivor's experience? Have you been able to express what the survivor saw and felt? Maybe he or she will think of additional information that you can add to your narrative.

Editing YOUR NARRATIVE

After you've revised your draft, work with a partner to edit your narrative. Read one another's narratives and check for errors in spelling, grammar, and punctuation. Correct your errors and make a publishable copy of your work. Turn to pages 110-111 to read the survival narrative that Kristen wrote.

Publishing YOUR COLLECTION OF NARRATIVES

Once you've finished your survival narrative, form a small group and share your work. Decide what stories you would like to combine into a booklet and plan carefully how you will do this. If you can, use a word processor to print your work. Maybe someone in your group can design an attractive cover by hand or on the computer. Then make copies available to your audience. You might even want to make audiotapes of your stories.

More Than Just a Snowfall
by Kristen Foster, Ellicott City, Maryland

Mr. and Mrs. Randolph turned on the television and listened to the morning weather report. The meteorologists had been forecasting a snow storm for nearly a week now, but no one really expected a full blown blizzard since they were not common in Maryland. But there was something about how the meteorologist described the severity of the storm that made Mr. Randolph call in his two sons, Chris and Tyler. The boys listened to the report with a hint of fear in their eyes. The family had never experienced a severe snow storm before, but Mrs. Randolph, having grown up in Massachusetts, knew what one was like and how to prepare for it.

Mr. Randolph cut firewood, while Mrs. Randolph took the children to the store to buy food. When they got back, they collected batteries, flashlights, and candles. The Randolphs had a strange feeling as they went to bed that night, but thanks to the reassuring confidence of Mrs. Randolph, they felt that they were secure and had everything under control.

When the family awoke the next morning, the wind was howling and branches were tapping against the windows. They peered out through a mosaic of snow on the window and saw birds digging through eight inches of snow, looking for seed that had been thrown there the day before.

Realizing that the blizzard was as serious as the meteorologists said it was, the Randolphs became a bit frightened. They were anxiously watching the weather report when, Bizz! The power went out! Everyone froze in shock. Soon they could feel the room getting colder. What the heck were they going to do? Where could they go? Nowhere!

Instead of panicking, Mrs. Randolph reacted calmly to the situation and put the rest of the family at ease. As she did not know how long the power would be out, Mrs. Randolph moved all the food from the refrigerator to the back porch. She also put water into milk cartons in case the pipes froze.

Another surprise came when they found out that the phone was dead. The radio reported that thousands of people were without power. The Randolphs then realized that the telephone and electric companies could take days to repair the lines.

As the storm worsened, the family collected blankets, sweatshirts, sweaters, and extra socks, and brought up clothes from their basement. To get their minds off the cold, the whole family sat together to play Monopoly and listen to the radio. The broadcaster suggested staying indoors. As the game went on, the Randolphs put on gloves. The temperature inside felt like the temperature outside. They could even see their breath when they talked.

They waited until nightfall to start a fire in the fireplace, as they did not have very much wood. At bedtime, the family wrapped up warmly and snuggled near the fire to sleep. When they awoke the next morning, it had stopped snowing. The house even felt a little warmer. Throughout the morning, the power went on and off. Around lunch time, the power stayed on, and the house started to heat up. Little by little, the family took off their layers of clothing. The feeling of survival, teamwork, and satisfaction filled every member of the Randolph family. The threat of having to survive had brought the Randolphs closer together.

Cooperative Learning

PRODUCING A SURVIVAL KIT

The PROBLEM

One of the Big Questions in this unit asks, "What survival challenges do people face?" This project gives you a chance to put together a collection of useful objects that will help you or someone you know survive a challenge—anything from a night lost in the woods to your first dance.

Work with a partner or with a group to produce your survival kit. First, choose a survival challenge and write it in your journal. Then decide who the users of your survival kit will be and describe this audience in your journal.

The SOLUTION

What objects can you collect that will solve the problems of your survival situation? Feel free to be funny if it's appropriate. Do some research if it's necessary. List the items in your journal, using a chart like the one below. Remember to ask these questions.

What is my survival challenge?

What items will I need to survive the challenge?

Survival Challenge	Item	Purpose of the Item

The PACKAGE

You can put all the items you need in a box or a bag—or you can find other ways to share your survival ideas. For example, if you can't bring in actual items, you could create a large poster, make a videotape, or develop an illustrated computer printout. What other forms could your survival kit take? In your journal, make a list of ideas for packaging a survival kit and then choose the best form for your kit.

Working with your partner or your writing group, think about all the steps needed to complete a practical survival kit. In your journal, make a project planner like the one below.

Task	Target Date	Person Responsible	Materials Needed

The PRESENTATION

Once you've finished your survival kit, arrange a time to present it to your classmates or to your school. Then make it available to the audience you've chosen. Take it home and keep it in your room, or store it in the bottom of your backpack. You could even offer samples of your survival kit to the librarian or to officials of your city or town. Perhaps the officials could make your kit available to your community—and make you famous!

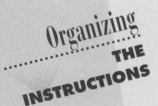

PROJECT 3

Helping Your Community

PREPARING A SURVIVAL MANUAL

One Big Question in this unit asks, "What decisions do people make to survive?" This project gives you a chance to recommend procedures during a survival challenge in your community. The situation could be as serious as an approaching tornado or as simple as the first day of school. The people who will use your manual—your **audience**—will need clear instructions on what to do. Your manual's **purpose** is to provide those instructions.

Choosing THE PROBLEM

In your journal, brainstorm a list of threatening situations that might occur in your community. Then choose the situation that interests you the most. Think carefully about who will use your survival manual as you write a brief description of the situation.

Organizing THE INSTRUCTIONS

Prewrite by brainstorming a list of instructions that readers of your manual would need to survive in the situation you've chosen. Do some research if it's necessary. Then put your instructions in **sequential** order—the order in which they'll have to be followed. Use the chart below—the first few steps for surviving a tornado—as a model.

Sequential Order		
First, listen carefully to weather advisories from the National Weather Service.		
Second, be sure to keep some windows open to reduce the difference in air pressure inside and outside the house and prevent an explosion.		
Third,	Next,	After that,

Drafting and Revising

YOUR MANUAL

Write a draft of your manual, starting with an introduction that clearly states the purpose of your survival manual. Include any illustrations, diagrams, or charts that will help your audience. Reread your draft carefully and revise it, asking the following questions:

- Does my introduction clearly state the purpose of my manual?
- Are my instructions in logical, sequential order?
- Do I use effective transitions from one set of instructions to the next?

Editing

YOUR MANUAL

Edit your survival manual carefully, checking your grammar and your punctuation. Make sure that you've spelled all the words correctly. Ask a partner or a member of your group to help.

Presenting

YOUR MANUAL

Think of the most effective way to publish your manual. Maybe you'll want to make a final copy on a word processor and offer it to a group that could really use it. Your town's newspaper, for example, might want to publish your manual, or your city hall might want to offer your survival manual to the people in your community. Brainstorm for some ideas for ways to present your manual to your school or to your community. Write your publishing ideas in your journal.

Putting It All Together
What Have You Learned About Survival?

Now that you've thought and read about different forms of survival, consider how your ideas on this theme have changed. Look back at the writing you've done for this unit—in your journal, in response to your reading, and in the Writing Workshop. Then show what you learned about survival by writing a journal entry for a challenging day that *you* survived.

A SURVIVOR'S STORY

Prewriting and Drafting   Have you ever had a day when everything went wrong? A day when you missed the bus after school and had to walk home in the rain only to find the front door locked and no one else around? Brainstorm a list of times that were particularly difficult or challenging for you. Then choose a day that you could reconstruct in the form of a journal entry. Make a note of how you survived that day.

Now draft your journal entry. Tell how you felt about the day's events and how you planned to survive your difficulties. Describe any decisions you might have made during your challenging day. Finally tell how you felt afterwards. Were there any lessons that you learned from your ordeals?

Revising and Editing   Work with a writing group or a partner. Exchange journal entries and ask for comments on and advice about the content of your writing. Ask questions that you have about your draft. Have your partner or writing group check for errors in grammar, spelling, and punctuation.

Publishing   After you have made your final revisions, write your journal entry out neatly and give it a title. Post it on a class bulletin board so that your classmates can read it. If you like, add your journal entry to a collection of your classmates' entries entitled *The Most Challenging Days of Our Lives*.

Evaluating Your Work

Think Back About the Big Questions

Think about the Big Questions on pages 10-11. Discuss your thoughts with a partner, especially your thoughts about questions that still seem hard to answer. Compare your ideas now with your ideas when you started this unit. Record your current thoughts in your journal.

Think Back About Your Work

Now think about the whole unit. What did you do? How did you do? To evaluate your work, including your reading, your writing, your activities, and your project, write a note to your teacher. Explain what you've done during this unit and what you've learned. Use the following questions to help you write your note.

- Which literature selections in this unit did you like the most? Why?

- What was your favorite activity in this unit? Why?

- What was your least favorite activity? Why?

- If you were to do your project again, what parts would you do the same way? What parts would you do differently?

- What did you learn as you worked on your project or projects?

- What have you learned in this unit about survival?

- How would you rate your work in this unit? Use the following scale and give at least three reasons for your rating.

  1 = Outstanding   3 = Fair
  2 = Good   4 = Not as good as it could have been

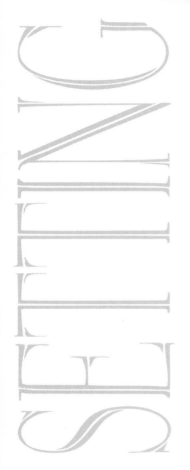

What Is Setting?

Setting is the time and place in which the action of a story or a poem occurs. The setting may be described at the beginning of the story, or it may be presented through details that appear as the story unfolds. Many of the literature selections in this unit are about human survival in a hostile or dangerous setting. In "To Build a Fire," for example, the setting is described in great detail as it poses a threat to the main character's existence: "The Yukon lay a mile wide and hidden under three feet of ice. On top of this ice were as many feet of snow. It was all pure white, rolling in gentle undulations where the ice-jams of the freeze-up had formed. North and south, as far as his eye could see, it was unbroken white . . ." In this case, the setting is described so well that the reader can almost see and feel this frozen world.

Write a Letter   Look through the literature selections you've read to find a setting that presented some kind of threat. Then imagine you've taken the place of the main character. Write a letter home, describing your situation and your setting. Make sure that you also explain how you intend to survive in this hostile environment.

Your Own Survival Story   Have you ever been caught in a thunderstorm or felt threatened by your surroundings? Write a survival story based on your experience. You may exaggerate some of the details to create a sense of danger, but make sure you describe your setting thoroughly.

What Is Character?

A **character** is a person or an animal that participates in the action of a work of literature. A good writer will allow each character's personality to express itself through his or her thoughts, words, and actions. We can also learn a lot about a character from the way he or she reacts to events. In many of the literature selections in this unit, for example, the main character's struggle for survival reveals many aspects of the character's personality. In *Pandora's Box*, for example, we learn a lot about Dorie Carson from the way she reacts to the terrible suffering around her: "The woman closes her eyes. There is a wall inside her too. The whole time she was in Vietnam, she did not cry. She was afraid that if she started, she wouldn't be able to stop." Throughout the play, Dorie's courage and compassion are expressed through her thoughts, words, and actions.

Compare Survivors Look through the literature selections you've read. Does the main character in each selection react to his or her situation in the same way? Write a short essay comparing how the main characters manage to survive in two selections you've read.

Write a Survival Story Look through a newspaper for reports of natural disasters, such as floods or earthquakes. Then write a story about a character who has survived such a catastrophe. Use details from the news report in your story, and be sure to reveal the character's personality as he or she struggles for survival.

GLOSSARY OF LITERARY TERMS

A

alliteration Repetition of the first sound—usually a consonant sound—in several words of a sentence or a line of poetry.

allusion An author's indirect reference to someone or something that is presumed to be familiar to the reader.

anecdote A short narrative about an interesting or a humorous event, usually in the life of a person.

antagonist The person or force opposing the protagonist, or main character in a literary work. [See also *protagonist*.]

autobiography A person's written account of his or her own life.

B

ballad A poem, often a song, that tells a story in simple verse.

biography An account of a person's life, written by another person.

blank verse Unrhymed poetry.

C

character A person or an animal that participates in the action of a work of literature. A *dynamic character* is one whose thoughts, feelings, and actions are changeable and lifelike; a *static character* always remains the same. [See also *protagonist, antagonist*.]

characterization The creation of characters through the characters' use of language and through descriptions of their appearance, thoughts, emotions, and actions. [See also *character*.]

chronology An arrangement of events in the order in which they happen.

cliché An overused expression that is trite rather than meaningful.

climax The highest point of tension in the plot of a work of literature. [See also *plot*.]

comedy An amusing play that has a happy ending.

conclusion The final part or ending of a piece of literature.

concrete poem A poem arranged on the page so that its punctuation, letters, and lines make the shape of the subject of the poem.

conflict A problem that confronts the characters in a piece of literature. The conflict may be *internal* (a character's struggle within himself or herself) or *external* (a character's struggle against nature, another person, or society). [See also *plot*.]

context The general sense of words that helps readers to understand the meaning of unfamiliar words and phrases in a piece of writing.

D

description An author's use of words to give the reader or listener a mental picture, an impression, or an understanding of a person, place, thing, event, or idea.

dialect A form of speech spoken by people in a particular group or geographical region that differs in vocabulary, grammar, and pronunciation from the standard language.

dialogue The spoken words and conversation of characters in a work of literature.

drama A play that is performed before an audience according to stage directions and using dialogue. Classical drama has two genres: *tragedy* and *comedy*. Modern drama includes *melodrama, satire, theater of the absurd*, and *pantomime*. [See also *comedy, play*, and *tragedy*.]

dramatic poetry A play written in the form of poetry.

E

epic A long narrative poem—written in a formal style and meant to be read aloud—that relates the adventures and

experiences of one or more great heroes or heroines.

essay   Personal nonfiction writing about a particular subject that is important to the writer.

excerpt   A passage from a larger work that has been taken out of its context to be used for a special purpose.

exposition   Writing that explains, analyzes, or defines.

extended metaphor   An elaborately drawn out metaphor. [See also *metaphor*.]

F

fable   A short, simple story whose purpose is to teach a lesson, usually with animal characters who talk and act like people.

fantasy   Imaginative fiction about unrealistic characters, places, and events.

fiction   Literature, including the short story and the novel, that tells about imaginary people and events.

figurative language
Language used to express ideas through figures of speech: descriptions that aren't meant to be taken literally. Types of figurative language include *simile*, *metaphor*, *extended metaphor*, *hyperbole*, and *personification*.

figure of speech   A type of figurative language, not meant to be taken literally, that expresses something in such a way that it brings the thing to life in the reader's or listener's imagination. [See also *figurative language*.]

flashback   A break in a story's action that relates a past happening in order to give the reader background information about a present action in the story.

folktale   A story that has been passed along from storyteller to storyteller for generations. Kinds of folktales include *tall tales*, *fairy tales*, *fables*, *legends*, and *myths*.

foreshadowing   The use of clues to create suspense by giving the reader or audience hints of events to come.

free verse   Poetry that has no formal rhyme scheme or metrical pattern.

 G

genre   A major category of art. The three major literary genres are poetry, prose, and drama.

H

haiku   A three-line Japanese verse form. In most haiku, the first and third lines have five syllables, while the second line has seven. The

traditional haiku describes a complicated feeling or thought in simple language through a single image.

hero/heroine   The main character in a work of literature. In heroic literature, the hero or heroine is a particularly brave, noble, or clever person whose achievements are unusual and important. [See also *character*.]

heroic age   The historical period in western civilization—from about 800 B.C. through A.D. 200—during which most works of heroic literature, such as myths and epics, were created in ancient Greece and Rome.

hubris   Arrogance or excessive pride leading to mistakes; the character flaw in a hero of classical tragedy.

hyperbole   An obvious exaggeration used for emphasis. [See also *figurative language*.]

I

idiom   An expression whose meaning cannot be understood from the ordinary meaning of the words. For example, *It's raining cats and dogs*.

imagery   The words and phrases in writing that appeal to the senses of sight, hearing, taste, touch, and smell.

irony An effect created by a sharp contrast between what is expected and what is real. An *ironic twist* in a plot is an event that is the complete opposite of what the characters have been hoping or expecting will happen. An *ironic statement* declares the opposite of the speaker's literal meaning.

J

jargon Words and phrases used by a group of people who share the same profession or special interests in order to refer to technical things or processes with which they are familiar. In general, jargon is any terminology that sounds unclear, overused, or pretentious.

L

legend A famous folktale about heroic actions, passed along by word of mouth from generation to generation. The legend may have begun as a factual account of real people and events but has become mostly or completely fictitious.

limerick A form of light verse, or humorous poetry, written in one five-line stanza with a regular scheme of rhyme and meter.

literature The branch of art that is expressed in written language and includes all written genres.

lyric poem A short poem that expresses personal feelings and thoughts in a musical way. Originally, lyrics were the words of songs that were sung to music played on the lyre, a stringed instrument invented by the ancient Greeks.

M

metamorphosis The transformation of one thing, or being, into another completely different thing or being, such as a caterpillar's change into a butterfly.

metaphor Figurative language in which one thing is said to be another thing. [See also *figurative language*.]

meter The pattern of rhythm in lines of poetry. The most common meter, in poetry written in English, is iambic pentameter, that is, a verse having five metrical feet, each foot of verse having two syllables, an unaccented one followed by an accented one.

mood The feeling or atmosphere that a reader senses while reading or listening to a work of literature.

motivation A character's reasons for doing, thinking, feeling, or saying something. Sometimes an author will make a character's motivation obvious from the beginning. In realistic fiction and drama, however, a character's motivation may be so complicated that the reader discovers it gradually, by studying the character's thoughts, feelings, and behavior.

myth A story, passed along by word of mouth for generations, about the actions of gods and goddesses or superhuman heroes and heroines. Most myths were first told to explain the origins of natural things or to justify the social rules and customs of a particular society.

N

narration The process of telling a story. For both fiction and nonfiction, there are two main kinds of narration, based on whether the story is told from a first-person or third-person point of view. [See also *point of view.*]

narrative poem A poem that tells a story containing the basic literary ingredients of fiction: character, setting, and plot.

narrator The person, or voice, that tells a story. [See also *point of view, voice.*]

nonfiction Prose that is factually true and is about real people, events, and places.

nonstandard English
Versions of English, such as slang and dialects, that use pronunciation, vocabulary, idiomatic expressions, grammar, and punctuation that differ from the accepted "correct" constructions of English.

novel A long work of narrative prose fiction. A novel contains narration, a setting or settings, characters, dialogue, and a more complicated plot than a short story.

O

onomatopoeia The technique of using words that imitate the sounds they describe, such as *hiss*, *buzz*, and *splash*.

oral tradition Stories, poems, and songs that have been kept alive by being told, recited, and sung by people over many generations. Since the works were not originally written, they often have many different versions.

P

parable A brief story—similar to a fable, but about people— that describes an ordinary situation and concludes with a short moral or lesson to be learned.

personification Figurative language in which an animal, an object, or an idea is given human characteristics. [See also *figurative language*.]

persuasion A type of speech or writing whose purpose is to convince people that something is true or important.

play A work of dramatic literature written for performance by actors before an audience. In classical or traditional drama, a play is divided into five acts, each containing a number of scenes. Each act represents a distinct phase in the development of the plot. Modern plays often have only one act and one scene.

playwright The author of a play.

plot The sequence of actions and events in fiction or drama. A traditional plot has at least three parts: the *rising action*, leading up to a turning point that affects the main character; the *climax*, the turning point or moment of greatest intensity or interest; and the *falling action*, leading away from the conflict, or resolving it.

poetry Language selected and arranged in order to say something in a compressed or nonliteral way. Modern poetry may or may not use many of the traditional poetic techniques that include *meter*, *rhyme*, *alliteration*, *figurative language*, *symbolism*, and *specific verse forms*.

point of view The perspective from which a writer tells a story. *First-person* narrators tell the story from their own point of view, using pronouns such as *I* or *me*. *Third-person* narrators, using pronouns such as *he*, *she*, or *them*, may be *omniscient* (knowing everything about all characters), or *limited* (taking the point of view of one character). [See also *narration*.]

propaganda Information or ideas that may or may not be true, but are spread as though they are true, in order to persuade people to do or believe something.

prose The ordinary form of written and spoken language used to create fiction, nonfiction, and most drama.

protagonist The main character of a literary work. [See also *character* and *characterization*.]

R

refrain A line or group of lines that is repeated, usually at the end of each verse, in a poem or a song.

repetition The use of the same formal element more than once in a literary work, for emphasis or in order to achieve another desired effect.

resolution The falling action in fiction or drama,

including all of the developments that follow the climax and show that the story's conflict is over. [See also *plot*.]

rhyme scheme   A repeated pattern of similar sounds, usually found at the ends of lines of poetry or poetic drama.

rhythm   In poetry, the measured recurrence of accented and unaccented syllables in a particular pattern. [See also *meter*.]

S

scene   The time, place, and circumstances of a play or a story. In a play, a scene is a section of an act. [See also *play*.]

science fiction   Fantasy literature set in an imaginary future, with details and situations that are designed to seem scientifically possible.

setting   The time and place of a work of literature.

short story   Narrative prose fiction that is shorter and has a less complicated plot than a novel. A short story contains narration, at least one setting, at least one character, and usually some dialogue.

simile   Figurative language that compares two unlike things, introduced by the words "like" or "as." [See also *figurative language*.]

soliloquy   In a play, a short speech spoken by a single character when he or she is alone on the stage. A soliloquy usually expresses the character's innermost thoughts and feelings, when he or she thinks no other characters can hear.

sonnet   A poem written in one stanza, using fourteen lines of iambic pentameter. [See also *meter*.]

speaker   In poetry, the individual whose voice seems to be speaking the lines. [See also *narration*, *voice*.]

stage directions   The directions, written by the playwright, to tell the director, actors, and theater technicians how a play should be dramatized. Stage directions may specify such things as how the setting should appear in each scene, how the actors should deliver their lines, when the stage curtain should rise and fall, how stage lights should be used, where on the stage the actors should be during the action, and when sound effects should be used.

stanza   A group of lines in poetry set apart by blank lines before and after the group; a poetic verse.

style   The distinctive way in which an author composes a work of literature in written or spoken language.

suspense   An effect created by authors of various types of fiction and drama, especially adventure and mystery, to heighten interest in the story.

symbol   An image, person, place, or thing that is used to express the idea of something else.

T

tall tale   A kind of folk tale, or legend, that exaggerates the characteristics of its hero or heroine.

theme   The main idea or underlying subject of a work of literature.

tone   The attitude that a work of literature expresses to the reader through its style.

tragedy   In classical drama, a tragedy depicts a noble hero or heroine who makes a mistake of judgment that has disastrous consequences.

V

verse   A stanza in a poem. Also, a synonym for poetry as a genre. [See also *stanza*.]

voice   The narrator or the person who relates the action of a piece of literature. [See also *speaker*.]

ACKNOWLEDGMENTS

Grateful acknowledgment is made for permission to reprint the following copyrighted material.

From *Hatchet* by Gary Paulsen. Reprinted with the permission of Bradbury Press, an Affiliate of Macmillan, Inc. Copyright © 1987 by Gary Paulsen.

"Staying Alive" by David Wagoner from *Staying Alive* by David Wagoner is used by permission of the author.

From *Mississippi Solo* by Eddy Harris. Copyright © 1988 by Eddy L. Harris. By permission of Lyons & Burford, Publishers.

"I, Hungry Hanna Cassandra Glen..." by Norma Fox Mazer, copyright © 1984 by Norma Fox Mazer from *Sixteen: Short Stories by Outstanding Writers for Young Adults* by Donald R. Gallo, ed. Used by permission of Dell Books, a division of Bantam Doubleday Dell Publishing Group, Inc.

"In Response to Executive Order 9066" by Dwight Okita, copyright © 1992 by Dwight Okita from his book *Crossing With the Light* (Tia Chucha Press, Chicago)

"La Bamba" by Gary Soto from *Baseball in April and Other Stories*, copyright © 1990 by Gary Soto is reprinted with permission of Harcourt Brace & Company.

"Life Doesn't Frighten Me" from *And Still I Rise* by Maya Angelou. Copyright © 1978 by Maya Angelou. Reprinted by permission of Random House.

Pandora's Box by Catherine Gourley from READ® Magazine, October 1992. Special reprint permission granted by READ® Magazine, published by Weekly Reader Corporation. Copyright © 1992 by Weekly Reader Corporation. All rights reserved.

Activity on pages 8 and 9 adopted from *Joining Together: Group Theory and Group Skills* by David W. Johnson and Frank P. Johnson, Prentice Hall, 1982.

ILLUSTRATION

34-35 Calligraphy by Colleen; **72-79** Fran O'Neill.

PHOTOGRAPHY

4 *l* Sarah Putnam/©D.C. Heath; *r* Harvey Lloyd/The Stock Market; **5** ©M.C. Escher Foundation-Baarn-Holland. All rights reserved; **6** *t* The National Museum of Women in the Arts. Gift of Wallace and Wilhelmina Holladay; *b* Skjold/The Image Works; **10** *t, b* Sarah Putnam/©D.C. Heath; **11** *t* John Owens/©D.C. Heath; *c* Jim Whitmer/Stock Boston; *b* Julie Bidwell/©D.C. Heath; **12-13** Barrie Rokeach; **13** *inset,* **14-15** Bob Daemmrich/The Image Works; **16-17** Jeff Hunter/The Image Bank; **18-21** Bob Daemmrich/The Image Works; **21** Courtesy of Penguin USA; **22** ©1950 M.C. Escher Foundation-Baarn-Holland. All rights reserved; **25** ©1952 M.C. Escher Foundation-Baarn-Holland. All rights reserved; **26** ©1948 M.C. Escher Foundation-Baarn-Holland. All rights reserved; **27** Courtesy of Indiana University Press; **28-31** *background* William H. Mullins/Photo Researchers, Inc.; **31** *inset* Tom Branch/Photo Researchers, Inc.; **32-33** *background* William H. Mullins/Photo Researchers, Inc.; **33** *inset* Photo by Mark Katzman/Ferguson & Katzman; **34-35, 37** *detail* NAA Thomas C. Woods Mem. Coll., 1962. N-138, Sheldon Memorial Art Gallery, University of Nebraska, Lincoln, 1962. N-138; **40, 43** *detail* **44** *detail* Erich Lessing/Art Resource, NY; **46** Crocker Art Museum, Sacramento, CA. Gift of Philip L. Elhert in memory of Dorothy Evelyn Elhert. ©1961 Paul LeBaron Thiebaud; **47** Courtesy of William Morrow & Company, Inc.; **69** AP/Wide World Photos; **70** Library of Congress; **71** Courtesy of Dwight Okita; **79** Photo by Carolyn Soto. Courtesy of Harcourt Brace and Company; **80-81, 82, 83** *details* The National Museum of Women in the Arts. Gift of Wallace and Wilhemina Holladay; **83** Courtesy of Lordly & Dame, Inc.; **84** Dirck Halstead/Gamma Liaison; **84-85** *background* Robert Ellison/Black Star; **88-89** Bruce Allen/Black Star; **89** Marc Riboud/Magnum Photos; **94** Bruno Barbey/Magnum Photos; **95, 100** *l* Philip Jones Griffiths/Magnum; **100** *r* Joel Gordon/Black Star; **101** *l* Courtesy of Catherine Gourley/Weekly Reader Corp.; *r* Bruno Barbey/Magnum Photos; **105** Nancy Sheehan/©D.C. Heath; **106** *t* Elizabeth Hamlin/Stock Boston; *b* Edi Ann Otto; **108** J. Messerschmidt/Leo de Wys, Inc.; **112** *t* Jean-Claude Lejeune/Stock Boston; *c, b,* **113** Ken O'Donoghue/©D.C. Heath; **114** ©J. Sulley/The Image Works; **115** ©1993 Mort Gerberg and the Cartoon Bank, Inc.

Back cover *t* Skjold/The Image Works; *c* John Owens/©D.C. Heath; *b* Sarah Putnam/©D.C. Heath.

Full Pronunciation Key for Footnoted Words

(Each pronunciation and definition is adapted from *Scott, Foresman Advanced Dictionary* by E.L. Thorndike and Clarence L. Barnhart.)

The pronunciation of each footnoted word is shown just after the word, in this way: **abbreviate** [ə brē′ vē āt]. The letters and signs used are pronounced as in the words below. The mark ′ is placed after a syllable with primary or heavy accent, as in the example above. The mark ′ after a syllable shows a secondary or lighter accent, as in **abbreviation** [ə brē′ vē ā′ shən].

Some words, taken from foreign languages, are spoken with sounds that do not otherwise occur in English. Symbols for these sounds are given in the key as "foreign sounds."

a	hat, cap	j	jam, enjoy	u	cup, butter	**foreign sounds**	
ā	age, face	k	kind, seek	u̇	full, put		
ä	father, far	l	land, coal	ü	rule, move	Y as in French *du*. Pronounce (ē) with the lips rounded as for (ü).	
b	bad, rob	m	me, am	v	very, save		
ch	child, much	n	no, in	w	will, woman	à as in French *ami*. Pronounce (ä) with the lips spread and held tense.	
d	did, red	ng	long, bring	y	young, yet		
				z	zero, breeze		
e	let, best	o	hot, rock	zh	measure, seizure	œ as in French *peu*. Pronounce (ā) with the lips rounded as for (ō).	
ē	equal, be	ō	open, go				
ėr	term, learn	ô	order, all	ə represents:		N as in French *bon*. The N is not pronounced, but shows that the vowel before it is nasal.	
		oi	oil, voice		a in about		
f	fat, if	ou	house, out		e in taken		
g	go, bag				i in pencil		
h	he, how	p	paper, cup		o in lemon	H as in German *ach*. Pronounce (k) without closing the breath passage.	
		r	run, try		u in circus		
i	it, pin	s	say, yes				
ī	ice, five	sh	she, rush				
		t	tell, it				
		th	thin, both				
		ᴛʜ	then, smooth				

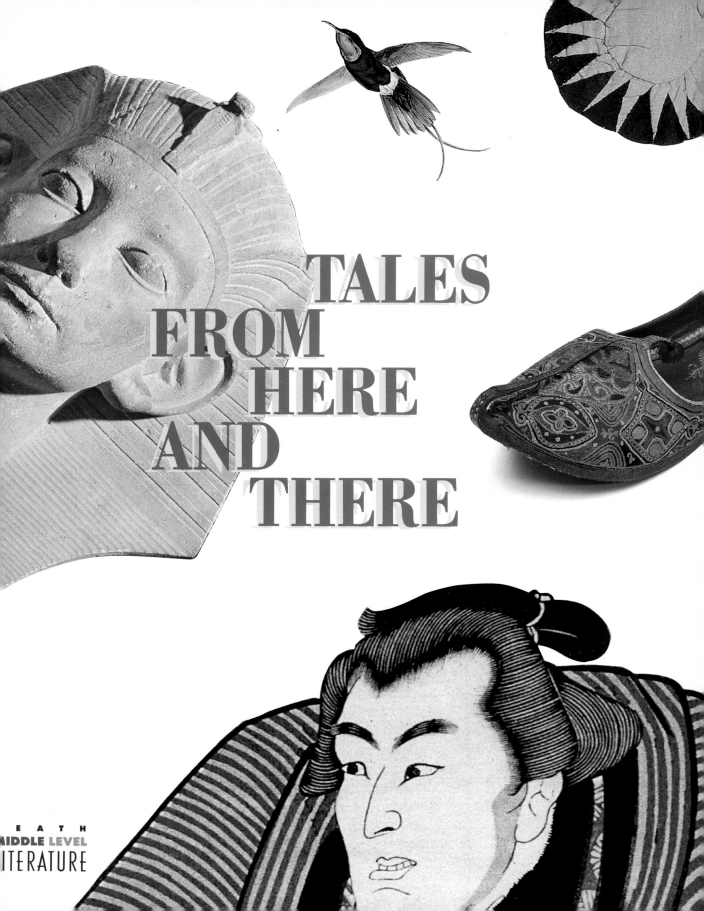

TALES FROM HERE AND THERE

H E A T H
MIDDLELEVEL
LITERATURE

Tales from Here and There

T H E M E
MYTHS, LEGENDS, AND FOLKTALES

A U T H O R S

Donna Alvermann
Linda Miller Cleary
Kenneth Donelson
Donald Gallo
Alice Haskins
J. Howard Johnston
John Lounsbury
Alleen Pace Nilsen
Robert Pavlik
Jewell Parker Rhodes
Alberto Alvaro Ríos
Sandra Schurr
Lyndon Searfoss
Julia Thomason
Max Thompson
Carl Zon

D.C. Heath and Company
Lexington, Massachusetts / Toronto, Ontario

927

Middle Level Authors

Donna Alvermann, University of Georgia
Alice Haskins, Howard County Public Schools, Maryland
J. Howard Johnston, University of South Florida
John Lounsbury, Georgia College
Sandra Schurr, University of South Florida
Julia Thomason, Appalachian State University
Max Thompson, Appalachian State University
Carl Zon, California Assessment Collaborative

Literature and Language Arts Authors

Linda Miller Cleary, University of Minnesota
Kenneth Donelson, Arizona State University
Donald Gallo, Central Connecticut State University
Alleen Pace Nilsen, Arizona State University
Robert Pavlik, Cardinal Stritch College, Milwaukee
Jewell Parker Rhodes, Arizona State University
Alberto Alvaro Ríos, Arizona State University
Lyndon Searfoss, Arizona State University

Teacher Consultants

Suzanne Aubin, Patapsco Middle School, Ellicott City, Maryland
Judy Baxter, Newport News Public Schools, Newport News, Virginia
Saundra Bryn, Director of Research and Development, El Mirage, Arizona
Lorraine Gerhart, Elmbrook Middle School, Elm Grove, Wisconsin
Kathy Tuchman Glass, Burlingame Intermediate School, Burlingame, California
Lisa Mandelbaum, Crocker Middle School, Hillsborough, California
Lucretia Pannozzo, John Jay Middle School, Katonah, New York
Carol Schultz, Jerling Junior High, Orland Park, Illinois
Jeanne Siebenman, Grand Canyon University, Phoenix, Arizona
Gail Thompson, Garey High School, Pomona, California
Rufus Thompson, Grace Yokley School, Ontario, California
Tom Tufts, Conniston Middle School, West Palm Beach, Florida
Edna Turner, Harpers Choice Middle School, Columbia, Maryland
C. Anne Webb, Buerkle Junior High School, St. Louis, Missouri
Geri Yaccino, Thompson Junior High School, St. Charles, Illinois

CONTENTS

Garden of the Mustard Seed Anonymous, China

ASKING BIG QUESTIONS ABOUT THE LITERATURE

PROJECTS

1 WRITING WORKSHOP

WRITING A STORY   108-113

Create and tell a children's story.

2 COOPERATIVE LEARNING

DRAMATIZING A STORY   114-115

Bring a tale to life by turning it into a play.

3 HELPING YOUR COMMUNITY

**HOLDING A STORYTELLING FESTIVAL
116-117**

Collect tales to share in a storytelling festival.

Myths for MODERNS

Can you identify the scenes on these pages? The pictures illustrate some of the most famous and best-loved folktales and myths of all time. Although they were first told hundreds of years ago, they continue to delight people of all ages . . . even today.

Select a tale.

With a group, select one of the stories pictured here or choose another folktale or myth. Then list the events of the plot and the details of the setting. Try not to leave anything out, even if it seems unimportant.

Modernize the tale.

Now modernize your story. Review your list of events and decide what details you could change to modernize the story. Could Cinderella ride in a stretch limo instead of a carriage? Could she lose her shoe outside the homecoming dance instead of her slipper at a ball?

Tell the tale.

Decide on how you want to present your Myth for Moderns. If you present it as a short story, one person could read the tale aloud with appropriate voice changes for all the different characters. If you present it as a short play, let group members choose their roles.

Class discussion.

After your presentation, hold a class discussion. Compare traditional and modern versions of the stories. Talk about how the time changes affect the story. Use these questions to guide your discussion.

- What can traditional tales tell you about life in the old days? How does this differ from the picture of modern life that you've created in your version?
- Which version works better? Why?
- What lessons do these stories teach?

Asking Big Questions
About the Theme

How are tales from around the world alike and different?

On the chalkboard, make a list of as many folktales and myths as you can think of. Group the stories into pairs. Beside each pair, make a diagram like the one here.

Then let members of the class take turns telling each story. After each pair of stories has been told, compare the tales in a class discussion. As you are discussing the stories, fill in the appropriate diagram, showing how the tales are alike and how they are different.

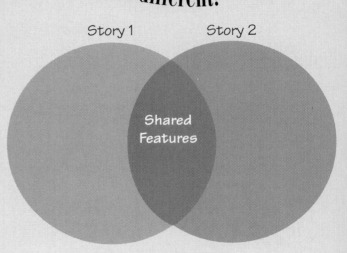

Story 1

Story 2

Shared Features

Why do people everywhere have myths and folktales?

Did you know that "Cinderella" was originally an Italian story, while "Snow White" was German? Why do people everywhere have tales like these? Are these stories simply to entertain children, or do they teach us important truths about life and death? Hold a discussion about why myths and folktales are important to people everywhere.

Why is it important for each generation to retell these tales?

Form groups of five or six students. Then draw a family tree of the members of your group like the one below. Write the name of each person in a different box to represent each generation. Then let the person whose name is at the top of the tree write a short story of no more than five or six sentences on a sheet of paper. The writer should then whisper the story to the person who represents the next generation. Take turns "handing down" this story in a whisper to only one person at a time. Let the person who represents the most recent generation write the story on a sheet of paper. Now compare the first with the most recent version of the story. What features of the original survived?

Then, in your journal, write a short essay explaining why you think myths and folktales should be passed down from generation to generation.

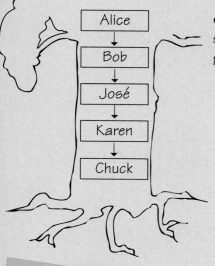

Alice
↓
Bob
↓
José
↓
Karen
↓
Chuck

NOW Think!

With one or more classmates, think of other questions about myths and folktales. Write them in your journal. Ask yourself these questions as you work through this unit. Watch how your original ideas about myths and legends grow and change.

DIRECTION

ALONZO LOPEZ

I was directed by my grandfather
To the East,
    so I might have the power of the bear;
To the South,
    so I might have the courage of the eagle;   5
To the West,
    so I might have the wisdom of the owl;
To the North,
    so I might have the craftiness of the fox;
To the Earth,   10
    so I might receive her fruit;
To the Sky,
    so I might lead a life of innocence.

ALONZO LOPEZ

Alonzo Lopez was born in 1947 in Crowhang Village, Arizona, and attended public school in Sells, Arizona, until the ninth grade. His high school years were spent studying at the Institute of American Indian Arts in Santa Fe, New Mexico. He graduated in 1967 and went east to college in Connecticut—first at Yale University and then at Wesleyan.

A second poem by Lopez, "I Go Forth to Move About the Earth," is a good companion to the poem "Direction." Both poems are found in Lopez's collection of poems, *The Whispering Wind*.

THE STORYTELLING

JOSEPH BRUCHAC

Long ago, the people had no stories to tell. It was hard for them to live without stories, especially during the long winter nights when the snow was deep outside the lodge and the people longed for something to give meaning to their lives.

"If only there were something we could listen to," the people would say. But there were no storytellers and no stories to be told.

In those days, in a certain village, there was a boy whose parents had died and whose other relatives would not care for him. This boy's name was Gah-ka, which means Crow. He lived by himself in a small lodge he made of branches. Among his few possessions

STONE

were a bow and some arrows which his father had made for him. Because he had to take care of himself, he became a very good hunter. He also carried a small tobacco pouch which his mother had made, telling him that it was good to make an offering of some tobacco to thank the animal's spirit whenever he was successful in hunting.

The people in that village did not treat Gah-ka well. They made fun of him and laughed at his ragged clothes. Finally, one autumn, Gah-ka decided to leave the village and find a better place to live. He traveled for many days. He walked and walked until he came to a place where a large stone stood. It looked like a good place to camp. He made a fire and sat in front of it, thinking about his life and wishing that he had something to offer his people, something which would lead them to respect him

It was dark now and Gah-ka felt lonely. He leaned back against the large stone and spoke.

"If only I had something interesting to hear," he said.

"Give me tobacco and I will tell you something," a deep voice said. It sounded as if it came out of the earth itself. Gah-ka looked around and could see no one.

"What will you tell me?" Gah-ka said.

"Give me tobacco and I will tell you something," the voice repeated.

Then Gah-ka realized that the voice was coming from the great standing stone. He reached into his pouch and placed some tobacco at the base of the stone.

"Speak, Grandfather," Gah-ka said.

"I will now tell a story," said the big standing stone. Then it began to relate a tale. It was a story of the creation of the earth itself, of the woman who fell from the sky and the animals and birds who helped her. Gah-ka listened to the story. It was the most wonderful thing Gah-ka had ever heard. He listened hard, trying to remember every detail. At last the story was over. Gah-ka waited and the voice spoke again.

"When a story has been told," the great stone said, "it will be the

custom to give the storyteller a small gift."

Gah-ka pulled some beads from the deerskin fringe on his old, worn jacket and placed them at the base of the stone.

"Here, Grandfather. Thank you for the story."

"From now on," the great stone said, "when one announces that they will tell a story, you must say *Nyo!* And when the storyteller says *Ho!* at any time in the story, you must

answer *Hey!* to show you are listening. I will now tell a story."

"Nyo!" Gah-ka said. Then the great stone began to relate a tale of the animal people and how the Bear's tail came to be short. Each time the stone said *Ho!* Gah-ka was quick to answer *Hey!* As before, Gah-ka listened closely, trying to remember every word of the story. Too soon, the story was ended and the great stone was silent. Then it spoke again.

"This is as long as my stories will go on this night."

Gah-ka was sorry to have the stories end, but he placed a few more beads at the base of the great stone.

"Thank you, Grandfather," he said. Then he went to sleep, trying to hold every word of the stories in his mind. When he woke the next day, he wondered if he had dreamed. But the bone beads were gone and he found that he still remembered the stories. He had eaten all of his food, so he took up his bow and arrows and went hunting. As always, his luck was good and he managed to shoot several birds. As he circled back toward his camp by the big stone, he came across a village. Some of the people in the village welcomed him and asked him to sit by the fire with them. As they sat there, Gah-ka thought of the stories.

"Would you like to hear something?" he said.

"Nyo!" the people said.

"Give me some tobacco and I will tell you the story of how the Earth came to be. Each time I say *Ho!* you must answer me by saying *Hey!*"

The people did as he said. They listened closely and answered each time he said *Ho!* Before the end of his tale, everyone in the village was gathered around to listen. When the story was done, they all gave him presents. They asked him for another tale, offering him more tobacco.

"I shall tell of how the Bear lost his tail," Gah-ka said. "Do you want to hear this story?"

"Nyo!" the people said.

When Gah-ka was done, the people begged for another story.

"No," Gah-ka said. "That is the length of my stories for this evening. I must return to my lodge." Then, after promising the people he would return again the next night, Gah-ka went back to his camp by the big standing stone, carrying his presents with him. He placed tobacco on the ground and spoke.

"Grandfather, I am ready to listen again."

"I shall now tell a story," said the deep voice of the big stone.

So it went on for a long time. Each evening Gah-ka would share the stories with his new friends and each night the big standing stone would tell new stories to the boy. Sometimes people from the village would follow Gah-ka back to his camp and see him sitting in front of his fire listening, but they could hear nothing. The voice from the big stone was for Gah-ka alone to hear.

One evening, after finishing his storytelling, a girl of about Gah-ka's age approached him. She handed him a decorated pouch.

"You have many stories," she said. "Perhaps you can use this pouch in which to keep them."

Gah-ka thanked the girl and took the pouch with him. From then on, each time he learned a new story, he would put something in the pouch which would help him remember that tale. A blue jay feather reminded him of the story of how the Birds got their clothing. A small wooden Turtle reminded him of the tale of Turtle's race with Bear. As the days and weeks passed, the pouch became filled with stories.

Each time Gah-ka went to the village, he saw that girl who gave him the pouch. They became good friends and finally the girl brought him to her house. As soon as he walked through the door, the girl's mother looked up at them and smiled.

"I see that my future son-in-law has finally come through my door."

The next day, the girl came to Gah-ka's camp carrying a basket of bread. "I have brought you this because my mother agrees that we should ask you to marry me."

Gah-ka took the bread and ate it and he and the girl were married. Now the two of them lived together in his lodge near the big stone. They lived well there because Gah-ka was such a good hunter and because he had been given so many useful things by the people of the village to thank him for his stories. All through the winter he listened to stories until it was time for spring. Then the big stone spoke.

"The time for stories has ended. Now the earth is waking up and the stories must sleep. After the first frost, I will tell more stories." The next day, Gah-ka told the same thing to the people of the village.

Gah-ka and his wife spent a happy spring and summer together. They planted corn and beans and squash and took a part in the life of the village. When the first frost came, the storytelling stone began once again to share its tales of the old days with Gah-ka, who was now a young man and no longer a boy.

So it went on for a long time. Finally, one day, the stone ended a story and was silent for a long time. Then it spoke one last time.

"Now I shall tell no more stories. I have told you all of the stories from the old time. From now on, the stories will be carried by the people, not kept in the stones. You, Gah-ka, are the first storyteller, but there will be many storytellers after you. Wherever they go, they will always be welcomed.

And from that time on, that is the way it has been.

JOSEPH BRUCHAC

Joseph Bruchac III was born in 1942 in Saratoga Springs, New York. He is part Native American, and most of his writing comes from that background.

Bruchac attended college and went to Ghana, West Africa, to teach at the Keta School. "Much of my writing and my life relates to the problem of being an American," he has written. "...I went to Africa to teach—but more than that to be taught." The most important lesson Bruchac learned is "how human people are everywhere." As a writer, Bruchac points out that his purpose is "not to be a man apart, but to share."

Bruchac has written poetry, novels, nonfiction, and folktales. "The Storytelling Stone" is part of a collection of northeastern Native American tales called *Return of the Sun*. You can also look up Bruchac's books of Iroquois tales, *Turkey Brother* and *Stone Giants*.

ALL STORIES ARE ANANSI'S

HAROLD COURLANDER

In the beginning, all tales and stories belonged to Nyame,[1] the Sky God. But Kwaku[2] Anansi, the spider, yearned to be the owner of all the stories known in the world, and he went to Nyame and offered to buy them.

The Sky God said: "I am willing to sell the stories, but the price is high. Many people have come to me offering to buy, but the price was too high for them. Rich and powerful families have not been able to pay. Do you think you can do it?"

Anansi replied to the Sky God: "I can do it. What is the price?"

"My price is three things," the Sky God said. "I must first have Mmoboro,[3] the hornets. I must then have Onini,[4] the great python. I must then have Osebo,[5] the leopard. For these things I will sell you the right to tell all stories."

Anansi said: "I will bring them."

He went home and made his plans. He first cut a gourd[6] from a vine and made a small hole in it. He

---

1. **Nyame** [nē ä′ mē]
2. **Kwaku** [kwä′ kü]
3. **Mmoboro** [mō bô′ rō]
4. **Onini** [ō nē′ nē]
5. **Osebo** [ō sē′ bō]
6. **gourd** [gôrd]: a fleshy fruit often hollowed into a bowl or cup.

Linguist staff c. 1950, carved wood with gold leaf, Ghana

took a large calabash[7] and filled it with water. He went to the tree where the hornets lived. He poured some of the water over himself, so that he was dripping. He threw some water over the hornets, so that they too were dripping. Then he put the calabash on his head, as though to protect himself from a storm, and called out to the hornets: "Are you foolish people? Why do you stay in the rain that is falling?"

The hornets answered: "Where shall we go?"

"Go here, in this dry gourd," Anansi told them.

The hornets thanked him and flew into the gourd through the small hole. When the last of them had entered, Anansi plugged the hole with a ball of grass, saying: "Oh, yes, but you are really foolish people!"

He took his gourd full of hornets to Nyame, the Sky God. The Sky God accepted them. He said: "There are two more things."

Anansi returned to the forest and cut a long bamboo pole and some strong vines. Then he walked toward the house of Onini, the python, talking to himself. He said: "My wife is stupid. I say he is longer and stronger. My wife says he is shorter and weaker. I give him more respect. She gives him less respect. Is she right or am I right? I am right, he is longer. I am right, he is stronger."

When Onini, the python, heard Anansi talking to himself, he said: "Why are you arguing this way with yourself?"

The spider replied: "Ah, I have had a dispute with my wife. She says

7. **calabash** [kal′ ə bash]: a gourd-like fruit whose dried shell is used to make bottles, bowls, or instruments.

you are shorter and weaker than this bamboo pole. I say you are longer and stronger."

Onini said: "It's useless and silly to argue when you can find out the truth. Bring the pole and we will measure."

So Anansi laid the pole on the ground, and the python came and stretched himself out beside it.

"You seem a little short," Anansi said.

The python stretched further.

"A little more," Anansi said.

"I can stretch no more," Onini said.

"When you stretch at one end, you get shorter at the other end," Anansi said. "Let me tie you at the front so you don't slip."

He tied Onini's head to the pole. Then he went to the other end and tied the tail to the pole. He wrapped the vine all around Onini, until the python couldn't move.

"Onini," Anansi said, "it turns out that my wife was right and I was wrong. You are shorter than the pole and weaker. My opinion wasn't as good as my wife's. But you were even more foolish than I, and you are now my prisoner."

Anansi carried the python to Nyame, the Sky God, who said: "There is one thing more."

Osebo, the leopard, was next. Anansi went into the forest and dug a deep pit where the leopard was accustomed to walk. He covered it with small branches and leaves and put dust on it, so that it was impossible to tell where the pit was. Anansi went away and hid. When Osebo came prowling in the black of night, he stepped into the trap Anansi had prepared and fell to the bottom. Anansi heard the sound of the leopard falling, and he said: "Ah, Osebo, you are half-foolish!"

When morning came, Anansi went to the pit and saw the leopard there.

"Osebo," he asked, "what are you doing in this hole?"

"I have fallen into a trap," Osebo said. "Help me out."

"I would gladly help you," Anansi said. "But I'm sure that if I bring you out, I will have no thanks for it. You will get hungry, and later on you will be wanting to eat me and my children."

"I swear it won't happen!" Osebo said.

"Very well. Since you swear it, I will take you out," Anansi said.

He bent a tall green tree toward the ground, so that its top was over the pit, and he tied it that way. Then he tied a rope to the top of the tree and dropped the other end of it into the pit.

"Tie this to your tail," he said.

Osebo tied the rope to his tail.

"Is it well tied?" Anansi asked.

"Yes, it is well tied," the leopard said.

"In that case," Anansi said, "you are not merely half-foolish, you are all-foolish."

And he took his knife and cut the other rope, the one that held the tree bowed to the ground. The tree straightened up with a snap, pulling Osebo out of the hole. He hung in the air head downward, twisting and turning. And while he hung this way, Anansi killed him with his weapons.

Then he took the body of the leopard and carried it to Nyame, the Sky God, saying: "Here is the third thing. Now I have paid the price."

Nyame said to him: "Kwaku Anansi, great warriors and chiefs have tried, but they have been unable to do it. You have done it. Therefore, I will give you the stories. From this day onward, all stories belong to you. Whenever a man tells a story, he must acknowledge that it is Anansi's tale."

In this way Anansi, the spider, became the owner of all stories that are told. To Anansi all these tales belong.

HAROLD COURLANDER

Harold Courlander was born in 1908 in Indianapolis, Indiana. After college he became a farmer and also began writing. Over the years, his interest in folklore led him to work in Ethiopia, India, and Washington, D.C., with the radio program *Voice of America* and the United Nations. Throughout his career, Courlander has studied and gathered oral literature and music of Indonesia, Africa, and Haiti as well as early African American and Native American folklore. His many books and recordings have introduced readers and listeners to many stories and songs. Courlander has said that his aim has been to use such folk material as a bridge between other cultures and his own.

To read more of the folktales collected by Courlander, you can look up Haitian stories in *The Piece of Fire and Other Haitian Tales*, Hopi legends in *People of the Short Blue Corn*, and African stories in *The Crest and the Hide*.

In olden days, the creatures used to plow in the fields and plant their crops the same as menfolks. When the rains came, the crops were good. But one year no rain came, and there was a famine in the land. The sun boiled down like a red ball of fire. All the creeks and ditches and springs dried up. All the fruit on the trees shriveled, and there was no food and no drinking water for the creatures. It was a terrible time.

But there was one place where there was plenty of food and a spring that never ran dry. It was called the Clayton Field. And in the field stood a big pear tree, just a-hanging down with juicy pears, enough for everybody.

So the poor hungry creatures went over to the field to get something to eat and something to drink. But a great big Bengal[1] tiger lived under the pear tree, and when the creatures came nigh, he rose up and said, "Wumpf! Wumpf! I'll eat you up. I'll eat you up if you come here!" All the creatures backed off and crawled to the edge of the woods and sat there with misery in their eyes, looking at the field. They were so starved and so parched that their ribs showed through their hides and their tongues hung out of their mouths.

Now, just about that time, along came Brer Rabbit, just a-hopping and a-skipping, as if he'd never been hungry or thirsty in his life.

---

1. **Bengal** [ben gôl′]: a former province in northeast India.

William J. Faulkner

"Say, what's the matter with you creatures?" asked Brer Rabbit.

"We're hungry and thirsty and can't find any food or water—that's what's the matter with us," answered the creatures. "And we can't get into the Clayton Field because Brer Tiger said he'd eat us up if we came over there."

"That's not right," said Brer Rabbit. "It's not right for one animal to have it all and the rest to have nothing. Come here. Come close. I'm going to tell you something." And Brer Rabbit jumped up on a stump so that

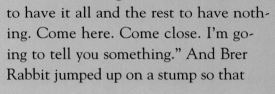

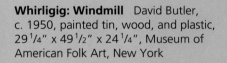

Whirligig: Windmill David Butler, c. 1950, painted tin, wood, and plastic, 29$\frac{1}{4}$" x 49$\frac{1}{2}$" x 24$\frac{1}{4}$", Museum of American Folk Art, New York

all could see him as they crowded around. When Brer Rabbit had finished whispering his plan, he said, "Now, you-all be at your posts in the morning; everyone be there before sunup."

The first animal to get to his post was Brer Bear. Before daybreak, he came toting a big club on his shoulder and took his place alongside an old hollow log. The next creature to arrive was Brer Alligator Cooter, a snapping turtle, who crawled in the hollow log. Then Brer Turkey Buzzard and Brer Eagle and all the big fowls of the air came a-sailing in and roosted in the tops of the tall trees. Next to arrive were the tree-climbing animals, like Brer Raccoon and his family and Sis Possum and all her little ones. They climbed into the low trees. Then followed the littler creatures, like Brer Squirrel, Brer Muskrat, Brer Otter, and all kinds of birds. They all took their posts and waited for Brer Rabbit.

Pretty soon, when the sun was about a half hour high, along came Brer Rabbit down the big road with a long grass rope wrapped around his shoulder. And he was just a-singing. "Oh, Lord, oh, Lord, there's a great big wind that's a-coming through the woods, and it's going to blow *all* the people off the earth!" And while he was singing his song, a powerful noise broke out in the woods.

There was Brer Bear a-beating on the hollow log with all his might, bic-a-bam, bic-a-bam, bic-a-bam, bam, bam! Inside the log Brer Cooter was a-jumping, bic-a-boom, bic-a-boom, bic-a-boom,

Skunk David Butler, c. 1975, painted tin and plastic, 6 1/2" x 16 5/8", from the collection of William A. Fagaly

Rabbit David Butler, c. 1975, painted tin and plastic, 9 1/4" x 13 1/4", from the collection of William A. Fagaly

boom, boom. Brer Turkey Buzzard, Brer Eagle, and Brer Chicken Hawk were a-flapping their wings and a-shaking the big trees, and the trees were a-bending, and the leaves were a-flying. Brer Raccoon and Sis Possum were stirring up a fuss in the low trees, while the littler creatures were a-shaking all the bushes. And on the ground and amongst the leaves the teeny-weeny creatures were a-scrambling around. All in all it sounded like a cyclone was a-coming through the woods!

All this racket so early in the morning woke Brer Tiger out of a deep sleep, and he rushed to the big road to see what was going on. "What's going on out there, huh?" he growled. "What's going on out there?"

All of the creatures were too scared to say anything to Brer Tiger. They just looked at him and hollered for Brer Rabbit to "Tie me! Please, sir, tie me!"

Now, all this time Brer Rabbit just kept a-hollering, "There's a *great* big cyclone a-coming through the woods that's going to *blow* all the people off the earth!" And the animals just kept a-making their noise and a-hollering, "Tie me, Brer Rabbit. Tie me."

When Brer Rabbit came around by Brer Tiger, Brer Tiger roared out, "Brer Rabbit, I want you to tie me. I don't want the big wind to blow *me* off the earth!"

"I don't have time to tie you, Brer Tiger. I've got to go down the road to tie those other folks to keep the wind from blowing *them* off the earth. Because it sure looks to me like a *great big hurricane* is a-coming through these woods."

Brer Tiger looked toward the woods, where Brer Bear was a-beating and Brer Cooter was a-jumping and the birds were a-flapping and the trees were a-bending and the leaves were a-flying and the bushes were a-shaking and the wind was a-blowing, and it seemed to him as if Judgment Day had come.

Old Brer Tiger was so scared he couldn't move. And then he said to Brer Rabbit, "Look-a-here, I've got my head up against this pine tree. It won't take but a minute to tie me to it. Please tie me, Brer Rabbit. Tie me, because I don't want the wind to blow me off the face of the earth."

Brer Rabbit shook his head. "Brer Tiger, I don't have time to bother with you. I have to go tie those other folks; I told you."

"I don't care about those other folks," said Brer Tiger. "I want you to tie *me* so the wind won't blow *me* off the earth. Look, Brer Rabbit, I've got my head here against this tree. Please, sir, tie me."

All right, Brer Tiger. Just hold still a minute, and I'll take out time to save your striped hide," said Brer Rabbit.

Now, while all this talking was going on, the noise kept getting louder and louder. Somewhere back yonder it sounded like thunder was a-rolling! Brer Bear was still a-beating on the log, bic-a-bam, bic-a-bam, bam, bam! Brer Cooter was still a-jumping in the log, bic-a-boom, bic-a-boom, boom, boom! And the birds were a-flapping and the trees were a-bending and the leaves were a-flying and the bushes were a-shaking and the creatures were a-crying—and Brer Rabbit was a-tying!

He wrapped the rope around Brer Tiger's neck, and he pulled it tight; he wrapped it around Brer Tiger's feet, and he pulled it tight. Then Brer Tiger tried to pitch and rear, and he asked Brer Rabbit to tie him a little tighter, "because I don't want the big wind to blow me off the earth." So Brer Rabbit wrapped him around and around so tight that even the biggest cyclone in the world couldn't blow him away. And then Brer Rabbit backed off and looked at Brer Tiger.

When he saw that Brer Tiger couldn't move, Brer Rabbit called out, "Hush your fuss, children. Stop all of your crying. Come down here. I want to show you something. Look, there's our great Brer Tiger. He had all the pears and all the drinking water and all of everything, enough for everybody. But he wouldn't give a bite of food or a drop of water to anybody, no matter how much they needed it. So now, Brer Tiger, you just stay there until those ropes drop off you. And you, children, gather up your crocus[2] sacks and water buckets. Get all the pears and drinking water you want, because the Good Lord doesn't love a stingy man. He put the food and water here for all His creatures to enjoy."

After the animals had filled their sacks and buckets, they all joined in a song of thanks to the Lord for their leader, Brer Rabbit, who had shown them how to work together to defeat their enemy, Brer Tiger.

2. **crocus** [krō′ kəs]: a small flowering plant that blooms in early spring.

WILLIAM J. FAULKNER

William J. Faulkner was born in South Carolina in 1891 and grew up there on his widowed mother's farm in Society Hill. Faulkner first became interested in African American folk literature when he was ten years old. Simon Brown, a former Virginia slave, came to work on the family farm and told young William both true stories of slave times and fanciful tales of talking animals. The boy never forgot these stories.

When he grew up, Faulkner graduated from Chicago Theological Seminary. Over the years, he worked as a YMCA secretary, as a pastor, and as Dean of Men at Fisk University. In every place, he became known as a teller of tales from what his children called "the book that's inside him." He found so much enthusiasm for Simon Brown's stories that he used them in his book, *The Days When Animals Talked*.

AUNT SUE'S STORIES

LANGSTON HUGHES

Aunt Sue has a head full of stories.
Aunt Sue has a whole heart full of stories.
Summer nights on the front porch
Aunt Sue cuddles a brown-faced child to her bosom
And tells him stories.   5

Black slaves
Working in the hot sun,
And black slaves
Walking in the dewy night,
And black slaves   10
Singing sorrow songs on the banks of a mighty river
Mingle themselves softly
In the flow of old Aunt Sue's voice,
Mingle themselves softly
In the dark shadows that cross and recross   15
Aunt Sue's stories.

And the dark-faced child, listening,
Knows that Aunt Sue's stories are real stories.
He knows that Aunt Sue never got her stories
Out of any book at all,   20
But that they came
Right out of her own life.

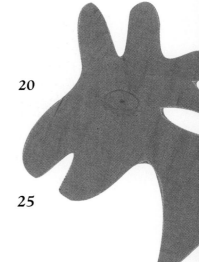

The dark-faced child is quiet
Of a summer night
Listening to Aunt Sue's stories.   25

Pictorial quilt Harriet Powers, 1895-98, cotton and yarn, 69" x 105", Museum of Fine Arts, Boston

LANGSTON HUGHES

Langston Hughes [1902-1967] was born in Joplin, Missouri. As he grew older, he held a dozen different jobs and traveled to many countries. All this experience taught him that the simple people, like "Aunt Sue" in this poem, were the important ones. He never lost his belief that, as he once put it, "most people are generally good, in every race and in every country where I have been." More of Hughes's work is waiting for you in *The Langston Hughes Reader.*

THE STORY OF THE SAILOR

ROGER LANCELYN

When Pharaoh Amen-em-het[1] ruled Egypt in about the year 2000 B.C. he brought peace and prosperity to a country that had been torn by civil war and rebellion for nearly two hundred years. During his reign adventurers and traders went on many expeditions to the south—either up the Nile[2] through Nubia and even as far as Ethiopia, or along the Red Sea and out into the Indian Ocean to the mysterious land of Punt, whence they brought back jewels and spices and other treasures.

The Royal Court, whether it was in residence at Thebes[3] or Memphis,[4] was thronged with ships' captains and the leaders of expeditions, each with a tale to tell—and each anxious to win a commission[5] from Pharaoh to command some royal venture on the strength of his past achievements.

One day such a wanderer stopped the Grand Vizier[6] in the palace courtyard at Thebes, and said to him, "My lord, harken to me a while. I come with costly gifts for Pharaoh, nor shall his councilors such as yourself be forgotten. Listen, and I will tell you of such adventures as have not been told: Pharaoh himself—life, health, strength be to him!—will reward you for bringing to his presence a man with such adventures to tell. I have been to a magic island in

1. **Pharaoh Amen-em-het** [fer′ ō äm′ ən em het′]: the first in a line of four Egyptian kings (pharaohs) of the Twelfth dynasty.
2. **Nile:** the longest river in the world, which runs through Egypt.
3. **Thebes:** an ancient Egyptian city located on the left bank of the Nile.
4. **Memphis:** an ancient city in lower Egypt, south of Cairo.
5. **commission** [kə mish′ ən]: an appointment or position.
6. **Grand Vizier** [vi zir′]: the minister of state.

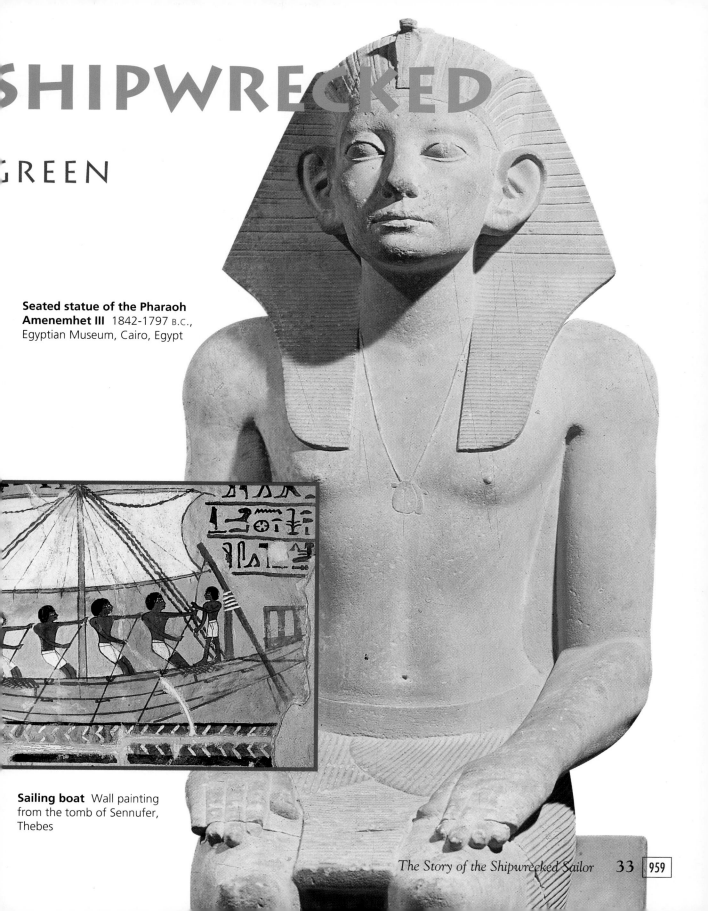

SHIPWRECKED

GREEN

Seated statue of the Pharaoh Amenemhet III 1842-1797 B.C., Egyptian Museum, Cairo, Egypt

Sailing boat Wall painting from the tomb of Sennufer, Thebes

the sea far to the south—far beyond Nubia, to the south even of Ethiopia. I beg of you to tell Pharaoh that I am here and would tell my tale to him."

The Grand Vizier was accustomed to such appeals, and he looked doubtfully at the wanderer and said, "It seems to me that you speak foolishly and have only vain things to tell. Many men such as you think that a tall story will win them a commission from Pharaoh—but when they tell their tale they condemn themselves out of their own mouths. If what you have to tell is one of these, be sure that I shall have you thrown out of the palace. But if it is of sufficient interest, I may bring you before Pharaoh. Therefore speak on at your own risk, or else remain silent and trouble me no more."

"I have such a tale to tell," answered the wanderer, "that I will risk your anger with an easy mind. When you have heard it, you will beg me to come before Pharaoh and tell it to him—even to the good god Pharaoh Amen-em-het who rules the world. Listen, then.

"I was on my way to the mines of Pharaoh in a great ship rowed by a hundred and fifty sailors who had seen heaven and earth and whose hearts were stronger than lions. We rowed and sailed for many days down the Red Sea and out into the ocean beyond.

"The captain and the steersman swore that they knew the signs of the weather and that the wind would not be strong but would waft us gently on our way. Nevertheless before long a tempest[7] arose suddenly and drove us toward the land. As we drew near the shore the waves were eight cubits[8] in height and they broke over the ship and dashed it upon the rocks. I seized a piece of wood and flung myself into the sea just as the ship ran aground: a moment later it was smashed to pieces and every man perished.

"But a great wave raised the board to which I clung high over the sharp rocks and cast me far up the shore, on level sand, and I was able to crawl into the shelter of the trees out of reach of the cruel, angry sea.

"When day dawned the tempest passed away and the warm sun shone out. I rose up to see where I was, giving thanks to the gods for

7. **tempest** [tem′ pist]: a wild storm.
8. **cubits** [kyu′ bits]: an ancient measure of length, about 20 inches or 50 centimeters.

my delivery when all the rest had perished. I was on an island with no other human being to be a companion to me. But such an island as no man has seen! The broad leaves of the thicket where I lay formed a roof over my head to shield me from the burning midday sun. When I grew hungry and looked about for food, I found all ready for me within easy reach: figs and grapes, all manner of good herbs, berries and grain, melons of all kinds, fishes and birds for the taking.

"So I satisfied my hunger on the fruits around me. And then I dug a pit and kindled a fire in it on which I made first of all a burnt offering to the gods, and then cooked meat and fish for myself.

"As I sat there comfortably after an excellent meal I suddenly heard a noise like thunder. Nearly beside myself with terror, I flung myself on the ground, thinking that it was some great tidal wave come to engulf the island: for the trees were lashing as if at the breath of the tempest and the earth shook beneath me.

"But no wave came, and at last I cautiously raised my head and looked about me. Never shall I forget the horror of that moment. Moving toward me I saw a serpent thirty cubits long with a beard of more than two cubits. Its body was covered with golden scales and the scales around its eyes shaded off into blue as pure as lapis lazuli.[9]

"The serpent coiled up its whole length in front of where I lay with my face on the ground, reared its head high above me, and said, 'What has brought you, what has brought you here, little one? Say, what has brought you to my island? If you do not tell me at once I will show you what it is to be burned with fire, what it is to be burned utterly to nothing and become a thing invisible. Speak quickly, I am waiting to hear what I have not heard before, some new thing!'

"Then the serpent took me in his huge jaws and carried me away to his cave, and put me down there without hurting me. Yes, though he had held me in his sharp teeth he had not bitten me at all: I was still whole.

"Then he said again, 'What has brought you, what has brought you here, little one? Say what has brought you to this island in the midst of the sea with the waves breaking on all sides of it?'

9. **lapis lazuli** [lap′ is laz′ ye lī]: a deep-blue stone.

Egyptian funerary model of a sailing boat
1800 B.C., The British Museum, London

"At this I managed to speak, crouching before him and bowing my face to the ground as if before Pharaoh himself.

"'I sailed by command of Amen-em-het, Pharaoh of Egypt, in a great ship one hundred and fifty cubits in length to bring treasure from the mines of the south. But a great tempest broke upon us and dashed the ship upon the rocks so that all who sailed in her perished except for myself. As for me, I seized a piece of wood and was lifted on it over the rocks and cast upon this island by a mighty wave, and I have been here for three days. So behold me, your suppliant,[10] brought hither by a wave of the sea.'

10. **suppliant** [sup′ lē ənt]: a person who asks humbly and earnestly.

"Then the serpent said to me, 'Fear not, fear not, little one, nor let your face show sadness. Since you have come to my island in this way, when all your companions perished, it is because some god has preserved and sent you. For surely Amen-Ra has set you thus upon this island of the blessed where nothing is lacking, which is filled with all good things. And now I will tell you of the future: here in this isle shall you remain while one month adds itself to another until four months have passed. Then a ship shall come, a ship of Egypt, and it shall carry you home in safety, and at length you shall die in your own city and be laid to rest in the tomb which you have prepared.

"'And now I will tell you of this island. For it is pleasant to hear strange things after fear has been taken away from you—and you will indeed have a tale to tell when you return home and kneel before Pharaoh, your lord and master. Know then that I dwell here with my brethren[11] and my children about me; we are seventy-five serpents in all, children and kindred. And but one stranger has even come among us: a lovely girl who appeared strangely and on whom the fire of heaven fell and who was turned into ashes. As for you, I do not think that heaven holds any thunderbolts for one who has lived through such dangers. It is revealed to me that, if you dwell here in patience, you shall return in the fullness of time and hold your wife and children in your arms once more.'

"Then I bowed before him, thanking him for his words of comfort, and said, 'All that I have told you is true, and if what you have said to me happens indeed, I shall come before Pharaoh and tell him about you, and speak to him of your greatness. And I will bring as offerings to you sacred oils and perfumes, and such incense as is offered to the gods in their temples. Moreover I shall tell him of all the wonders of this isle, and I shall sacrifice donkeys to you, and Pharaoh shall send out a ship filled with the riches of Egypt as presents to your majesty.'

"The king serpent laughed at my words, saying, 'Truly you are not rich in perfumes—for here in this island I have more than in all the

11. **brethren** [breᵻH′ rən]: the fellow members of a society.

land of Punt. Only the sacred oil which you promise me is scarce here—yet you will never bring it, for when you are gone this island will vanish away and you shall never more see it. Yet doubtless the gods will reveal it in time to come to some other wanderer.'

"So I dwelt happily in that enchanted island, and the four months seemed all too short. When they drew to a close I saw a ship sailing over the smooth sea toward me, and I climbed into a high tree to see better what manner of men sailed in it. And when I perceived that they were men of Egypt, I hastened to the home of the serpent king and told him. But he knew already more than I did myself, and said to me, 'Farewell, brave wanderer. Return in safety to your home and may my blessing go with you.'

"Then I bowed before him and thanked him, and he gave me gifts of precious perfumes—of cassia[12] and sweet woods, of khol and cypress,[13] of incense, of ivory and of other precious things. And when I had set these upon the ship and the

sailors would have landed, the island seemed to move away from them, floating on the sea. Then night fell suddenly, and when the moon shone out there was no island in sight but only the open waves.

"So we sailed north and in the second month we came to Egypt, and I have made haste to cross the desert from the sea to Thebes. Therefore, I pray you, lead me before Pharaoh, for I long to tell him of my adventures and lay at his feet the gifts of the King of the Serpents, and beg that he will make me commander of a royal ship to sail once more into the ocean that washes the shores of Punt."

12. **cassia** [kash′ ə]: the spicy bark of a tree native to China.
13. **cypress** [sī′ prəs]: the hard wood of an evergreen tree.

When the wanderer's tale was ended, the Grand Vizier laughed heartily, crying, "Whether or not I believe your adventures, you have told a tale such as delights the heart of Pharaoh—life, strength, health be to him! Therefore come with me at once, and be sure of a rich reward: to you who tell the tale, and to me who brings before him the teller of the tale."

So the wanderer passed into the presence of the good god Pharaoh Amen-em-het, and Pharaoh delighted in the story of the shipwrecked sailor so much that his chief scribe Ameni-amdn-aa was set to write it down upon a roll of papyrus[14] where it may be read to this very day.

14. **papyrus** [pə pī′ rəs]: a kind of paper made from a tall water plant.

Detail from **Sailing Boat**

R O G E R   L A N C E L Y N   G R E E N

Roger Lancelyn Green was born in 1918 in Norwich, England. His love of myth and storytelling began very early and led him to writing through work as an actor, an antiquarian bookseller, a librarian, and a teacher. Green published a book of poems right after finishing his studies at Oxford University. His second book, *Tellers of Tales*, appeared a year later. Green went on to write biographies of such children's storytellers as Beatrix Potter, Lewis Carroll, and Rudyard Kipling. His studies of mythology have taken him to Greece more than twenty times.

Green has retold fairy tales, great myths, and folktales of many lands. His books include *Tales of Ancient Egypt*, *The Tale of Ancient Israel*, and *Folktales of the World*.

THE BAMB

Last year during the planting season, I helped Mama plant seeds on our hill. "One seed for each of my brothers and sisters," she said, and she covered up seven seeds with dark dirt. Mama's family lives on the other side of the island, so we hardly ever see them.

Each day I watched Mama water the dark mounds of dirt and weed around them. Soon, flowers grew up. They were red as the evening sun. But one day the floods came and swept them to the sea.

"Poor Mama," I said.

"They'll grow again," she replied.

OO BEADS

LYNN JOSEPH

She looked at her gardening gloves hanging on a nail. "If they don't grow back, we'll plant some more." And she smiled.

That night the moon was round and white as my Sunday hat. I told Daddy how Mama's flowers had drowned in the flood rains. He said, "Did I ever show you how *I* count my brothers and sisters?"

"No," I answered.

Then Daddy showed me the fisherman stars. "They point fishermen to the way home," he said. "There are eight of them. I named one each for my brothers and sisters."

"How do you know which is which?" I asked.

Daddy pointed again to the bright stars. "Well, there's Rupert and Hazel, Anthony and Derek, Peter, Janet, and Neil."

"You forgot Auntie Sonia," I said.

Daddy smiled and pointed to a tiny star. "That one's her."

I nodded my head as Daddy moved his finger around although I couldn't tell which star was who.

After that, Daddy and I looked for the fisherman stars each night. Some nights when the sea breezes blew dark clouds in the sky, we couldn't see them. But Daddy would say, "They'll come back." And he'd smile.

"I wish I had brothers and sisters to plant flowers for or to count stars on," I told Mama and Daddy one day. "I'm tired of having only myself."

"What about all your cousins?" asked Mama.

"You can count them on something," said Daddy.

"What can I count them on?" I wondered.

"Maybe Tantie can help find you something," said Mama. "She's the one who keeps track of all yuh."

So, the next time Tantie came to visit, I said, "Tantie, Mama said you keep track of me and my cousins."

"That's right, chile," said Tantie. "And is plenty of all yuh to keep track of, too."

"I know," I said, "but how you do it? I want something that I can name after each one of my cousins. Something I can count them on. Like Mama has flowers and Daddy has his fisherman stars."

Well, Tantie looked me in the eye for a long time. Then from underneath the neck of her dress she pulled out a brown string full of bright, colorful beads.

"Tantie, where you get those pretty beads from?" I asked.

"These, my dear, is a story by itself, and if you have de time to listen, I'll tell it to you."

I nodded and sat down on the porch swing next to Tantie. As Tantie told her story, I kept trying to push the swing with my foot.

But Tantie was too heavy. The swing sat quiet quiet. The only sound was Tantie's voice.

"A long, long time ago," she began, "when I was in my bare feet still, I went to market with a basket of bread and red-currant[1] buns to sell. Market day was de busiest time. There was plenty to see as I set up my little stall and tucked cloths around de bread and buns so de flies wouldn't get them.

"I hadn't sold one thing yet when an old man came up. His clothes were ragged and he didn't have on no shoes. His feet didn't look like no ordinary feet. They looked like cow hooves. I didn't stare, though, because it rude to do that.

"He asked for a piece of bread. Well, I remember Mama telling me that morning to get good prices for de bread, but I was sure Mama hadn't meant from this man too. So, I cut off a hunk of bread, wrapped it in brown paper, and handed it to him. He looked so hungry that I reached for a bun and gave him that too. De man smiled and bowed his head at me. Then he went his way.

"After that I was busy selling bread. De buns went even faster. By afternoon, I had sold them all. Then I saw de old man coming over again. He didn't look so ragged anymore. His hair was combed and he had on a new shirt.

" 'I'm sorry,' I said. 'No more bread left.'

"He didn't answer. Instead he handed me something. It was a piece of brown string. It looked like an ordinary old string, but I didn't tell him that.

" 'Thank you for de bread, child,' he said. Then he shuffled off and was gone.

"I looked at de string for a while. I could use it to tie up my bread cloths, I thought. Or I could use it as a hair ribbon. But I decided I would put de string around my neck and wear it like a necklace."

---

1. **currant** [kėr′ ənt]: a small, seedless raisin, native of eastern Mediterranean countries.

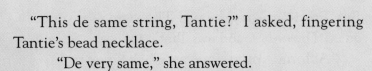

"This de same string, Tantie?" I asked, fingering Tantie's bead necklace.

"De very same," she answered.

"Well, that evening, Mama was so proud I had sold all de bread that she gave me a treat. It was a small blue bamboo bead. It was de exact color of Mama's best blue head scarf.

" 'Where you get this bead, Mama?' I asked.

" 'Found it in de yard,' she replied.

"I wondered how it got there but it didn't matter. I pulled out my brown string and untied it. Then I slipped de blue bead on and tied it around my neck again. It looked like a real necklace now that it had Mama's bead on it."

"Is this your mama's bead?" I asked, touching a bright blue bead on Tantie's string.

"Yes, that's it, chile," said Tantie. "And it shines more now than de day I got it.

"Two days later, Daddy found a smooth black bead down by de sea. He brought it home in his pocket.

" 'I thought you might like this,' he said and handed it to me. It sparkled like a black sun. I untied my necklace and slipped it on next to de blue bead. Now my string was beautiful with Mama's and Daddy's bamboo beads on it.

"During de next few days, Mama and Daddy and I kept finding shiny bamboo beads in de strangest places. I found a red one under de bed. Mama found a green one in de garden, and Daddy found a yellow one in his shoe. Mama and Daddy didn't think nothing of it but as I added each new bead to my necklace, I got a strange, trembly feeling.

"De next week when I took Mama's bread and currant buns to market, I saw de old man who had given me my string. His clothes were still ragged and he clumped around on his hooves.

" 'Hello, mister,' I said when he came over. I wrapped up a chunk of bread and two buns this time and gave them to him. He smiled and shuffled off.

"Again my day of selling flew by. Before lunchtime I had sold everything. Mama hugged me hard when I got home. But then she sat down at de kitchen table and looked serious.

"'What's wrong?' I asked.

"'Look,' she said, pointing to a bowl on the table. I looked inside and there were de most beautiful, shiny bamboo beads I'd ever seen. Lots and lots of them. I put my hand in and touched de smooth wood.

"'Where they come from?' I asked.

"'Don't know,' said Mama. 'They were here when I turned around from de sink this morning. I thought you might know something about them, since you're collecting beads.'

"'No,' I said. 'I don't know about these.'

"Then Mama said, 'Let me see that string of beads around your neck, girl.'

"I showed it to Mama. She looked and looked at de beads and tugged on de string until I thought she'd break it. Then she looked at me and said, 'You've met Papa Bois.'[2]

"'Papa who?'

"'Papa Bois,' she murmured. 'He lives in de forest and protects de trees and forest animals from hunters. He spends his time whittling bamboo beads from fallen bamboo shoots. He's de only one who could make these beads. They're priceless.'

"Mama looked at me and gave me back de necklace. 'Have you met an old man without any feet?' she asked.

"I immediately thought of de old man from de market. 'Yes, Mama, I met him last week at de market. An old man in ragged clothes and no feet. He had cow hooves instead.'

"Mama closed her eyes and nodded her head. 'That's Papa Bois,' she said. 'He can be dangerous. Once he meets someone, he keeps track of them by

2. **Papa Bois** [pä pä´ bwä]

The Bamboo Beads 45

counting their sins, their blessings, even their teeth, on his whittled beads. You never know with Papa Bois just what he's counting for you. The last time Papa Bois gave someone beads, the beads represented de number of days he had left to live. These beads on de table must be for you. He's counting something for you.'

"'What?' I whispered, almost too frightened to speak.

"'We won't know till he's ready to say. Were you kind or mean to him?'

"'I gave him some bread to eat because he looked hungry,' I said.

"'Good,' said Mama, and she pulled me into her arms. 'That was very kind. Now you might as well put de beads on de string and wait until Papa Bois comes back and tells you what he's counting.'

"I put de pretty beads on de string. I didn't think they would all fit, but no matter how many I put on, de string never filled up. When every bead was on I counted thirty-three beads. Then I tied it around my neck once more. It wasn't any heavier than when I wore de string empty.

"As de days passed, Mama, Daddy, and I kept our eyes open for Papa Bois. We thought he might come by anytime. I wondered over and over what Papa Bois could be counting on my beads."

"Were you scared, Tantie?" I interrupted.

"A little," she answered. "But I knew I had been kind to Papa Bois, and that was all that mattered.

"De next time I went to market for Mama, she wanted to come with me. I told her Papa Bois might not come to our stall if she was there.

"At the stall I laid de bread and buns out nicely and covered them with clothes. I saw de old man shuffling up to my table.

"'*Bonjour, vieux Papa,*'[3] I said. Mama had told me that to say hello in French was de polite way to greet Papa Bois. She also said not to look at his feet no matter what.

"'*Bonjour,*' said de old man.

"'Would you like some bread?' I asked. Papa Bois nodded.

"As I cut him a chunk of bread, I said, 'Thank you for de pretty necklace.'

"'It's for you to wear always,' he said. 'Until you find someone who should wear it instead.'

"Papa Bois' eyes looked kind in his wrinkled face. I decided I go ask him what de beads were for.

"'De beads,' he answered, 'are for all de little children you'll one day have.'

"'Thirty-three children?' I asked.

"'Yes, they'll be yours, but they won't be yours,' " he said mysteriously. But then he smiled a big smile.

"'All right,'" I said, and I handed him de bread and buns.

"That was de last time I ever see Papa Bois. Mama said he only comes out of his forest when he's lonely for human company. Otherwise his friends are de deer, de squirrels, and de trees. The first person he meets when he leaves his forest early in de morning is de one who counts. If that person stares at his feet or laughs at him— watch out!"

"But Tantie, what happen to de thirty-three children?" I asked.

"You're one of them," she said. "Ever since your oldest cousin Jarise was born, I been de one helping to take care of all yuh. I have thirty grandnieces and nephews now. That mean three more to come. And all yuh are *my* children, just like Papa Bois said."

Tantie reached up and unhooked her bamboo bead necklace. Then she laid it in my hands.

3. *Bonjour, vieux Papa* [boN zhür′ vyoe pä pä´]: French for "Hello, old dad."

"Oh," I said, looking at Tantie's necklace again. "I'd like to be de red bead."

Tantie took the necklace out of my hands and put it around my neck. She tied the string. The necklace felt cool and smooth against my skin.

"I wish I had a mirror," I said.

"It looking beautiful," said Tantie. "And it for you now. You can count your cousins on them beads."

"You're giving this to me, Tantie?" I asked, not believing what I had heard.

"Papa Bois said I go find someone who should wear it."

"Thank you," I said. I ran my fingers over the bamboo smoothness of the beads and admired the pretty colors.

"And since you wear Papa Bois' beads, you can start helping me tell these stories," said Tantie. "I been doing de work alone for too long."

Tantie reached over and adjusted the bead string on my neck.

I looked down at the shiny red bead that was me and smiled and smiled.

LYNN JOSEPH

Lynn Joseph was born in Trinidad, West Indies. Her childhood memories are of that two-island country where summer lasts all year and she heard many stories like "The Bamboo Beads."

Joseph moved to the United States with her parents and went to Colorado University. She went on to study law in New York, and continued living there. The tale of "The Bamboo Beads" is from her book of six stories from Trinidad, *A Wave in Her Pocket*. Joseph has also written *Coconut Kind of Day: Island Poems*.

The Wonderful

JAMES RIORDAN

Once upon a time there was an orphan girl called Wa, who lived on the banks of the Mekong River.[1] Ever since she had been a little girl and could carry a basketful of rice upon her back, she had worked for the village headman.

Like the other villagers, she toiled long and hard for her master, and was hardly given enough to eat in return. She had to cut down the biggest trees that even the strongest men could barely fell. And when the rice was ripe, she had to peel the husks from dawn till dusk. Her hands were always blistered from cutting wood, and when the skin had hardened, her palms would itch from the coarse rice husks. Each night she would gather herbs to put on her raw, itching hands, and other workers would come to her for their wounds to be soothed—for she had a great knowledge of wild plants and their healing powers.

One day she was cleaning the new harvest of rice with her friend, Ho. Ho was so thin that his ribs stuck through his tattered shirt. As they worked they spoke of the drudgery[2] of their lives and wondered, sadly, how many of their people would die of starvation before the year was out.

1. **Mekong River** [māʹ kon]: a river that flows from South China to South Vietnam, where it empties into the South China Sea.
2. **drudgery** [drujʹ ər ē]: work that is difficult and tiresome.

Pearl

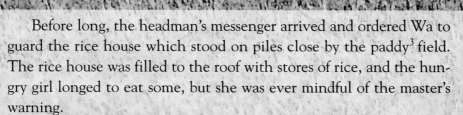

Before long, the headman's messenger arrived and ordered Wa to guard the rice house which stood on piles close by the paddy[3] field. The rice house was filled to the roof with stores of rice, and the hungry girl longed to eat some, but she was ever mindful of the master's warning.

"An evil spirit protects my rice. If you eat even one grain, the spirit will jump inside you. Then you will die and turn into a grain of rice!"

In her fear, poor Wa went hungry.

As darkness came, Wa was overcome with tiredness and she fell asleep. In her dreams she saw her master growing fat and rich from the store of rice, which grew bigger and bigger from the toil of her fellow villagers, while they grew thin and sick.

All of a sudden, she was rudely awakened by a vicious kick in her side. It was the headman's son. "You lazy pig!" he screamed in her ear. "Fill this pail with water by my return."

Wa jumped up in alarm as he went laughing on his way. She took the pail and ran swiftly to the river to fill it up.

The waters of the river were ruffled by a gentle breeze as they lapped softly at the girl's sore and aching feet. She sighed and bent

3. **paddy** [pad′ ē]: a flooded area with raised banks, usually used for growing rice.

down to fill the pail. All of a sudden, the waters began to foam and ring out like the torong's[4] twanging strings, making her scamper back to dry land in fear.

Out of the silver foam appeared a maiden, tall and proud, wearing a long shimmering dress. She approached Wa and, taking her trembling hand, softly said, "The Water Spirit's young daughter has fallen ill. And our sprites say that you, Wa, are wise with herbs and can cure her. Come with me and see the girl."

"No, no, I cannot," Wa cried out. "I have to guard the rice house. The master would kill me if he should find me gone."

"Do not anger us, Wa. The Water Spirit is mightier even than your village chief. If you do not come, the sprites will punish you."

A dry pathway suddenly opened before her and the stately[5] maid led Wa down into the underwater depths.

Wa was told that the Water Spirit's daughter had had a scorpion sting while playing on the shore. Ever since she had been ill. All the underwater doctors—the shrimps and eels—were fussing about the poor sick girl, but none could cure the strange sickness that had overcome her. For three months she had lain in a fever, unable to eat or sleep.

Wa gently touched the wound and told the sprites what herbs they should collect. When these were ready, she used them on the girl, and three days later she was well.

The Water Spirit was overjoyed. "Dear Wa," he said, "what will you take as reward?"

"My only wish is to save my people from need," Wa replied.

Thereupon, the Spirit handed her a precious pearl, saying, "This pearl will make any wish come true."

Wa thanked the Water Spirit and returned to dry land along the underwater path. When she reached the rice house, she saw in horror the tracks of birds, big and small, all around it. They had helped themselves to half the unprotected rice!

An old man passed by just then, and stared at Wa in surprise. "Where did you get to, Wa, these past three months?" he said. "Be

4. **torong** [tȯ′ rông]: an instrument made from split bamboo cane.
5. **stately** [stāt′ lē]: dignified, majestic.

warned, for you're in trouble. Just look about you: those thieving birds have stolen the master's rice. He is searching for you and his rage is terrible."

Wa went sadly on her way. Eventually she sat down on the ground and hung her head in woe. Her thin dress became drenched with tears. And then, all at once, she remembered the precious pearl. Taking out the Spirit's gift, she murmured, "Pearl, wonderful pearl, bring me rice to eat."

Right away, a huge bamboo dish of rice appeared before her, filled with all manner of tasty food. And at her back a store of rice grew up three times higher than the master's rice house.

She clapped her hands with joy and began to eat to her heart's content. Yet suddenly she stopped. Her thoughts were of her dear friend Ho. He too was poor and had to toil in the master's paddy fields all day. So she took out the pearl again and said, "Pearl, wonderful pearl, bring me a house, a pair of oxen and some hens. And then bring my friend Ho to me."

Hardly had Wa spoken than, to her right, a tall house on bamboo stilts grew up, with hens scratching round about; and there beneath it was a pair of milk-white oxen. Inside the house she saw gongs and copper pans, a brass kettle on a stove and jars of candy. Just then an astonished Ho appeared and together they walked into the house as Wa told him her wonderful story.

Next morning Wa made her way to the headman's house. As soon as he set eyes on the girl, he roared like a stricken ox.

"Ahrr-rrr, here comes the lump of oxen dung, the one who stole my rice. I'll have her fed to the tigers in the hills!"

"It was not my fault you lost your rice," Wa spoke up boldly. "No matter, I'll make up what you lost. Just send your son to collect it."

"Lead on," snarled the headman's son. "I'll take it now. And if you fail by a single grain, I'll bring your head back on a tray."

When the son set eyes on Wa's rich house, his mouth dropped open in surprise and his eyes grew wide like a bullock's.[6]

"Hey there, Ho!" shouted Wa. "The master's son has come for rice. Give him all he wants. I'm going to the river to fish."

When the man recovered from his shock, he hurried down to the riverbank and stared at the girl with fresh respect. He thought that she looked stronger and sturdier than the finest jungle tree.

"I do n-n-not want your r-r-rice, dear Wa," he stammered. "I wish to m-m-marry you."

Wa only laughed. "Take your rice and go," she said. "I cannot stand the sight of you."

Slowly he made his way back home and reported all to his father. In a rage, the headman called his guards.

"Gather up your spears, your swords, your bows and arrows," he yelled. "We go to slay that low-born girl and take her riches for ourselves."

But the good people of the village ran swiftly to warn Wa of the master's plans. At once, the bold young girl took out the magic pearl and said, "Pearl, wonderful pearl, protect us from this evil man."

Suddenly a chain of lofty[7] mountains sprang up around the headman's house. He and his men tried to scale the heights. But after three whole months they had only managed to climb an eighth of the mountain and eventually they had to give up. They were forced

6. **bullock** [bůl′ ək]: an ox.
7. **lofty** [lôf′ tē]: very high.

to return defeated to their narrow valley and were never able to bother the poor again.

Meanwhile, on the other side of the mountain, Wa and Ho lived in contentment. The wise, just Wa shared out her wealth among the people, who never went hungry again, and she protected them always with her wonderful pearl.

JAMES RIORDAN

James Riordan was born in 1936 in Portsmouth, England, and studied in England and Moscow. Among other occupations, Riordan has worked as a translator and served as British Olympic attaché at the Moscow Olympic Games in l980. Riordan most enjoys writing folktales and writing about sports.

Riordan says his interest in folktales has grown from "a personal acquaintance with the people and the land." He wrote his book *Russian Tales* after spending five years visiting fifteen republics of the former Soviet Union. Visiting his wife's relatives provided him with sources for *Tales from Tartary*. Riordan has also written a book about the Moscow Olympics, stories of King Arthur, and other books. This Vietnamese tale comes from his collection, *The Woman in the Moon and Other Tales of Forgotten Heroines*.

BAUCIS AND PHILEMON

·············· EDITH HAMILTON ··············

OVID[1] IS THE ONLY SOURCE FOR THIS STORY.
IT SHOWS ESPECIALLY WELL HIS LOVE OF DETAILS
AND THE SKILLFUL WAY HE USES THEM TO MAKE
A FAIRY TALE SEEM REALISTIC. THE LATIN NAMES
OF THE GODS ARE USED.

In the Phrygian hill-country there were once two trees
which all the peasants near and far pointed out as a great marvel, and no wonder, for one was an oak and the other a linden,
yet they grew from a single trunk. The story of how this came
about is a proof of the immeasurable power of the gods, and also
of the way they reward the humble and the pious.

Sometimes when Jupiter[2] was tired of eating ambrosia and
drinking nectar up in Olympus and even a little weary of listening to Apollo's lyre and watching the Graces dance, he would
come down to the earth, disguise himself as a mortal and go
looking for adventures. His favorite companion on these tours
was Mercury,[3] the most entertaining of all the gods, the
shrewdest and the most resourceful. On this particular trip
Jupiter had determined to find out how hospitable the people of

1. **Ovid:** (43 B.C.–A.D. 17?) famous Roman poet.
2. **Jupiter:** known as Zeus in Greek mythology, Jupiter was the chief god.
3. **Mercury:** known as Hermes in Greek mythology, Mercury was the messenger god.

Phrygia were. Hospitality was, of course, very important to him, since all guests, all who seek shelter in a strange land, were under his especial protection.

The two gods, accordingly, took on the appearance of poor wayfarers and wandered through the land, knocking at each lowly hut or great house they came to and asking for food and a place to rest in. Not one would admit them; every time they were dismissed insolently and the door barred against them.

They made trial of hundreds; all treated them in the same way. At last they came upon a little hovel of the humblest sort, poorer than any they had yet found, with a roof made only of reeds. But here, when they knocked, the door was opened wide and a cheerful voice bade them enter. They had to stoop to pass through the low entrance, but once inside they found themselves in a snug and very clean room, where a kindly-faced old man and woman welcomed them in the friendliest fashion and bustled about to make them comfortable.

The old man set a bench near the fire and told them to stretch out on it and rest their tired limbs, and the old woman threw a soft covering over it. Her name was Baucis,[4] she told the strangers, and her husband was called Philemon.[5] They had lived in that cottage all

4. **Baucis** [bô′ sis]
5. **Philemon** [fi′ lē mən]

their married life and had always been happy. "We are poor folk," she said, "but poverty isn't so bad when you're willing to own up to it, and a contented spirit is a great help, too." All the while she was talking, she was busy doing things for them. The coals under the ashes on the dark hearth she fanned to life until a cheerful fire was burning. Over this she hung a little kettle full of water and just as it began to boil her husband came in with a fine cabbage he had got from the garden. Into the kettle it went, with a piece of the pork which was hanging from one of the beams. While this cooked Baucis set the table with her trembling old hands. One table-leg was too short, but she propped it up with a bit of broken dish. On the board she placed olives and radishes and several eggs which she had roasted in the ashes. By this time the cabbage and bacon were done, and the old man pushed two rickety couches up to the table and bade his guests recline and eat.

Presently he brought them cups of beechwood and an earthenware mixing bowl which held some wine very like vinegar, plentifully diluted with water. Philemon, however, was clearly proud and happy at being able to add such cheer to the supper and he kept on the watch to refill each cup as soon as it was emptied. The two old folks were so pleased and excited by the success of their hospitality that only very slowly a strange thing dawned upon them. The mixing bowl kept

full. No matter how many cups were poured out from it, the level of the wine stayed the same, up to the brim. As they saw this wonder each looked in terror at the other, and dropping their eyes they prayed silently. Then in quavering voices and trembling all over they begged their guests to pardon the poor refreshments they had offered. "We have a goose," the old man said, "which we ought to have given your lordships. But if you will only wait, it shall be done at once." To catch the goose, however, proved to be beyond their powers. They tried in vain until they were worn out, while Jupiter and Mercury watched them greatly entertained.

But when both Philemon and Baucis had had to give up the chase panting and exhausted, the gods felt that the time had come for them to take action. They were really very kind. "You have been hosts to the gods," they said, "and you shall have your reward. This wicked country which despises the poor stranger will be bitterly punished, but not you." Then they escorted the two out of the hut and told them to look around them. To their amazement all they saw was water. The whole countryside had disappeared. A great lake surrounded them. Their neighbors had not been good to the old couple; nevertheless standing there they wept for them. But all of a sudden their tears were dried by an overwhelming wonder. Before their eyes the tiny, lowly hut which had been their home for so long was turned into a stately pillared temple of whitest marble with a golden roof.

"Good people," Jupiter said, "ask whatever you want and you shall have your wish." The old people exchanged a hurried whisper, then Philemon spoke. "Let us be your priests, guarding this temple for you—and oh, since we have lived so long together, let neither of us ever have to live alone. Grant that we may die together."

The gods assented, well pleased with the two. A long time they served in that grand building, and the story does not say whether they ever missed their little cozy room with its cheerful hearth. But one day standing before the marble and golden magnificence they fell to talking about that former life, which had been so hard and yet so happy. By now both were in extreme old age. Suddenly as they exchanged memories each saw the other putting forth leaves. Then bark was growing around them. They had time only to cry, "Farewell, dear companion." As the words passed their lips they became trees, but still they were together. The linden and the oak grew from one trunk.

From far and wide people came to admire the wonder, and always wreaths of flowers hung on the branches in honor of the pious and faithful pair.

EDITH HAMILTON

Edith Hamilton [1867-1963] was born in Dresden, Germany, to American parents and studied both in the United States and Germany. At the age of seven, she discovered the Greek and Latin classics and fell in love with them. They became her major studies in college.

Hamilton was headmistress of Bryn Mawr School in Baltimore, Maryland, for twenty-seven years. During that time she modeled her ideas of education on the Greeks, believing that each person should be educated according to individual talents and should have the freedom to develop them. Hamilton hated television as a destroyer of these individual interests.

Hamilton did not become a full-time writer until 1922, when she retired from Bryn Mawr. She was sixty-three years old when her first book, *The Greek Way,* was published. It was not a book for scholars. Instead, she introduced everyday readers to her enthusiasm for the values of the ancient Greeks. She followed this with *The Roman Way* and then began her retellings of the classic myths for her book *Mythology.*

Hamilton saw these myths as lively fables from a time when the world was young. She also felt that they were full of meaning for our own time.

Waters of Gold

Laurence Yep

Many years ago, there lived a woman whom everyone called Auntie Lily. She was Auntie by blood to half the county and Auntie to the other half by friendship. As she liked to say, "There's a bit of Heaven in each of us." As a result, she was always helping people out.

Because of her many kind acts, she knew so many people that she couldn't go ten steps without meeting someone who wanted to chat. So it would take her half the day to go to the village well and back to her home.

Streams and Mountains Under Fresh Snow Liu Sung-nien, ink and color on silk, 16³/₈" x 95⁷/₁₆", Metropolitan Museum of Art, New York

Eventually, though, she helped so many people that she had no more money. She had to sell her fields and even her house to her neighbor, a rich old woman. "If you'd helped yourself instead of others, you wouldn't have to do this," the neighbor said smugly. "Where are all those other people when you need them?"

"That isn't why I helped them," Auntie Lily said firmly. She wound up having to pay rent for the house she had once owned. She supported herself by her embroidery;[1] but since her eyes were going bad, she could not do very much.

One day an old beggar entered the village. He was a ragbag of a

---

1. **embroidery** [əm broi′ dər ē]: an art of ornamenting something with a pattern of stitches or raised design.

man—a trash heap, a walking pig wallow. It was impossible to tell what color or what shape his clothes had once been, and his hair was as muddy and matted as a bird's nest. As he shuffled through the village gates, he called out, "Water for my feet. Please, water for my feet. One little bowl of water—that's all I ask."

Everyone ignored him, pretending to concentrate on their chores instead. One man went on replacing the shaft of his hoe. A woman swept her courtyard. Another woman fed her hens.

The beggar went to each in turn, but they all showed their backs to him.

The Peach Blossom Spring Tao-chi, c. 1641-1717, light color on paper, Freer Gallery of Art, Washington, D.C.

After calling out a little while longer, the beggar went to the nearest home, which happened to belong to the rich old woman.

When he banged at her door, he left the dirty outline of his knuckles on the clean wood. And when the rich woman opened her door, his smell nearly took her breath away.

Now it so happened that she had been chopping vegetables when the beggar had knocked. When the beggar repeated his request, she raised her cleaver menacingly.[2] "What good would one bowl of water be? You'd need a whole river to wash you clean. Go away."

"A thousand pardons," the old beggar said, and shambled on to the next house.

Though Auntie Lily had to hold her nose, she asked politely, "Yes?"

"I'd like a bowl of water to wash my feet." And the beggar pointed one grimy finger toward them.

Her rich neighbor had stayed in her doorway to watch the beggar. She scolded Auntie Lily now. "It's all your fault those beggars come into the village. They know they can count on a free meal."

It was an old debate between them, so Auntie Lily simply said, "Any of us can have bad luck."

"Garbage," the rich old woman declared, "is garbage. They must have done something bad, or Heaven wouldn't have let them become beggars."

Auntie Lily turned to the beggar. "I may be joining you on the road someday. Wait here."

Much to the neighbor's distress,[3] Auntie Lily went inside and poured water from a large jar in her kitchen into a bucket. Carrying it in both hands, she brought it outside to the beggar and set it down.

The beggar stood on one leg, just like a crane,[4] while he washed one callused,[5] leathery sole over the bucket. "You can put mud on any other part of me, but if my feet are clean, then I feel clean."

As he fussily continued to cleanse his feet, Auntie Lily asked kindly, "Are you hungry? I don't have much, but what I have I'm willing to share."

2. **menacingly** [men′ əs ing lē]: threateningly.
3. **distress** [dis tres′]: anxiety, unhappiness.
4. **crane** [krān]: a large, wading bird, with long legs, neck, and bill.
5. **callused** [kal′ əsd]: hardened.

The beggar shook his head. "I've stayed longer in this village than I have in any other. Heaven is my roof, and the whole world my house."

Auntie Lily stared at him, wondering what she would look like after a few years on the road. "Are you very tired? Have you been on the road for very long?"

"No, the road is on me," the beggar said, and held up his hands from his dirty sides. "But thank you. You're the first person to ask. And you're the first person to give me some water. So place the bucket of water by your bed tonight and do not look into it till to-morrow morning."

As the beggar shuffled out of the village again, Auntie Lily stared down doubtfully at the bucket of what was now muddy water. Then, even though she felt foolish, she picked it up again.

"You're not really going to take that scummy water inside?" laughed the rich neighbor. "It'll probably breed mosquitoes."

"It seemed important to him," she answered. "I'll humor him."

"Humoring people," snapped the neighbor, "has got you one step from begging yourself."

However, Auntie Lily carried the bucket inside anyway. Setting it down near her sleeping mat, she covered the mouth of the bucket with an old, cracked plate so she wouldn't peek into it by mistake, and then she got so caught up in embroidering a pair of slippers that she forgot all about the beggar and his bucket of water.

She sewed until twilight, when it was too dark to use her needle. Then, because she had no money for oil or candles, she went to sleep.

The next morning Auntie Lily rose and stretched the aches out of her back. She sighed. "The older I get, the harder it is to get up in the morning."

She was always saying something like that, but she had never stayed on her sleeping mat—even when she was sick. Thinking of all that day's chores, she decided to water the herbs she had growing on one side of her house.

Her eyes fell upon the beggar's bucket with its covering plate. "No sense using fresh water when that will do as well. After all, dirt's dirt to a plant."

Squatting down, she picked up the bucket and was surprised at how heavy it was. "I must have filled it fuller than I thought," she grunted.

She staggered out of the house and over to the side where rows of little green herbs grew. "Here you go," she said to her plants. "Drink deep."

Taking off the plate, she upended the bucket; but instead of muddy brown water, there was a flash of reflected light and a clinking sound as gold coins rained down upon her plants.

Auntie Lily set the bucket down hastily and crouched, not trusting her weak eyes. However, where some of her herbs had been, there was now a small mound of gold coins. She squinted in disbelief and rubbed her aching eyes and stared again; but the gold was still there.

She turned to the bucket. There was even more gold inside. Scooping up coins by the handful, she freed her little plants and made sure that the stalks weren't too bent.

Then she sat gazing at her bucket full of gold until a farmer walked by. "Tell me I'm not dreaming," she called to him.

The farmer yawned and came over with his hoe over his shoulder. "I wish I were dreaming, because that would mean I'm still in bed instead of having to go off to work."

Auntie Lily gathered up a handful of gold coins and let it fall in a tinkling, golden shower back into the bucket. "And this is real?"

The farmer's jaw dropped.

Garden of the Mustard Seed China, late 17th–early 18th century

He picked up one coin with his free hand and bit into it. He flipped it back in with the other coins. "It's as real as me, Auntie. But where did you ever get that?"

So Auntie Lily told him. And as others woke up and stepped outside, Auntie told them as well, for she still could not believe her luck and wanted them to confirm that the gold was truly gold. In no time at all, there was a small crowd around her.

If the bucket had been filled with ordinary copper cash, that would have been more money than any of them had ever seen. In their wildest dreams, they had never expected to see that much gold. Auntie Lily stared at the bucket uncomfortably. "I keep thinking it's going to disappear the next moment."

The farmer, who had been standing there all this time, shook his head. "If it hasn't disappeared by now, I don't think it will. What are you going to do with it, Auntie?"

Auntie Lily stared at the bucket, and suddenly she came to a decision. Stretching out a hand, she picked up a gold coin. "I'm going to buy back my house, and I'm going to get back my land."

The farmer knew the fields. "Those old things? You could buy a valley full of prime land with half that bucket. And a palace with the other half."

"I want what I sweated for." Asking the farmer to guard her bucket, Auntie Lily closed her hand around the gold coin. Then, as the crowd parted before her, she made her way over to her neighbor.

Now the rich old woman liked to sleep late; but all the noise had woken her up, so she was just getting dressed when Auntie knocked. The old woman yanked her door open as she buttoned the last button of her coat. "Who started the riot? Can't a person get a good night's sleep?"

With some satisfaction, Auntie Lily held up the gold coin. "Will this buy back my house and land?"

"Where did you get that?" the old woman demanded.

"Will it buy them back?" Auntie Lily repeated.

The rich old woman snatched the coin out of Auntie Lily's hand and bit into it just as the farmer had. "It's real," the old woman said in astonishment.

"Will it?" Auntie asked again.

"Yes, yes, yes," the old woman said crabbily. "But where did you ever get that much gold?"

When Auntie Lily told her the story and showed her the bucket of gold, the rich old woman stood moving her mouth like a fish out of water. Clasping her hands together, she shut her eyes and moaned in genuine pain. "And I sent him away. What a fool I am. What a fool." And the old woman beat her head with her fists.

That very afternoon, the beggar—the ragbag, the trash heap, the walking pig wallow—shuffled once more through the village gates with feet as dirty as before. As he went, he croaked, "Water for my feet. Please, water for my feet. One little bowl of water—that's all I ask."

This time, people dropped whatever they were doing when they heard his plea. Hoes, brooms, and pots were flung down, hens and pigs were kicked out of the way as everyone hurried to fill a bucket with water. There was a small riot by the village well as everyone fought to get water at the same time. Still others rushed out with buckets filled from the jars in their houses.

"Here, use my water," one man shouted, holding up a tub.

A woman shoved in front of him with a bucket in her arms. "No, no, use mine. It's purer."

They surrounded the old beggar, pleading with him to use their water, and in the process of jostling one another, they splashed a good deal of water on one another and came perilously close to drowning the beggar. The rich old woman, Auntie Lily's neighbor, charged to the rescue.

"Out of the way, you vultures,"[6] the rich old woman roared. "You're going to trample him." Using her elbows, her feet, and in one case even her teeth, the old woman fought her way through the mob.

No longer caring if she soiled her hands, the old woman seized the beggar by the arm. "This way, you poor, misunderstood creature."

Fighting off her neighbors with one hand and keeping her grip on

6. **vultures** [vul′ chərz]: large birds of prey of the eagle family that eat dead animals.

the beggar with the other, the old woman hauled him inside her house. Barring the door against the rest of the village, she ignored all the fists and feet thumping on her door and all the shouts.

"I really wasn't myself yesterday, because I had been up the night before tending a sick friend. This is what I meant to do." She fetched a fresh new towel and an even newer bucket and forced the beggar to wash his feet.

When he was done, he handed her the now filthy towel. "Dirt's dirt, and garbage is garbage," he said.

However, the greedy old woman didn't recognize her own words. She was too busy trying to remember what else Auntie Lily had done. "Won't you have something to eat? Have you traveled very far? Are you tired?" she asked, all in the same breath.

The old beggar went to the door and waited patiently while she unbarred it. As he shuffled outside, he instructed her to leave the bucket of water by her bed but not to look into it until the morning.

That night, the greedy old woman couldn't sleep as she imagined the heap of shiny gold that would be waiting for her tomorrow. She waited impatiently for the sun to rise and got up as soon as she heard the first rooster crow.

Hurrying to the bucket, she plunged her hands inside expecting to bring up handfuls of gold. Instead, she gave a cry as dozens of little things bit her, for the bucket was filled not with gold but with snakes, lizards, and ants.

The greedy old woman fell sick—some said from her bites, some claimed from sheer frustration. Auntie Lily herself came to nurse her neighbor. "Take this to heart: Kindness comes with no price."

The old woman was so ashamed that she did, indeed, take the lesson to heart. Though she remained sick, she was kind to whoever came to her door.

One day, a leper came into the village. Everyone hid for fear of the terrible disease. Doors slammed and shutters banged down over windows, and soon the village seemed deserted.

Only Auntie Lily and her neighbor stepped out of their houses. "Are you hungry?" Auntie Lily asked.

"Are you thirsty?" the neighbor asked. "I'll make you a cup of tea."

The leper thanked Auntie Lily and then turned to the neighbor as if to express his gratitude as well; but he stopped and studied her. "You're looking poorly, my dear woman. Can I help?"

With a tired smile, the rich old woman explained what had happened. When she was finished, the leper stood thoughtfully for a moment. "You're not the same woman as before: You're as kind as Auntie Lily, and you aren't greedy anymore. So take this humble gift from my brother, the old beggar."

With that, the leper limped out of the village; and as he left, the illness fell away from the old woman like an old, discarded cloak. But though the old woman was healthy again, she stayed as kind as Auntie Lily and used her own money as well and wisely as Auntie Lily used the waters of gold.

LAURENCE YEP

Laurence Yep was born in 1948 in San Francisco and has lived there most of his life. He grew up, Yep has said, having two mythical homelands. One of them—China—he has yet to visit. The other—West Virginia—is where his mother grew up. As a child in California, he thought that a land like West Virginia, with four very different seasons, seemed as mythical as the land of China.

Yep has researched old Chinese myths as well as ones that have been retold more recently by Chinese immigrants to the United States. "Waters of Gold" is from his book of tales, *Tongues of Jade*. Another, similar, collection is called *The Rainbow People*.

The King and the Shoemaker

John W. Spellman

Once upon a time long ago there was a shoemaker. He made very good shoes, but he was growing old and his eyes were weak. He worked slowly because he could not see very well.

People said, "We will go to another shoemaker. We want our shoes to be made quickly, and we cannot wait so long. Your work is too slow."

So the poor old shoemaker had no money to buy new leather. He had no sons to look after him and he lived all alone. It was not long before he became tired and ill because he did not have enough food to eat.

Now, the shoemaker had one beautiful piece of leather which

he had bought many years before. It was a fine soft piece of red leather. He had never made it into shoes because he liked it very much and wanted to keep it with him always. But now he took it out of his cupboard and looked at it again.

"I will make this leather into a beautiful pair of shoes," he said. "It cost a lot of money so the shoes will be expensive. Perhaps someone will pay me thirty *rupees*[1] for them, and I can buy food and more leather with the money."

So the shoemaker got out his tools and made a pair of red shoes. He worked slowly and carefully, and they were the most beautiful shoes he had ever made. He displayed them in his shop and waited for someone to come and buy them.

The next day a man came into the shop. "What is the price of those red shoes?" he asked.

"Thirty rupees," said the man.

"The young shoemaker across the street can make me a pair of shoes for fifteen rupees."

"But this is very good leather," explained the old shoemaker. "And I have made the shoes very carefully. You will be able to wear them for many years."

"I like to buy a new pair of shoes every year," said the man. "And I do not want to pay thirty rupees for them."

He walked out of the shop.

The same thing happened again and again. People saw the beautiful red shoes in the shop, but they all said they would not pay thirty rupees for one pair of shoes. They all went to the young shoemaker who lived across the street. The poor old shoemaker was very unhappy.

One evening he was sitting sadly in his house. He had spent his last two *annas*[2] and had bought himself a cup of coffee and a loaf of bread.

1. *rupees* [rü pēz´]: plural of *rupee*, a unit of money in India.
2. *annas* [a´ nəz]: plural of *anna*, a former unit of money in India equivalent to one-sixteenth of a rupee.

"Tomorrow I shall have no food," he thought. "What is to become of me?"

It was raining outside and a cold wind was blowing. Suddenly the shoemaker heard a knock on his door. He got up and opened the door. A poor beggar stood shivering outside.

"Please, will you give me an anna?" asked the beggar. "I am cold and wet, and I have had no food today."

"I, too, have no money and no food," said the old shoemaker. "I have just spent my last two annas. But come in anyway and dry yourself beside my fire. You can sleep here tonight."

The beggar came inside and sat beside the fire. He had no shoes, and his feet were sore where the stones had cut them as he walked along the roads.

"Why have you no money, old man?" he asked.

"I am too old," the shoemaker replied. "I cannot work quickly, and everyone buys shoes from the young shoemaker who lives across the street."

The beggar picked up the new red shoes and looked at them. "These are very beautiful shoes," he said. "Why do you not sell these?"

"No one will buy them," said the shoemaker. "They say the shoes are too expensive."

"I should like a pair of shoes like that," said the beggar sadly. "My feet are sore and bleeding. But, of course, I have no money at all."

"Take the red shoes," the shoemaker said. "No one will buy them, and perhaps they will bring you good luck."

Then the shoemaker went to bed and left the beggar sitting by the fire.

When the old man woke up next morning the beggar had gone. He had taken the new red shoes with him. The shoemaker lighted his fire and heated a cup of water to drink. He had nothing to eat. All morning he sat beside the fire, wondering what could have happened to the beggar.

At one o'clock he heard a knock on his door. He went to

open it and was very surprised to see a finely dressed servant standing outside. The servant was holding a brass food carrier. "I have brought your food," he said.

"My food!" cried the shoemaker. "I don't understand. I think there must be some mistake."

The servant smiled. "There is no mistake," he said. "Last night you gave my master a pair of shoes, and he wants to repay you."

"But I gave the shoes to a beggar," said the puzzled shoemaker. "Who is your master?"

"My master is the Maharajah,"[3] said the servant. "This village belongs to him. Sometimes he gets tired of living in his palace, and he dresses like a beggar and walks through the villages. In this way he can find out whether the people are happy. Last night you thought he was a poor beggar and you gave him the only thing you had. You gave him your beautiful red shoes. Today my master sends you food, and he says he will take care of you all your life."

So the shoemaker was happy and well fed in his old age. The Maharajah never forgot him, and sometimes he would come to the village and talk to the old man. And whenever he came, the Maharajah wore the beautiful red shoes.

3. **Maharajah** [mä′ hə rä′ jə]: a ruling prince of a state in India.

JOHN W. SPELLMAN
....

John W. Spellman was born in 1934 in Tewksbury, Massachusetts. As he grew up, Spellman developed a deep interest in Asia. This interest eventually brought him to the London School of Oriental and African Studies. Spellman has taught in India, Pakistan, the Middle East, and Japan.

Most of Spellman's writing has been scholarly work about the history of India. However, in one book, *The Beautiful Blue Jay and Other Tales of India,* he collected folktales such as "The King and the Shoemaker."

THREE STRONG WOMEN

千年川竜藏

1002

Long ago, in Japan, there lived a famous wrestler, and he was on his way to the capital city to wrestle before the Emperor.

He strode down the road on legs thick as the trunks of small trees. He had been walking for seven hours and could, and probably would, walk for seven more without getting tired.

The wrestler hummed to himself, "Zun-zun-zun," in time with the long swing of his legs. Wind blew through his brown robe, and he wore no sword at his side. He felt proud that he needed no sword, even in the darkest and loneliest places. The icy air on his body only reminded him that few tailors would have been able to make expensive warm clothes for a man so broad and tall. He felt much as a wrestler should—strong, healthy, and rather conceited.

He thought: They call me Forever-Mountain because I am such a good strong wrestler—big, too. I'm a fine, brave man and far too modest ever to say so. . . .

Just then he saw a girl who must have come up from the river, for she steadied a bucket on her head.

Her hands on the bucket were small, and there was a dimple on each thumb, just below the knuckle. She was a round little girl with red cheeks and a nose like a friendly button. Her eyes looked as though she were thinking of ten thousand funny stories at once. She clambered up onto the road and walked ahead of the wrestler, jolly and bounceful.

"If I don't tickle that fat girl, I shall regret it all my life," said the wrestler under his breath. "She's sure to go 'squeak' and I shall laugh and laugh. If she drops her bucket, that will be even funnier—and I can always run and fill it again and even carry it home for her."

He tiptoed up and poked her lightly in the ribs with one huge finger.

"Kochokochokocho!" he said, a fine, ticklish sound in Japanese.

The girl gave a satisfying squeal, giggled, and brought one arm down so that the wrestler's hand was caught between it and her body.

Sumo Wrestler Kunisada, 1862, woodblock print, 10" x 14 ¼"

"Ho-ho-ho! You've caught me! I can't move at all!" said the wrestler, laughing.

"I know," said the jolly girl.

He felt that it was very good-tempered of her to take a joke so well, and started to pull his hand free.

Somehow, he could not.

He tried again, using a little more strength.

"Now, now—let me go, little girl," he said. "I am a very powerful man. If I pull too hard I might hurt you."

"Pull," said the girl. "I admire powerful men."

She began to walk, and though the wrestler tugged and pulled until his feet dug great furrows in the ground, he had to follow. She couldn't have paid him less attention if he had been a puppy—a small one.

Ten minutes later, still tugging while trudging helplessly after her, he was glad that the road was lonely and no one was there to see.

"Please let me go," he pleaded. "I am the famous wrestler Forever-Mountain. I must go and show my strength before the Emperor"—he burst out weeping from shame and confusion—"and you're hurting my hand!"

The girl steadied the bucket on her head with her free hand and dimpled sympathetically over her shoulder. "You poor, sweet little Forever-Mountain," she said. "Are you tired? Shall I carry you? I can leave the water here and come back for it later."

"I do not want you to carry me. I want you to let me go, and then I want to forget I ever saw you. What do you want with me?" moaned the pitiful wrestler.

"I only want to help you," said the girl, now pulling him steadily up and up a narrow mountain path. "Oh, I am sure you'll have no more trouble than anyone else when you come up against the other wrestlers. You'll win, or else you'll lose, and you won't be too badly hurt either way. But aren't you afraid you might meet a really *strong* man someday?"

Forever-Mountain stumbled. He was imagining being laughed at throughout Japan as "Hardly-Ever-Mountain."

She glanced back.

"You see? Tired already," she said. "I'll walk more slowly. Why don't you come along to my mother's house and let us make a strong man of you? The wrestling in the capital isn't due to begin for three months. I know, because Grandmother thought she'd go. You'd be spending all that time in bad company and wasting what little power you have."

"All right. Three months. I'll come along," said the wrestler. He felt he had nothing more to lose. Also, he feared that the girl might become angry if he refused, and place him in the top of a tree until he changed his mind.

"Fine," she said happily. "We are almost there."

She freed his hand. It had become red and a little swollen. "But if you break your promise and run off, I shall have to chase you and carry you back."

Soon they arrived in a small valley. A simple farmhouse with a thatched roof stood in the middle.

"Grandmother is at home, but she is an old lady and she's probably sleeping." The girl shaded her eyes with one hand. "But Mother should be bringing our cow back from the field—oh, there's Mother now!"

She waved. The woman coming around the corner of the house put down the cow she was carrying and waved back.

"Excuse me," she said, brushing some cow hair from her dress and dimpling, also like her daughter. "These mountain paths are full of stones. They hurt the cow's feet. And who is the nice young man you've brought, Maru-me?"[1]

The girl explained. "And we have only three months!" she finished anxiously.

"Well, it's not long enough to do much, but it's not so short a time that we can't do something," said her mother, looking thoughtful. "But he does look terribly feeble. He'll need a lot of good things to eat. Maybe when he gets stronger he can help Grandmother with some of the easy work about the house."

1. **Maru-me** [mä rů mā]

"I'm coming!" came a creaky voice from inside the house, and a little old woman leaning on a stick and looking very sleepy tottered out of the door. As she came toward them she stumbled over the roots of a great oak tree.

"Heh! My eyes aren't what they used to be. That's the fourth time this month I've stumbled over that tree," she complained and, wrapping her skinny arms about its trunk, pulled it out of the ground.

"Oh, Grandmother! You should have let me pull it up for you," said Maru-me.

Her mother went to the tree, picked it up in her two hands, and threw it—clumsily and with a little gasp.

Up went the tree, sailing end over end, growing smaller and smaller as it flew. It landed with a faint crash far up the mountainside.

"Ah, how clumsy," she said. "I meant to throw it *over* the mountain."

The wrestler was not listening. He had very quietly fainted.

"Oh! We must put him to bed," said Maru-me.

"I hope we can do something for him. Here, let me carry him, he's light," said the grandmother. She slung him over her shoulder and carried him into the house, creaking along with her cane.

The next day they began the work of making Forever-Mountain over into what they thought a strong man should be. They gave him the simplest food to eat, and the toughest. Day by day they prepared his rice with less and less water, until no ordinary man could have chewed or digested it.

Every day he was made to do the work of five women, and every evening he wrestled with Grandmother. Maru-me and her mother agreed that Grandmother, being old and feeble, was the least likely to injure him accidentally. They hoped the exercise might be good for the old lady's rheumatism.[2]

He grew stronger and stronger but was hardly aware of it. Grandmother could still throw him easily into the air—and catch him again—without ever changing her sweet old smile.

---

2. **rheumatism** [rü′ mə tiz′ əm]: a disease with swelling and stiffness of the joints.

He quite forgot that outside this valley he was one of the greatest wrestlers in Japan and was called Forever-Mountain. His legs had been like logs; now they were like pillars.

Soon he could pull up a tree as well as the grandmother. He could even throw one—but only a small distance. One evening, near the end of his third month, he wrestled with Grandmother and held her down for half a minute.

"Heh-heh!" She chortled[3] and got up, smiling with every wrinkle. "I would never have believed it!"

Maru-me squealed with joy and threw her arms around him—gently, for she was afraid of cracking his ribs.

"Very good, very good! What a strong man," said her mother, who had just come home from the fields, carrying, as usual, the cow. She put the cow down and patted the wrestler on the back.

They agreed that he was now ready to show some *real* strength before the Emperor.

"Take the cow along with you tomorrow when you go," said the mother. "Sell her and buy yourself a belt—a silken belt. Buy the fattest and heaviest one you can find. Wear it when you appear before the Emperor, as a souvenir from us."

"I wouldn't think of taking your only cow. You've already done too much for me. And you'll need her to plow the fields, won't you?"

Sumo Referee's Ceremonial Fan Kunisada, 1850, woodblock print, 4¹⁄₄" high

3. **chortled** [chôr′ tld]: chuckled with glee.

They burst out laughing. Maru-me squealed, her mother roared. The grandmother cackled so hard and long that she choked and had to be pounded on the back.

"Oh, dear," said the mother, still laughing. "You didn't think we used our cow for anything like *work!* Why, Grandmother here is stronger than five cows!"

"The cow is our pet." Maru-me giggled. "She has lovely brown eyes."

"But it really gets tiresome having to carry her back and forth each day so that she has enough grass to eat," said her mother.

"Then you must let me give you all the prize money that I win," said Forever-Mountain.

"Oh, no! We wouldn't think of it!" said Maru-me. "Because we all like you too much to sell you anything. And it is not proper to accept gifts of money from strangers."

Next morning Forever-Mountain tied his hair up in the topknot that *all* Japanese wrestlers wear, and got ready to leave. He thanked Maru-me and her mother and bowed very low to the grandmother, since she was the oldest and had been a fine wrestling partner.

Then he picked up the cow in his arms and trudged up the mountain. When he reached the top, he slung the cow over one shoulder and waved good-bye to Maru-me.

At the first town he came to, Forever-Mountain sold the cow. She brought a good price because she was unusually fat from never having worked in her life. With the money, he bought the heaviest silken belt he could find.

When he reached the palace grounds, many of the other wrestlers were already there, sitting about, eating enormous bowls of rice, comparing one another's weight and telling stories. They paid little attention to Forever-Mountain, except to wonder why he had arrived so late this year. Some of them noticed that he had grown very quiet and took no part at all in their boasting.

All the ladies and gentlemen of the court were waiting in a special courtyard for the wrestling to begin.

Behind a screen sat the Emperor—by himself, because he was too noble for ordinary people to look at. He was a lonely old man with a

Sumo Wrestler at a Celebratory Banquet Kuniaki, 1869, woodblock print,
9³/₄" x 14¹/₄"

kind, tired face. He hoped the wrestling would end quickly so that he could go to his room and write poems.

The first two wrestlers chosen to fight were Forever-Mountain and a wrestler who was said to have the biggest stomach in the country. He and Forever-Mountain both threw some salt into the ring. It was understood that this drove away evil spirits.

Then the other wrestler, moving his stomach somewhat out of the way, raised his foot and brought it down with a fearful stamp. He glared fiercely at Forever-Mountain as if to say, "Now *you* stamp, you poor frightened man!"

Forever-Mountain raised his foot. He brought it down.

There was a sound like thunder, the earth shook, and the other wrestler bounced into the air and out of the ring, as gracefully as any soap bubble.

He picked himself up and bowed to the Emperor's screen.

"The earth-god is angry. Possibly there is something the matter with the salt," he said. "I do not think I shall wrestle this season." And he walked out, looking very suspiciously over one shoulder at Forever-Mountain.

Five other wrestlers then and there decided that they were not wrestling this season, either.

From then on, Forever-Mountain brought his foot down lightly. As each wrestler came into the ring, he picked him up very gently, carried him out, and placed him before the Emperor's screen, bowing most courteously every time.

The court ladies' eyebrows went up even higher. The gentlemen looked disturbed and a little afraid. They loved to see fierce, strong men tugging and grunting at each other, but Forever-Mountain was a little too much for them. Only the Emperor was happy behind his screen, for now, with the wrestling over so quickly, he would have that much more time to write his poems. He ordered all the prize money handed over to Forever-Mountain.

"But," he said, "you had better not wrestle any more." He stuck a finger through his screen and waggled it at the other wrestlers, who were sitting on the ground weeping with disappointment like great fat babies.

Forever-Mountain promised not to wrestle any more. Everybody looked relieved. The wrestlers sitting on the ground almost smiled.

"I think I shall become a farmer," Forever-Mountain said, and left at once to go back to Maru-me.

Maru-me was waiting for him. When she saw him coming, she ran down the mountain, picked him up together with the heavy bags of prize money, and carried him halfway up the mountainside. Then she giggled and put him down. The rest of the way she let him carry her.

Forever-Mountain kept his promise to the Emperor and never fought in public again. His name was forgotten in the capital. But up in the mountain sometimes, the earth shakes and rumbles, and they say that is Forever-Mountain and Maru-me's grandmother practicing wrestling in the hidden valley.

CLAUS STAMM

Claus Stamm was born in 1929 in Germany. As a native speaker, he is naturally fluent in German. But when he joined the U.S. Army just after World War II, the army needed specialists in Japanese. Stamm was sent to language school and learned that language too.

In Japan, Stamm became fascinated by the legends he heard being told to children. After his military service, he went to Columbia University, majored in English composition, and continued his study of Japanese. Eventually he went to live in Japan again.

Stamm began to write down the Japanese stories and folktales he heard. Sometimes he added a new character or changed an ending. "Three Strong Women" is one of these tales.

ARACHNE

Olivia Coolidge

Arachne was a maiden who became famous throughout Greece, though she was neither wellborn nor beautiful and came from no great city. She lived in an obscure little village, and her father was a humble dyer of wool. In this he was very skillful, producing many varied shades, while above all he was famous for the clear, bright scarlet which is made from shellfish, and which was the most glorious of all the colors used in ancient Greece. Even more skillful than her father was Arachne. It was her task to spin the fleecy wool into a fine, soft thread and to weave it into cloth on the high, standing loom within the cottage. Arachne was small and pale from much working. Her eyes were light and her hair was dusty brown, yet she was quick and graceful, and her fingers, roughened as they were, went so fast that it was hard to follow their flickering movements. So soft and even was her thread, so fine her cloth, so gorgeous her embroidery, that soon her products were known all over Greece. No one had ever seen the like of them before.

At last Arachne's fame became so great that people used to come from far and wide to watch her working. Even the graceful nymphs[1] would steal in from stream or forest and peep shyly through the dark doorway, watching in wonder the white arms of Arachne as she stood at the loom and threw the shuttle from hand

---

1. **nymphs** [nimfs]: Greek goddesses of nature, found in seas, fountains, hills, or woods.

Greek vase c. 430 B.C.,
The Louvre, Paris, France

to hand between the hanging threads, or drew out the long wool, as fine as a hair, from the distaff [2] as she sat spinning. "Surely Athene[3] herself must have taught her," people would murmur to one another. "Who else could know the secret of such marvelous skill?"

Arachne was used to being wondered at, and she was immensely proud of the skill that had brought so many to look on her. Praise was all she lived for, and it displeased her greatly that people should think anyone, even a goddess, could teach her anything. Therefore when she heard them murmur, she would stop her work and turn round indignantly to say, "With my own ten fingers I gained this skill, and by hard practice from early morning till night. I never had time to stand looking as you people do while another maiden worked. Nor if I had, would I give Athene credit because the girl was more skillful than I. As for Athene's weaving, how could there be finer cloth or more beautiful embroidery than mine? If Athene herself were to come down and compete with me, she could do no better than I."

One day when Arachne turned round with such words, an old woman answered her, a grey old woman, bent and very poor, who stood leaning on a staff and peering at Arachne amid the crowd of onlookers. "Reckless girl," she said, "how dare you claim to be equal to the immortal gods themselves? I am an old woman and have seen much. Take my advice and ask pardon of Athene for your words. Rest content

2. **distaff** [dis taf′]: a staff on a spinning wheel for holding wool or flax.
3. **Athene** [ə thē′ nē]: the Greek goddess of wisdom, art, industry, and prudent warfare.

with your fame of being the best spinner and weaver that mortal eyes have ever beheld."

"Stupid old woman," said Arachne indignantly, "who gave you a right to speak in this way to me? It is easy to see that you were never good for anything in your day, or you would not come here in poverty and rags to gaze at my skill. If Athene resents my words, let her answer them herself. I have challenged her to a contest, but she, of course, will not come. It is easy for the gods to avoid matching their skill with that of men."

At these words the old woman threw down her staff and stood erect. The wondering onlookers saw her grow tall and fair and stand clad in long robes of dazzling white. They were terribly afraid as they realized that they stood in the presence of Athene. Arachne herself flushed red for a moment, for she had never really believed that the goddess would hear her. Before the group that was gathered there she would not give in; so pressing her pale lips together in obstinacy and pride, she led the goddess to one of the great looms and set herself at the other. Without a word both began to thread the long wooden strands that hang from the rollers, and between which the shuttle moves back and forth. Many skeins lay heaped beside them to use, bleached white, and gold, and scarlet, and other shades, varied as the rainbow. Arachne had never thought of giving credit for her success to her father's skill in dyeing, though in actual truth the colors were as remarkable as the cloth itself.

Soon there was no sound in the room but the breathing of the on-lookers, the whirring of the shuttles, and the creaking of the wooden frames as each pressed the thread into place or tightened the pegs by which the whole was held straight. The excited crowd in the doorway began to see that the skill of both in truth was very nearly equal, but that, however the cloth might turn out, the goddess was the quicker of the two. A pattern of many pictures was growing on her loom. There was a border of twined branches of the olive, Athene's favorite tree, while in the middle, figures began to appear. As they looked at the glowing colors, the spectators realized that Athene was weaving into her pattern a last warning to Arachne. The central figure was the goddess herself competing with Poseidon[4] for possession of the city of Athens; but in the four corners were mortals who had tried to strive with gods and pictures of the awful fate that had overtaken them. The goddess ended a little before Arachne and stood back from her marvelous work to see what the maiden was doing.

Never before had Arachne been matched against anyone whose skill was equal, or even nearly equal to her own. As she stole glances from time to time at Athene and saw the goddess working swiftly, calmly, and always a little faster than herself, she became angry instead of frightened, and an evil thought came into her head. Thus as Athene stepped back a pace to watch Arachne finishing her work, she saw that the maiden had taken for her design a pattern of scenes which showed evil or unworthy actions of the gods, how they had deceived fair maidens, resorted to trickery, and appeared on earth from time to time in the form of poor and humble people. When the goddess saw this insult glowing in bright colors on Arachne's loom, she did not wait while the cloth was judged, but stepped forward, her grey eyes blazing with anger, and tore Arachne's work across. Then she struck Arachne across the face. Arachne stood there a moment, struggling with fear and pride. "I will not live under this insult," she cried, and seizing a rope from the wall, she made a noose and would have hanged herself.

The goddess touched the rope and touched the maiden. "Live on, wicked girl," she said. "Live on and spin, both you and your descendants. When men look at you they may remember that it is not wise to strive with Athene." At that the body of Arachne shrivelled up, and her legs grew tiny, spindly, and distorted. There before the eyes of the spectators hung a little dusty brown spider on a slender thread.

All spiders descend from Arachne, and as the Greeks watched them spinning their thread wonderfully fine, they remembered the contest with Athene and thought that it was not right for even the best of men to claim equality with the gods.

4. **Poseidon** [pə sīd′ n]: the Greek god of the sea.

OLIVIA COOLIDGE

Olivia Coolidge was born in 1908 in London, England. Her father was a historian and journalist, which meant that Coolidge grew up hearing about both ancient and current events.

Today, Coolidge has taught Latin, Greek, and English in the United States, where she has made her home. She has written many books of mythology and a number of biographies of famous people, both ancient and modern. The story of Arachne is one of the stories Coolidge retold in her book, *Greek Myths.* You can find more tales of ancient Greece in her book, *The Trojan War.*

THE BUILDING OF THE WALL

Fantastic City Vera Stravinsky, 1976-1977, gouache, 7 $^5/_{16}$" x 10 $^{15}/_{16}$"

PADRAIC COLUM

Always there had been war between the Giants and the Gods—between the Giants who would have destroyed the world and the race of men, and the Gods who would have protected the race of men and would have made the world more beautiful.

There are many stories to be told about the Gods, but the first one that should be told to you is the one about the building of their City.

The Gods had made their way up to the top of a high mountain and there they decided to build a great City for themselves that the Giants could never overthrow. The City they would call "Asgard," which means the Place of the Gods. They would build it on a beautiful plain that was on the top of that high mountain. And they wanted to raise round their City the highest and strongest wall that had ever been built.

Now one day when they were beginning to build their halls and their palaces a strange being came to them. Odin the Father of the Gods, went and spoke to him. "What dost thou want on the Mountain of the Gods?" he asked the Stranger.

"I know what is in the mind of the Gods," the Stranger said. "They would build a City here. I cannot build palaces, but I can build great walls that can never be overthrown. Let me build the wall round your City."

"How long will it take you to build a wall that will go round our City?" said the Father of the Gods.

"A year, O Odin," said the Stranger.

Now Odin knew that if a great wall could be built around it the Gods would not have to spend all their time defending their City, Asgard, from the Giants, and he knew that if Asgard were protected, he himself could go amongst men and teach them and help them. He thought that no payment the Stranger could ask would be too much for the building of that wall.

That day the Stranger came to the Council of the Gods, and he swore that in a year he would have the great wall built. Then Odin made oath that the Gods would give him what he asked in payment if the wall was finished to the last stone in a year from that day.

The Stranger went away and came back on the morrow. It was the first day of Summer when he started work. He brought no one to help him except a great horse.

Now the Gods thought that this horse would do no more than drag blocks of stone for the building of the wall. But the horse did more than this. He set the stones in their places and mortared them together. And day and night and by light and dark the horse worked, and soon a great wall was rising round the palaces that the Gods themselves were building.

"What reward will the Stranger ask for the work he is doing for us?" the Gods asked one another.

Odin went to the Stranger. "We marvel at the work you and your horse are doing for us," he said. "No one can doubt that the great wall of Asgard will be built up by the first day of Summer. What reward do you claim? We would have it ready for you."

The Stranger turned from the work he was doing, leaving the great horse to pile up the blocks of stone. "O Father of the Gods," he said, "O Odin, the reward I shall ask for my work is the Sun and the Moon, and Freya, who watches over the flowers and grasses, for my wife."

Now when Odin heard this he was terribly angered, for the price the Stranger asked for his work was beyond all prices. He went amongst the other Gods who were then building their shining palaces within the great wall and he told them what reward the Stranger had asked. The Gods said, "Without the Sun and the Moon the world will wither away." And the Goddesses said, "Without Freya all will be gloom in Asgard."

They would have let the wall remain unbuilt rather than let the Stranger have the reward he claimed for building it. But one who was in the company of the Gods spoke. He was Loki, a being who only half belonged to the Gods; his father was the Wind Giant. "Let the Stranger build the wall round Asgard," Loki said, "and I will find a way to make him give up the hard bargain he has made with the Gods. Go to him and tell him that the wall must be finished by the first day of Summer, and that if it is not finished to the last stone on that day the price he asks will not be given to him."

The Gods went to the Stranger and they told him that if the last stone was not laid on the wall on the first day of the Summer not Sol or Mani, the Sun and the Moon, nor Freya would be given him. And now they knew that the Stranger was one of the Giants.

The Giant and his great horse piled up the wall more quickly than before. At night, while the Giant slept, the horse worked on and on, hauling up stones and laying them on the wall with his great forefeet. And day by day the wall around Asgard grew higher and higher.

But the Gods had no joy in seeing that great wall rising higher and higher around their palaces. The Giant and his horse would finish the work by the first day of Summer, and he would take the Sun and the Moon, Sol and Mani, and Freya away with him.

But Loki was not disturbed. He kept telling the gods that he would find a way to prevent him from finishing his work, and thus he would make the Giant forfeit the terrible price he had led Odin to promise him.

It was three days to Summer time. All the wall was finished except the gateway. Over the gateway a stone was still to be placed. And the Giant, before he went to sleep, bade his horse haul up a great block of stone so that they might put it above the gateway in the morning, and so finish the work two full days before Summer.

It happened to be a beautiful moonlit night. Svadilfare, the Giant's great horse, was hauling when he saw a little mare come galloping towards him. The great horse had never seen so pretty a little mare and he looked at her with surprise.

"Svadilfare, slave," said the little mare to him and went frisking past.

Svadilfare put down the stone he was hauling and called to the little mare. She came back to him. "Why do you call me 'Svadilfare, slave'?" said the great horse.

"Because you have to work night and day for your master," said the little mare. "He keeps you working, working, working, and never lets you enjoy yourself. You dare not leave that stone down and come and play with me."

"Who told you I dare not do it?" said Svadilfare.

"I know you daren't do it," said the little mare, and she kicked up her heels and ran across the moonlit meadow.

Now the truth is that Svadilfare was tired of working day and

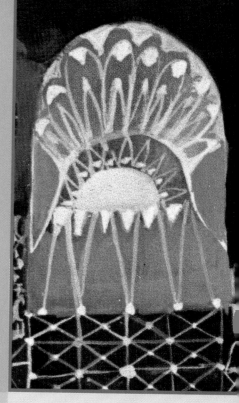

Detail from
Fantastic City
Vera Stravinsky

Detail from
Fantastic City
Vera Stravinsky

night. When he saw the little mare go galloping off he became suddenly discontented. He left the stone he was hauling on the ground. He looked round and saw the little mare looking back at him. He galloped after her.

He did not catch up on the little mare. She went on swiftly before him. On she went over the moonlit meadow, turning and looking back now and again at the great Svadilfare, who came heavily after her. Down the mountainside the mare went, and Svadilfare, who now rejoiced in his liberty and in the freshness of the wind and in the smell of the flowers, still followed her. With the morning's light they came near a cave and the little mare went into it. They went through the cave. Then Svadilfare caught up on the little mare and the two went wandering together, the little mare telling Svadilfare stories of the Dwarfs and the Elves.

They came to a grove and they stayed together in it, the little mare playing so nicely with him that the great horse forgot all about time passing. And while they were in the grove the Giant was going up and down, searching for his great horse.

He had come to the wall in the morning, expecting to put the stone over the gateway and so to finish his work. But the stone that was to be lifted was not near him. He called for Svadilfare, but his great horse did not come. He went to search for him, and he searched all down the mountainside and he searched as far across the earth as the realm of the Giants. But he did not find Svadilfare.

The Gods saw the first day of Summer come and the gateway of the wall stand unfinished. They said to each other that if it were not finished by the evening they need not give Sol and Mani to the Giant, nor the maiden Freya to be his wife. The hours of the summer day went past and the Giant did not raise the stone over the gateway. In the evening he came before them.

"Your work is not finished," Odin said. "You forced us to a hard bargain and now we need not keep it with you. You shall not be given Sol and Mani nor the maiden Freya."

"Only the wall I have built is so strong I would tear it down," said the Giant. He tried to throw down one of the palaces, but the Gods laid hands on him and thrust him outside the wall he had built. "Go, and trouble Asgard no more," Odin commanded.

Then Loki returned to Asgard. He told the Gods how he had transformed himself into a little mare and had led away Svadilfare, the Giant's great horse. And the Gods sat in their golden palaces behind the great wall and rejoiced that their city was now secure, and that no enemy could ever enter it or overthrow it. But Odin, the Father of the Gods, as he sat upon his throne was sad in his heart, sad that the Gods had got their wall built by a trick; that oaths had been broken, and that a blow had been struck in injustice in Asgard.

PADRAIC COLUM

Padraic Colum [1881-1972] was born in Longford, Ireland. As a young boy, he lived with his grandmother, who was a born storyteller. She brought him up on the legends, songs, and poetry that would shine through his own writings later. Colum was educated in local schools and worked for the railroad briefly before becoming a full-time writer by the time he was twenty.

Colum was famous as a poet and a playwright as well as a teller of tales. Some of his poems have become familiar Irish folksongs. As he put it, "Poems are . . . for our voices, not just for our eyes."

Colum came to the United States in 1914. He began writing children's books because, he once said, "we must see to it that young people's imaginations are not clipped or made trivial."

In 1923, Colum went to Hawaii, at the request of the government, to retell their traditional tales in *Legends of Hawaii*. Colum's stories range from Greek myths to Arabian tales—and Norse stories like *The Children of Odin*, from which this story comes.

The
Legend *of the*
Hummingbird

P U R A   B E L P R É

Crimson Topaz Hummingbird
Louis Agassiz Fuertes, pencil and watercolor

Between the towns of Cayey[1] and Cidra,[2] far up in the hills, there was once a small pool fed by a waterfall that tumbled down the side of the mountain. The pool was surrounded by pomarosa trees,[3] and the Indians used to call it Pomarosa Pool. It was the favorite place of Alida, the daughter of an Indian chief, a man of power and wealth among the people of the hills.

One day, when Alida had come to the pool to rest after a long walk, a young Indian came there to pick some fruit from the trees. Alida was surprised, for he was not of her tribe. Yet he said he was no stranger to the pool. This was where he had first seen Alida, and he had often returned since to pick fruit, hoping to see her again.

1. **Cayey** [kä′ yā]: a town in Southeast Puerto Rico.
2. **Cidra** [sēd′ rə]: a town in East Central Puerto Rico.
3. **pomarosa trees** [pō′ mä rō′ sä]: apple trees found in the West Indies.

He told her about himself to make her feel at home. He confessed, with honesty and frankness, that he was a member of the dreaded Carib tribe[4] that had so often attacked the island of Boriquen.[5] As a young boy, he had been left behind after one of those raids, and he had stayed on the island ever since.

Alida listened closely to his story, and the two became friends. They met again in the days that followed, and their friendship grew stronger. Alida admired the young man's courage in living among his enemies. She learned to call him by his Carib name, Taroo, and he called her Alida, just as her own people did. Before long, their friendship had turned into love.

Their meetings by the pool were always brief. Alida was afraid their secret might be discovered, and careful though she was, there came a day when someone saw them and told her father. Alida was forbidden to visit Pomarosa Pool, and to put an end to her romance with the stranger, her father decided to marry her to a man of his own choosing. Preparations for the wedding started at once.

Alida was torn with grief, and one evening she cried out to her god: "O Yukiyú, help me! Kill me or do what you will with me, but do not let me marry this man whom I do not love!"

And the great god Yukiyú took pity on her and changed her into a delicate red flower.

Meanwhile Taroo, knowing nothing of Alida's sorrow, still waited for her by Pomarosa Pool. Day after day he waited. Sometimes he stayed there until a mantle of stars was spread across the sky.

One night the moon took pity on him. "Taroo," she called from her place high above the stars. "O Taroo, wait no longer for Alida! Your secret was made known, and Alida was to be married to a man

Crimson Topaz Hummingbird
Louis Agassiz Fuertes, pencil and watercolor

4. **Carib tribe** [kar′ əb]: Native Americans who lived in the northern part of South America and on islands in the southern part of the Caribbean Sea.
5. **Boriquen** [bōr ə′ kän]: early name of Puerto Rico.

of her father's choosing. In her grief she called to her god, Yukiyú; he heard her plea for help and changed her into a red flower."

"Ahee, ahee!" cried Taroo. "O moon, what is the name of the red flower?"

"Only Yukiyú knows that," the moon replied.

Then Taroo called out: O Yukiyú, god of my Alida, help me too! Help me to find her!"

And just as the great god had heard Alida's plea, he listened now to Taroo and decided to help him. There by the Pomarosa Pool, before the moon and the silent stars, the great god changed Taroo into a small many-colored bird.

"Fly, Colibrí, and find your love among the flowers," he said.

Off went Colibrí, flying swiftly, and as he flew his wings made a sweet humming sound.

In the morning the Indians saw a new bird darting about among the flowers, swift as an arrow and brilliant as a jewel. They heard the humming of its wings, and in amazement they saw it hover in the air over every blossom, kissing the petals of the flowers with its long slender bill. They liked the new bird with the music in its wings, and they called it Hummingbird.

Ever since then the little many-colored bird has hovered over every flower he finds, but returns most often to the flowers that are red. He is still looking, always looking, for the one red flower that will be his lost Alida. He has not found her yet.

PURA BELPRÉ

Pura Belpré was born in Cidra, Puerto Rico, and came to the United States in the 1920s. She began her career as a storyteller in the New York Public Library program. To add to her storytelling, she became a skillful puppeteer, designing her own puppets to fit her stories. Belpré has also translated English language stories into Spanish, including several well-known books for young children.

Belpré published her first story in 1932. She has retold scores of Puerto Rican folktales ever since. *Once in Puerto Rico* has long been a popular book; also popular are her stories of the folk character Juan Bobo.

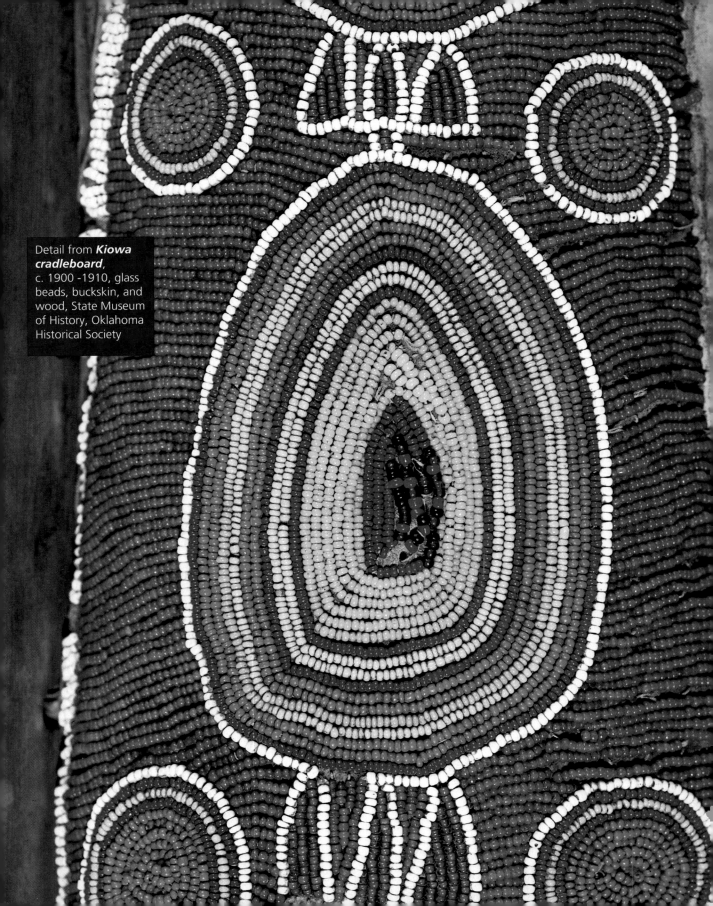

Detail from *Kiowa cradleboard*, c. 1900 -1910, glass beads, buckskin, and wood, State Museum of History, Oklahoma Historical Society

CARRIERS OF THE *Dream Wheel*

N. SCOTT MOMADAY

THIS IS THE WHEEL OF DREAMS
WHICH IS CARRIED ON THEIR VOICES,
BY MEANS OF WHICH THEIR VOICES TURN
AND CENTER UPON BEING.
IT ENCIRCLES THE FIRST WORLD,   5
THIS POWERFUL WHEEL.
THEY SHAPE THEIR SONGS UPON THE WHEEL
AND SPIN THE NAMES OF THE EARTH AND SKY,
THE ABORIGINAL[1] NAMES.
THEY ARE OLD MEN, OR MEN   10
WHO ARE OLD IN THEIR VOICES,
AND THEY CARRY THE WHEEL AMONG THE CAMPS,
SAYING: COME, COME,
LET US TELL THE OLD STORIES,
LET US SING THE SACRED SONGS.   15

1. **aboriginal** [ab′ ə rij′ ə nəl]: original, existing from the beginning.

N. SCOTT MOMADAY

N(avarre) Scott Momaday was born in 1934 in Lawton, Oklahoma, and grew up on the reservations of the Southwest. Momaday has described his boyhood as a time when he saw "people who were deeply involved in their traditional life, in the memories of their blood."

Momaday has taught English at several large universities and exhibited his paintings in many galleries. He is known as a writer of both poetry and prose. His first novel, *House Made of Dawn*, won the Pulitzer Prize in 1969, but he thinks of himself primarily as a poet. One collection of his poems is called *The Gourd Dancer*. Momaday has also retold the Kiowa folktales in *The Way to Rainy Mountain*.

Asking Big Questions About the Literature

How are tales from around the world alike and different?

LITERATURE STUDY

Theme

The main idea of a work of literature is called the **theme**. The theme is often presented in the form of a lesson. For example, many folktales teach that kindness to strangers will be rewarded. List all the literature selections you've read and tell the theme of each one. (*See "Theme" on page 120.*)

COMPARE SELECTIONS

Choose two literature selections from this unit. Then make a chart like the one below comparing and contrasting these two selections. Use the chart to help you write a short essay comparing and contrasting the themes.

Create A FOLKTALE

In a group, discuss the similarities and differences between the literature selections you've read. Then write a universal folktale that includes features and characters from several myths and folktales you've read.

Selection Title	Differences	Shared Features
"Waters of Gold"	The rich woman does not help the beggar.	Kindness is rewarded.
"The King and the Shoemaker"	The only rich character in the story disguises himself as a beggar.	Both Auntie Lily and and the shoemaker are poor, but give what they have to a beggar.

PLAY

Join a group of five or six classmates. Then choose a literature selection you've all read. Write a short play based on the story. After each group has performed its play, hold a class discussion of the differences and similarities between the stories.

LITERATURE STUDY

Plot

Plot is the sequence of actions and events in a work of literature. The plot is often the most important element of a story, because it tells you what happens. Think about the plot of two selections with a similar theme, such as "The Storytelling Stone" and "All Stories are Anansi's," and write an essay comparing the two plots. (*See "Plot" on page 121.*)

PLOT *a Chart*

Several of the selections in this unit feature similar events. For example, both "Baucis and Philemon" and "Arachne" feature disguised gods who suddenly reveal their identity. Make a plot chart like the one here, showing the differences and similarities between the plots of two or more selections you've read. Show the similarities in the same box.

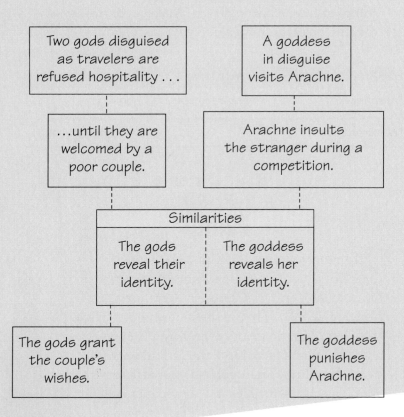

Two gods disguised as travelers are refused hospitality . . .

A goddess in disguise visits Arachne.

. . . until they are welcomed by a poor couple.

Arachne insults the stranger during a competition.

Similarities

The gods reveal their identity.

The goddess reveals her identity.

The gods grant the couple's wishes.

The goddess punishes Arachne.

Asking Big Questions About the Literature

Why do people everywhere have myths and folktales?

HOLD a Discussion

Hold a class discussion about why people all over the world have myths and folktales. Are folktales meant to entertain, to explain something, or to teach some truth? Make a chart like the one below to help guide your discussion.

Selection Title	To explain . . .	To teach us . . .
"Arachne"	why spiders spin.	humility.
"Waters of Gold"		to help the poor.

LITERATURE STUDY
Plot

In most folktales the **plot**—the sequence of the story's events—features fantastic or unbelievable happenings. Choose a literature selection you've read. Then write a newspaper article that describes the story's events as if they had actually taken place. Give the article a sensational headline. Then publish your article with your classmates' articles in a newspaper called "The Tall Tale Times." (*See "Plot" on page 121.*)

Write a
CHILDREN'S BOOK

Look through the selections you've read for stories that explain something. Then write a folktale that tells why people all over the world have myths and folktales. Publish it in the form of an illustrated children's book.

LITERATURE STUDY

Theme

Most stories have a **theme**, or main idea. The theme is often not stated directly but is revealed through the plot. For example, in "Baucis and Philemon," the events of the plot show that hospitality is rewarded. For each literature selection you've read, draw two circles like the ones below. Write the theme of the selection in the inner circle. Then write the events of the plot in the outer circle. Number the plot events in the order in which they happen. (*See "Theme" on page 120.*)

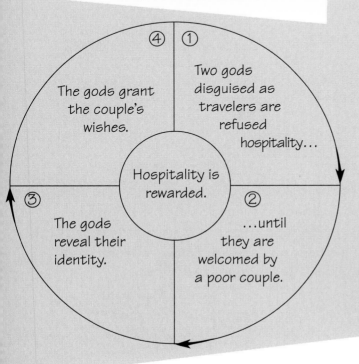

④ The gods grant the couple's wishes.

① Two gods disguised as travelers are refused hospitality...

Hospitality is rewarded.

③ The gods reveal their identity.

② ...until they are welcomed by a poor couple.

Write AN ESSAY

Look through the literature selections you've read. Then write a short essay explaining why you think it is important for each generation to retell the myths and folktales they've learned.

Write a

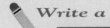
RESEARCH PAPER

Many of the literature selections in this unit are very old, having been handed down for generations. Choose a literature selection you've read and research some historical aspect of the story. For example, if you choose "The Story of the Shipwrecked Sailor," research ancient Egyptian boats. Then write a research paper on the subject.

NOW

Choose a Project!

Three projects involving myths and folktales are described on the following pages. Which one is for you?

Writing Workshop

WRITING A STORY

The impulse to tell a story and the need to listen to it have made storytelling fun for all ages. In this project, your **purpose** will be to write a tale and be a storyteller for an **audience** of nursery school or kindergarten children.

To find a story idea that will appeal to this audience, think back to the kinds of questions you asked at that age, such as "Where do lights go when they're turned off?" Write down a question, like the one shown here, and make a cluster of possible answers.

Prewriting
CHOOSING A STORY IDEA

evaporate into the air — Where do lights go when they're turned off? — into the lamp base

follow cord into outlet

Another way to generate story ideas is to start with the theme you want to communicate. For example, if you want your message to be that you can help yourself by helping others, think of situations in which this theme would be true. In your journal, try freewriting for three to five minutes. Then circle the idea that would appeal to your young audience the most.

Think of a story as a kaleidoscope—a collection of bits of colored glass that can be arranged and rearranged into beautiful patterns. Like the bits of colored glass, the elements of a story must also work together to create meaning.

To help you develop your story idea, think about the following elements. Then organize your ideas by creating a story outline using these elements.

Story Elements

Theme: the writer's message
Setting: the time and place
Conflict: the problem the main character faces
Characters: the people or animals with the details of their name, age, physical appearance, and personality traits
Plot: the events that trigger the action and tell the story
Resolution: the way in which the conflict is settled

To help you organize the action of the story, list the events in the story in the shape of a pyramid. Keep in mind that the events should build tension until the plot reaches its climax—*the highest point in the story.* Notice how the pyramid below lists the events in the student model written by Dara Bloom on pages 112 and 113.

Climax

Becomes bored with the holidays

Elf grants wish

Returns to brook

Goes to magical brook

Elf takes wish back

Kelsey is sad

Kelsey no longer
unhappy with life

Beginning

Resolution

Drafting
YOUR STORY

With your story outline filled in and your pyramid developed, you're ready to draft your story. Use the following guidelines to help you.

- Start your story with pizzazz! "Once upon a time . . . " or "Long ago in the land of . . . " are reliable beginnings, but you can also capture your young audience's attention with dialogue, action, or description. For example, Dara Bloom, a student writer, uses description to introduce her story on pages 112 and 113. "Looking at the sea of wrapping paper covering the floor, Kelsey sighed deeply."

- Use dialogue or a character's thoughts to illustrate the central conflict in your story. For example, Dara develops her story entirely through Kelsey's thoughts and the use of dialogue. The conflict is created by Kelsey's first wish. "I wish that every day was a holiday."

- Be sure to keep your audience and purpose in mind as you write your draft. Explain each event logically and dramatically and make sure that your word choice and sentence structure are simple enough for children to grasp.

- Draft a conclusion for your story. Your ending is the natural result of the story's design. It resolves the conflict, completes the action, and leaves your readers satisfied. For example, Dara conveys the theme of her story in Kelsey's last statement: "I won't forget the cloudy days when I think of the sunny ones!"

- End by drafting a title that shouts "Read Me!" Experiment with several different ways to grab the attention and curiosity of your audience. Notice how Dara's title, "One Wish Too Many," makes you curious about what the wish could be.

Revising YOUR STORY

Taking a second look at your story gives you the chance to polish it before you share it with others. Treat your draft like someone else's work. Find a place to read it out loud to a partner. Then ask for a response to the following questions. Is the story interesting? Is the conflict clearly understood? Is there a climax or turning point? Are there any irrelevant actions or details? Does the dialogue help develop the conflict and the characters? Is the conflict resolved at the end of the story? Would an audience of young children like the subject of my story? Is my word choice simple and clear enough for them to understand?

Editing YOUR STORY

Since your story will be read aloud to nursery school or kindergarten children, it's important to correct any errors in grammar, usage, spelling, and punctuation. A misspelled word or a clumsy sentence will confuse both the reader and the listeners.

Publishing YOUR STORY

Now you're ready to share your story with your intended audience of kindergarten and nursery school children. In your journal, brainstorm several different ways to publish your story. The following ideas may help you get started.

- Collect your classmates' stories into an illustrated anthology. Display the anthology in your school library.
- Make an audiotape to accompany your story. Present the story and tape to a kindergarten or nursery school classroom.
- Visit a neighborhood school or library and ask permission to hold a story hour.

ONE WISH TOO MANY

by Dara Bloom
Katonah, New York

ooking at the sea of wrapping paper covering the floor, Kelsey sighed deeply. What a wonderful day it had been! How she loved birthdays! The day, though, was now over and upstairs to bed she had to go.

Reluctantly, Kelsey said goodnight and went to bed. Comforted by thoughts of the wonderful day, she quickly fell into a sound sleep. It was the middle of the night when Kelsey woke and felt a tremendous sadness as she realized that her birthday was all over and her relatives had gone home. Finding it hard to go back to sleep, Kelsey went downstairs. Sitting down on a large chair, she closed her eyes and listened to the sounds of the night, especially the small brook in her back yard. The brook—that was it! It was such a magical place! Quickly she ran out of the house and down to the brook, where she made a wish.

"I wish that every day was a holiday—lots of presents, lots of fun, and no school!"

"Is that what you really want?" inquired a gruff voice.

Kelsey stood up and looked around. There by the side of the brook sat a strange little man. "Well, is that really what you want? You do have a wish coming to you, for it is the night of your seventh birthday and there is a full moon."

Kelsey looked in awe at the little man. He was an elf—no larger than her hand.

"Yes," she replied. "I wish that every day would be a marvelous holiday!"

"So it will be," he said as he disappeared.

....

"Good morning! It's 8:30 and you're listening to WA85! Looks like we have another holiday today, so just lie back and take a break!"

And so on it went! Day after day, there was one holiday after another. Yet now Kelsey discovered a new problem. Holidays had become boring.

"Why aren't holidays fun anymore?" Kelsey asked her mother.

"Well, I think we've had too much of a good thing," she answered. "You need a cloudy day to appreciate the beauty of a sunny one."

That night when Kelsey went to bed, she thought, "It's all my fault! I've got to do something to get things back to normal. I must go back to the brook."

Quickly she ran down to the brook. "Little man, little man, where are you? I want to take back my wish!" she cried.

"Okay," he said, "but this is it! No more wishes for you!" As Kelsey smiled in agreement, he vanished.

....

Good morning! It's 8:30 and you're listening to WA85! Looks like we have heavy traffic out there this morning. Be careful as everyone heads back to work.

Kelsey smiled as she realized that her nightmare was over. "I'll always love holidays," she thought as she got up to go to school. "But I won't forget the cloudy days when I think of the sunny ones!"

2

Cooperative Learning

Did you know that the earliest drama in the world was created when people turned their myths into plays? This project will give you an opportunity to dramatize, or make a play out of, a myth or a folktale of your choice.

Develop
THE SCRIPT

As a class, choose a myth or folktale from this unit or from any other source. Make sure that the story is simple enough to dramatize in the time you have.

Let everyone read the story you've chosen. On the chalkboard, make a list of the characters and the scenes you want to dramatize. Then *improvise*, or perform without a script, the first scene. Imagine what the characters would say and how they might feel. Let one person record the best lines of the actors as they improvise. Use your improvised performance as the basis of your dialogue.

Now divide into teams of three to five students. Let each team choose a scene to work on, using the method suggested above. For the scene that your group has chosen to write, select actors and a writer who will record the dialogue and develop the script. Make a chart like the one below to help you.

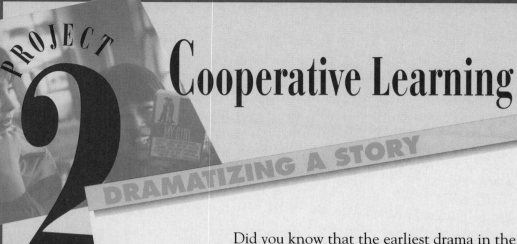

ARACHNE
a play by the Students of Class 7-B

CHARACTERS

ARACHNE	a young Greek maiden about eighteen
ARACHNE'S FATHER	a humble man
ATHENE	(appears in two forms), a grey old woman a beautiful Greek goddess
GREEK VILLAGERS	onlookers
SPIDER	Arachne transformed

ACT 1

Stage shows the interior of a room in a very modest Greek dwelling that existed centuries ago. The furnishings are quite simple and basic, such as a couple of wooden chairs and small table. In the center of the room is a spinning wheel and stool. A basket of wool is positioned on the floor next to the spinning wheel. Morning light filters into the room. As the curtain rises, we see Arachne in the process of spinning wool. Her father enters the room.

Description of Scene

....

Actor(s) _____

_____

Writer(s) _____

_____

ARACHNE'S FATHER (enters...
Well, h...
with y...

ARACHNE (neve...
Why,...
Som...
the...

1040

ARACHNE'S FATHER Wh...
th...
p...
t...

Rehearse
THE PLAY

After you've written the dialogue, perform the scene for your class. Study the performance of the other groups so that you can choose an actor who will play the same character in every scene. Then, working together as a class, choose a director who will guide the rehearsals and suggest improvements to the actors' gestures, tone of voice, and movement. Some of these improvements should be added to the script in the form of *stage directions*, which tell the actors what to do.

The actors should now memorize their lines. Now is also the time to choose a set designer and a costume designer to work on the production. You might also need someone to control the lighting and someone else to provide music and sound effects. Make a chart like the one here to keep track of the tasks and who will be responsible for each one.

Rehearse until everyone knows their cues and the production runs smoothly.

Task Chart

Costume designer _____
Set designer _____
Lighting technician _____
Sound technician _____

Stage
THE PLAY

Decide on the time and place for your performance. After your performance, consider presenting it in some other form, such as a video or a tape recording.

Helping Your Community

HOLDING A STORYTELLING FESTIVAL

Just about everyone has a favorite childhood story or legend that he or she would enjoy sharing with others. Your task in this project is to seek out those stories and their tellers and to organize them into a community Storytelling Festival.

Choosing THE TIME AND PLACE

With your classmates, begin your planning by deciding when and where to hold your festival. Should it be day or evening? Would you prefer a small gathering or a large audience? Where could you possibly have it?

Organizing THE PROJECT

Once you and your classmates decide on the time and the place, make two columns on the chalkboard: one for tasks to be done prior to the festival and one for tasks to be done the day of the festival. Then form committees of five or more students and assign tasks. For example, a committee assigned to find a place also needs to get permission to use the place. That committee should also check the seating, the acoustics, and the lighting. Other committees will be needed for publicity, program planning, storyteller selections, tickets, and technical equipment.

On the day of the festival, all of the committees need to make sure that everything is ready—from arranging chairs to checking out the sound system. To ensure that everything goes smoothly, each committee should make up a checklist of their responsibilities for the day of the festival.

Finding STORYTELLERS

Start recruiting storytellers close to home. Ask your relatives, neighbors, and friends if they have a favorite childhood story or legend to tell at the festival.

As you interview the people who would like to participate in the festival, take careful notes that you can record on a chart like this one. Try to get as much variety as possible—a good balance of age of the storyteller, subject matter, and country of origin will be educational as well as fun. Be sure the stories are suitable for all ages.

Storyteller	Story Title	Place of Origin	Subject	Theme

Staging THE EVENT

Using the information in your chart, plan the sequence of storytellers. You might want to group them by subject matter, by theme, or by culture. Be sure to give a copy of the schedule to the participants. Assign someone to be responsible for providing the music or working the lights. You'll also need to write an introduction to the program, some short remarks about each of the storytellers and their tales, and a conclusion. Don't forget to choose a *master of ceremonies* to welcome the audience and introduce the storytellers.

If your program is well received, you may want to make the Storytelling Festival an annual event!

Putting It All Together

What Have You Learned About the Theme?

Now that you've finished *Tales from Here and There*, think about how your ideas about myths and folktales have changed. Look over your writing—in your journal, in response to your reading, and in the Writing Workshop—and the other activities you did for this unit. Then write a myth or folktale with a modern theme, such as the importance of protecting nature. When you have written your myth or folktale, add it to a collection of your classmates' stories and publish it in book form.

A MODERN THEME

Prewriting and Drafting   Many literature selections in this unit present themes that have concerned people for centuries, such as the importance of kindness and generosity. Brainstorm a list of modern concerns, such as protecting the environment or helping the homeless. Choose a theme from this list. Then think about how you can express this theme through the plot of your myth or folktale. It may help you organize the action of your story if you draw a pyramid like the one on page 109.

Now draft your story about the theme you've chosen. Describe the setting in detail. Let the events of your plot reveal your theme. Remember to use a mix of dialogue and description.

Revising and Editing   Now work with a partner or writing group. Exchange tales and read with a critical eye. Ask questions that you have about your draft, or ask your partner or group to suggest improvements to the content of your writing. Have your partner check for errors in grammar, punctuation, and spelling, too.

Publishing   Make your final revisions and publish your story with your classmates' stories in a book of myths and folktales. You might also want to add illustrations of the most important events in your stories.

Evaluating Your Work

Think Back About the Big Questions

Discuss the Big Questions on pages 10-11 with a partner. Can you answer all the questions easily now? In your journal, write two or three sentences to tell how your responses to the Big Questions have changed after your work in this unit.

Think Back About Your Work

Think back on your work in this unit and evaluate what you did—your reading, writing, activities, and projects. Don't be too hard on yourself, but do be honest.

Finally write a note to your teacher. Explain what you did as you worked through the unit and what you learned from the experience. Use the following questions to help you write your note.

- Which literature selections in this unit did you enjoy most?
- Which selections did you enjoy least?
- Which activity in the unit did you enjoy most?
- Which activity did you enjoy least?
- If you were to repeat your project, what would you do the same way? What would you do differently?
- What did you learn from working on the project?
- What did you learn in this unit about myths and folktales?
- How would you rate your work in this unit? Use the following scale and give at least three reasons for your rating.

  1 = Outstanding   3 = Fair
  2 = Good   4 = Not as good as it could have been

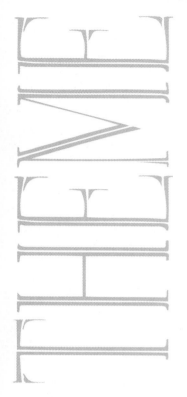

What Is Theme?

Many works of literature have a **theme**, which expresses the author's opinion about some aspect of life. In the case of myths and folktales, the story's theme may also express the beliefs and values of an entire people or culture. This theme can be revealed through dialogue or through the story's plot. For example, the plot of "Arachne" shows the reader that human arrogance offends the gods, so the theme of the story is the importance of humility.

Classifying Themes   Folktales and myths are like people: although they come from different parts of the world, they have many things in common, which is why many of the literature selections in this unit have similar themes. Hold a class discussion about the similarity of values represented by these themes. Why do people everywhere value kindness, hospitality, and humility so highly? As you discuss the themes, you might want to locate each selection's country of origin on a large world map. Then, on the chalkboard, group together the titles of selections with related themes. When you have finished listing the titles of selections from this unit, think of other stories you know with similar themes. Add the titles of these stories to your list.

Write a Myth   Look through the literature selections from this unit that you've read, paying special attention to the theme of each selection. Choose a theme that seems particularly important. How would you express the same theme if you were to write a myth of your own? Write a myth with a plot that expresses this theme. You could set your myth in any period of history, from the distant past to the present. When you have finished, let a classmate read your myth and identify the theme.

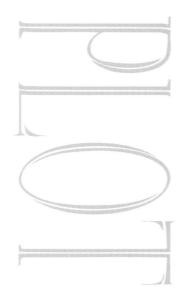

What Is Plot?   **Plot** is the sequence of actions and events in fiction or drama. Most plots have three parts: the *rising action* that leads to the most important event in the story; the *climax* or turning point of the action; and the *falling action*—the events that occur after the most important event has taken place. In "Baucis and Philemon," for example, the rising action occurs as the gods search for hospitality and are unable to find it. The climax comes when they reveal their identity to Baucis and Philemon and grant the couple's wishes, while the falling action shows the consequences of these wishes.

Plot Pyramids   Think about the plot in each literature selection you've read in this unit. Were there three parts to each plot? Make a plot pyramid for each literature selection in this unit that you've read, showing the rising action on one slope of the pyramid, the climax at the apex, or top, of the pyramid, and the falling action on the other slope. Write the name of the selection in the pyramid itself. Compare your plot pyramids with those of another classmate.

Write a Folktale   Many of the myths and folktales in this unit have plots that feature sudden changes of fortune. For example, in the Vietnamese tale "The Wonderful Pearl," the main character acquires a pearl that transforms her life from one of hungry poverty to one of comfortable wealth. Write a folktale in which a sudden change of fortune is the climax of the plot.

GLOSSARY OF LITERARY TERMS

A

alliteration   Repetition of the first sound—usually a consonant sound—in several words of a sentence or a line of poetry.

allusion   An author's indirect reference to someone or something that is presumed to be familiar to the reader.

anecdote   A short narrative about an interesting or a humorous event, usually in the life of a person.

antagonist   The person or force opposing the protagonist, or main character in a literary work. [See also *protagonist*.]

autobiography   A person's written account of his or her own life.

B

ballad   A poem, often a song, that tells a story in simple verse.

biography   An account of a person's life, written by another person.

blank verse   Unrhymed poetry.

C

character   A person or an animal that participates in the action of a work of literature. A *dynamic character* is one whose thoughts, feelings, and actions are changeable and lifelike; a *static character* always remains the same. [See also *protagonist, antagonist*.]

characterization   The creation of characters through the characters' use of language and through descriptions of their appearance, thoughts, emotions, and actions. [See also *character*.]

chronology   An arrangement of events in the order in which they happen.

cliché   An overused expression that is trite rather than meaningful.

climax   The highest point of tension in the plot of a work of literature. [See also *plot*.]

comedy   An amusing play that has a happy ending.

conclusion   The final part or ending of a piece of literature.

concrete poem   A poem arranged on the page so that its punctuation, letters, and lines make the shape of the subject of the poem.

conflict   A problem that confronts the characters in a piece of literature. The conflict may be *internal* (a character's struggle within himself or herself) or *external* (a character's struggle against nature, another person, or society). [See also *plot*.]

context   The general sense of words that helps readers to understand the meaning of unfamiliar words and phrases in a piece of writing.

D

description   An author's use of words to give the reader or listener a mental picture, an impression, or an understanding of a person, place, thing, event, or idea.

dialect   A form of speech spoken by people in a particular group or geographical region that differs in vocabulary, grammar, and pronunciation from the standard language.

dialogue   The spoken words and conversation of characters in a work of literature.

drama   A play that is performed before an audience according to stage directions and using dialogue. Classical drama has two genres: *tragedy* and *comedy*. Modern drama includes *melodrama, satire, theater of the absurd*, and *pantomime*. [See also *comedy, play*, and *tragedy*.]

dramatic poetry   A play written in the form of poetry.

E

epic   A long narrative poem—written in a formal style and meant to be read aloud—that relates the adventures and

experiences of one or more great heroes or heroines.

essay   Personal nonfiction writing about a particular subject that is important to the writer.

excerpt   A passage from a larger work that has been taken out of its context to be used for a special purpose.

exposition   Writing that explains, analyzes, or defines.

extended metaphor   An elaborately drawn out metaphor. [See also *metaphor*.]

F

fable   A short, simple story whose purpose is to teach a lesson, usually with animal characters who talk and act like people.

fantasy   Imaginative fiction about unrealistic characters, places, and events.

fiction   Literature, including the short story and the novel, that tells about imaginary people and events.

figurative language   Language used to express ideas through figures of speech: descriptions that aren't meant to be taken literally. Types of figurative language include *simile, metaphor, extended metaphor, hyperbole,* and *personification*.

figure of speech   A type of figurative language, not meant to be taken literally, that expresses something in such a way that it brings the thing to life in the reader's or listener's imagination. [See also *figurative language*.]

flashback   A break in a story's action that relates a past happening in order to give the reader background information about a present action in the story.

folktale   A story that has been passed along from storyteller to storyteller for generations. Kinds of folktales include *tall tales, fairy tales, fables, legends,* and *myths*.

foreshadowing   The use of clues to create suspense by giving the reader or audience hints of events to come.

free verse   Poetry that has no formal rhyme scheme or metrical pattern.

G

genre   A major category of art. The three major literary genres are poetry, prose, and drama.

H

haiku   A three-line Japanese verse form. In most haiku, the first and third lines have five syllables, while the second line has seven. The

traditional haiku describes a complicated feeling or thought in simple language through a single image.

hero/heroine   The main character in a work of literature. In heroic literature, the hero or heroine is a particularly brave, noble, or clever person whose achievements are unusual and important. [See also *character*.]

heroic age   The historical period in western civilization—from about 800 B.C. through A.D. 200—during which most works of heroic literature, such as myths and epics, were created in ancient Greece and Rome.

hubris   Arrogance or excessive pride leading to mistakes; the character flaw in a hero of classical tragedy.

hyperbole   An obvious exaggeration used for emphasis. [See also *figurative language*.]

I

idiom   An expression whose meaning cannot be understood from the ordinary meaning of the words. For example, *It's raining cats and dogs*.

imagery   The words and phrases in writing that appeal to the senses of sight, hearing, taste, touch, and smell.

irony   An effect created by a sharp contrast between what is expected and what is real. An *ironic twist* in a plot is an event that is the complete opposite of what the characters have been hoping or expecting will happen. An *ironic statement* declares the opposite of the speaker's literal meaning.

J

jargon   Words and phrases used by a group of people who share the same profession or special interests in order to refer to technical things or processes with which they are familiar. In general, jargon is any terminology that sounds unclear, overused, or pretentious.

L

legend   A famous folktale about heroic actions, passed along by word of mouth from generation to generation. The legend may have begun as a factual account of real people and events but has become mostly or completely fictitious.

limerick   A form of light verse, or humorous poetry, written in one five-line stanza with a regular scheme of rhyme and meter.

literature   The branch of art that is expressed in written language and includes all written genres.

lyric poem   A short poem that expresses personal feelings and thoughts in a musical way. Originally, lyrics were the words of songs that were sung to music played on the lyre, a stringed instrument invented by the ancient Greeks.

M

metamorphosis   The transformation of one thing, or being, into another completely different thing or being, such as a caterpillar's change into a butterfly.

metaphor   Figurative language in which one thing is said to be another thing. [See also *figurative language*.]

meter   The pattern of rhythm in lines of poetry. The most common meter, in poetry written in English, is iambic pentameter, that is, a verse having five metrical feet, each foot of verse having two syllables, an unaccented one followed by an accented one.

mood   The feeling or atmosphere that a reader senses while reading or listening to a work of literature.

motivation   A character's reasons for doing, thinking, feeling, or saying something. Sometimes an author will make a character's motivation obvious from the beginning. In realistic fiction and drama, however, a character's motivation may be so complicated that the reader discovers it gradually, by studying the character's thoughts, feelings, and behavior.

myth   A story, passed along by word of mouth for generations, about the actions of gods and goddesses or superhuman heroes and heroines. Most myths were first told to explain the origins of natural things or to justify the social rules and customs of a particular society.

N

narration   The process of telling a story. For both fiction and nonfiction, there are two main kinds of narration, based on whether the story is told from a first-person or third-person point of view. [See also *point of view*.]

narrative poem   A poem that tells a story containing the basic literary ingredients of fiction: character, setting, and plot.

narrator   The person, or voice, that tells a story. [See also *point of view, voice*.]

nonfiction   Prose that is factually true and is about real people, events, and places.

nonstandard English
Versions of English, such as slang and dialects, that use pronunciation, vocabulary, idiomatic expressions, grammar, and punctuation that differ from the accepted "correct" constructions of English.

novel   A long work of narrative prose fiction. A novel contains narration, a setting or settings, characters, dialogue, and a more complicated plot than a short story.

O

onomatopoeia   The technique of using words that imitate the sounds they describe, such as *hiss*, *buzz*, and *splash*.

oral tradition   Stories, poems, and songs that have been kept alive by being told, recited, and sung by people over many generations. Since the works were not originally written, they often have many different versions.

P

parable   A brief story—similar to a fable, but about people— that describes an ordinary situation and concludes with a short moral or lesson to be learned.

personification   Figurative language in which an animal, an object, or an idea is given human characteristics. [See also *figurative language*.]

persuasion   A type of speech or writing whose purpose is to convince people that something is true or important.

play   A work of dramatic literature written for performance by actors before an audience. In classical or traditional drama, a play is divided into five acts, each containing a number of scenes. Each act represents a distinct phase in the development of the plot. Modern plays often have only one act and one scene.

playwright   The author of a play.

plot   The sequence of actions and events in fiction or drama. A traditional plot has at least three parts: the *rising action*, leading up to a turning point that affects the main character; the *climax*, the turning point or moment of greatest intensity or interest; and the *falling action*, leading away from the conflict, or resolving it.

poetry   Language selected and arranged in order to say something in a compressed or nonliteral way. Modern poetry may or may not use many of the traditional poetic techniques that include *meter*, *rhyme*, *alliteration*, *figurative language*, *symbolism*, and *specific verse forms*.

point of view   The perspective from which a writer tells a story. *First-person* narrators tell the story from their own point of view, using pronouns such as *I* or *me*. *Third-person* narrators, using pronouns such as *he*, *she*, or *them*, may be *omniscient* (knowing everything about all characters), or *limited* (taking the point of view of one character). [See also *narration*.]

propaganda   Information or ideas that may or may not be true, but are spread as though they are true, in order to persuade people to do or believe something.

prose   The ordinary form of written and spoken language used to create fiction, nonfiction, and most drama.

protagonist   The main character of a literary work. [See also *character* and *characterization*.]

R

refrain   A line or group of lines that is repeated, usually at the end of each verse, in a poem or a song.

repetition   The use of the same formal element more than once in a literary work, for emphasis or in order to achieve another desired effect.

resolution   The falling action in fiction or drama,

including all of the developments that follow the climax and show that the story's conflict is over. [See also *plot*.]

rhyme scheme   A repeated pattern of similar sounds, usually found at the ends of lines of poetry or poetic drama.

rhythm   In poetry, the measured recurrence of accented and unaccented syllables in a particular pattern. [See also *meter*.]

S

scene   The time, place, and circumstances of a play or a story. In a play, a scene is a section of an act. [See also *play*.]

science fiction   Fantasy literature set in an imaginary future, with details and situations that are designed to seem scientifically possible.

setting   The time and place of a work of literature.

short story   Narrative prose fiction that is shorter and has a less complicated plot than a novel. A short story contains narration, at least one setting, at least one character, and usually some dialogue.

simile   Figurative language that compares two unlike things, introduced by the words "like" or "as." [See also *figurative language*.]

soliloquy   In a play, a short speech spoken by a single character when he or she is alone on the stage. A soliloquy usually expresses the character's innermost thoughts and feelings, when he or she thinks no other characters can hear.

sonnet   A poem written in one stanza, using fourteen lines of iambic pentameter. [See also *meter*.]

speaker   In poetry, the individual whose voice seems to be speaking the lines. [See also *narration*, *voice*.]

stage directions   The directions, written by the playwright, to tell the director, actors, and theater technicians how a play should be dramatized. Stage directions may specify such things as how the setting should appear in each scene, how the actors should deliver their lines, when the stage curtain should rise and fall, how stage lights should be used, where on the stage the actors should be during the action, and when sound effects should be used.

stanza   A group of lines in poetry set apart by blank lines before and after the group; a poetic verse.

style   The distinctive way in which an author composes a work of literature in written or spoken language.

suspense   An effect created by authors of various types of fiction and drama, especially adventure and mystery, to heighten interest in the story.

symbol   An image, person, place, or thing that is used to express the idea of something else.

T

tall tale   A kind of folk tale, or legend, that exaggerates the characteristics of its hero or heroine.

theme   The main idea or underlying subject of a work of literature.

tone   The attitude that a work of literature expresses to the reader through its style.

tragedy   In classical drama, a tragedy depicts a noble hero or heroine who makes a mistake of judgment that has disastrous consequences.

V

verse   A stanza in a poem. Also, a synonym for poetry as a genre. [See also *stanza*.]

voice   The narrator or the person who relates the action of a piece of literature. [See also *speaker*.]

ACKNOWLEDGMENTS

Grateful acknowledgment is made for permission to reprint the following copyrighted material.

"Direction" by Alonzo Lopez from *The Whispering Wind* by Terry Allen. Copyright © 1972 by the Institute of American Indian Arts. Used by permission of Doubleday, a division of Bantam Doubleday Dell Publishing Group, Inc.

"The Storytelling Stone" from *Return of the Sun* by Joseph Bruchac, copyright © 1989 by Joseph Bruchac, published by The Crossing Press, Freedom, CA. By permission of The Crossing Press.

"All Stories Are Anansi's" from *The Hat-Shaking Dance and Other Ashanti Tales from Ghana* by Harold Courlander. Copyright © 1957, 1985 by Harold Courlander. By permission of the author.

"Brer Tiger and the Big Wind" by William J. Faulkner from *The Days When the Animals Talked* by William J. Faulkner. Copyright © 1977 by Follett Publishing Co. Republished 1989 by Marie Faulkner Brown. By permission of Marie Faulkner Brown.

"Aunt Sue's Stories" by Langston Hughes from *Selected Poems by Langston Hughes*. Copyright 1926 by Alfred A. Knopf, Inc. and renewed 1954 by Langston Hughes. Reprinted by permission of the publisher.

"The Story of the Shipwrecked Sailor" by Roger Lancelyn Green from *Tales of Ancient Egypt*, selected and retold by Roger Lancelyn Green, copyright © 1967 by Roger Lancelyn Green.

"The Bamboo Beads" from *A Wave in Her Pocket* by Lynn Joseph. Text copyright © 1991 by Lynn Joseph. Reprinted by permission of Clarion Books/Houghton Mifflin Co. All rights reserved.

"The Wonderful Pearl" from *The Woman in the Moon* by James Riordan. Copyright © 1984 by James Riordan. Used by permission of Dial Books for Young Readers, a division of Penguin Books USA, Inc.

"Baucis and Philemon" from *Mythology* by Edith Hamilton. Copyright 1942 by Edith Hamilton. © renewed 1969 by Dorian Fielding Reid and Doris Fielding Reid. By permission of Little, Brown and Company.

"Waters of Gold" by Laurence Yep from *Tongues of Jade*, text copyright © 1991 by Laurence Yep. Reprinted by permission of HarperCollins Publishers.

"The King and the Shoemaker" from *The Beautiful Blue Jay and Other Tales of India* collected and edited by John W. Spellman. Copyright © 1967 by John W. Spellman. By permission of Little, Brown and Company.

"Three Strong Women" by Claus Stamm is reprinted from *Stories for Free Children*, edited by Letty Cottin Pogrebin, copyright © 1982 by Ms. Foundation for Education and Communication, Inc.

"Arachne" by Olivia Coolidge from *Greek Myths*. Copyright 1949, © renewed 1977 by Olivia E. Coolidge. Reprinted by permission of Houghton Mifflin Company. All rights reserved.

"The Building of the Wall" from *The Children of Odin* by Padraic Colum. Copyright 1920 by Macmillan Publishing Company, copyright renewed 1948 by Padraic Colum. Reprinted with the permission of Macmillan Publishing Company.

"The Legend of the Hummingbird" from *Once in Puerto Rico* by Pura Belpré. Copyright © 1973 by Pura Belpré. Used by permission of Frederick Warne Books, a division of Penguin Books USA, Inc.

"Carriers of the Dream Wheel" from *The Gourd Dancer* by N. Scott Momaday. Copyright © 1976 by N. Scott Momaday. Reprinted by permission of the author.

ILLUSTRATION

11 Heidi Lutts; 72-75 Rani Sarin.

PHOTOGRAPHY

4 *tr* Harvey Lloyd/The Stock Market; *l* John Owens/©D.C. Heath; **5** *b* Giraudon/Art Resource, NY; **8** *Popular Fairy Tales for the Young,* 1861; **9** Walter Crane, *The Blue Beard Picture Books,* 1876; **10** *t* Mary Kate Denny/PhotoEdit; *b* John Owens/©D.C. Heath; **11** *t* Sarah Putnam/©D.C. Heath; *c* Jim Whitmer/Stock Boston; *b* Sarah Putnam/©D.C. Heath; **13** David Muench Photography; **14-17** Stephen Trimble; **19** Photo by Carol Bruchac. Courtesy of Crossing Press; **20-21** Doran H. Ross; **23** Photo by Herbert Cohen; **24-25** Collection of the Museum of American Folk Art, New York. Gift of William A. Fagaly, 1977.15.1; **26-27** Collection of William A. Fagaly; **30-31** *details, Pictorial Quilt* by Harriet Powers. Bequest of Maxim Karolik. Courtesy of Museum of Fine Arts, Boston. (#64.619); **31** *b* UPI/The Bettmann Archive; **33** *l* Michael Holford; *r* Giraudon/Art Resource, NY; **36, 38-39** Michael Holford; **40-49** Melina Freedman/©D.C. Heath; **49** *b* Courtesy of Clarion Books; **50-51** Jeffrey Alford/Asia Access; **53** William Lesch/Swanstock; **54-55** Jeffrey Alford/Asia Access; **55** *inset* Courtesy of James Riordan, University of Surrey; **56-61** Melina Freedman/©D.C. Heath; **62-63** The Metropolitan Museum of Art. Gift of John M. Crawford, Jr., 1984. (1984.274); **64** Courtesy of the Freer Gallery of Art, Smithsonian Institution, Washington, D.C., #57.4; **67** Giraudon/Art Resource, NY; **71** Photo by K. Yep. Courtesy of HarperCollins Publishers; **72** Courtesy of the Trustees of the Victoria and Albert Museum. Photo by M. Kitcatt; **76, 81, 83** Asian Art and Archaeology, Inc.; **86-87** Erich Lessing/Art Resource, NY; **86-87** *background* Stephen J. Krasemann/DRK Photo; **88** Nimatallah/Art Resource, NY; **88-91** *background* Stephen J. Krasemann/DRK Photo; **91** *t* Courtesy of Russell & Volkening, Inc.; **92-96** Courtesy of Robert Craft; **97** Courtesy of Macmillan Children's Book Group; **98** Ted Horowitz/The Stock Market; **98-99** Suzanne L. Murphy/DDB Stock Photo; **99, 100** Division of Rare and Manuscript Collections, Cornell University Library; **102** Jeff Briley, State Museum of History, Oklahoma Historical Society; **106** Nancy Sheehan/©D.C. Heath; **108** *t* Elizabeth Hamlin/Stock Boston; *b* Tony Stone Images; **114** Jean-Claude Lejeune/Stock Boston; **115** Ken O'Donoghue/©D.C. Heath; **116** J. Sulley/The Image Works; **117** Lawrence Migdale.
Back cover *t, c* Sarah Putnam/©D.C. Heath; *b* John Owens/©D.C. Heath.

Full Pronunciation Key for Footnoted Words

(Each pronunciation and definition is adapted from *Scott, Foresman Advanced Dictionary* by E.L. Thorndike and Clarence L. Barnhart.)

The pronunciation of each footnoted word is shown just after the word, in this way: **abbreviate** [ə brē′ vē āt]. The letters and signs used are pronounced as in the words below. The mark ′ is placed after a syllable with primary or heavy accent, as in the example above. The mark ′ after a syllable shows a secondary or lighter accent, as in **abbreviation** [ə brē′ vē ā′ shən].

Some words, taken from foreign languages, are spoken with sounds that do not otherwise occur in English. Symbols for these sounds are given in the key as "foreign sounds."

a	hat, cap	j	jam, enjoy	u	cup, butter	**foreign sounds**
ā	age, face	k	kind, seek	u̇	full, put	Y as in French *du*.
ä	father, far	l	land, coal	ü	rule, move	Pronounce (ē) with
		m	me, am	v	very, save	the lips rounded as
b	bad, rob	n	no, in	w	will, woman	for (ü).
ch	child, much	ng	long, bring	y	young, yet	
d	did, red			z	zero, breeze	à as in French *ami*.
		o	hot, rock	zh	measure, seizure	Pronounce (ä) with
e	let, best	ō	open, go			the lips spread and
ē	equal, be	ô	order, all	ə represents:	held tense.
ėr	term, learn	oi	oil, voice		a in about	
		ou	house, out		e in taken	œ as in French *peu*.
f	fat, if				i in pencil	Pronounce (ā) with the
g	go, bag	p	paper, cup		o in lemon	lips rounded as for (ō).
h	he, how	r	run, try		u in circus	
		s	say, yes			N as in French *bon*.
i	it, pin	sh	she, rush			The N is not pro-
ī	ice, five	t	tell, it			nounced, but shows
		th	thin, both			that the vowel before
		ŦH	then, smooth			it is nasal.

H as in German *ach*. Pronounce (k) without closing the breath passage.

GLOSSARY

This glossary is an alphabetical list of words found in the literature selections in this book. Most of the words in the glossary are also defined in footnotes on the pages where they appear. A few foreign words, proper nouns, and words with meanings that are very specific to the literature selection are not listed here but are defined in footnotes on the pages where they appear.

Many English words have several different meanings. This glossary gives you the meanings that apply to the words as they are used in the literature selections in this book.

Unless a word is very easy to pronounce, its pronunciation is given in brackets. A key to the pronunciation symbols appears on the previous page (page 128).

A

a.s.a.p.: abbreviation for "as soon as possible."

abated [ə bat′ əd]: lessened in force.

aboriginal [ab′ ə rij′ ə nəl]: original, existing from the beginning.

abysses [ə bis′ əz]: deep openings in the earth.

adders [ad′ ərz]: small, poisonous snakes.

ado [ə dü′]: fuss, trouble, or excitement.

aerodynamics [er′ ō dī nam′ iks]: branch of science that deals with pressure or resistance on flying bodies by air or other gases in motion.

affidavits [af′ ə dā′ vitz]: statements written down and sworn to be true.

afghan [af′ gən]: blanket made of knitted yarn.

aghast [ə gast′]: surprised, amazed.

agitation [aj′ ə tā′ shən]: vigorous shaking.

aka [ā kā ā]: also known as.

alders [ôl′ dərz]: type of birch trees that grow in moist areas.

aliens [ā′ lyənz]: people who are not citizens of the country in which they live.

altruist [al′ trü ist]: a person who helps others without expecting anything in return.

amphibious [am fib′ ē əs]: able to travel on land or water.

anaesthetic [an′ əs thet′ ik]: a substance, like ether, that causes loss of feeling or pain.

annas [a′ nəz]: a former unit of money in India equivalent to one-sixteenth of a rupee.

antechambers [an′ ti chām′ bərz]: small waiting rooms.

aperture [ap′ ər chùr]: an opening.

apex [ā′ peks]: the highest point.

aphorisms [af′ ə riz′ əmz]: short sentences that express a truth or piece of wisdom.

appeasingly [ə pēz′ ing lē]: calmly, quietly.

appendage [ə pen′ dij]: a thing attached to something larger.

apprehension [ap′ ri hen′ shən]: dread of danger, fear.

arid [ar′ id]: dry, having little rainfall.

aristocratic [ə ris′ tə krat′ ik]: noble.

asset [as′ et]: something of value.

asthmatic [az mat′ ik]: having asthma, a disease that causes breathing difficulties.

atone [ə tōn′]: make up for.

audacity [ô das′ ə tē]: reckless daring, boldness.

audible [ô′ də bəl]: loud enough to be heard.

avalanche [av′ ə lanch]: large mass of snow, ice, dirt, or rocks falling quickly down the side of a mountain.

awe [ô]: a feeling of wonder.

B

balaclava [bä lə klä′ və]: close-fitting, knitted woolen cap that covers the head, neck, and tops of the shoulders.

bamboo [bam bü′]: a sturdy, tree-like grass with tall, hollow stems used for making canes, furniture, and even houses.

bandsaw: saw consisting of a steel belt running over two pulleys.

barrack [bar′ ək]: building where soldiers live.

battalion [bə tal′ yən]: a large group of people with a common purpose.

begrudged [bi grudjd′]: was reluctant to admit.

belfry [bel′ frē]: church tower.

beseechingly [bi sēch′ ing lē]: in a manner of asking or begging.

besieged [bi sējd′]: surrounded by armed forces in order to force surrender.

bifocals [bī fō′ kəlz]: lenses on glasses that have two sections, one for distant vision and the other for near vision.

biologist [bī ol′ ə jist]: an expert in biology, which is the scientific study of plant and animal life.

blissful [blis′ fəl]: extremely happy, joyful.

boonie hat: a hat worn in the jungle for camouflage purposes.

bootie [bü′ tē]: covering for the dogs' paws.

botching [boch′ ing]: ruining or spoiling.

break a leg: what actors say to each other before a performance; it means "Good luck."

brethren [bre ⧢н rən]: the fellow members of a society.

bric-à-brac [brik′ ə brak′]: curious decorative ornaments, such as vases or china.

briers [brī′ ərz]: bushes that have prickly stems, such as the blackberry plant or wild rose.

bullock [bùl′ ək]: an ox.

bushplanes [bùsh′ plānz′]: airplanes used to fly over unsettled areas.

C

cacophony [kə kof′ ə nē]: harsh clashing sound.

calabash [kal′ ə bash]: a gourd-like fruit whose dried shell is used to make bottles, bowls, or other instruments.

callused [kal′ əsd]: hardened.

cassia [kash′ ə]: the spicy bark of a tree native of China.

catechism [kat′ ə kiz əm]: a book of questions and answers about religion.

caucus [kô′ kəs]: consult, ask.

centimetre [sen′ tə mē′ tər]: British spelling of "centimeter": unit of length: one inch equals 2.54 centimeters.

chaplet [chap′ lit]: a string of jewels.

charade [shə rād′]: meaningless or false action or series of actions.

chemises [shə mēz′ əz]: shirtlike undergarments for women and girls.

chemotherapy [kēm′ ō ther′ ə pē]: treatment of a disease with chemicals that destroy the organisms of the disease.

chidden [chid′ ən]: scolded, blamed.

chitlins [chit′ linz]: the intestines of pigs, cooked as food.

chortled [chôr′ tld]: chuckled with glee.

christen [kris′ n]: to give a name to someone or something, as in baptism.

chronic [kron′ ik]: lasting a long time.

circuit [sėr′ kit]: route or way around.

cirrus [sir′ əs]: high, thin, feathery, white clouds.

Civil Rights Act: a federal law of 1964 that authorized federal action against segregation in employment and in public places.

civil rights movement: movement that aimed to assure

that every United States citizen, regardless of race or sex, has the rights guaranteed by the Constitution.

clod-hopper [klod′ hop′ ər]: strong, heavy shoes.

cocoon [kə kün′]: protective silk covering spun by larvae of various insects.

cod-liver oil [kod′ liv′ ər]: oil from the liver of codfish, used in medicine as a source of vitamins A and D.

coherent [kō hir′ ənt]: logical, sensible.

colours [kul′ ərz]: British spelling of "colors."

commencement [kə mens′ ment]: graduation.

commission [kə mish′ ən]: a percentage of the amount of money earned by a business deal, paid to the agent who does the business; an appointment or position.

commotion [kə mō′ shən]: bustle or stir; confusion.

commune [kə myün′]: communicate effortlessly as with a good friend.

communion [kə myü′ nyən]: the act of receiving bread as a part of some Christian religious services.

compliance [kəm plī′ əns]: doing as another wishes.

conceivable [kən sē′ və bəl]: possible to imagine.

concentration camp: place where the Nazis held, tortured, and killed Jewish people and others during World War II.

concocted [kon kokt′ əd]: made up.

concussed [kən kushd′]: injured in the head by a blow.

conjectural [kən jek′ chər əl]: based on a guess.

conjured [kon´ jərd]: caused to appear by using magic.

conspire [kən spīr´]: plan secretly together.

constitution: [kon´ stə tü´ shən]: nature or makeup.

contemplating [kon´ təm plāt ing]: looking at for a long time.

contemptuously [kən temp´ chü əs lē]: scornfully, with disrespect.

contrition [kən trish´ ən]: sorrow for having hurt someone, guilt.

convulsive [kən vul´ siv]: unintentionally violent and fast.

coquettish [kō ket´ ish]: attracting attention.

coquina [kō kē´ nə]: soft, porous limestone formed of fragments of sea shells and corals.

counterpane [koun´ tər pān´]: bedspread.

coupès [kü pāz´]: closed, horse-drawn carriages holding passengers inside and the driver outside.

crane [krān]: a large, wading bird, with long legs, neck, and bill.

crocus [krō´ kəs]: a small flowering plant that blooms in early spring.

crypts [kripts]: hidden depths like an underground room.

crystal [kris´ tl]: a clear plastic or glass cover on the face of a watch.

crystalled [kris´ tld]: warm breath turned to ice in the frigid air; looks like bits of glass.

cubits [kyu´ bits]: an ancient measure of length, about 20 inches or 50 centimeters.

cue [kyü]: an action, a speech, or a word that gives a signal to an actor, singer, or musician.

culvert [kul´ vərt]: a small channel or drain.

cure [kyùr]: preserve meat or fish by drying, salting, smoking, or pickling.

currant [kėr´ ənt]: a small, seedless raisin, native of eastern Mediterranean countries.

cypress [sī´ prəs]: the hard wood of an evergreen tree.

D

dale [dāl]: valley.

dark lantern: a lantern with a shutter to hide the light.

de facto [dē fak´ tō]: in fact, in reality.

de jure [dē jùr´ ē]: by right, according to law.

deadeye [ded´ ī]: round, flat, wooden block that fastens the shrouds of a ship.

debilitating [di bil´ ə tāt ing]: causing to become weak.

debut [dā´ byü]: a first public appearance.

deductions [di duk´ shənz]: answers found by reasoning.

defiant [di fī´ ənt]: challenging authority, bold.

descent [di sent´]: family line; ancestry.

dexterous [dek´ stər əs]: skillful.

discharge [dis chärj´]: release, let go.

disinfectant [dis´ in fek´ tənt]: a substance that destroys germs and may prevent infection.

disposition [dis´ pə zish´ ən]: nature, way of acting.

dissolute [dis´ ə lüt]: living an immoral life.

distaff [dis taf´]: a staff on a spinning wheel for holding wool or flax.

distress [dis tres´]: anxiety, unhappiness.

dogcart: a small, open, horse-drawn carriage with two seats placed back to back.

dominant [dom´ ə nənt]: powerful, controlling.

donned [dond]: put on clothing.

drudgery [druj´ ər ē]: work that is difficult and tiresome.

duo [du´ ō]: two people performing together.

dust years: the Great Depression in the 1930s, when the American Midwest and Southwest suffered droughts and destructive dust storms.

dyslexia [dis lek´ sē ə]: a brain problem that causes difficulty in reading.

E

electrophoresis [i lek´ trō fə rē´ sis]: movement of extremely small particles of matter influenced by an electric field.

embedded [em bed´ əd]: fastened firmly.

embroidery [əm broi´ dər ē]: an art of ornamenting something with a pattern of stitches or raised design.

empowered [em pou´ ərd]: given the authority, permitted.

erratic [ə rat´ ik]: not steady, irregular.

erstwhile [ėrst´ hwīl]: former, past.

ethereal [i thir´ ē əl]: light, airy.

evacuated [i vak´ yü āt əd]: forced to leave.

evolved [i volvd´]: developed gradually.

excruciating [ek skrü´ shē ā ting]: very painful.

exuberant [eg zü´ bər ənt]: in high spirits, happy.

exultation [eg´ zul tā´ shən]: a great rejoicing, triumph.

F

fain [fān]: willingly.

feed merchants: those who sell food for farm animals.

fissures [fish´ ərz]: long, narrow splits.

five bells: 2:30, 6:30, or 10:30; on ships, a certain number of bells are sounded each half hour to give the time.

fivescore [fīv skōr′]: one hundred; one score is a group of twenty.

flailing [flā′ ling]: moving or swinging about forcefully.

flatbed truck: truck with flat back section for carrying items.

folly [fol′ ē]: foolishness.

foraging [fôr′ ij ing]: searching for food.

foremost [fôr′ mōst]: first.

fortnight [fôrt′ nīt]: two weeks.

fossilized [fos′ ə līzd]: changed by time into a rock-like material.

frailty [frāl′ tē]: weakness.

frantic [fran′ tik]: wild with grief, fear, or pain.

frond: leaflike plant.

fufu [fü fü′]: dish comprised of bananas, squash, or yams.

G

gaiters [gā′ tərz]: coverings for the lower leg or ankle, made of cloth or leather, for walking outdoors.

galleons [gal′ ē ənz]: large, high, sailing ships with three or four decks, used in the 1400s and 1500s, especially by Spain.

galley [gal′ ē]: kitchen of a ship.

galoshes [gə losh′ iz]: high plastic or rubber overshoes worn in wet weather.

gantry [gan′ trē]: bridge-like framework for supporting the space shuttle while on the ground.

gawked [gôkd]: stared idly or rudely.

genetic [je net′ ik]: inherited, inborn.

gig [gig]: a light, open, two-wheeled carriage drawn by one horse.

girth: strap.

gladiolus [glad′ē ō′ ləs]: a plant with sword-shaped leaves and spikes of large flowers in various colors.

glister [glis′ tər]: shine, glitter.

glockenspiels [glok′ ən spēlz]: musical instruments played by striking two hammers on metal bells, bars, or tubes that are mounted in two rows in a frame.

gospel music [gos′ pəl]: intense, joyful songs about the teachings of Jesus and the Apostles.

gourd [gôrd]: a fleshy fruit often hollowed into a bowl or cup.

greens: leaves and stems of plants, such as beets, used for food.

grenadiers [gren′ ə dirz′]: soldiers in a special regiment of the British Army.

guineas [gin′ ēz]: guinea fowl: large, dark, speckled birds, similar to pheasants, which are often raised for food.

gumption [gump′ shən]: fearlessness, energy.

gurney [gėr′ nē]: stretcher or wheeled cot.

H

half nelson: in wrestling, a hold applied by hooking one arm under the opponent's armpit and putting a hand on the back of the opponent's neck.

hallowed [hal′ ōd]: holy, sacred.

haphazardly [hap′ haz′ ərd lē]: without being planned ahead.

haughty [hô′ tē]: too proud, scornful of others.

hawthorn [hô′ thôrn]: small tree of the rose family with fragrant white, red, or pink flowers.

headland: a point of high land jutting into the water.

hermit crab: a crab with a soft body who lives in the empty shells of snails for protection.

hibernation [hī bėr nā′ shən]: inactive state, like sleep, into which bears enter during the winter.

honorary doctorate [on′ ə rer′ ē dok′ tər it]: a university doctor's degree given as an honor rather than earned through regular duties.

horizon [hə rī′ zn]: line where the earth and sky seem to meet.

horizontal [hôr′ ə zon′ tl]: at right angles to a vertical line.

housing project [proj′ ekt]: group of apartment houses run as a unit, especially as a part of public housing.

hovering [huv′ ər ing]: suspended in air.

hula hoop [hōōl′ ə hōōp′]: a brand-name for a ring-shaped, plastic toy that is spun around the hips, introduced in the 1950s.

hypocrisy [hi pok′ rə sē]: state of pretending to be good and polite.

I

immaculate [i mak′ yə lit]: absolutely clean, without spot or fault.

imperceptible [im′ pər sep′ tə bəl]: very slight.

impetuous [im pech′ ü əs]: acting suddenly.

indelible [in del′ ə bəl]: permanent.

indifferently [in dif′ ər ənt le′]: without interest or attention.

indigo [in′ də gō]: deep violet-blue.

indolently [in′ dl ənt lē]: lazily, idly.

inflation [in flā′ shən]: sharp increase in prices caused by the circulation of too much paper money or bank credit.

initiative [i nish ē ə tiv]: the first step in starting a task.

inlets [in′ letz]: narrow bays or channels of water extending inland from a large body of water.

inoculated [in ok′ yə lāt əd]: injected with a material made of germs in order to prevent disease.

intangible [in tan′ jə bəl]: not able to be felt or touched.

interposition [in tər pə zish′ ən]: interruption, interference.

intimated [in′ tə māt əd]: hinted.

intuition [in′ tü ish′ ən]: immediate understanding of truths or facts without reasoning.

isolated [ī′ sə lāt əd]: set apart.

J

jargon [jär′ gən]: the language of a special profession.

jauntily [jôn′ tə lē]: in a carefree way.

jester [jes′ tər]: a man who told amusing stories to kings and their guests.

jousted [joust′ əd]: fought on horseback, armed with spears called lances.

jowls [jouls]: folds of flesh under the jaw.

K

knave [nāv]: tricky, dishonest man.

knickers [nik′ ərz]: short, loose trousers gathered at the knee.

L

lamprey [lam′ prē]: ocean and freshwater animal with a body like an eel's and a large, round mouth for attaching itself to other fish.

languished [lang′ gwishd]: suffering in sadness and neglect.

lapis lazuli [lap′ is laz′ ye lī]: a deep-blue stone.

lean-to [len′ tü′]: rough shelter built against a post or tree and open on one side.

leukemia [lü kē′ mē ə]: cancer in which there are too many white cells in the blood.

lichen-blotched [lī′ kən blochd]: stained with lichen: moss-like, flowerless plants that grow on trees, rocks, and walls.

limelight [līm līt]: the center of public attention.

local [lō′ kəl]: local resident or person native to the area.

lofty [lôf′ tē]: very high.

lopsided [lop′ sī′did]: leaning to one side.

louis [lü′ ē]: a former French gold coin, worth 20 francs.

lubber [lub′ ər]: big, clumsy, stupid fellow.

luminous [lü′ mə nəs]: shining, full of light.

lute [lüt]: a musical instrument, similar to a guitar, used in the 1500s and 1600s.

M

machetes [mə shet′ ēs]: large, heavy knives for cutting brush.

magpie [mag′ pī]: a black and white bird, known for its chatter, with a long tail and short wings.

malicious [mə lish′ əs]: cruel and spiteful.

manacles [man′ ə kəlz]: chains or restraints.

maneuvered [mə nü′ vər əd]: moved skillfully.

manifold [man′ ə fōld]: many and varied.

mansard [man′ särd]: a roof with two slopes on each side, named after the seventeenth-century French architect François Mansard.

marathon [mar′ ə thon]: a race run over a long distance, usually 26 miles, 385 yards.

marsh: soft, wet land.

masonry [mā′ sn rē]: the trade of building with stone or brick.

mattock [mat′ ək]: a large tool with a steel head and a flat blade, used for loosening soil and cutting roots.

menacing [men′ is ing]: threatening.

mesa [mā′ sə]: a small, high plateau with a flat top and steep sides.

metabolism [mə tab′ ə liz′ əm]: bodily processes that maintain life in a living being.

metronome [met′ rə nōm]: device that moves back and forth in musical time for practicing on musical instruments.

metropolis [mə trop′ ə lis]: the capital or chief city of a country or region.

migraine [mī′ grān]: a severe headache.

migrant [mi′ grənt]: person who moves from place to place, especially for farm work.

mincingly [min′ sing lē]: with very exact short steps.

molar [mō′ lər]: back tooth with a broad surface for grinding food.

monotonous [mə not′ n əs]: not changing tone or pitch.

monotonously [mə not′ n əs lē′]: continuously without change.

monotony [mə not′ nē]: sameness.

moor: open, rolling land, usually covered with short grasses and other vegetation.

motivated [mō′ tə vā′ tid]: wanting to act.

murky [mėr′ kē]: dark and thick.

must [must]: mold.

muster: group, gathering.

muzzle [muz′ əl]: nose, mouth, and jaws of an animal.

myopic [mī op′ ik]: near-sighted.

myriads [mir′ ē ədz]: a very great number.

N

nocturnal [nok tėr′ nl]: of the night.

nonchalantly [non′ shə länt′ lē]: indifferently, casually.

nostalgia [no stal′ jə]: a painful loneliness that results from thinking about one's home, country, city, and so forth.

nullification [nul′ ə fə kā′ shən]: act of causing something to cease to exist.

nurseryman [nėr′ sər ē mən]: person who grows or sells young trees and plants.

nymphs [nimfs]: Greek goddesses of nature, found in seas, fountains, hills, or woods.

O

ocelots [os′ ə lotz]: spotted cats smaller than leopards.

okra [ō′ krə]: a tall plant with sticky pods used in soups and as a vegetable.

orb [ôrb]: a form in the shape of a circle, usually in the sky.

organdy [ôr′ gən dē′]: fine, transparent material.

organic [ôr gan′ ik]: from plants or animals.

orthodontic [ôr′ thə don′ tik]: having to do with straightening teeth.

P

paddy [pad′ ē]: a flooded area with raised banks, usually used for growing rice.

palate [pal′ it]: roof of the mouth.

palisade [pal′ ə sād′]: a strong fence of large, wooden stakes set close together to enclose or defend.

pall [pôl]: a dark, gloomy covering.

palomino-colored [pal′ ə mē′ nō]: the cream color of a palomino horse.

palpable [pal′ pə bəl]: can be touched or felt.

pantomime [pan′ tə mīm]: a gesture without words.

papyrus [pə pī ′ rəs]: a kind of paper made from a tall water plant.

parapet [par′ ə pit]: a low wall or barrier at the edge of a balcony, roof, or bridge.

passably [pas′ ə blē]: fairly.

pavilions [pə vil′ yənz]: tent-like open buildings used for shelter.

peanut gallery [pē′ nut′]: *slang;* people offering uninvited, insignificant comments or advice.

pedigreed [ped′ ə grēd]: having record of breeding, or ancestry.

pension [pen′ shən]: a fixed amount of money paid regularly by the government to a war veteran, especially one who has been wounded.

peremptorily [pə remp′ tə ri lē]: with authority.

perilous [per′ ə ləs]: dangerous.

perpendicular [pėr′ pən dik′ yə lər]: very steep, vertical.

pervading [pər vād′ ing]: spreading everywhere.

pestles [pes′ əlz]: club-shaped tools for pounding substances into powder.

petitioner [pə tish′ ən ər]: someone who asks a person in authority for a benefit.

phantom [fan′ təm]: ghostly, shadowy in appearance

phenomenon [fə nom′ ə non]: an extraordinary occurrence.

pike [pīk]: a dive in which the diver bends at the waist, keeps the knees straight, and usually touches the toes.

pilchards [pil′ chərdz]: small fish related to herrings.

pinnace [pin′ is]: a light boat.

piston [pis′ tən]: a cylinder that is quickly moved back and forth by the force of steam.

pittance [pit′ ns]: a small amount.

plaguing [plāg′ ing]: tormenting, troubling.

plaintive [plān′ tiv]: sorrowful.

plausible [plô′ zə bəl]: believable.

plod: walk heavily or slowly.

pomarosa trees [pō′ mä rō′ sä]: apple trees found in the West Indies.

pomegranate [pom′ gran′ it]: a tree that bears a reddish-yellow fruit with many seeds.

popple [pop′ əl]: poplar tree.

posse [pos′ ē]: group working together.

pout [pout]: push out the lips as a sulky child does.

precaution [pri kô′ shən]: something done beforehand in the hope of getting good results.

precipice [pres′ ə pis]: very steep, almost vertical mountainside.

preliminaries [pri lim′ ə ner′ ēz]: contests that come before the main event.

preternatural [prē′ tər nach′ ər əl]: something above or beyond nature.

primly [prim′ lē]: extremely neatly.

prodigy [prod′ ə jē]: young person who is extremely brilliant and talented.

promissory note [prom′ ə sôr′ ē]: a written promise to pay a sum of money to a certain person at a certain time.

promontories [prom′ ən tôr′ ēz]: high points of land extending from the coast into the water.

proprietor [prə prī′ ə tər]: owner.

proverb [prov′ ėrb]: a short, wise saying used for a long time by many people.

psychology [sī kol′ ə jē]: study of the mind.

puce [pyüs]: purplish brown.

puffin [puf′ ən]: a sea bird with a thick body, a large head, and a bill of several colors.

put-out [pût′ out′]: an action that puts the batter or base-runner out of the game.

Q

querulous [kwer′ ə ləs]: complaining.

queue [kyü]: line of people waiting their turn.

R

rain forests: very dense forests in regions, usually tropical, where rain is heavy all year.

rapturous [rap′ chər əs]: full of joy.

ratlines: small ropes that cross the shrouds of a ship, used as steps for climbing.

recoiled [ri koild′]: drew back, reacted.

redcoats: British soldiers.

reinvigorating [rē in vig′ ə rāt ing]: filling again with life and energy.

reiterated [rē it′ ə rāt′ əd]: frequently repeated.

replicated [rep′ lə kat əd]: exactly reproduced, copied.

reservation [rez′ ər va′ shən]: place set aside by the government as a place for Native Americans to live.

resolutions [rez′ ə lü′ shənz]: decisions or intentions.

restitution [res′ tə tü′ shən]: act of making up for damage or injury done.

retrace [re tras′]: go or trace back over.

rhapsodizes [rap′ sə dīz əz]: talks or writes in an overly enthusiastic way.

rheumatism [rü′ mə tiz′ əm]: a disease with swelling and stiffness of the joints.

rigging: the masts, sails, and ropes on a ship.

riveted [riv′ it əd]: fixed firmly.

royal yard: the highest beam fastened across the mast, used to support the sail.

ruffed grouse [rufd grous]: brown bird with a tuft of gleaming black feathers on each side of the neck.

rupees [rü pēz′]: a unit of money in India.

rural [rùr′ əl]: in or of the country.

S

scant [skant]: barely enough.

scones [skōnz]: thick, round biscuits.

scythe [sīth]: a long, curved blade on a long handle, for cutting grass.

sea urchin: a small, round sea animal with a spiny shell.

self-sufficiency [self′ sə fish′ ən sē]: ability to take care of one's own needs.

senna [sen′ ə]: dried leaves used as an herbal medicine.

sensational [sen sā′ shə nəl]: trying to arouse strong feelings.

sentinel [sen′ tə nəl]: guard.

serene [sə rēn′]: calm, peaceful.

serrated [ser′ ā tid]: notched like the edge of a saw.

shied [shīd]: started back or aside suddenly.

shoepacs: insulated boots for cold weather.

shrouds [shrouds]: covering made of cloth or some protective material; pairs of ropes that reach from a mast to the side of a ship.

sidled [sī′ dld]: slowly moved sideways.

simile [sim′ ə lē]: a comparison of two different things that shows a likeness between them.

simulators [sim′ yə lāt ərz]: mock space shuttles that imitate a real journey into space to prepare the astronauts for the real thing.

slewed [slüd]: turned or twisted.

sloop [slüp]: a sailboat, usually having one sail.

sloshing [slosh′ ing]: splashing.

sloths [slôths]: slow-moving mammals of South and Central America that live in trees and hang upside down from tree branches.

smite [smīt]: strike with a weapon to cause serious injury or death.

smote [smōt]: struck or came with great force.

snickering [snik′ ər ing′]: laughing in a disrespectful way.

solid fuel booster: rocket engine used as the principal force that allows a rocket or a missile to take off.

sou [sü]: a former French coin, worth 1/20 of a franc.

sparsely [spärs′ lē]: thinly; very little spread out.

spasmodically [spaz mod′ ik lē]: suddenly, very irregularly.

species [spē′ shēz]: kind, type.

spectral [spek′ trəl]: ghostly.

spits: sharp-pointed, slender bars on which meat is roasted.

sporadic [spə rad′ ik]: occasional, happening at uneven intervals.

squire [skwīr]: young nobleman who served a knight until he himself became a knight.

stately [stāt′ lē]: dignified, majestic.

stealthy [stel′ thē]: quiet and secretive.

steward [stü′ ərd]: man who has charge of food and table service.

stile [stīl]: a step or steps for getting over a fence or wall.

stoically [stō′ ə kəl lē]: calmly and without showing feelings.

stolidly [stol′ id lē]: showing no emotion.

stoutly: bravely.

straight-furrowed [fėr′ ōd]: cut in long, narrow grooves by a plow.

stupor [stü′ pər]: a dazed condition.

subsequent [sub′ sə kwənt]: following or happening next.

suede [swād]: a soft leather that feels velvety on one or both sides.

supercilious [sü′ pər sil′ ē əs]: proud and filled with contempt for others.

suppliant [sup′ lē ənt]: a person who asks humbly and earnestly.

supplication [sup′ lə kā′ shən]: humble begging.

sycamore tree [sik′ ə môr]: tall shade tree with broad leaves.

T

tangibles [tan′ jə bəlz]: whatever is real and can be touched, such as property and money.

tapirs [tā′ pərz]: large piglike animals of tropical America with hooves and a flexible snout.

tarry [tär′ ē]: covered with tar.

teetered [tē′ tərd]: swayed or rocked unsteadily.

tempest [tem′ pist]: a wild storm.

tenement [ten′ ə mənt]: an apartment house in a large city.

tentatively [ten′ tə tiv lē]: carefully, hesitatingly.

terse [tėrs]: brief and to the point.

thistledown [this′ əl doun′]: soft, feathery fluff from thistle seeds.

tiara [tē är′ ə]: a band of gold, jewels, or flowers worn around the head as an ornament.

tidewater [tīd′ wô′ tər]: low-lying land along a seacoast through which the tide flows.

timber-jams [tim′ bər jams]: logs pressed together in a creek stopping the flow of water.

topaz [tō′ paz]: golden brown.

topsail spar [top′ sāl′ spär]: strong pole used to support the sail that is above the lowest sail on a mast.

torong [tō′ rông]: an instrument made from split bamboo cane.

tracers: bullets with a burning substance that leaves a trail.

tranquil [trang′ kwəl]: calm, peaceful.

trap [trap]: a light, two-wheeled horse-drawn carriage.

trawling [trôl′ ing]: fishing with a net.

triage : three categories of casualties: immediate care , delayed treatment, and comfort care only.

tunic [tü′ nik]: a long shirt.

two-by-fours: pieces of lumber four inches wide and two inches thick used in building.

tyrant [tī′ rənt]: cruel or unjust ruler.

U

unalienable [un ā′ lyə nə bəl]: that cannot be given or taken away.

unanimous [yü nan′ ə məs]: in complete agreement.

uncanny [un kan′ e]: strange and mysterious; weird.

undertow [un′ dər tō′]: the backward flow of water from waves breaking on the shore.

undulations [un′ jə lā′ shəns]: a series of wavelike curves.

universal [yü nə ver′ səl]: belonging to all.

unsullied [un sul′ ēd]: not soiled, clean.

unsurpassed [un′ sər pasd′]: not equaled.

unwonted [un wun′ tid]: not usual.

upstanding [up stan′ ding]: honorable.

V

veritable [ver′ ə tə bəl]: real, actual.

vestibule [ves′ tə byül]: a hall between the outer door and the inside of a building.

viciously [vish′ əs lē]: in a severely unpleasant way.

vise [vīs]: a very strong grip.

voyageurs [vwä yä zhėr′]: French-Canadian woodsmen, boaters, guides, and workers for early fur-trading companies; the word is French for "traveler."

vultures [vul′ chərz]: large birds of prey of the eagle family that eat dead animals.

W

waned [wānd]: lessened, grown smaller.

water-immersion tank [i mėr′ zhən]: tank in which astronauts prepare for the weightlessness of space.

weathercock: weather vane in the shape of a rooster.

whittled [hwit′ ld]: carved.

whorls [hwėrlz]: circular fingerprint patterns on the fingertips by which people can be identified.

win my spurs [spėrz]: idiom meaning "succeed."

winsome [win′ səm]: charming, pleasing.

wistfully [wist′ fəl ē]: longingly, yearningly.

wither [with′ ər]: to become dry and lifeless.

Y

yearned [yėrnd]: felt a longing or desire for something.

INDEX OF FINE ART

INDEX OF SKILLS

LITERATURE STUDY

WRITING

Advice column/booklet: 120, 524, 639

Comparison and Contrast: 118, 511, 522, 525, 769, 784, 898, 915, 1030, 1031

Diary/journal entry: 135, 154, 769, 912

Directions: 250, 910-911

Guide/brochure: 388-389, 518-519, 520-521, 772-775, 900, 910-911

Journal Writing: 24-25, 154, 286, 380, 545, 638, 641, 654, 675, 677, 768, 898, 900, 901, 908

Letter: 118, 120, 248, 395, 512-515, 524, 639, 641, 770, 914

News Report/article: 379, 770, 771, 1032

Outline: 511, 525, 545, 547

Poem: 262, 265, 392, 525

Script/dialogue: 378, 380, 381, 509, 641, 654, 899, 1031, 1040-1041

Speech: 251

SPEAKING AND LISTENING

24-25, 119, 120, 121, 125, 128-129, 130-131, 132, 133, 154-155, 156, 157, 249, 251, 255, 258-259, 260-261, 262, 263, 264, 265, 284-285, 287, 378, 379, 380, 381, 388-389, 390-391, 393, 395, 414-415, 416, 417, 508, 509, 510, 511, 515, 518-519, 520-521, 523, 524, 544-545, 546, 547, 639, 640, 645, 648-649, 650-651, 653, 674-675, 676, 770, 778-779, 780-781, 783, 785, 804-805, 806, 807, 898, 899, 901, 902-905, 908-909, 912, 913, 934-935, 936, 937, 1030, 1031, 1032, 1037, 1040-1041, 1042-1043, 1044, 1045, 1046

CRITICAL THINKING

Analyzing: 24-25, 118, 121, 132, 250, 264, 265, 378, 379, 380-381, 414-415, 508, 509, 520-521, 547, 638, 640, 641, 768, 898, 900, 934-935, 1030, 1031, 1032, 1033, 1046

Applying: 390-391, 520-521, 642-645, 654, 780-781, 908-909, 910-911, 912, 1040-1041

Classifying: 156, 249, 380, 416, 509, 769, 1046

Comparing and Contrasting: 118, 249, 285, 287, 509, 511, 522, 768, 769, 806, 898, 914, 934-935, 936, 1030, 1031, 1046

Defining: 122-125, 154-155, 156, 284, 380, 390-391, 512-515, 768, 807, 1030

Drawing Conclusions: 249, 284-285, 379, 934-935, 936, 1030, 1032, 1033

Evaluating: 24-25, 26, 119, 132-133, 250, 262-263, 284-285, 378, 379, 392-393, 395, 518-519, 522-523, 638, 639, 642-645, 650-651, 652-653, 771, 772-775, 780-781, 782-783, 899, 900, 901, 912-913, 1040-1041, 1044-1045

Extending: 119, 120, 121, 262, 380, 381, 382-385, 509, 510, 524, 639, 641, 648-649, 654, 768, 770, 784, 900, 912, 1030, 1033, 1046

Generalizing: 154-155, 512-515, 768, 934-935, 1032, 1033

Imagining: 118, 119, 120, 121, 128-129, 130-131, 134, 135, 248, 258-259, 262, 264, 378, 380, 381, 388-389, 395, 414-415, 509, 510, 524, 544-545, 546, 547, 639, 674-675, 676, 768, 769, 771, 778-779, 782, 784, 785, 804-805, 899, 900, 901, 914, 1030, 1032, 1034-1037, 1040-1041, 1044, 1047

Inferring: 249, 898, 1032

Interpreting: 249, 250, 378, 380, 414-415, 784, 934-935, 1030, 1032, 1033, 1046

Organizing: 24-25, 118, 119, 120, 121, 122-125, 128-129, 156, 157, 248, 250, 251, 252-255, 258-259, 260-261, 284, 286, 287, 378, 379, 380, 382-385, 388-389, 390-391, 416, 417, 508, 509, 510, 511, 512-515, 518-519, 525, 544-545, 639, 640, 642-645, 648-649, 650-651, 677, 768, 769, 770, 772-775, 778-779, 807, 898, 899, 902-905, 908-909, 910-911, 1030, 1031, 1032, 1034-1037, 1040-1041, 1042-1043, 1047

Predicting Outcomes: 394, 655

Summarizing: 128-129, 132, 157, 249, 251, 252-255, 417, 510, 511, 512-515, 520-521, 522, 641, 642-645, 768, 780-781, 902-905, 1030

Synthesizing: 132-133, 262-263, 392-393, 522-523, 652-653, 782-783, 912-913, 1044-1045

Understanding Relationships Between Characters: 134, 250, 380, 381, 382-385, 394, 524, 642-645, 650-651, 769, 771, 782, 807, 934-935, 1031, 1034-1037, 1040-1041, 1044, 1046, 1047

Understanding Relationships Between Events: 122-125, 135, 382-385, 509, 510, 524, 544-545, 546, 642-645, 650-651, 652, 655, 676, 769, 771, 782, 784, 804-805, 807, 902-905, 914, 934-935, 1030, 1031, 1032, 1033, 1034-1037, 1040-1041, 1044, 1046, 1047

Understanding Relationships Between Ideas: 642-645, 652, 1030, 1031, 1032

Understanding Causal Relationships: 121, 252-255, 381, 382-385, 394, 414-415, 509, 544-545, 642-645, 652, 655, 769, 804-805, 899, 902-905, 914, 1031, 1032, 1033, 1034-1037, 1040-1041, 1044, 1046, 1047

Understanding Chronological Relationships (Sequencing): 382-385, 509, 544-545, 546, 642-645, 650-651, 652, 676, 771, 782, 807, 902-905, 914, 934-935, 1032, 1033, 1034-1037, 1040-1041, 1044, 1046, 1047

261, 262, 263, 264, 265, 287, 378, 379, 380, 381, 385, 388-389, 390-391, 393, 414-415, 416, 417, 509, 510, 511, 515, 518-519, 520-521, 523,524, 544-545, 546, 547, 639, 641, 645, 648-649, 650-651, 652, 653, 676, 677, 770, 775, 778-779, 780-781, 782, 783, 785, 804-805, 807, 899, 900, 905, 908-909, 912, 913, 934-935, 936, 937, 1030, 1031,1032, 1040-1041, 1042-1043, 1044, 1045

COLLABORATIVE LEARNING

27, 118, 119, 120, 121, 125,128-129, 130-131, 132, 133, 154-155, 157, 249, 251, 255, 258-259, 260-

COMMUNITY SERVICE

130-132, 260-261, 390-391, 520-521, 650-651, 780-781, 910-911, 1042-1043.

INDEX OF GENRES

F I C T I O N

P O E T R Y

N O N F I C T I O N

D R A M A

INDEX OF AUTHORS AND TITLES